AS/A2

Information and Communication Technology

Geoffrey Knott BA, AIB, Cert Ed
Nick Waites BSc, MSc, Cert Ed

Business Education Publishers
2000

©Geoffrey Knott and Nick Waites 2000
ISBN 1901 888 22 3
First published 2000
Reprinted 2001

Cover Design by Tim Murphy, Creative Solutions
Graphical illustrations by Nick Waites and Geoffrey Knott
Production and Editing by Geoffrey Knott

Published in Great Britain by
Business Education Publishers Limited
The Solar Building
Doxford International
Sunderland
SR3 3XW

Tel: 0191 5252400
Fax: 0191 5201815

British Cataloguing-in-Publications Data
A catalogue record for this book is available from the British Library

Printed in Great Britain by Athenaeum Press, Gateshead

To Anne and Carolyn with love

The Authors

Geoffrey Knott and Nick Waites have long experience in Computing and IT education and have been producing highly successful course text books for well over a decade. They are authors of Computer Studies, Computing for BTEC Nationals, GNVQ Advanced Communication and Information Technology, GNVQ Intermediate Information Technology, Information Processing, Computing, Small Business Computer Systems, Information Technology Skills - A Student Guide, GCSE Information Systems and co-authors of Business GNVQ Advanced and Core Skills for GNVQ. They are also the authors and developers of the ICT 2000 CD-ROM.

Acknowledgements

We would like to thank our friend Jim Morton for his meticulous proofing of several of the more technical topics in this book and Rosalind Murphy for her equally careful general proofing of the remainder of the book.

Preface

This text provides comprehensive coverage of the subject matter required by the new GCE AS/A2 modular award in Information and Communication Technology offered by the OCR, Edexcel and AQA examining boards.

To cater for the significant variations in the Examining Boards' syllabuses for this Award, the text has been carefully organised into over 60 'bite-sized' Topics, allowing students and teachers to identify relevant material as easily as possible.

The Topics cover the complete spectrum of ICT, from computer architecture and network topologies to software, the Internet and event-driven programming. To provide a valuable learning aid and revision tool, each Topic is followed by Exercises testing knowledge and understanding.

The book is divided into three Parts:

Part 1   Fundamentals of ICT - contains topics relating primarily to the AS Level.

Part 2   Further ICT - covers the additional topics required for the A2 Level

Part 3   Applications Development - concentrates on skills required for practical work. This part includes substantial coverage of event-driven programming using Visual Basic.

Each Part is divided into Sections which form logical groupings of Topics. A summary of the Parts, Sections and Topics is provided overleaf. The summary is followed by a full Table of Contents.

The accompanying CD-ROM contains a variety of learning resources, including printable programming guides for Visual Basic, Pascal, C and COBOL.

Summary of Topics

Contents

Part 1
Fundamentals of ICT

Part 2
Further ICT

Systems and systems management

Further networking

Part 1

Fundamentals of ICT

Sections

- Introduction to ICT
- Computer hardware
- Computer software
- Files and file processing
- Databases
- Networking
- Social and legal issues
- Applications software

Part 1

Fundamentals of ICT

Sections

1. Introduction
2. Computer hardware
3. Computer software
4. Files and file processing
5. Databases
6. Networking
7. Social and legal issues
8. Application software

Section 1

Introduction to ICT

Topics

What is ICT?

Information and Communication Technology, or *ICT*, is a general term used to describe producing, storing, communicating and processing information using computers and other forms of electronic technology.

In everyday life we are surrounded by examples of ICT. For instance, if you own a computer that is connected to the Internet, you have a perfect example of ICT. When you use a spreadsheet you will be *producing* and *processing* information; when you create a document using a word processor and then save it, you are *storing* the document on your hard drive; and when you send an e-mail to a friend you are *communicating* electronically.

A personal computer system is an obvious form of ICT, but there are many other examples that are perhaps not quite so apparent. For instance, ordinary domestic devices such as hi-fi systems, video recorders, telephones and mobile 'phones all use ICT. Digital wrist watches can store information, perform calculations and even communicate with TV sets. Digital cameras store visual information and can transmit images to computers. Many modern cars now have computerised engine management systems. The list of devices that now rely on ICT is endless.

ICT also pervades industry and commerce and is absolutely crucial to their operation. Banks, building societies and other financial services rely on ICT for storing, processing and communicating customer information. Businesses ranging from sole traders to large corporations use electronic systems for design, advertising, accounting, stock control, payroll and many other applications. Moreover, as a direct result of the explosion in the use of the Internet, there are now thousands of *e-businesses* (electronic-businesses) that sell goods, services and information partly or wholly by electronic means. As well as using ICT for business management and administration purposes, many industries also use ICT to automate manufacturing processes. A good example is the use of robots in the manufacture of cars and other machines.

At the heart of ICT are the concepts of data, information and knowledge. Sometimes 'data' and 'information', and 'information' and 'knowledge' are used synonymously but, in terms of ICT, their meanings are quite distinct as we see in the next section.

✎ Exercises

1. List household devices that are likely to use ICT. For each device say whether it produces, stores, processes or communicates information.
2. Suggest ways that a range of businesses make use of ICT.
3. List industrial processes that are likely to make use of ICT.
4. Name some types of businesses that may not use ICT at all.

Data, Information and Knowledge Topic 2

Though 'data' and 'information', and 'information' and 'knowledge' are often used synonymously in everyday language, their meanings are quite different in the context of ICT. Data can be a series of measurements, a set of observations or a collection of facts. When we summarise or interpret data it becomes information. And if we refine information into, say, a 'rule of thumb' for some activity or task, it can then be classed as knowledge. Figure 2.1 illustrates these ideas.

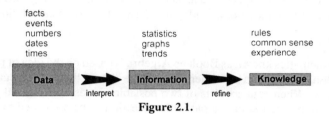

Figure 2.1.

In the next sections data, information and knowledge are discussed in detail.

Data

The term 'data' refers to collections of basic facts, meaningless until put into context or interpreted in some way, and also often in coded form. For example, the following list of letters could mean many things and is therefore meaningless without further information:

C, B, C, A, D

However, if we were told that the they represented the examination grades for Eric Walters in English, Mathematics, Science, Information Technology and Religious Education, they then make sense.

Computers process raw data to produce meaningful information. Computer programs, which define how the data is to be used by computers, can help us to interpret it. In other words, we can use computers to convert meaningless data into meaningful information.

Types of data

In the context of ICT, data is either numeric, alphabetic or alphanumeric (a combination of numeric, alphabetic and other symbols such as punctuation marks). Even if it is in electrical or digital form so that it can be used by a computer or transmitted over a telecommunications link, data still is represented by the symbols we use for written communication. However, within these three categories, we can identify certain special forms of data that occur very frequently: real numbers, integers, strings, Boolean values and dates.

Real numbers

These are numbers such as $123 \cdot 345$, $-3 \cdot 1428$ and $0 \cdot 001$. They can be positive or negative values and have several figures before and after the decimal point.

Integers

These are positive and negative whole numbers, such as 123 and −9, which do not include a decimal point.

Strings

The term 'string' is a computing term meaning a sequence of alphabetic or alphanumeric characters. For example, the text of this sentence is an alphabetic string. A street address such as "24, Balmoral Crescent" is also a string, this time an alphanumeric string. A telephone number containing numeric digits and spaces, such as 01432 765123, is a string. Strings are generally sequences of characters that are not intended to be used directly in calculations.

Boolean values

The branch of mathematics known as Boolean Algebra is based on the idea of two-valued logic. 'Statements' in Boolean Algebra are either true or false, that is, they can evaluate to only one of two possible values. When data consists of two possible values, it is classed as Boolean. For example, if a questionnaire requires a particular question to be answered by choosing either 'yes' or 'no', the data provided by this answer is said to be 'Boolean'. Other commonly used Boolean pairs include True/False, 0/1 and zero/non-zero.

Dates

Though it could be argued that a date such as 29-Feb-2000 is a string as described above, because computer software often needs to perform calculations on dates, they can be regarded as a special form of data. For instance, a computerised library system may perform a calculation using the date a book was borrowed and the current date, in order to determine whether the book is overdue for return. Using examples based on the date given above, other common date formats include 29/2/2000, 2/29/2000, 2000-02-29.

Sources of data

In the context of ICT, data originates from only two distinct sources: people and machines. People provide data by completing forms and questionnaires, performing and recording market surveys or by using devices such as keyboards and keypads that are connected to computers.

However, many electronic and mechanical devices produce or record data automatically, without direct human intervention. For example, meteorological instruments record wind speed and direction, air pressure, humidity and temperature; telephone systems automatically log the duration and type of calls, air traffic control systems monitor and record passenger aircraft traffic; gas and electricity meters log fuel consumption; automobile odometers record distance travelled; under the control of programs, computers can generate data. Figure 2.2 illustrates these ideas.

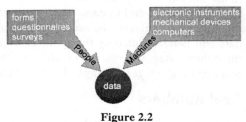

Figure 2.2

Coding data

Codes are widely used in computer applications. Where the same data items occur repeatedly, where data processing speed and data storage requirements are considerations, or where there are other important reasons for doing so, data may be coded. *Encoding* is the term for converting data into its coded form; *decoding* is the reverse process of returning a data code to its original form.

Coding schemes are commonly used for the following tasks:

❑   Data compression

❑   Data identification

❑   Data processing

Data compression

A full discussion of data compression techniques is beyond the scope of this text but a simple form relevant to data coding is explained in the following.

When identical items of data occur frequently, short codes may be used to compress the original data. For instance, a college administration system might allocate the numeric codes shown below for their different departments

01	Science
02	Engineering
03	Humanities
04	Art
05	Business Studies
06	Information Technology

Alternatively more meaningful alphabetic codes could be used:

SCI	Science
ENG	Engineering
HUM	Humanities
ART	Art
BUS	Business Studies
ICT	Information and Communication Technology

Both coding schemes shown above reduce the amount of information that needs to be recorded and stored. Thus, each record in the college's student file will contain only a short code to represent the department in which a student is studying instead of the complete name. Where there are hundreds or even thousands of students, this scheme would greatly reduce the amount of work involved in creating student records and, assuming the data was to be stored in a computer system, the amount of storage space required.

When this form of data compression is used for encoding, a *look-up table* is required to decode the data. Using the college example described previously, let us suppose that the computer system is able to print individual student enrolment details. The department code, for example, 'ICT', stored in the student's record may not be meaningful to many people, so it is preferable for a printed report to show the full name of the student's department ('Information and Communication Technology' in this example). A separate table containing each code and its original meaning is stored in the computer system and, when a code needs to be expanded to its original state (decoded), this look-up table is consulted.

The disadvantage of using this form of coding is that it increases the complexity of processing.

Data identification

Unique identification codes are frequently used for applications such as stock control. Each stock item is given a different code, often with built-in error prevention safeguards (see 'validation methods'), so that it can be uniquely identified. The code may be purely numeric or a mixture of alphabetic and numeric characters. The code identifies a collection of information concerning the stock item. For instance, a mail order company might allocate unique six-digit integers to each of its stock items. This code will be used to retrieve and update data such as a description of the item, its cost, how many are in stock, the supplier code, and so on. This identification code is frequently termed a *key field*, or *primary key*.

A familiar form of coding is the use of post codes. These short alphanumeric codes, such as DL14 8HZ and SR1 2PN, are used to identify the location of every street in every village, town and city in the UK. You may have noticed that if you order goods over the telephone, you will often be asked only for your post code and your house number. Telephone operators simply enter this number using a keyboard connected to a computer which then decodes the post code and supplies the address, complete except for the house number.

Data processing

Some data retrieval systems use coding to improve their performance. A good example of this is the use of the *soundex coding* system. Suppose that a user of a personnel records system is verbally asked to retrieve a record for an employee with surname Waites, then it is unlikely that the record would be retrieved if the operator entered Whaites or Waits.

Similar situations arise when searches need to be made on other alphabetic data that is prone to spelling variations. A possible solution is to convert the name to a soundex code as follows:

- ❏ the first letter of the name becomes the first letter of the code
- ❏ all vowels and the letters H, W and Y are ignored
- ❏ double letters are replaced by a single instance of the letter
- ❏ the remaining letters are replaced by values according to Table 2.1.

Letter	Replace with
B, F, P ,V	1
C, G, J, K, Q, S, X, Z	2
D, T	3
L	4
M, N	5
R	6

Table 2.1

❑   the code is restricted to four characters in length

❑   if the code contains less than four characters, it is padded with trailing zeros.

Table 2.2 provides some examples of names converted to soundex codes.

Soundex coding techniques are used by the police force for searching criminal records. It is important to find all similar sounding names from their files because of the high probability of a name being reported incorrectly.

Soundex coding is also very useful for helping to make interactive information retrieval systems more user friendly. For example, rather than the computer saying, "There are no personnel records with the name JOHNSON", it reported, "There are no personnel records with the name JOHNSON, but here is a list of records closely matching this name: A. JONSON, B. JOHNSEN... etc", this would be much more useful to the user.

Name	Soundex Code
Waites	W320
Whaites	W320
Waits	W320
Williams	W452
Johnson	J525
Jonson	J525
Johnsen	J525
Morton	M635
Morten	M635
Summerville	S561
Sommerset	S562

Table 2.2

Guidelines for coding data

A new coding system should use codes that are:

❑   Unique

❑   As short as possible

❑   Easily interpreted if they are to be used manually

❑   Able to be validated/verified

❑   Unambiguous (for example, avoiding confusion between 1(numeric) and I(alphabetic), 0 (numeric) and O (alphabetic)

❑   Consistent within the coding scheme

In general, the coding scheme should be:

❑   Easily expanded to accommodate more codes

❑   Consistent with other schemes used by the organisation

Quality of data

The quality of data has a direct effect on the accuracy of the information derived from it. For this reason the data control systems within an organisation are vitally important. As a simple example, suppose that a catalogue-based store uses a coding system for stock items. Without data control procedures, mistakes made recording stock items might remain undetected, resulting in inaccurate stock level figures and serious loss of sales or other administrative problems. Data control procedures are examined in Topic 19.

Information

We have seen earlier that *information* is derived from interpreting *data*. In the following paragraphs we examine the concept of information in more detail, starting with a discussion of information quality.

Quality of information

The quality of information depends on several factors, but the larger and more complex the organisation, the more difficult it is to maintain high quality information, without highly systematised procedures. Conversely, a larger organisation tends to have more specialist staff to assist in its efficient operation. Small organisations have to employ multi-skilled staff with responsibility for a number of different tasks. A sole trader, with only a few products and customers may be able to control the whole business, but not necessarily in the most efficient manner. As the volume of data to be processed increases, there will be pressures for increased staffing and an introduction or extension of computerisation.

To use a computer merely to process and produce operational information is often an under-use of computer power. Computerisation can lead to an improvement in the quantity and quality of management information, as well as the accuracy and availability of operational information.

Technological developments in stand-alone and networked computer systems have lessened the importance of the centralised data processing department and brought processing power closer to the user. Although this brings many benefits, the loss of central control can make it more difficult to maintain some of the qualities of information. The following characteristics contribute to high quality information.

Accuracy

This is of primary importance because good decisions can only be made on the basis of accurate information. For example, a decision to increase factory production, based on last year's sales figures (which prove to be inaccurate) and market research (which proves to be unreliable) may result in disaster for a business, leaving it with large stocks of unsold goods. Inaccurate information may result from hardware, software or transmission errors, but these may be controlled and largely prevented. More seriously, inaccurate information may result from data input errors.

Validation and verification techniques, discussed later, attempt to prevent such inaccuracies.

Tailored information

The presentation, layout and detail of information presented to a user can affect its usefulness. For example, a three-page report on a customer's credit history is probably too detailed for a sales order clerk, who wishes to check the credit limit before processing an order. Similarly, if a report is required for the shareholders of a holding company, a column chart showing comparative trading profits for two subsidiaries may be of more use than a tabular presentation of the figures.

Figures 2.3 and 2.4 illustrate these two forms of presentation. It is important that information is tailored to the user's needs.

Annual Trading Profits of Daybreak Ltd and Sunrise Ltd, 1993 to 1997

	Daybreak	**Sunrise**
	£	**£**
1993	140,000	90,000
1994	230,000	180,000
1995	250,000	200,000
1996	340,000	270,000
1997	350,000	220,000

Figure 2.3. *Comparison of annual trading profits in tabular form*

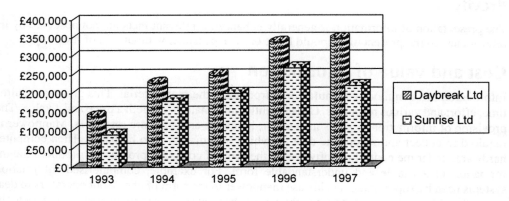

Figure 2.4. *Chart view of annual trading profits*

Relevance

Information should be relevant to the purpose for which it was provided. For example, it would not be relevant to produce outstanding debit balances for all customers' accounts, if management merely required information on customers who live within a specific geographical area, such as the West Midlands.

Timeliness

Information must be as up-to-date as necessary. In some circumstances, information may retain its usefulness for months. For example, a six-month cash flow forecast may be referred to throughout the period of the forecast.

Conversely, for example, if market research for a new product is not completed until after its planned launch date, the launch may be delayed or it may proceed with the risk that the marketing information will not prove positive.

Legibility

The user must be able to read and understand the information. This requires that the information is presented clearly and in a form which the user can readily understand.

Significance

The significance of information must be apparent to the recipient. Usually, proper presentation, format and a suitable report heading will ensure this characteristic.

Completeness

The recipient should be satisfied that he or she has received all the information needed. If information is missing and the recipient is unaware of this fact, any decision based on the incomplete information may be ill-founded. Even if the recipient is aware that it is incomplete, pressure of time may force him or her to act before the rest can be obtained.

Brevity

The presentation of information is generally enhanced if relevant facts are not obscured by irrelevancies, so the presentation should be as brief as possible, without loss of meaning.

Cost and value of information

Information is a commodity manufactured from data, the raw material. This process requires time, effort and various resources. Consequently, information has both a price and a value. The provision of information requires manpower, hardware and software resources. Manpower is required to collect and record the data on which information is to be based. Then computer hardware, under the control of software (in the form of computer programs), produces the information in a usable and understandable form. For example, computerised information systems used by supermarket chains use manpower in the form of check-out operators to deal manually with purchases, hardware in the form of bar code scanners connected to a computer to record items sold, and software to control the whole process and generate information such as stock statistics reports.

Information also has value to individuals as well as organisations. As individuals we pay for information all of the time. For instance, we buy newspapers, periodicals, books and electronic sources of information such as CD ROMs, and we subscribe to information sources such as organisations specialising in market research reports, mailing lists and stock market trend analysis.

Knowledge

A dictionary definition of 'knowledge' might go something like this:

"The facts or experiences known by a person or group of people" or

"Specific information about a subject".

Though there are similarities, knowledge has a more specific meaning in ICT terms. Knowledge is in the form of rules which can be used to arrive at conclusions in some area of expertise. Collections of these rules are known as 'knowledge bases' just as sets of data are called 'databases'. Computer systems that use knowledge bases are called 'knowledge-based systems' or 'intelligent knowledge-based systems', which are described below.

Knowledge-based systems

A knowledge-based system embodies human knowledge in a form suited to processing by a computer program. Such a system will store facts about a certain subject area, and relationships, often in the form of rules, that allow conclusions to be drawn from the facts.

The most common type of knowledge-based system is the *expert system*, and this is discussed in some detail in the following section.

Expert systems

Research in the field of artificial intelligence has had a number of practical spin-offs, one of which has been the development of programs known as *expert systems*, or intelligent knowledge-based systems. These are programs designed to be able to give the same sort of help or advice, or make decisions, as a human expert in some narrow field of expertise. For instance, a program called PROSPECTOR is capable of predicting the existence of mineral ores given various pieces of information gathered from physical locations. In the same way that, given certain evidence, an expert might say that a particular site looked favourable for containing ore, PROSPECTOR indicates the probability of the existence of the ore. PROSPECTOR is in fact attributed with the discovery of an extremely valuable quantity of molybdenum which had previously been overlooked by human experts.

Expert systems have been developed in numerous areas which traditionally have been the province of human experts. For example, several expert systems have been developed to aid medical diagnosis and treatment. However, decisions in areas such as this are often so critical that it would be foolish to blindly accept the pronouncement of a computer. For this reason, expert systems have the built-in ability to justify the chain of logical reasoning leading to any conclusion, so that it can be checked and verified (or rejected) by a human.

Another characteristic of many expert systems is the use of *fuzzy logic* which allows degrees of uncertainty to be built in to logical deduction processes. Such expert systems are able to state conclusions that are qualified by a probability value indicating the chances of the conclusion being correct. Probabilities are represented by positive numeric values in the range 0 to 1.An event that has been assigned a probability value of 0 cannot ever occur, the number 7 showing when a standard dice is thrown, for instance; a value of 1 indicates a certainty such as a value between 1 and 6 inclusive showing when a normal dice is thrown; probabilities greater than 0 and less than 1 indicate that there is some degree of uncertainty in the chance of a event occurring. For instance when a coin is thrown, the face that shows could be either a head or a tail, each with an equal probability of 0.5 of occurring. On a **particular** throw of a coin, no one can predict with absolute certainty whether a head or a tail will show, but if the coin is thrown many times, **approximately** half the time a head will show and **approximately** half the time a tail will show. This mathematical representation of real-world situations using probability values is incorporated in certain types of expert systems, where rules will be true most, rather than all, of the time.

Other successful expert systems include:

❑   MYCIN - diagnosis of infections

❑   HEURISTIC DENDRAL - identifies organic compounds

❑   XCON - for configuring (VAX) computer systems

❑   SACON - for advice on structural analysis

An expert system has three main components:

❑   A *knowledge base* consisting of rules which use facts supplied by some external source, typically a user.

❑   An *inference engine* which processes the knowledge base.

❑   A *user interface* to facilitate communication with the user.

As an example, the following knowledge base is for a simple botanical expert system to identify whether a particular plant is a shrub, tree, herb or vine.

Four rules are to be used:

1.   IF STEM IS GREEN THEN TYPE IS HERB.

2.   IF STEM IS WOODY AND ATTITUDE IS CREEPING THEN TYPE IS VINE.

3.   IF STEM IS WOODY AND ATTITUDE IS UPRIGHT AND ONE MAIN TRUNK IS TRUE THEN TYPE IS TREE.

4.   IF STEM IS WOODY AND ATTITUDE IS UPRIGHT AND ONE MAIN TRUNK IS FALSE THEN TYPE IS SHRUB.

This forms the knowledge base.

The inference engine starts by attempting to satisfy a primary goal, in this instance to determine the TYPE of the plant. To this end, it searches its knowledge base for the goal by looking for a rule containing the word TYPE in the conclusion part of the rule (after the THEN part of a rule). This process of examining conclusions to rules while attempting to resolve goals is called backward chaining (or goal-driven inference).

Rule 1 satisfies this requirement, but in order to establish if the plant is a HERB, the system must obtain information regarding the STEM. Initially this information will not be available and must be supplied by the user. Consequently, obtaining the STEM information is added to a list of subgoals to be evaluated, along with rule 1, and the system looks for another rule containing the goal in its conclusion. The subgoal list also notes the rule which generated the subgoal in question.

After the remaining rules have been processed in a similar fashion, the system must then attempt to satisfy the subgoal list. Consequently, the user interface is invoked. This generates a question of the form

IS THE STEM OF THE PLANT GREEN?

Let us suppose that the plant is a SHRUB (which has a woody stem, grows upright, and has more than one main trunk). The user answers NO which is stored as a fact relating to the stem of the plant.

Having succeeded with a subgoal, the inference engine again searches for a rule conclusion containing TYPE. It can attempt to evaluate the first rule now that it has all the necessary information. The rule does not produce a conclusion since the STEM is not green. This rule is therefore discarded since it can never cause the primary goal to succeed in this particular consultation.

Examination of the second rule reveals to the inference engine that it cannot be resolved until the ATTITUDE of the plant is in its list of facts, so this is added to its list of subgoals.

Eventually, all the necessary facts are available and the inference engine is able to discard all rules except rule 4 which establishes that the plant is a SHRUB. In the course of a consultation the user might wish to know why the system is asking a certain question. The information required to answer this question is easy to find: the subgoal generating the question being asked was stored along with the rule from which it came, and this contains all the necessary information. For example, if the inference engine was attempting to resolve rule 4 by asking about the number of TRUNKS, the user interface might respond,

```
I am trying to determine the TYPE.
I know that the STEM is woody.
I know that the ATTITUDE is upright.
If ONE MAIN TRUNK is false then I will know that the TYPE is
SHRUB.
```

Expert system shells

The term shell is given to expert systems which have been given no specific knowledge base, only the inference engine and user interface; the knowledge base has to be provided by the user. A single expert system shell can thus be used to provide advice or help in a number of areas of expertise, providing it is given the appropriate knowledge base for each area. For example, an expert system shell could be used to give advice on the procedures and sequence of steps necessary for selling a house (what solicitors call 'conveyancing'), or to give advice about possible causes and cures of diseases in houseplants, or diagnosing faults in cars. Not only could these applications be of practical use, but they could also be instructive because the user could ask for and obtain the reasons behind any conclusions.

One of the problems of using such shells is the determination of the rules which represent the wisdom of a human expert; many experts are not consciously aware of the precise reasoning processes they themselves use in order to come to some conclusion, yet in order to produce an expert program, these processes must be defined in a form that is usable. The process of determining the knowledge base rules is known as 'knowledge elicitation' or 'knowledge acquisition' and is performed by 'knowledge engineers'.

✍️Exercises

1. For the past 30 years, a weather monitoring station has logged the ambient temperature at noon each day. Use this example to distinguish between *data*, *information* and *knowledge*.

2. State the data type represented by each of the following data examples:

    (i)   "The cat sat on the mat"

    (ii) 434·55

    (iii) −55

    (iv) 0191 5252400

    (v)   18-Mar-2000 *(N.B. This could represent two data types)*

3. A company wishes to record in its computerised personnel system whether each member of staff is a member of the pension scheme. Identify a suitable data type to hold this information and explain your choice.

4. Give two examples of ICT systems which uses data received from:

    (i)   people;

    (ii) machines.

5. The following lookup table is used by a company to decode the two-letter codes which identify each of its branches. It plans to open new branches in many other cities and towns. Each of its 5000 account customers records is identified with a particular branch.

SC	Scarborough
CA	Cambridge
DU	Durham
LO	London
ED	Edinburgh
MA	Manchester

    (i)   Explain the purpose and benefits of the lookup table

    (ii) identify a potential difficulty with the table in its present form and suggest a solution.

6. How may the *soundex* coding system be of benefit in the operation of a police criminal records system?

7. A company is planning to launch an upgrade of one of its products and is undertaking market research. Two major sources of market information are: (i) its sales records; (ii) customer user surveys.

    (i)   For each source, identify **two** particular aspects of its *quality* which would affect the value of the information.

    (ii) Use the example to distinguish between the cost and value of information.

8. Give one example of an expert system and use it to explain the purpose of each of its component parts, namely its knowledge base, inference engine and user interface.

Section 2

Computer Hardware

Topics

- 📖 3: Computer systems
- 📖 4: Input and output devices
- 📖 5: Storage systems
- 📖 6: Computer architecture
- 📖 7: Emerging technologies

Computer systems

A computer system, like any system, is made up of a number of separate parts which work together to serve a purpose. A car is a system and it will only work as such if all the vital parts are there, including the driver. Although different models of car have different specifications, they must all have some essential components, such as an engine (to power it), wheels (to move along the ground) and brakes (to stop it). Specifications for computer systems also vary. For example, one will calculate more quickly or store more data than another, but all computer systems must have certain vital *hardware*, or physical, components. A car is useless without a driver and a computer system is worthless without computer programs to control it. All the programs used to make a computer perform useful work are known collectively as *software*. To be effective the hardware and software components must meet user needs.

Hardware components

The hardware components of a computer system can be categorised by function, as follows:

Input

To allow the computer to process data it must be in a form which the machine can handle. Before processing, data is normally in a human-usable form, for example, printed text on a page, images received through a video camera, the spoken word, live music or heat from a boiler. Such data cannot be handled directly by the internal circuitry of the computer. Firstly, it has to be translated into the binary format which makes the data *machine-sensible*; this is the function of an input device. There is a wide variety of such devices, each designed for a particular form of data and method of input. The keyboard, mouse, scanner and microphone are all examples of input devices. Data is transferred from the input device to main memory. As part of an information system, input devices are used for *data collection*.

Main memory

This element, also commonly known as *RAM*, has two main functions:

- ❏ to temporarily store programs currently in use for processing data;
- ❏ to temporarily store data:
    - entered through an input device and awaiting processing;
    - currently being processed;
    - which results from processing and is waiting to be output.

Central processing unit (CPU)

Often referred to as the *processor*, the CPU handles program instructions and data and consists of two elements:

- ❏ *Arithmetic/logic unit (ALU)*. The ALU carries out arithmetic operations such as addition, multiplication, subtraction and division. It can also make logical comparisons between items of data, for example, it can determine whether one value is greater than another. Such logical operations can also be performed on non-numeric data.

❑ *Control unit*. The control unit governs the operation of all hardware, including input and output devices and the CPU. It does this by fetching, interpreting and executing each instruction in turn, in an automatically controlled cycle referred to as the *fetch-execute cycle*.

Output

Output devices perform the opposite function of input devices by translating machine-sensible data into a human-readable form, for example, on to a printer or the screen of a visual display unit (VDU). Sometimes, the results of computer processing may be needed for further processing, in which case, they are output to a storage medium (Topic 5) which retains it in machine-sensible form for subsequent input. As part of an information system, output devices are used for the *presentation* of data or information.

Backing storage

Backing, or auxiliary, storage performs a filing function within the computer system. In this context it is important to consider a couple of important concepts.

❑ *Memory volatility*. It is not practical to store data files and programs in main memory because of its volatility. This means that the contents of the main memory can be destroyed, either by being overwritten as new data is entered for processing and new programs used, or when the machine is switched off. Such volatile memory is termed random access memory (RAM).

❑ *Retrievable data*. Backing storage media provide a more permanent store for programs (which may be used many times on different occasions) and data files (which are used for future reference or processing).

Peripherals

Those hardware devices which are external to the CPU and main memory, namely those devices used for input, output and backing storage, are called *peripherals*. Figure 3.1 illustrates the logical structure of the computer and thereby, the relationships between various hardware elements. It shows the data flow through the system and the flow of control signals from the processor.

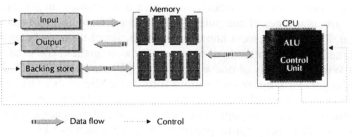

Figure 3.1. *Logical configuration of a computer system*

Software

Software can be divided into two main groups:

(i)   systems software;

(ii)   applications software.

Systems software

Systems software is dedicated to the general organisation and running of a computer system. Standard tasks, such as handling files on backing storage and controlling programs in memory, are common to all applications and are managed by a particular group of systems programs known collectively as the operating system. Familiar examples include Windows 98, NT and 2000, OS/2, Unix and Linux.

Types of operating system

Different types of operating system are necessary to handle different computer configurations and the variety of processing modes in which they can operate. For example, a microcomputer with keyboard, mouse, screen, printer and disk drives requires a much less sophisticated operating system than a mainframe computer system, which has a large variety and number of input, output and storage devices. Computer systems which allow multi-user operation (where multiple users access shared files and programs at the same time) require a *multi-user* operating system, with facilities for controlling individual user access and security. Conversely, a microcomputer designed for single-user operation can be operated with a simpler, single-user operating system. There is a variety of operating systems which serve the requirements of different computer processing methods, including *real-time*, *batch* and *time-share* processing (Topic 20).

Applications software

Applications programs make the computer function in a specific way, for a particular user requirement. Common examples are stock control and invoicing programs. Although an application may be tailored for a particular user, most applications can be catered for by off-the-shelf packages.

Hardware and software standards

Where standards exist in hardware and software the transfer of information between computers, applications and users is simplified.

Although there are no universal standards for hardware or software, in particular user areas the popularity of particular types of computer system and software products has resulted in some standardisation. For example, most home and small business users and many corporate users have adopted the PC based on the Intel processor (or a compatible competitor processor) and the Microsoft Windows family of operating systems (Windows 95, 98, NT, 2000). Similarly, the most popular general-purpose applications software is Microsoft's Office suite which contains a word processor, spreadsheet, presentation package and database. In the microcomputer world the Macintosh is the most popular choice for artist and designer and it is generally difficult to transfer, for example, graphics produced on a Macintosh to a PC.

Portability of information can also be difficult between different versions of the same package.

For example, a document produced with Word 7 cannot be opened by Word 6, unless the document was specifically saved as a Word 6 file. It is common practice for new versions of software to contain options to save files in earlier version formats.

There are variations in standards in all areas of computer hardware. For example, hard disk drives are produced with a number of different connection or interface standards, including SCSI (Small Computer Systems Interface, Ultra Wide SCSI and UDMA (Ultra Direct Memory Access).

Lack of standardisation leads to more complexity in the design of operating systems, applications software and in the hardware configurations of computer systems. For example, a standard PC with a UDMA hard drive interface will not allow the connection of a Jaz drive (Topic 5) without the addition of a SCSI interface. Operating systems of less popular computer systems, such as the Macintosh have to include facilities for handling information from PCs and software packages usually include options for handling files produced by competitor packages.

A similar lack of standardisation exists in larger computer configurations based on the Unix operating system or one of several others specific to particular computer manufacturers. Despite the variation in standards, the Internet is able to connect computer systems of all types through the use of common communication standards, or *protocols* (Topic 26).

✎Exercises

1. Distinguish between *hardware* and *software*.
2. Give three examples of 'human-usable' data and use them to explain the role of input devices and output devices.
3. Give two reasons why backing storage is an essential component of a computer system.
4. Using suitable examples, distinguish between systems software and applications software.
5. What extra facilities does a multi-user operating system require which are not needed in a single users operating system?
6. A company has a number of PCs with Microsoft Office installed on each machine, but some are using Office 97 and some are using Office 2000. Identify problems which may arise and how they may be overcome.

Input and output devices

Input and output devices allow users to communicate with the computer, in different ways, according to their requirements. For a given type of device, such as a printer, there are many different product specifications, each designed to meet a particular need. For example, when judging a printer specification, its speed of output and the quality of the print it can produce need to be considered. The first part of this Topic deals with input devices and the second with output devices.

Input devices

Input devices enable information to be entered into a computer for processing or storage on magnetic media. The computer can only process or store information if it is in an electronic, binary coded form, so input devices are needed to convert, for example, letters of the alphabet, digits in our number system, the sounds of the human voice or musical instruments, into the computer's code. The most commonly used input device is the keyboard, which converts key presses into the computer's code. So, for example, pressing the 'A' key produces electrical signals which the computer uses to represent that letter. The computer uses a different code for each character on the keyboard. The ASCII (American Standard Code for Information Interchange) binary code is recognised by all computers. Similarly, a *scanner* allows typed or hand-written documents to be read into a computer and a microphone enables the entry of sounds, perhaps to give voice commands to the computer. Each input device needs its own *driver* software to make it work on a particular computer system.

Standard keyboard

The arrangement of keys on the main part of the keyboard is the same as for any typewriter. This QWERTY layout comes from mechanical typewriters and has little to do with the requirements of a computer keyboard. It has continued as the favoured design because many people are used to it and changing the layout of the keys would mean retraining for millions of keyboard users. The computer keyboard does have other keys, specifically designed for the computer. Function keys, for example, are programmable and are used by software packages to access particular options, such as Help menus. Some common examples of keyboard use are:

- ❑ entering text and numbers into the computer, perhaps using a word processor;
- ❑ entering keywords into a *search engine,* a type of program used to find information on the World Wide Web;
- ❑ controlling animated graphics characters in computer games;

Concept keypads

In specialist applications, the standard keyboard is not always the most convenient method of input. In a factory, for example, a limited number of functions may be necessary for the operation of a computerised lathe. These functions can be set out on a touch-sensitive pad and clearly marked. This is possible because all inputs are anticipated and the range is small. The operator is saved the trouble of typing in the individual characters which form instructions.

Concept keypads are used in shops, restaurants and bars. For example, each key position on the pad can be assigned to a particular drink. Pressing a key automatically enters the charge for the specified drink. Concept keypads are also useful in education, particularly for the mentally and physically handicapped.

The grid shown on the keypad is divided into a grid of 16 × 8 (128) programmable cells and the example overlay shows that the grid is to be programmed into 4 areas. Each area occupies 32 cells (128 ÷ 4) and pressure on any of the cells in one area indicates that the user has selected a particular picture. This may result, for example, in the matching word being displayed on screen. Alternatively, the input may be the user's response to the word shown on screen. Figure 4.1 illustrates a concept keypad and overlay.

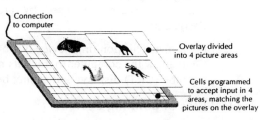

Figure 4.1. *Educational concept keypad with sample overlay*

Pointing devices

Apart from the keyboard, which is an essential part of every computer system, pointing devices are the next most popular option for input. The devices in this group use different mechanisms and technologies, but they all allow the user to draw, erase, select and format text and graphics on screen. Pointing devices are an essential component for the effective use of modern software. Two of the most popular types are described below.

Mouse

A mouse is a hand-held device which the user can move on a flat surface to direct a pointer on the computer screen. It has two or more buttons, which allow the user to draw, erase, select and format text and graphics on screen. Most computer systems are equipped with a mouse facility and many packages, including those for art, design, word processing and desktop publishing can only be operated effectively with a mouse. Graphical user interfaces (GUIs - see Topic 10) such as that provided by the Microsoft Windows 98 operating system, also depend heavily on its use.

Tracker ball

A tracker (or roller) ball is another variation of a mouse and is used for the same purposes. As shown in Figure 4.2, a tracker ball is a bit like an upside-down mouse, with the ball visible on the top of the base. To use a tracker ball you simply move the ball in the required direction using your fingers. Buttons are supplied just like on a mouse. Like *joysticks*, tracker balls have the advantage over mice that a flat surface is not required for its operation and are often used with portable computers.

Figure 4.2. *Tracker ball*

Other pointing devices

Although the mouse and tracker ball are very popular, they are not the most suitable for every application. Three other pointing devices are described below.

> ❑ *Touch screen*. A touch sensitive display allows selection of screen options with a finger. It is commonly used in banks and tourist agencies to allow customers to

obtain information on certain topics.

❏ *Digitising tablet.* A stylus (pen-like device) is used to 'draw' on the tablet (Figure 4.3); the movements of the stylus are reflected on screen.

A digitising tablet allows more precise drawing than a mouse and is used by architects and designers.

Figure 4.3. *Digitising tablet*

❏ *Light pen.* This pointing device is moved over the screen and uses a light sensitive tip to allow the computer to track its movements. It can only be used with cathode ray tube (CRT) displays and cannot be used with laptop or notebook computers

Typical uses of pointing devices

For most users, the mouse is standard equipment, but for architects, graphic artists and other designers, the mouse does not provide the precision control possible with a graphics tablet. The light pen is a possible alternative to the graphics tablet; it is cheaper but is not capable of the same accuracy. The roller or tracker ball is suitable for a portable computer because it does not need a flat surface. Touch-sensitive screens are suited to public display information systems, because no keyboard or other input device is needed. The user simply uses a finger to touch the required option on screen.

Sensors and ADCs

Sensors are used to detect continuously varying values, such as temperature, pressure, light intensity, humidity, wind speed and so on. These sensors detect analogue signals which are not compatible with digital computers. So, apart from several other components, an *analogue-to-digital converter* (ADC) is needed to convert analogue signals into the digital values a computer can understand.

Suppose that the temperature of a washing machine is computer controlled, using a built-in microprocessor programmed for that purpose. The microprocessor can only handle discrete, that is separate, values, so the ADC in this machine takes a sample from the sensor every minute. Figure 4.4 illustrates the analogue wave form which represents the temperature variations detected by the sensor, over a 5 minute period. The figure also shows that temperature readings at each sample point (S1 to S5). For example, at the 3rd minute sample S3 = 40°C.

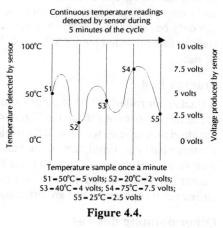

Temperature sample once a minute
S1 = 50°C = 5 volts; S2 = 20°C = 2 volts;
S3 = 40°C = 4 volts; S4 = 75°C = 7.5 volts;
S5 = 25°C = 2.5 volts

Figure 4.4.

If the microprocessor-controlled washing machine allowed you to select several temperature settings for the water, it might use a temperature sensor in conjunction with an ADC to convert water temperatures between 0°C and 1000°C to a binary signal in the range 0 to 255, as illustrated in Figure 4.5.

The diagram shows a temperature sensor immersed in the water. This will produce a small electrical signal, proportional to the water temperature, which must be amplified so that it produces a voltage in the range 0 volts to 10 volts, for example. The ADC then converts this voltage to a binary signal in the range 0 to 255 (11111111 in binary), so that 0ºC is represented by 0 and 100ºC is represented by 255. Thus a temperature of 25ºC would produce about 2·5 volts from the amplifier and this would translate to binary 63 (00111111).

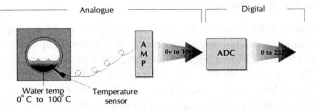

Figure 4.5. *Example of analogue to digital conversion*

The term *digitiser* is usually reserved for more complex ADCs used for converting whole frames of photographic film into digital images which, with the aid of suitable software, can be displayed on a computer screen and edited. The output from a video camera, or medical scanning equipment can also be digitised for use in a computer. Digitisers which are designed for textual or graphical documents are usually termed *scanners*.

Microphone

A microphone acts as a sensor, converting sound waves to equivalent electrical voltage levels. The voltages are sampled and converted by the sound card inside the system casing into the binary codes which the computer can store and process. Most personal computers are equipped with a microphone to allow, with appropriate software, sound recording or the input of commands and text.

Input devices for the physically disabled

Physical disability may prevent many people from using conventional input devices of keyboard and hand-held mouse and a number of specialist devices have been developed to meet their needs, including those controlled by:

❑ **head movement**. This 'head tracking' device can emulate mouse movements and clicks. Using head movements, the user can direct movement of the cursor on screen and left and right mouse clicks can be executed with a suck-puff switch. Using a virtual keyboard on screen, the user can carry out text entry. To allow the user to move around freely, communication between the device and the computer is normally carried out via an infra-red transmitter and receiver.

❑ **foot movement**. All the normal mouse operations can be carried out with a *foot-mouse*. The device is also helpful to those who have temporary disablement through, for example, repetitive strain injury (RSI), which can result from intensive and lengthy use of the hand-held mouse.

Other input devices

There are a number of devices designed to capture information, in the form of pictures or text, already printed on paper.

These devices include the following.

❑ *Scanners*. These devices allow whole documents to be scanned optically and converted into digital images. Text can be captured in this way and then converted for use in a word processor. The conversion is carried out by *optical character recognition (OCR)* software.

❑ *Optical mark reader (OMR)*. An OMR is designed to read simple pencil marks placed in pre-set positions on a document. A common application for OMR is a multi-choice examination paper, where the answer to each question has to be indicated by a pencil mark in one of several boxes located after the question number. The OMR can then scan the paper for the pencil marks and work out a grade. National Lottery tickets are completed and checked in a similar fashion.

❑ *Bar code readers*. Bar codes are commonly used to store a variety of data such as prices and stock codes relating to products in shops and supermarkets. A sticker with the relevant bar code is attached to each product, or alternatively, the packaging may be pre-coded. By using the data from the code, the cash register can identify the item, look up its latest price and print the information on the customer's receipt.

❑ *Cameras*. Images captured through video cameras and still cameras can be input and processed by computer. In the case of tape-based video cameras the images must be digitised by the computer's graphics card, which is acting as an analogue to digital converter or ADC. To edit a video sequence, the computer requires a special video capture card which allows each frame in a sequence to be separately manipulated. If the video camera uses a digital format no analogue to digital conversion is required. Pictures taken with a digital still camera can similarly be captured and edited in the computer. Architects and other designers find digital cameras particularly useful in that there are no film development costs and pictures can be viewed on screen whilst working on drawings or designs.

The USB (universal serial bus) is a standard *port* (connection point) on modern computers and can be used to attach devices such as scanners and cameras.

Output devices

Just as input devices allow us to communicate with computers, so output devices convert computer code into the information we can use. In this section we describe the devices that form part of typical personal and office computer systems.

Visual display unit

The most commonly used device for communicating with a computer is the *visual display unit* (VDU). The term VDU *terminal* is normally used to describe the screen and keyboard as a combined facility for input and output. On its own, the screen is called a *monitor* or *display*.

Technical features of monitors

Screen size

A screen's size is quoted as a measurement across the diagonal. For desktop personal computers, 14" or 15" is standard, but 17", 19" and 21" are also available. The larger screens are needed for applications such as computer-aided design (CAD). This is because the level of detail on some designs cannot be properly seen on a standard screen. Notebook computer screens, which use a different technology to desktop models, are obviously smaller and typically around 12" across the diagonal.

Screen resolution and video memory

A screen's *resolution* is one measurement indicating the clarity or sharpness of displayed text or graphics. Images are formed on the screen with pixels (picture elements). A pixel is one dot in a graphic image. A display screen is divided into thousands or millions of such pixels, organised in rows and columns. By varying the colours and luminosity (brightness) of individual pixels, text and graphic images are displayed. A high resolution screen packs pixels more densely to produce sharper images. A lower resolution will produce a more 'grainy' image, rather like a photograph which has been enlarged to many times its original size.

Any given screen has a *maximum resolution*. This is the number of pixels it is capable of displaying. This maximum may be reduced, depending on several other things, such as the number of colours to be used and the amount of *video memory* on the graphics card. The software which controls the graphics card can then be used to set the screen's resolution to the user's requirements (up to the screen's maximum).

Screen size and resolution

A resolution of more than 1024 × 768 is only practical for screen sizes of 17" or larger. This is because higher resolutions on a small screen make the images too small to see.

Refresh rate

The contents of a display must be continually refreshed, that is re-displayed. Flicker occurs when the eye can detect a gap between each screen refresh cycle. If the refresh rate is quick enough, the eye will not detect any flicker. Refresh rates are measured in Hz (cycles per second) and a typical rate is around 75 Hz.

Monochrome and colour

A monochrome monitor uses one colour for the text or graphic images and one for the background, for example, white, green or amber on black. Colour monitors use red, green and blue, which can be mixed together in different quantities to produce different colours. For example, when red, green and blue are mixed in exactly the same quantities, we see white light; red and green in equal quantities produces yellow; two parts red and one part green gives orange. In fact, by varying the quantities and the mixtures, any colour can be produced.

Resolution and colour range

The more colours a screen can display, the more memory is required, so graphics cards (or adapters) have their own memory. In practice, the maximum number of colours, which can be up to 16·7 million, is set by the graphics adapter. Higher resolutions also use more memory, so although a graphics card may allow 16·7 million colours at a resolution of 1024 × 768, it may only permit 256 colours when the resolution is increased to 1600 × 1200. Typically, such a graphics card would have several megabytes of its own special RAM.

Text mode

For some applications, graphics display is not needed and when operated in text mode, the computer system needs to use less power and memory. This is an advantage when numerous VDUs are controlled by a central computer.

In text mode, characters are formed using a matrix of *pixels* as shown in the adjacent example and the clarity of individual characters is determined by the number of pixels used. The same principle is used in character printers, such as the ink-jet (see Printers). Selected dots within the matrix are illuminated to display particular characters. There are various main text modes, including one that displays 40 characters and another that displays 80 characters in each of 25 rows.

VDU applications

Although specific recommendations cannot be given here, it is possible to provide advice for broad application areas. Text displays are suitable for standard applications, such as ordering, sales and stock control systems where there is no graphics requirement. Text-based displays are often used at supermarket checkouts or a in car spares departments.

General office applications make use of word processors, spreadsheets and databases. They all run under operating systems such as Windows 98, through a mouse-driven, graphical interface. For general office applications, a 15" monitor is probably the norm. Although larger screens are generally better, they take up more desk space and, of course, are more expensive.

Graphics-intensive applications include computer-aided design (CAD), photo-editing, graphic design, desktop publishing, video-editing and animation and larger monitors, from 17" to 21" are essential for these applications.

Higher resolutions of 1024×768, 1280×1024 and 1600×1200 need greater screen areas to ensure that images are large enough to allow detailed working.

Ferroelectric liquid crystal display (FLCD)

Portable devices, such as laptop and notebook computers and personal digital devices (PDAs) demand flat screen displays with low power consumption. Ferroelectric liquid crystal display or FLCD fulfils these requirements and is the most widely used technology for portable devices. It uses ferroelectric materials as bistable (two state) devices. Computer components use bistable devices to indicate a binary 1 or 0. Binary coding is used throughout a computer system to represent every kind of information which it handles; such information could be, for example, text, numbers or bit mapped (see earlier) screen images. The ferroelectric bistable device remains in one of two stable states until an electric field is applied. The field causes the material to switch to its second state; this state remains until another electric field is applied. The full display consists of FLC cells, sandwiched between two glass plates. When a positive charge is applied to a cell, light is blocked and the image appears dark. A negative charge changes the orientation of the molecules in the FLC cell and light is able to pass through. Cells are arranged in rows and columns, like the pixels (picture elements - the dots which make up the screen image) on a CRT display. Filters are used to provide colour images.

Display qualities are improving and now provide an alternative to the CRT screen, and power consumption is very low. A CRT screen image is updated (scanned) 50 to 60 times per second (Hz), whereas the refresh rate for an FLC display can be as low as 10Hz. Low power consumption is an important quality for battery powered devices, such as notebook computers. The need for 'greener' (less environmentally damaging) computer systems is likely to advance the cause of this type of display. Larger FLC displays (up to 21 inches) are available.

Printers

Computer printers vary according to the technology they use for the printing process, the quality of their printed output, the speed of printing and whether they can print in black and shades of grey, or in colour, or both.

Liquid ink jet

Ink jet printers spray high-speed streams of ink droplets from individual nozzles in the print head on to the paper to form individual characters or smooth graphical images. Individual text characters are formed by the print head as a matrix of dots.

By a series of passes and adjustments to the head's position, graphics can also be produced. Although the output quality is high, print speeds for graphical work are very slow. Liquid ink jets produce their best quality output on special paper, which is considerably more expensive than standard copier paper. The best glossy paper costs around £1 per sheet. The fastest liquid ink jets can print 2 pages per minute (ppm) in economy mode (low resolution), but $0 \cdot 5$ ppm is more usual. Colour printing at the best resolutions of 600 to 700 dots per inch (dpi) is even slower. At these resolutions, near photographic quality can be achieved.

Solid ink jet

A *solid ink jet* uses sticks of ink (rather like crayons) and these are turned to liquid by being heated. In contrast to the more common liquid ink jet, the solid ink jet is quick at 3 to 4 ppm, using the base resolution of 300 dpi; this is good enough for general business graphics, but not for photographic quality. The solid ink jet achieves its high speed by using a print head the full width of an A4 sheet. Solid ink jet printers cost several thousand pounds.

Laser printers

Laser printers are called *page printers*, because they effectively print a complete page at one time. To do this, the printer must have received the contents of an entire page from the controlling computer, before it starts printing. Laser printers may be monochrome only or both monochrome and colour. Printing speeds are far superior to ink jet printers, with similar quality output.

Monochrome laser printer

A *personal* model will print at between 12 and 17 ppm, typically at 600 dpi, but also up to 1200 dpi. The highest resolutions are used where very high quality output is needed, for example, in publishing.

Some models of *network* laser, designed to serve the printing needs of many users, can print 32ppm at 600 dpi or even 50 ppm at 300 dpi. The lower of these two resolutions in perfectly good for standard printing, including invoices and general correspondence. However, such printers are expensive and aimed at high volume use, perhaps a maximum of 900,000 pages per month.

Colour laser printer

Alongside the solid ink jet, the colour laser produces the highest print speeds, ranging from 2 to 5 ppm. Resolutions are similar to the monochrome models, up to 1200 dpi. An advantage of colour lasers over liquid ink jets is that they can produce the best quality on standard paper. The quality of liquid ink jet printing depends on the quality of paper used. As you would expect, these advantages are gained at a price, colour laser printers costing several thousands of pounds. However, the speed of the laser printer allows it to be shared on a network, so the cost per user for colour printing may be little more than that of buying a personal ink jet for each user. Running costs are also much lower than for ink jet printers.

Other types of printers

Line impact

As the name suggests, this type of printer uses hammers to print the characters on to the continuous stationery, a complete line at a time. There are two main types, chain and drum. They are used as system printers, for internal, high volume reports and can achieve speeds of between 500 and 1400 lines per minute (lpm).

Large format plotter (drum plotter)

Used for design work, a large format printer can handle poster images up to 150 feet long and 54 inches wide. Monochrome and colour models are available. Figure 4.6 shows a typical example.

Flatbed plotter

This type of plotter looks like a drafting board with pens mounted on a carriage which moves along guide tracks. The paper is placed on the bed. The pens can be raised or lowered as the image being created requires and different coloured pens can be brought into use at various stages of the process. Drawing movements are executed by movement of the carriage along the tracks and by the pens along the carriage (Figure 4.7). The size of paper which can be accommodated is limited by the size of the plotter bed, but this can be extremely large.

Figure 4.6. *Large format drum plotter*

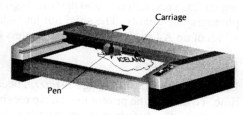

Figure 4.7. *Flat bed plotter*

Voice processing - recognition and synthesis

The recognition process is used for input and the synthesis for output. Human speech varies in accent, personal style of speech and pitch and the interpretation of the spoken word makes the development of systems capable of handling the full range of spoken communication a difficult process. In recent years, voice recognition systems have been developed which will allow both command and general text input to be effected by voice input. These systems can be trained by the user to recognise his or her particular speech patterns and to learn new vocabulary.

The effectiveness of voice recognition systems may be limited by, for example, a poor quality microphone, an inability to adjust to the differing speeds of speech and regional accents, or to distinguish between words which have the same spelling or sound the same, but have different meanings (homonyms - grate, great, know, no, you, yew and so on).

Devices can be used to give commands for machinery control, for example, up, down, left, right, fast, slow etc. Paralysed persons can control a wheelchair or lighting and heating through a voice recognition device controlled by a microprocessor. There are also applications which operate effectively because the communications are highly specialised and the conversation requirements extremely limited. Banks provide telephone banking through interactive voice response (IVR) systems; customers can obtain account balances, order statements or cheque books and make money transfers by spoken commands or by tone entry with the telephone keypad. Interaction is very carefully controlled by the system and callers are interrogated for precise information, such as their account number. By using a highly structured series of questions and answers, IVR systems only need to recognise key values such as the digits from 0 to 9 and the words 'yes' and 'no'. A caller's spoken request for information is digitised and sent to the host computer; the response is converted into synthesised speech and read out to the caller. IVR systems speak by forming pre-recorded words and phrases into sentences and playing them. For example, a request for an account balance may bring the response "Your balance is", followed by a series of digits which were recorded separately, interspersed by the word "pounds" and "credit" or "debit", as appropriate.

Other systems using voice recognition and voice synthesis include robot operation, telephone answering and information provision concerning the time, share prices, and railway timetables.

Screen readers allow the user to hear what is on screen, such as text or menu commands as the mouse is moved over them.

✐Exercises

1. Give an example of an application of each of the following: *OMR*; *OCR*.
2. List the names of *hand-held* input devices which provide alternatives to a keyboard and give an example when each device may be essential or desirable.
3. Using the example of greenhouse ventilation, briefly explain circumstances when an *analogue to digital converter* (ADC) may be used.
4. Give two reasons why a publisher would need a *laser printer*, in preference to other types of printer.
5. Identify and explain the benefits of two input devices which are specially designed to help the physically disabled.
6. Explain the term *screen resolution* and identify an application when high screen resolution would be important.
7. Give two advantages which FLCD screens have over CRT screens.
8. Suggest two applications of voice recognition systems and explain the particular difficulties which the technology has to overcome.

Storage systems

Backing storage is needed to hold programs and data files, from where they can be recalled as necessary by the computer. They are all *non-volatile* - their contents are not lost when power is removed. The purpose of main memory or RAM, which is volatile, is to hold programs and data currently in use - it is not a permanent storage area. A wide range of different backing storage systems is available, to suit every kind of computer system and user requirement. They vary according to:

❏ the technology they use and the way they operate;

❏ the speed with which they can record and retrieve data;

❏ capacity, that is, the amount of data they can hold;

❏ whether they are read-only (the contents cannot be changed) or read-write (the contents can be changed).

A common feature of all disk storage systems is the way in which they are addressed by the computer system. Magnetic disk addressing principles are described in the following section.

Magnetic disk

All disk storage systems provide *direct access* to data. This is in contrast to tape systems where data has to be accessed *serially*, that is, the order in which it is organised. When data is to be written to or read from disk, a specific *location* can be identified, by its address. Tape devices do not have locations which can be addressed, so data can only be accessed serially.

Magnetic disk addressing

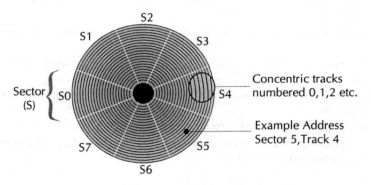

Figure 5.1. *Addressing structure on disk surface*

In a similar fashion to the first line of a typical postal address of house number and street, magnetic disks use *sector* and *track*. This structure in Figure 5.1 is simplified and shows 8 sectors numbered 0 to 7, a number of tracks, numbered from 0, starting with the outermost track (in reality, on a hard disk, there would be hundreds of tracks) and an example address, Sector 5,

Track 4. To read from or write to a disk location directly, the software must specify the address.

Hard disks and other high capacity systems use a number of disks within the one device and this makes the address structure slightly more complicated (Topic 18).

Hard disk

A typical microcomputer has an internal hard disk with a capacity measured in gigabytes (GB).

An illustration of its internal components is provided in the Figure 5.2. The pack of disks are rotated at high speed, between 4,500 and 10,000 revolutions per minute (rpm). The read/write heads move in or out across the surface of the disk to reach the required track.

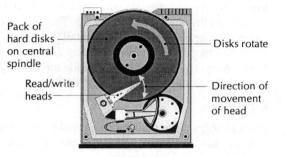

Pack of hard disks on central spindle

Read/write heads

Disks rotate

Direction of movement of head

Figure 5.2. *Hard disk drive components*

Access speed

The speed with which data can be read from, or written to, a hard disk is measured as the *average seek time*, in thousandths of a second, or milliseconds (ms). This means that to access a location, the read/write heads have to move to the required track. The time taken to reach the track is known as the *seek time*. A typical average seek time is between 7 ms (milliseconds) and 10 ms. The seek time is usually better in systems which use higher spin speeds. This means that the correct sector comes into position more quickly.

When a read or write instruction is issued, the head is not usually positioned over the sector where the required data are stored, so there is some *rotational delay* while the disk rotates into the proper position. On average, the time taken is half a revolution of the disk pack. This average time is known as the latency of the disk.

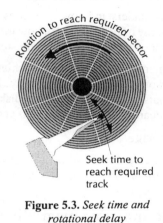

Rotation to reach required sector

Seek time to reach required track

Figure 5.3. *Seek time and rotational delay*

Another major influence on the speed of a disk drive is its *controller*. This is the interface between the disk drive and the computer system.

Hard drive interface standards

SCSI stands for Small Computer Systems Interface. It is a high speed, parallel interface (or device controller) standard, defined by ANSI (American National Standards Institute). SCSI interfaces are widely available for connecting microcomputers to a range of peripheral devices, including hard disks and printers; SCSI interfaces are also used for connecting computers to one another, and to local area networks. Separate ports (a port is a location for passing data in or out of a computer) do not have to be used for each attached device. Instead, one device can be connected directly to a SCSI port in the computer and other devices (a maximum total of seven) can be linked to the first, in a "daisy chain". Only one device can communicate through the SCSI port at any one time, so each device in a chain is given a separate logical address, which indicates its priority. The device with the highest address is given top priority. Macintosh computers and some computers in the IBM range include an SCSI port as standard.

PCs and 'compatibles' can be upgraded to include an SCSI port, with the use of an expansion card; this is necessary for the connection of a Jaz drive (see later). The SCSI interface was of particular value for the attachment of high speed devices, such as hard disk drives, because it allowed more rapid data transfer than was the norm for the IDE (Industry Device Electronics) based hard drives, used in most PCs. The IDE interface has become most popular with PCs because it is cheaper and easier to install than the SCSI interface. IDE performance has now been increased to that of a SCSI interface. Newer standards, the Enhanced IDE and UDMA (Ultra Direct Memory Access) now provide *data transfer rates* which are superior to those of SCSI and similar to those of the new SCSI Wide.

Capacity

Modern software, with its provision of an ever-increasing range of features and the use of multimedia images, such as photographs and video clips, demand larger capacity disk drives. Typical capacities used to be measured in megabytes (MB), but are now measured in gigabytes (GB) - thousands of megabytes.

To understand how capacities can be increased in this way, it is necessary to be familiar with some basic ideas about how the data is stored on magnetic disk. The binary codes used to represent data in a computer are stored as magnetic dots along the length of disk tracks.

Increases in capacity are achieved by packing the magnetic dots more closely together, that is, more densely. Until recently, it was thought that optical media, such as CD-ROM would far outstrip capacities of hard disk drives. This has not been the case, because technical advances mean that the magnetic dots can be packed more densely than was previously thought possible.

Usage

The hard disk, with its huge capacity and fast access times, remains the best product for the *primary drive* in a computer system, holding the operating system and main applications programs.

Removable magnetic disk

The products in this category include: floppy disk; Iomega Zip disk; Jaz disk.

Floppy disk

The floppy disk has, until recently, been the main product for securing small files. Although several developments have increased its capacity, the 1·44 MB of the 3·5" floppy disk (see below), is insufficient for many users. A graphics image, for example, is often too large to fit on a floppy. It also provides very slow access times, with a spin speed of only 360 rpm.

Usage

Floppy disks are extremely cheap and a 3·5" drive is still standard equipment in a microcomputer system. For many home and small business users, it is adequate for making backup copies of individual data files held on the primary hard drive or passing copies of data files to other users. The increasing use of e-mail, which allows the *attachment* of such files, is likely to reduce the need for this practice. The 1·44 MB floppy disk is inadequate for many applications, such as the production and storage multimedia presentations and large volume file backup.

Data compression programs

It is possible to compress files so that they will fit on to a floppy disk, through the use of data compression programs, such as WinZip. Bitmap files, in particular, will compress to about 2% or 3% of their original size. Compression may allow, for example, text and graphics files with a total capacity of 50MB (which would take at least 35 disks) to be stored on around 10 disks.

Backing up to even 10 floppy disks is still a laborious task and likely to discourage the vital task of frequent and regular backup.

Iomega Zip

A Zip disk cartridge holds 100MB or 250MB of data on its single platter. The Zip drive can be attached *externally*, to the parallel printer port or the printer and Zip drive connectors can be 'piggy backed' to allow both to connect to the port. An internal option is also available which allows it to be connected, as another drive, to the hard disk controller.

Access speed

Attached externally, the Zip drive is still relatively slow, but when attached internally to the main hard drive controller, it has a seek time of around 30 ms. This compares with a typical hard drive seek time of between 7 and 12 ms.

Usage

Its 100MB capacity makes it ideal for users who need to store large files, such as those producing design and multimedia presentations. The quickness of the internal drive encourages regular backup and although not matching the speed of the hard disk drive, it can be effective as an extension to the on-line storage system. Files could be retrieved directly from the Zip without first copying them to the hard drive.

Iomega Jaz

A single Jaz cartridge contains two platters and will store 1GB of data (2GB with data compression). It can be attached internally or externally, but only to a SCSI drive controller;

Access speed

The Jaz drive has an average seek time of between 10 and 12 ms, making it as quick as most fixed hard disks.

Usage

Its huge capacity and hard drive performance make the Jaz drive a true extension to on-line storage. Files can be retrieved from a Jaz cartridge as quickly as from the main hard drive. It is highly suitable for backing up the contents of the primary hard drive.

Magnetic tape

In contrast to disk, tape does not have locations which can be separately *addressed*. For this reason tape storage systems provide only *serial access* to data, that is, the order in which it is stored. Although magnetic tape systems can be used for some data processing applications, such as payroll, which do not need direct access, the systems described here are used primarily for security backup. Although the arrangement of data on tape is different from that on disk, the magnetic storage principles are the same.

Tape backup systems

To prevent permanent loss of data, it is vital that a computer system's main hard drive is regularly backed up. The more frequently the contents of files change, the more frequent should be the backups. For a single microcomputer hard drive, a single tape is often sufficient. A single tape device is often referred to as a *tape streamer*.

When several tapes are required for a complete backup, such as for a large network server, a *tape library* is essential. This device includes an *autochanger*, which rather like a juke box, automatically loads the next tape. The alternative is to insert new tapes manually, which for a process that may take hours, is not desirable.

Capacity

The most popular tape backup systems use Digital Audio Tape (DAT) cartridges. For example, a 120 metre tape can store up to 4GB, and 8GB using data compression. A tape library system, capable of holding 8 such tapes, would be able to backup 64GB of data.

Data transfer rate

Typically, tape backup systems can transfer data to the tape at between 35 and 60MB per minute. If compression is being used the rate will vary during backup, because some kinds of data take longer to compress than others. At an average of 50MB per minute, a 4GB drive would take 80 minutes (4000MB ÷ 50MB).

Optical media

Instead of using magnetism to record data, optical media are read or recorded using laser light. To *record*, a high intensity laser beam burns tiny holes into the surface of the disk, each hole representing a binary 1 or a binary 0. To *read*, a lower intensity laser is used to detect the holes and the binary digits they represent. The binary digits are recorded along tracks in a similar fashion to magnetic disk, but instead of using concentric tracks, optical disks use a spiralling track, similar to the old gramophone records.

Compact disk (CD)

CDs are optical media and a single disk can hold approximately 650MB of data. Although data transfer rates are continually being improved, CD drives are slower than hard magnetic disks. There are three types of CD.

❑   CD-ROM (compact disk-read only memory). As the name indicates, the data is recorded during manufacture and can only be read by a CD-ROM drive. The main uses of the CD-ROM are for multimedia applications, such as games and encyclopaedia and software installation. The large memory requirement of many software packages means that delivery on floppy disk is impractical, whereas one CD-ROM disk is often sufficient to deliver an entire package

❑   CD-R (recordable - once only). This is a CD which can be written to once, with a suitable CD-Writer. Provided the contents do not need to be updated, this can be a useful medium for archiving documentary and other material. The falling cost of

CD-Writers and the small cost of each disk makes it possible for businesses and other organisations to produce their own multimedia training programmes.

❑ CD-E (erasable - read and write). Because data can be erased and updated, this type of CD is an alternative to magnetic disk, although its data transfer rates are still relatively slow.

DVD (digital versatile disk)

Using the same basic principles as the CD, DVD packs the data more densely and can store 4.7GB, compared with the CD's 650MB. With this capacity and its quicker data transfer rate, a single DVD disk can hold 133 minutes of video, with Dolby surround sound. It is probable that DVD drives will be an increasingly important removable storage device, particularly with the increasing use of video in multimedia products.

✍️Exercises

1. (i) Identify one application which requires *direct* access to records and one application which handles records *serially*.

   (ii) Which feature of magnetic disk allows it to be used for *direct access*?

2. A disk's performance may be indicated by its *average seek time*. What does this signify?

3. (i) Review a hardware catalogue and draw up a comparative list of read/write storage devices, of all available types, and for each device detail its capacity, performance rating and the interface standard it uses.

   (ii) Identify three applications which have radically different storage requirements and suggest which of the items from the list in (i) would be most appropriate. Justify your choice, making reference to capacity and performance rating.

4. What is the purpose of a tape streamer?

5. What major advantage does an optical storage medium have over a magnetic storage medium?

6. Give two examples when an organisation may make use of DVD.

Computer architecture

This Topic looks at a number of aspects of computer systems architecture and builds on some of the basic ideas dealt with in Topic 3. The technical specification for any particular computer system will not only refer to the types of component, but also their performance and capacity ratings, which individually and in combination with one another contribute to the overall system performance. The following sections explain the operation and function of each component within the architecture of a computer system. Typical capacity and performance ratings are also given.

Memory

RAM

RAM constitutes the working area of the computer and is used for storage of program(s) and data currently in use. Computer memory is measured in Kb (kilobytes), where 1 Kb is 1024 bytes; for larger memory, the unit of measurement is Mb (megabyte), which is 1024 Kb. Generally, the performance of a computer system can be improved by the addition of more memory. Other upgrading measures, such as the addition of a *hard disk controller* will make less impact on system performance if main memory capacity is inadequate. If there is too little memory, more frequent access to disk is required. As a hard disk drive is a relatively slow component, compared with main memory, frequent disk accesses slow down overall system performance.

Large main memory enables the system to keep *resident* all the files it needs for an application. RAM is volatile (the current contents are lost when power is removed or different programs and data are entered), so all programs and data files are held more permanently on a magnetic storage medium; invariably this is floppy or hard disk.

Technical features

RAM is directly accessible by the processor and memory/processor transfers which occur during a program's execution have to be made as quickly as possible to maximise the use of the processor's power. The section on processors describes the use of a 'clock' which generates regularly timed pulses to synchronise the activities of the processor and explains that different activities take different numbers of clock pulses. Memory/processor transfers, although extremely quick, typically 60 to 80 nanoseconds (ns) for a read from RAM, are relatively slow when compared with typical processor speeds. Thus, the quicker the transfer can be carried out, the less time that the processor spends unoccupied. One quality RAM should possess, therefore, is speed. Predictably, the higher the speed, the greater is the cost.

Types of RAM

Broadly, two types of RAM are used in computers. They are: static RAM (SRAM); dynamic RAM (DRAM).

A number of comparisons can be drawn between the two types:

- ❑ DRAMs are easier to make than SRAMs;

❑   more DRAM can be packed on to a single integrated circuit or 'chip' than is possible with SRAM;

❑   DRAM consumes less power than SRAM;

❑   static RAM, as the term suggests, retains its contents as long as power is maintained, whereas Dynamic RAM needs to be refreshed (the contents of each location are rewritten) at intervals not exceeding 2 milliseconds (ms);

❑   SRAM can be written to and read from more quickly, but is more expensive than DRAM.

The most important features for comparison relate to speed of access and cost. To maximise use of a powerful processor SRAM is the obvious choice. Unfortunately, the needs of modern software for large main memory would make computer systems based wholly on SRAM very expensive. The use of *graphical user interfaces*, such as Windows 98 and the increasing sophistication of software packages, incrementally increases the amount of RAM which is needed. So, for economic reasons, main memory consists of DRAM chips grouped together on a memory board. A conflict exists between processor speed and memory cost. Doubling the clock speed of a processor from 200 MHz to 400 MHz does not necessarily double the speed of the computer's overall operation because of other factors, including *disk access* time and memory read time. To help improve the speed of memory accesses and still keep down the cost of memory, a system of *cache memory* can be used.

EDO (*extended* or *enhanced data out*) RAM has been used in many of the most recent microcomputer systems because of its superior access times. Despite this performance improvement, *cache memory* is still an essential part of a computer's configuration.

SDRAM (Synchronous DRAM) synchronises with the processor bus and running at 100MHz is around twice as fast as EDO RAM. As processor speeds increase, new memory technologies have to be designed to keep up.

Cache memory

To understand the function of cache memory it is necessary to refer to a feature identified in the section on the processor, namely *wait-state*. A wait-state is an extra clock pulse added to a processor cycle when it accesses memory. The slower the memory, the more wait-states which have to be added to processor cycles to give the memory time to respond. The greater the number of wait-states, the lower the overall computer system performance. Thus, a high performance processor is wasted if it is used with a slow memory system which requires many wait-states.

A memory system which requires zero wait-states will allow the system (ignoring peripheral device performance) to function at the maximum performance of the processor. It must be emphasised that overall system performance depends on all components forming a computer system and that *disk access time* also plays a major part in determining such performance. A cache memory system aims to provide the performance of fast Static RAM (SRAM) but at the lower cost of Dynamic RAM (DRAM). A cache is a small amount of very fast SRAM located between the processor and main memory.

Figure 6.1 illustrates the relationship between main memory, the processor and the cache.

The cache size is typically 256Kb to 512Kb and its purpose is to hold a copy of frequently used code and data. Instead of accessing the slower main memory (consisting of DRAM) for such data, the processor can go directly to the cache memory without incurring any wait-states. The effectiveness of

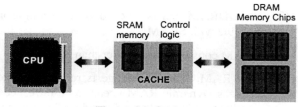

Figure 6.1. *Cache memory*

cache memory is based on the principle that once a memory location has been accessed, it is likely to be accessed again soon. This means that after the initial access, subsequent accesses to the same memory location need go only to the cache. Much computer processing is repetitive, so a high hit rate in the cache can be anticipated. The cache hit rate is simply the ratio of cache hits to the total number of memory accesses required by the processor. Systems using cache memory may achieve an 85 to 90 per cent hit rate. Thus, system performance can be radically improved beyond that possible with other systems using the same processor but lacking a cache memory system.

Cache memory aims to improve memory access times and keep down memory costs. The larger the cache, the greater the hit rate but the greater the cost of the memory. For example, a cache the same size as the main memory would obviously give a 100 per cent hit rate but would defeat the object of having a cache. Modern processors have an integral cache (on the same chip) which provides even better cache performance.

ROM (read only memory)

The term *firmware* is used to describe programs and data which are hard-wired into the computer, using integrated circuit ROM chips. ROM is non-volatile, so its contents are not lost when the machine is switched off and they cannot be overwritten by other programs or data. ROM is normally used to store an initial set of instructions which allow the booting of a computer system and the subsequent loading of the rest of the operating system. ROM (Read Only Memory) is a permanent storage area for special programs and data which have been installed during the process of computer manufacture. The contents are hard-wired and cannot be altered by software.

The software contained within ROM is fairly standard for most machines and generally includes part of the BIOS (Basic Input/Output System). As the name suggests, the BIOS handles the basic hardware operations of input and output. The aim of the BIOS is to provide an interface between the programmer and the computer. The interface relieves the programmer of concern about the physical characteristics of the hardware devices which form the system. As such, the BIOS is machine orientated and will vary from one make of machine to another.

There are two other types of ROM:

❑ *PROM* or programmable ROM chips, which can be purchased content-free and used to store software, such as word processors and spreadsheets, which are used regularly. Plugged into vacant slots inside a computer's system casing, the software they contain can then be accessed without reference to conventional backing storage, but simply by transfer to RAM (Random Access Memory - main memory). It has to be said that this is now less common, and most packages are stored on either a CD-ROM or hard disk drive, from where they can be loaded very quickly. Software is frequently being upgraded and the trouble of replacing ROM chips makes it an unattractive option. Once recorded upon, PROM chips cannot be re-used for any other purpose;

❑ *EPROM* or erasable programmable ROM chips fulfil a similar function to PROM chips, except for the fact that their contents can be erased by exposure to ultra-violet light and then replaced using a special EPROM programmer device.

Flash memory

The main memory in notebook computers is sometimes provided by flash memory, which requires no battery power to maintain its contents. Power is required to read from and write to the memory. Unfortunately, the access times are slower than those available with conventional forms of RAM and a flash memory card will wear out after approximately 10,000 erasures. Of course, they can be replaced when this happens. A flash memory card can be write-protected and because it includes a standard *interface*, it can be made to appear as a hard disk to the rest of the computer system.

Processor

The processor is a CPU (Central Processing Unit) on a chip and provides the central base for a machine's power. The speed with which a computer system is able to handle and process data depends on all of its hardware components, including the processor(s), RAM and disk storage systems. Generally, the most significant component in determining the speed of a system is the processor which fetches, decodes and executes the instructions needed to make the system form particular tasks, such as input, output, storage and calculation.

Most computers still use processors designed according to the Von Neumann model in which a stored program is executed by sequentially stepping through instructions stored in the main memory or RAM of a computer system. This repetitive and automatic process is known as the *fetch-execute cycle*. Apart from increases in the speed of the processor, performance improvements are also obtainable by the use of multiple processors which can, for example, work on separate tasks at the same time, or work simultaneously on the same task but with different sets of data. Before describing such parallel processing, we explain the factors which control the speed of a single processor.

Clock speed

As the initiator of all the activities in a computer, the processor has a wide range of tasks to perform and to ensure that these tasks are properly synchronised, an internal clock mechanism is used. The speed of the clock is one determinant of how quickly a processor can *execute* instructions.

Synchronising operations

To synchronise the processor's operations, the clock generates regularly timed pulses, at rates of hundreds of millions per second. A technical specification will express this rating in MHz (Megahertz or million *cycles* per second). For example a 500 MHz processor operates with a clock running at 500 million pulses or cycles per second.

Different processor activities take different times to complete. For example, it takes longer to read the contents of a memory location (a *memory read*) than to increment a value stored in one of the registers within the processor. Any such processor activity must be synchronised with a clock cycle. The number of clock cycles which the processor needs to complete an operation will depend on the type of operation. For example, one operation may be completed within a single clock cycle, whilst another may take several cycles. The most recent processors are able to execute one or more instructions for each clock pulse.

Wait state

When a processor handles data more quickly than it can be accessed from main memory, a memory read may take more than one clock cycle to complete. Each additional clock cycle is known as a wait state. The topic is referred to earlier, in the section on *cache memory*. Subject to certain limitations to be explained later, the greater the clock rate, the quicker the computer system (as a whole) will perform. For example, a 500 MHz processor will carry out processing more quickly than a 200 MHz processor.

Word length

Any given processor is designed to handle a particular number of bits as a unit. The size of this unit is known as the processor's *word length*. A processor with a word length of, for example, 32 bits, uses that unit size during the execution of arithmetic, logic, data transfer or input/output instructions. In addition, any working registers within the processor are also equal to the word length of the processor.

Processor data bus and motherboard

Within the processor, data are transmitted along a set of parallel lines called an *internal data bus*. An *external data bus* acts as the interface with the system's *motherboard*. The motherboard is a circuit board into which the system components are plugged. If the board is designed for the needs of a particular processor, the data path between the processor and memory components is at least as wide as the processor's internal bus. Thus, a motherboard designed to take a 32 bit processor has a 32 bit data path to connect it to other processor or memory chips. The processor's external data bus (which connects with the motherboard) is also 32 bits wide. The motherboard is connected to a *system data bus,* which acts as the communication channel between the motherboard and the other system components.

Table 6.1 shows the word lengths of generations of Intel processors.

Processor	word length	internal bus	external bus
8080	8 bits	8 bits	8 bits
8088	16 bits	16 bits	8 bits
8086	16 bits	16 bits	16 bits
80286	16 bits	16 bits	16 bits
i386	32 bits	32 bits	32 bits
i486	32 bits	32 bits	32 bits
P24T	32 bits	64 bits	32 bits
Pentium	32 bits	64 bits	64 bits

Table 6.1. *Generations of Intel processors showing word lengths and bus widths*

Processor architecture

The internal structure of a processor is generally referred to as its *architecture*. Within the integrated circuits that form the processor are contained a complex collection of component units, including registers, counters, arithmetic and logic circuits and memory elements. Although the details of such architecture are mainly of concern to the programmer working at machine code level, two main approaches to processor design are briefly described below. All the instructions available with a particular processor are known as its *instruction set*. CISC is an acronym for *complex instruction set computer* and RISC stands for *reduced instruction set computer*.

CISC architecture

For some time, the view was that longer word lengths should be used to create more complex instruction sets and thus, more powerful processors. This approach has given way to the RISC design, which makes more effective use of the increased word lengths available in modern processors.

RISC architecture

A RISC processor exhibits a number of particular design features:

❑   A reduced instruction set processor, as the name suggests, is one which provides only a small number of different instructions compared with the prevailing standards for its CISC competitors. Research into conventional CISC architecture has suggested that the average processor spends most of its time executing only a handful of simple instructions. Each instruction type in a RISC processor can be executed in only one clock pulse. More complex instructions can take several clock pulses.

❑   Super scalar execution. This is the ability to execute more that one instruction at once (in parallel pipelines). Thus, for example, a floating point arithmetic calculation can be executed in one pipeline, at the same time as an integer operation in the other. A separate arithmetic unit is available to deal with each. Intel's Pentium processor can, therefore, execute two instructions in one clock pulse, compared with its predecessor's (the i486) one.

❑   Integral cache memory. The topic of cache memory is examined earlier, but the location of this component on the processor provides faster data flow than is possible with a separate cache memory component.

❑   Branch prediction. The processor contains circuitry to predict the outcome of conditional branch instructions (when a certain condition is true, the program branches to an instruction out of the usual sequence) before they even enter the pipeline. Predictions are based on previous execution history. A correct prediction avoids retrieval of irrelevant instructions into the pipeline; instead, the valid instruction is fetched from the branch target address. An incorrect prediction means that the pipeline has to be cleared, but the algorithms for prediction achieve a high success rate, which makes the technique worthwhile.

A British microcomputer manufacturer, Acorn, was among the first to produce a RISC microcomputer called the ARM (Acorn RISC Machine). Now, all the world's major computer manufacturers produce their own RISC-based machines. Notable examples of modern RISC processors include the IBM RISC/6000 series, IBM/Motorola PowerPC601, DEC Alpha AXP and the Sun Microsystems/Texas Instruments SuperSparc. Such processors are designed for high performance systems, to be used as *file servers* or *workstations* in networks, rather than as stand-alone machines, where the power would be wasted. Unlike the Alpha, PowerPC and SuperSparc processors, which have been designed purely as RISC processors, the Intel i486 and Pentium processors have had to retain some CISC features, to remain compatible with the huge range of PC software designed for the i386 and its predecessors. The Alpha, PowerPC and SuperSparc processors are pure RISC processors and not compatible with software designed for the Intel range. This means that they are excluded from the lucrative PC software market. Although the Pentium still includes some complex instruction support, its design includes all the RISC features outlined earlier.

Parallel processing architectures

The potential for increasing computation speed through parallelism has long been recognised, its first real manifestation being in the change from computers which handled data serially bit by bit with a single processor to those manipulating parallel bit groupings or words, albeit still with only one processor. Parallelism as described here is concerned with the use, in a variety of approaches, of multiple processors to act upon either single or multiple streams of data. A number of factors have permitted the research and development of parallel processing architectures, which previously had not been cost-effective.

The development of VLSI (Very Large Scale Integration) circuits has allowed tremendous progress to be made in the miniaturisation of computer components, most significantly in terms of processor and memory chips, but although users have felt the benefits of significant speed improvements, they have not been of the same order. They continue to improve, but it has been apparent for some time that the power needs of some applications go beyond single processor systems. It is also recognised that the greatest increases in speed can be obtained through changes in system architecture. The RISC (Reduced Instruction Set Computer) approach is already bringing about significant benefits, but parallel architectures, despite the particular difficulties they present for the design of software which can take full advantage, probably hold the greatest potential for radical performance gains. Parallel hardware is, of course, only half the solution and it must be also possible to write programs that can execute in parallel. The Occam programming language developed by Inmos, addresses the special requirements of writing code for arrays of *transputers* (see later).

Parallel processing applications

A number of applications likely to benefit particularly from parallel processing are outlined below.

❑ *Weather forecasting*, which requires number crunching operations on huge volumes of data, gathered globally and from monitoring satellites, in time to produce accurate weather forecasts, rather than comments on existing weather conditions!

❑ *Graphics applications*. Ray tracing, for example, where a set of descriptors of three-dimensional objects in three-dimensional space is mapped onto a flat screen complete with shadows, refraction and reflections, needs considerable computation to trace where the light on each screen pixel came from. The application is most easily implemented on pipeline architecture, where it benefits from both the faster maths and the faster communication. With about 10 million calculations to generate a single screen picture, speed is vital when generating sequences of images. A major application is in aircraft flight simulators, where the scenes to be shown are not known exactly in advance, as they depend on the pilot's actions. To be of any use they need to be generated virtually instantaneously in real-time.

❑ *Simulation.* Engineering design problems benefit hugely from computer simulation. The designers of North Sea oil platforms could ill afford to build prototypes to test to destruction, so they carry out all the structural analysis on a Cray supercomputer costing around 20 million; the process only takes about 9 hours, but the time taken still makes extensive prototyping very expensive. A car body designer using a 1 million mainframe has to wait about 20 hours for a typical run to complete. These lengthy run-times mean that computer simulation tends to be used to validate designs already completed, rather than as a development tool.

❑ *Image processing.* A particularly exciting example involves the use of computers to assist the plastic surgeon in the repair of facial injuries or deformities. The patients head is scanned by cameras and the image digitised for display on a computer screen. This image can be rotated or tilted on screen by the surgeon and experimental cuts made, the results of which can then be viewed on screen from any angle. In this way, a plastic surgeon can study the results of a variety of strategies before making a single mark on the patient. The complexity of such image processing requires parallel processing if rapid response to user input is to be achieved. Industrial processes frequently require robots which can recognise different shaped components and possess sufficient spatial awareness to allow accurate assembly to take place. Artificial intelligence techniques are applied to both these areas, so that robots can learn and the power of parallel processing greatly enhances the opportunity for such developments.

❑ *Speech recognition* is an enormously complex process if a system is to be capable of handling a wide range of vocabulary, pronunciation and intonation, let alone the meaning of phrases and even sentences. Artificial intelligence techniques are being applied to the speech recognition process and parallel processing power greatly improves the opportunities for its evolution.

❑ *Financial and economic system modelling.* To make realistic assessments of the effectiveness of various economic strategies requires the processing of huge volumes of raw data.

Multi-processing
Parallel processing should not be confused with multi-processing architectures which allow the simultaneous running of several separate programs, but with each program only having control of one processor at a time.

Transputers
The Transputer is effectively a building block for parallel processing architectures; while it contains its own memory and processing elements, it also features unique serial links which allow it to communicate with other Transputers. A matrix of Transputers can be created with

each one solving a small part of a complete task. The addition of extra Transputers to a system incrementally adds the full power of each unit to the overall system performance. In theory, if one Transputer operates at 10 million instructions per second (mips), then two will give a system performance of 20 mips, 10 will give 100 mips and so on. In practice, the problem still remains of splitting computer processing problems into separate parts for each of the transputers to handle.

Buses

All computers have the same basic functional components, but the architectural details in some are far more complex than in others. A particular area of variation relates to the arrangement of the bus systems which permit communication between the various parts of the computer system. A number of features concerning buses can be identified:

❏ a bus is a group of parallel wires, one for each bit of a word, along which data can flow (as electrical signals);

❏ the *system* bus comprises a number of such communication channels, connecting a computer's processor and its associated components of memory and input/output(I/O) devices;

❏ a single bus may carry data for different functions at separate times or it may be dedicated to one function. A computer will usually have several buses, used for specific purposes, for example, the I/O bus or main memory to processor bus;

❏ some buses are *bi-directional*, that is data can flow in one direction or the other;

❏ the *width* of a bus determines the length of word which can be handled at one time. For example, a processor which used a 16-bit bus, but required a 32-bit word to address memory, would have to concatenate two 16-bit words in two separate fetch operations.

Communication is required within a processor, to allow movement of data between its various registers, between the processor and memory and for I/O transfers. In a *single* bus system, both I/O and memory transfers share the same communication channel, whereas in a *two-bus* system, I/O and memory transfers are carried out independently; similarly, in small systems with few I/O devices, they usually share the same bus, but a larger system requires several I/O buses to ensure efficient operation.

Each of the separately identified functions of memory, register-to-register and I/O transfers (assuming that the I/O bus is shared by a number of devices), must have the use of:

❏ a *data bus*, for the transfer of data subject to processing or manipulation in the machine;

❏ an *address bus* which carries the address of, for example, a memory word to be read or the output device to which a character is to be transmitted;

❏ a *control bus*, which as the name suggests, carries signals concerning the timing of various operations, such as memory write, memory read and I/O operations.

All signals on a bus follow strict timing sequences, some operations taking longer than others.

Expansion slots

These are slots into which expansion boards or cards can be plugged, to add extra features to a system. For example, a user may wish to install a sound card, to allow full use of multi-media software, or an additional *serial* port to connect to a modem. Expansion slots are connected to the system bus (it makes electrical contact), so when an expansion card is plugged in, it becomes part of the system.

I/O ports and interfacing

To allow an I/O device to communicate with the I/O bus, for example, to place data entered through a keyboard onto the data bus, requires the use of an I/O port. A number of I/O ports are usually available, the number and types depending on the range of devices which the system is designed to support. Each port has an *interfacing* role which must convert the data signals, as presented by the connected device, into the form required by the processor, as well as the converse for output data. Thus, for example, the *external* ASCII code used for data storage on a particular tape storage system, will probably have to be converted by the interface into the machine's particular *internal* code

✍️Exercises

1. What is *cache memory* and why is it used?
2. What do the abbreviations *CISC* and *RISC* stand for?
3. Why may a 'clock-doubled' processor not necessarily double the speed of the overall computer system?
4. What is meant by *parallel processing*?
5. What significance have parallel processing architectures for the way software is designed?
6. What are the functions of the: (i) data bus; (ii) address bus; (iii) control bus?
7. Research PC magazines for differing computer configurations and draw up a table which compares their specifications (RAM size, type, processor type, speed etc.). Judge the suitability of each for particular kinds of application (graphic design, word processing, accounts etc.).

Emerging technologies

The technology of Information and Communication Technology, labelled as ICT, arises from the convergence of the computer and communications technologies. The expansion and spread of ICT has profound implications for our society, in particular its erosion of the importance of location. This is particularly noticeable in the area of e-commerce and video conferencing. We begin with a summary of the major developments in ICT infrastructure, including the concept of the Information Super Highway, which are crucial to the expansion and increased sophistication of applications

Developments in the ICT infrastructure

Although communication between computers through networks is not a recent innovation (large institutions such as banks have been using data communications since the mid 1960s) the nature, range and facilities of networked systems have expanded massively since the early 1990s. A number of developments have been instrumental in the convergence of the IT (information technology) and communications technologies, to produce what we now refer to as Information Communications Technology or ICT. These developments include the following.

❑ Miniaturisation of electronic components and the advent of the microprocessor (a computer on a chip). The microprocessor is the central component of general purpose computers and of the embedded systems used in almost every electronic device.

The microprocessor has dramatically reduced costs of all electronic devices and made personal computing power affordable for many. It has also made all the other developments possible.

❑ Digitisation of existing and all new communications networks. The public switched telephone network (pstn) in the UK used to be entirely analogue and could not directly support the transmission of digital computer data. Today, the only analogue sections are those which connect domestic and some small business users to the network. Similarly, the first cellular networks used analogue signals to make connections between mobile phone users, but these networks are now digital. Television and radio networks are also being digitised. Digital signals maintain data integrity (the message is not corrupted) which means that in the case, for example, of radio and television communications, there is no interference such as crackle on sound or 'snow' on pictures. This integrity allows different signal channels to be closer together than is the case in analogue networks; this is why digital broadcasting networks can provide many more radio stations and television channels through the same networks.

For computer networks, *wideband* communications mean that text, sound and pictures from many different network users can be transmitted at the same time.

❑ Optical fibre cable, a communication medium which supports a much greater bandwidth than metal cable, and thus the ability to transmit more data.

❑ Expansion of the infrastructures for network communications. Satellite communications provide global reach at a fraction of the cost of cable and terrestrial transmitter systems. The fall in computer hardware costs has allowed massive growth in the number of computer systems which form the Internet and exponential growth in the number of users who communicate through it.

The most significant applications result from the expansion of the Internet (Topic 52) and the increasing numbers of people who have access to it. However, the popularity of the Internet would not have been as great if it could only support the transmission of text. Wideband communications have allowed the development of a World Wide Web of information represented by text, sound and images. This, in turn has allowed the Internet to be used for two new applications which are of major importance: e-commerce; video conferencing.

Information Super Highway

The term "information super highway" is used to describe an ICT infrastructure needed to support the development of an "information society" in which all citizens and organisations are able to take part. The information super highway must be accessible, mobile and sufficiently cheap to encourage its widespread use. The infrastructure will comprise fixed and mobile networks and for many applications must be able to carry multimedia information as well as traditional computer data, frequently in large volumes. Fixed and mobile sectors of the highway should integrate seamlessly, that is, users should be able to access information irrespective of the kind of network they are tapping into.

Multimedia is important for many educational and training applications and to deliver them remotely requires the use of *wideband* communications. Video conferencing is another area of growing importance which also requires wideband communications. The technology can reduce the need for face-to-face meetings and the travel costs they incur. According to BT, the business travel market is valued at £20 billion per annum, so even a two or three percent reduction in travel would bring significant environmental and economic benefits.

Wideband communications support can be increased with the use of fibre optic cabling and improved data compression techniques to squeeze more data down media which are presently regarded as narrow band.

The UK Government has sought to liberalise the telecommunications industry, partly to drive down the costs of communications technology and partly to encourage innovation. The growth of the mobile communications networks, for example, has been helped by the controversial policy of waiving normal local planning controls in respect of communication masts. The cost of connecting to a mobile network has fallen dramatically and a very high percentage of the UK population now use mobile phones. The development of phones with Internet access brings some ICT services to the many people who do not own a home computer. To further improve access efforts are being made to install computer with Internet access in, for example, community halls and libraries.

SuperJANET (Super Joint Academic Network) is a high speed, variable bandwidth network. One of its uses is to provide a service for teaching hospitals and relevant university sites for the transfer of high resolution images to support diagnosis and treatment of medical conditions. A logical development of this service would be to enable remote diagnosis.

The development of an information society has huge commercial and economic implications for a country, leading to improved productivity, more highly skilled jobs and higher wages.

Need for rapid response systems

A common characteristic of ICT applications such as e-commerce, telephone or Internet banking, share trading, booking systems, telephone directory enquiries and police, fire and ambulance emergency services is the need for rapid systems response. In share trading, for example, when a dealer decides to buy or sell shares at a particular moment, even a short delay in executing the transaction could see the price change significantly. When an emergency call is made to ambulance services, the information concerning location of the emergency and the state of injured persons must be communicated rapidly to the appropriate ambulance crew. Breakdown or overload of mobile communications would significantly damage the effectiveness of an emergency service.

Recent innovations

Interactive television (iTV)

As the term suggests, iTV television allows the viewer to interact and respond to information received through the set. Two-way communication allows viewers to ask for information, request to see particular programmes or films (video on demand), participate in studio discussions, buy goods from shopping channels or the Internet or use home banking services. Effectively, the television becomes a personal computer, albeit with a limited range of functions. Providers of iTV will include digital satellite broadcasters, cable television companies and Internet service providers.

It is likely that some television sets will have limited functions, perhaps for programme and information requests and audience participation. Other sets will include enhanced features which allow, for example, Internet shopping.

The division between the functions of personal computers and iTV are also starting to blur. Microsoft's Windows 98 operating system, for example, includes WebTV which supports some of the features of interactive television. With a TV tuner card installed, standard and interactive television broadcasts can be viewed on the computer screen. WebTV also handles Internet content and other data transmitted over broadcast networks. Even if a tuner card is not installed, TV program listings can be downloaded from broadcaster web sites and viewed through WebTV.

However, the presence of television sets in almost every home means that the greatest potential for the development of iTV is likely to be through that medium. Low-end iTV sets are likely to be much cheaper than home computer systems and for many people, the facilities provided by iTV may be all that they require. To allow Web browsing through an iTV set a new version of TV-HTML is being developed. An essential pre-requisite of iTV is the conversion of analogue television networks to digital networks.

Video phone

Modern video phones are fully-featured video conferencing systems which can be used with or without a computer. Internet video phones are available for connection through a computer modem, although the speed of the connection needs to support a video frame rate which gives a reasonably steady picture. Other phones are adapted for connection to ISDN and a variety of other network connection types. A video phone may include the following features:

❑ personal phonebook for storing names and user details and for quick dialling. The details and image of anyone in the phonebook can be called up at any time.

❑ video and voice mail which allow messages to be sent and stored for users who are unavailable to take a call;

❑ answer machine;

❑ caller and self-view windows;

❑ display controls to enlarge the video display or switch to full screen (in which case the self-view window is reduced in size;

❑ frame rate control. It may be necessary, for example, to slow the frame rate to keep the image synchronised with audio, which tends to lag slightly behind;

❑ remote camera operation. This allows the adjustment of your caller's camera to give you the view you want.

Wearable computers

The term personal computer applies to the current technology which sits on a desktop and its smaller offspring of notebooks and palmtops. None of them can be described as wearable and they all still rely on the familiar input devices of keyboard, mouse or stylus. Research into wearable computers is targeted at the development of more natural and spontaneous methods of computer input and control. To date, wearable computer research is centred around the idea of a head set with various sensors, such as a small digital camera and microphone, to the environment around the wearer. Input can be through speech recognition or finger gestures picked up by the small camera in the head set. Output to the wearer may be in the form of a small earpiece or a small display attached to the headset. Until recently, wearable computers were quite unwieldy, requiring a quite bulky headset and similarly awkward, though miniature PC attached to a waist belt. Although such devices have been used in specialist applications, they would not have found acceptance for general use. To be accepted, the wearable computer must be no more obtrusive than a pair of spectacles. One feature of the wearable computer is called *augmented memory*, which allows recognition of faces or physical items within the view of the wearer, allowing immediate recall of data relevant to the person or their physical surroundings. This would allow the wearer to be prompted with a person's name and other details, gathered from a previous meeting. Internet services can be made available through cellular networks.

Other possible applications of wearable computer include:

❑ manufacturing and assembly work. Training and technical support can be given to workers on site and the need for printed guides is reduced. Guidance can be readily updated, if necessary, through wireless networks.

❑ remote patient monitoring. Sensors on a patient's body can provide information for immediate diagnosis and treatment.

❑ education and training, particularly outside conventional classrooms.

❑   military. Immediate feedback on environment can be used, for example, by military personnel on reconnaissance.

Potential technologies

This section looks at those ICT technologies which are currently under development and the applications of which are still uncertain.

E-paper and e-ink

There are numerous e-books for sale on the Internet, such as Stephen King's short novel "Ride the Bullet" which costs just over a £1 to download and for which the publishers, Barnes and Noble, received over 200,000 download requests in the first 24 hours of its publication. A special reader program attempts to give the computer screen a paper-like quality, but e-books still tend to be short because of the difficulty of reading copious amounts of text on screen. Special portable e-book readers can also be bought from the publisher. Microsoft researchers have produced software called ClearType, which enhances the font to make for easier reading. Despite their success, e-books have not yet made significant inroads into the printed book market, partly because of the difficulty of reading text on screen, but also probably because e-books lack the tactile pleasures of conventional books, such as page turning.

An emerging technology for the production of *e-paper* may have the potential to be a true replacement for the printed page. The technology, called Gyricon and being developed by the Xerox Corporation, is thin sheets of plastic formed from millions of minute beads, similar to the toner particles used in laser printers and copiers. Each bead has one white side and one black side and fits into an oil-filled cavity in which it can rotate. Low power electrical impulses cause the beads to rotate and thus form black and white patterns for image or text representation. The researchers claim that the printing process could be effected through a pocket-sized device and once printed, no power source would be required to read it. Because the material can be rolled up and carried around it may be suitable for use as a newspaper, the contents of which could be updated daily.

Lucent/Bell laboratories are also working on an e-paper with E-Ink, the developer of an electronic ink technology which the researchers claim will both look and feel like paper. This e-ink is a coloured liquid formed from tiny spheres, each of which has a transparent outer surface and a filling of blue dye mixed with positively charged, microscopic chips of white pigment. The e-ink is held between two transparent sheets which can conduct the electrical charges which make the white pigment rise or fall to create the patterns for text or pictures. The researchers hope that this technology will allow the production of true electronic paper which will overcome the current loyalty to the printed word. It is likely that newspapers will be the first application for such a technology once it is fully developed.

Microchip implants

Research into the development and application of microchip implants for the human body is still very much in its infancy and if seriously developed will be the subject of considerable ethical and social controversy. Here is a list of possible developments and applications:

❑   Brain implant to give immediate access to reference sources such as a thesaurus, dictionary or newspaper archives;

❑   An internal alarm clock;

❑   Retinal implant to record everything the subject sees throughout his or her life. This chip has been nicknamed 'The Soul Catcher';

❑   Motor cortex implants to allow thought control of a computer have been developed and allowed a disabled man to select screen icons which indicated his needs, for example for food or drink, and feelings, such as discomfort. The signals from the implants were amplified

❑   Body implants to activate systems at work and home. Such implants could be used to authenticate employees entering restricted areas, automatically download e-mail when a person enters a room, switch on and off house alarms as appropriate, turn on the TV and so on. This is probably the area which has greatest potential for the near future.

All these applications are open to abuse and may well be considered a 'step too far' by most people.

Screen display technologies

Thin, low power consumption, FED (Field Emission Display) screens provide the image quality and viewing angle of the bulky cathode ray tube (CRT) monitors which currently form part of most PC systems.

Micro displays are of thumbnail size and can be placed on top of a silicon chip. The image it displays can then be magnified using a variety of optical techniques, making it suitable for use in notebooks, PDAs (Topic 4) and mobile phones.

Research is also taking place into the development of head sets which project the image directly on to the retina at the back of the eye. This technology would be particularly appropriate for the delivery of virtual reality systems.

Storage technology

The miniaturisation of storage media and increases in storage capacity are strong candidates for continued innovation. An example of current product development is IBM's Compact Flash 2 Microdrive which can hold 340MB. Researchers at California Institute of Technology are attempting to use laser beams to alter the states of particles within crystals to represent particular data values. Lasers would also be used to read the data contents. Theoretical capacities suggest that around 12GB could be stored in a sugar cube sized crystal. The massive storage density would enable very rapid, random, data retrieval at rates of about one billion bits per second.

✍️Exercises

1. List examples of products which use *embedded* microprocessors.
2. What perceived benefits do television viewers receive from *digital* television networks which they do not receive from *analogue* networks?
3. Using suitable examples of applications, what is meant by the *Information Super Highway*?
4. Identify two applications of *interactive TV* (iTV) and the features of the technology which support them.
5. Research video phone products and identify the main features they provide.
6. E-books are increasing in popularity, but there are aspects of current technology which will inhibit their replacement of conventional books. What advantages does this book have over an electronic version? What particular benefits would an e-version provide?
7. Identify applications of microchip implants for the human body and comment on any ethical considerations which should be taken into account.
8. Research current developments in hardware technologies.

Section 3

Computer Software

Topics

Introduction to software

The term *software* is used to describe the complete range of computer programs which convert a general purpose digital computer system into one capable of performing a multitude of specific functions. The term software implies its flexible, changeable nature, in contrast to the more permanent characteristics of the hardware or equipment which it controls.

The particular piece of software controlling the computer system at any particular moment determines the manner in which the system functions. For example, a certain type of software might cause the computer to behave like a word processor; another might allow it to perform accounting or stock control functions, or any one of a huge variety of other useful tasks. Whatever the task, it is software which directs the computer system.

Computer programs

The terms software and program tend to be used interchangeably so what precisely is meant by the term *computer program*?

At the level at which the computer operates, a program is simply a sequence of numeric codes. Each of these codes can be directly converted by the hardware into some simple operation. Built into the central processing unit (CPU - the heart of the computer) is a set of these simple operations, combinations of which are capable of directing the computer to perform complex tasks. Computer programs, in this fundamental form, are termed *machine code*, that is code which is directly understandable by the machine.

The numeric codes of the program are stored electronically in the main memory of the computer. Because this memory is volatile (its contents can be changed), it is possible to exchange the program currently held in the memory for another when the computer is required to perform a different function. For this reason the term *stored program* is often used to describe this fundamental characteristic of the modern digital computer.

Programming languages

When it is considered that a typical program might contain tens of thousands of machine code instructions it might seem that programming is a formidable task, well beyond the capabilities of all but the most determined and meticulous of computer professionals. Indeed, if machine code were the only computer language in use, it is extremely unlikely that society would today be experiencing such a widespread presence of computers in almost every aspect of industrial, commercial, domestic and social life.

Fortunately for the computer industry, programming techniques have evolved along with advances in hardware. There is now a proliferation of programming languages designed to allow the programmer to concentrate most of his or her attention on solving the problem, rather than on the tedious task of converting the solution to machine code form. Such computer languages are termed *high-level languages*. High-level languages provide a method of specifying complex processing tasks in a form relatively easy to use and understand by programmers, but not immediately understandable by a computer; the computer itself, using another program called a *language processor* or *translator*, performs the task of converting the high-level instructions into a usable form. Examples of commonly used languages are COBOL, Pascal, BASIC and C.

Categories of software

The tree diagram shown in Figure 8.1 illustrates the different categories of software and their broad relationships to each other.

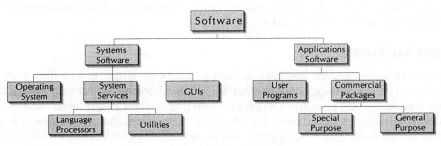

Figure 8.1. *Categories of software*

The term *systems software* covers the collection of programs usually supplied by the manufacturer of the computer. These programs protect the user from the enormous complexity of the computer system, and enable the computer to be used to maximum effect by a wide variety of people, many of whom will know very little about the inner workings of computers. Without systems software a modern digital computer would be virtually impossible to use; as computer hardware has evolved, so systems software has been forced to become more and more complex in order to make effective use of it. Broadly speaking, systems software comprises three elements:

❑   those programs concerned with the internal control and co-ordination of all aspects of the computer system, namely the *operating system;*

❑   a number of other programs providing various services to users. These services include *translators* for any *programming languages* supported by the system and *utility programs* such as program editors and other aids to programming;

❑   *user interfaces* providing access to the facilities made available by the computer system.

Applications software

Applications software refers to programs which have some direct value to an organisation, and will normally include those programs for which the computer system was specifically purchased. For example, a mail order company might acquire a computer system initially for stock control and accounting purposes, when its volume of business begins to make these functions too difficult to cope with by manual means. Applications programs would be required to record and process customers' orders, update the stock file according to goods sent or received, make appropriate entries in the various accounts ledgers, etc. Commercially produced applications software falls into two main categories:

❑   Software for *special-purpose* applications, such as a company payroll system or a production control system may be implemented with the use of *off-the-shelf packages* or, if necessary, *tailor-made* software. Such specially written software may be developed in-house, if the company employs staff for that purpose, or by a software development company.

❑   *general-purpose* packages which may be used for a wide variety of purposes. An example of a general-purpose package is a word processor which is appropriate to numerous text processing tasks.

Systems software

First generation computers are normally defined in hardware terms, in that they were constructed using valve technology, but another important characteristic of this generation of computers was the equally primitive software support provided for programmers and other users. Modern computers perform automatically many of the tasks that programmers in those days had to handle themselves: writing routines to control peripheral devices, allocating programs to main store, executing programs, checking peripheral devices for availability, as well as many other routine tasks.

In subsequent generations of computers, manufacturers started addressing themselves to the problem of improving the programming environment by providing standard programs for many routine tasks. Many of these routines became linked together under the control of a single program called the *executive, supervisor,* or *monitor,* whose function was to supervise the running of user programs and, in general, to control and co-ordinate the functioning of the whole computer system, both hardware and software. Early programs of this type have evolved into the sophisticated programs collectively known as *operating systems.*

Modern systems software now performs a wide variety of tasks, including

❑   supporting user programs;

❑   improving the performance of the computer system;

❑   providing assistance with program development;

❑   simplifying the use of the computer system.

The operating system, in conjunction with system *utilities*, program *translators* and *user interfaces,* support these four important functions

System user documentation

Comprehensive documentation is vital if users are to make effective use of an operating system and its interface. In the early days of computing, operating systems were less complex and use of operating systems was largely restricted to experts in centralised computer services departments. The growth of personal computing has required the development of more user friendly systems and on-line Help systems are now an essential part of all operating systems documentation. The Help system is installed as part of the operating system installation and the guidance given in printed documentation tends to be at an introductory "Getting Started" level. Most PCs are now sold with Internet access capability and the Help system will also include links to

Web-based support. This is particularly important for the provision of help with system 'bugs' that appear from time to time. The complexity of modern operating systems makes it certain that this will happen for some time after its launch and bug 'fixes' can be placed on the manufacturer's web site for downloading by users. The site may also include FAQs (frequently asked questions) to help users with common problems.

Figure 8.2 shows the on-line Help system which forms part of the Windows 98 operating system.

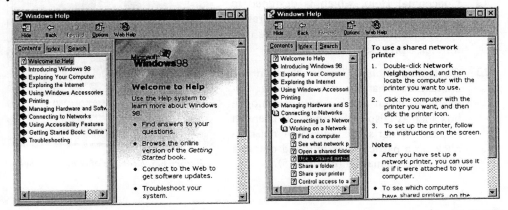

Figure 8.2. *Microsoft Windows 98 on-line help* **Figure 8.3.** *About sharing a network printer*

Typical contents of Help systems include:

❑ Introduction. Figure 8.2 shows the introduction page, which briefly lists the range of help that is provided.

❑ How to use Help. In Figure 8.2 this is within the section "Welcome to Windows 98".

❑ Specific help areas, such as Printing, Networking, Utilities and Accessories, etc. Figure 8.3 shows the "Connecting to Networks" section expanded to reveal help topics on a range of networking facilities.

❑ Getting started. This is a guided tour of the operating system and covers essential areas such as mouse techniques, file and folder management, installation of applications and so on.

❑ Troubleshooting guide. This provides help with common problems and difficulties. A series of multi-choice questions of the form shown in Figure 8.4 take the user through a problem step-by-step. The system works on a process of elimination to identify the user's particular problem and then suggests a solution or refers the user to technical or manufacturer support.

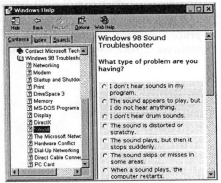

Figure 8.4. *Troubleshooting guide*

On-line Help systems provide different forms of assistance.

❑ Procedural Help. As the name suggests, the user is guided through as a series of steps to achieve a particular result. The Help window stays 'on top' so that the user can carry out the steps without losing sight of the Help window.

❑ Conceptual Help, which is designed to explain a technical term or an operating system facility rather than guide the user through a process.

❑ Contextual Help. This is Help in the context of what the user is doing. For example, when dealing with a dialogue box such as Display Settings, the user can use the 'What's this' question mark to click on a particular setting and obtain a 'pop-up' explanation (Figure 8.5).

Figure 8.5. *Example of contextual help*

✍❚Exercises

1. Draw up a table of programming languages and identify the main types of problem each is designed to solve, for example, business, scientific, artificial intelligence.

2. Why are *language translators* or processors needed?

3. Distinguish between the processes of language *interpretation* and *compilation*.

4. Distinguish between special-purpose and general-purpose software, giving two examples of each.

5. Draw up a list of functions fulfilled by systems software, identifying each function with the relevant type of systems software.

6. Identify the sources of help for the operating system you are using and comment on the usefulness or otherwise of each source.

7. Use the on-line help for an operating system or software package and identify an example of *procedural* help, *conceptual* help and *contextual* help. Use the examples to explain the differences between these various forms of help.

Software installation and configuration opic 9

This Topic deals with the following aspects of setting up a computer system:

❑ Installing device drivers, such as printer drivers.

❑ Tailoring a GUI 'desktop'.

❑ Installing and configuring applications software.

Installing device drivers

Device drivers are programs which control the way a device works. All attached devices, including for example, the graphics card (to control the display), sound card, disk drive controller and printer need device drivers. For example, without the appropriate driver, the computer system will be unable to take advantage of all the printer's features. So, a particular make of printer, with facilities to print text and graphics at a resolution of 600 dpi, will only provide all those facilities with the correct driver. The incorrect driver may prevent printing of graphics or even print 'gobbledygook'. A printer driver can be installed with the installation program provided by the printer manufacturer, or with the appropriate operating system utility.

Printer install program

A new printer will include its associated software on disk, and the driver is installed through the use of this software. The following Figures show a typical printer install process.

❑ The operating system is instructed to 'Run Setup.exe' (Figure 9.1).

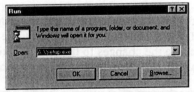

Figure 9.1. *Run printer setup.exe*

❑ Setup prompts (Figure 9.2) for the parallel port to be used by the printer. In this case, the system only has one such port, LPT1, so this is the only option.

Figure 9.2. *Selection of printer port*

❏   The user is asked to confirm the hard disk directory into which the programs will be installed. Generally, the default is chosen, unless there is a particular reason for changing it.

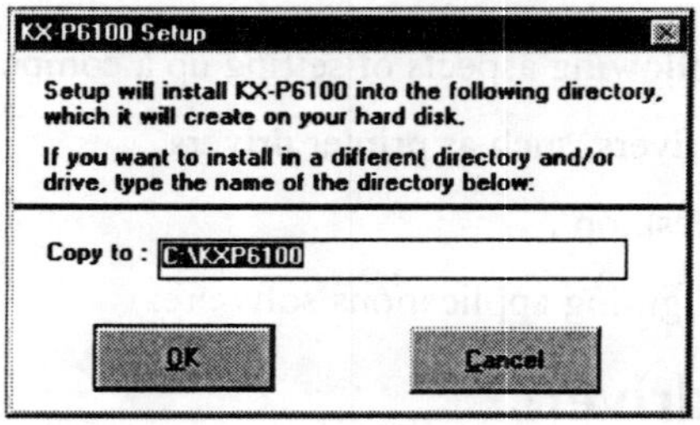

Figure 9.3. *Choose installation directory*

❏   The setup continues with the copying of files from the floppy to the named directory on hard disk (Figure 9.4). If the setup programs occupy more than one floppy disk, the user is prompted when the next one is needed.

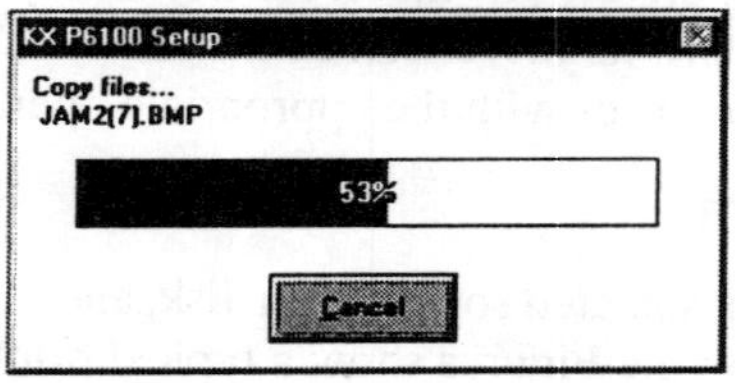

Figure 9.4. *Copying installation files to hard drive*

❏   When the setup is complete, various configuration files may be altered and the process is completed. For the changes to take effect, the operating system has to be restarted. This is because the changes to the configuration files are detected when the operating system is first loaded. The next figure shows the prompt to restart.

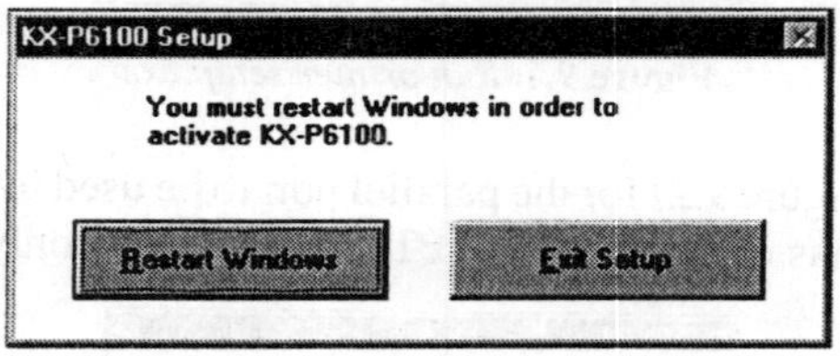

Figure 9.5. *Prompt to restart operating system*

Printer install utility

In the case of Windows 9x, a new printer can be installed with printer Install Wizard. Figure 9.6 shows the Printers window with two installed printers and the 'Add Printer' utility.

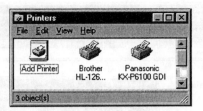

Figure 9.6. *'Add Printer' install utility*

Running the 'Add Printer' utility, calls up the Wizard. This provides the options of selecting a driver already available on the hard drive, or one held on another disk (such as that provided by the manufacturer). Figure 9.7 shows a list of drivers already available on the hard drive.

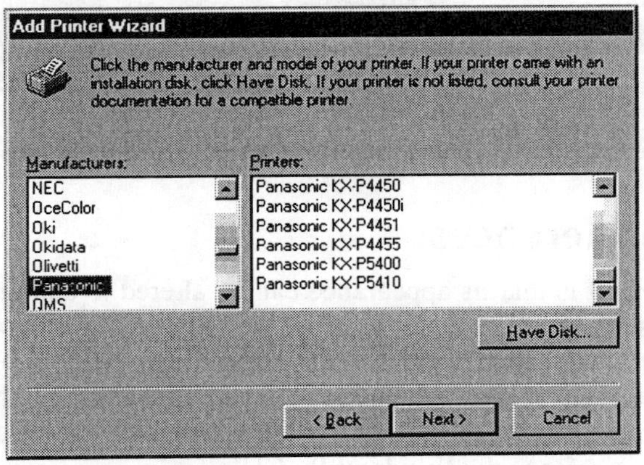

Figure 9.7. *List of printer drivers available with installed operating system*

The latest version of a driver may also be downloaded from the manufacturer's Internet Web site.

Downloading drivers from the Internet

Manufacturers often modify their device drivers to improve the features or performance of the devices they control. It is often worth downloading the latest device driver from the manufacturer's Web site, to take advantage of such improvements. Obtaining the latest graphics driver can improve the performance of a computer system, for example, by speeding up screen redraws.

Continuing with the example of printer drivers, the Figure 9.8 shows the download page on the Brother.com Web Site. To download a particular driver, the user simply clicks on the appropriate driver name. The figure shows that the user has requested the download of the Brother 1260 printer driver. The dialogue box indicates that the downloaded file can be copied straight to memory or to the hard disk. The downloaded file will normally include a program to automate the installation process.

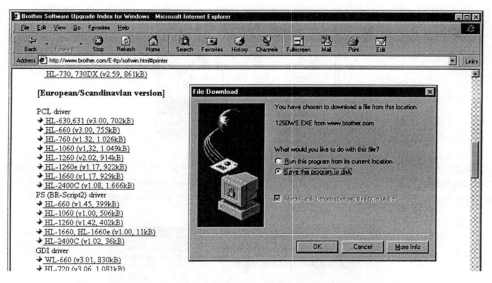

Figure 9.8. *Downloading printer driver from the Brother.com web site*

Setting GUI preferences

A major benefit of a GUI is that its appearance can be altered to suit an individual user or a group of users. If the settings are made for a group, then a generally accepted appearance has to be agreed. If one user in the group decides to change settings, without proper agreement, this can be annoying or even confusing for the other members of the group. There are too many different settings to deal with them all here, so we will concentrate on some of the most important. The examples used here refer to the Windows 9x GUI.

Display properties

The Windows 9x Display Properties window is shown in Figure 9.9. Each tab deals with a different aspect of the display. The displayed tab gives access to screen saver and energy saving controls.

Setting a screen saver prevents a static image from remaining on screen and burning a permanent shadow into it. Energy saving features can only be used if the screen is compatible. This switches the monitor power down or off after a certain period. The Settings tab allows the user to control the appearance of the screen display, including screen resolution, number of colours and the font size.

Figure 9.9 also shows an MGA settings tab, which is specific to the installed graphics card, an MGA Matrox Millennium. It provides more varied controls than the standard Settings tab.

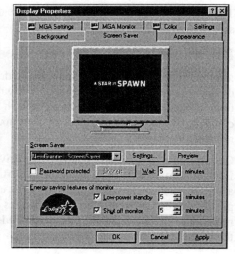

Figure 9.9. *Display properties*

Appearance

These settings can be selected from a number of different standard models, or the user can alter individual parts of the screen, such as the colour of the desktop or spacing of icons. Figure 9.10 shows the Appearance tab and a drop down list of items which can be altered.

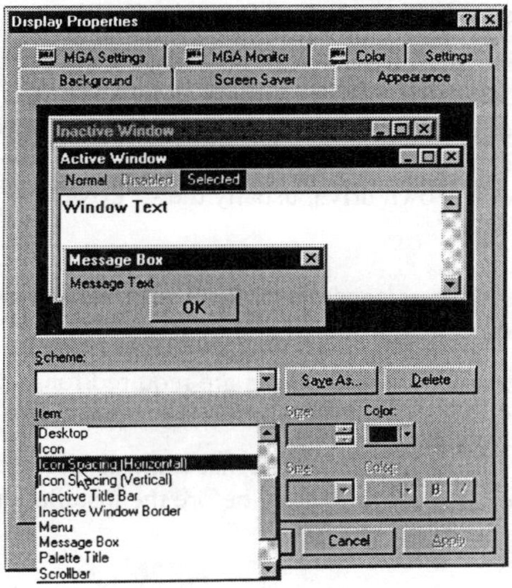

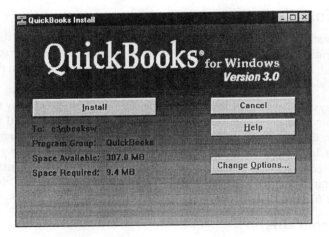

Figure 9.10. *Appearance tab*

Software installation

Much of this process is automated through an *install program.* Figure 9.11 shows an example.

Figure 9.11. *QuickBooks installation program*

Install settings

Some installations are quite straightforward and the only major decision to be made concerns:

❏   The drive and directory in which the programs are to be stored. The above example, shows that the directory is \qbooksw, on the E: drive. The default is usually C:, but E: was chosen because of limited space on the C: drive.

Although the drive and directory can be changed from that suggested by the install program, it is usually sensible to accept the default. The C:\ drive is normally the preferred location for applications programs, but another hard drive, or partition of the hard drive can be used. If an alternative is chosen, the operating system will still require some files on its own drive, usually the C: drive.

Other entries include:

❏   Acceptance of licence arrangements. This restricts the number of machines on which the software can be installed at the same time.

❏   User name and company; these details are required for technical support from the software supplier.

❏   Key code. This is supplied to the licensee and is designed to discourage pirate copies. The key code must be entered before the installation can continue.

Type of installation

The *typical* installation is useful if you wish to be certain that the facilities required by most users are provided. However, if you are knowledgeable about the facilities, a custom installation is usually better. Custom installation ensures that all the facilities you require are installed (your needs may not be typical) and that facilities you do not need are not installed. This can save considerable disk space.

Testing the installation

Completion on installation involves copying of program files to the named directory and alteration of configuration files which 'tell' the operating system that the program is installed and where it is located. In the Windows operating systems, the *Registry* holds all details of installed software.

Sometimes, the system needs to be restarted for the settings to be detected by the operating system. Once the above tasks are completed, the program can be run and tested with sample tasks or data. Whether the installation meets all of the user's requirements cannot be thoroughly checked until the full range of tasks has been attempted. Obviously, if the range of tasks is wide, this may take a considerable time. If a required option has not been installed, the install program may require the full installation to be repeated or allow the additional option to be installed without full installation.

Removing programs

Most commercial programs provide an *uninstall* program. The uninstall program should be used wherever possible. It is generally a bad idea to simply delete the program files. The configuration files will still contain details and the operating system will still 'think' that the program is installed. At best, only space will be wasted. At worst, the operating system may display error messages on startup, which although not damaging are a great nuisance. Figure 9.12 shows the Windows 9x utility for starting the removal of programs from the system, with a list of the installed software.

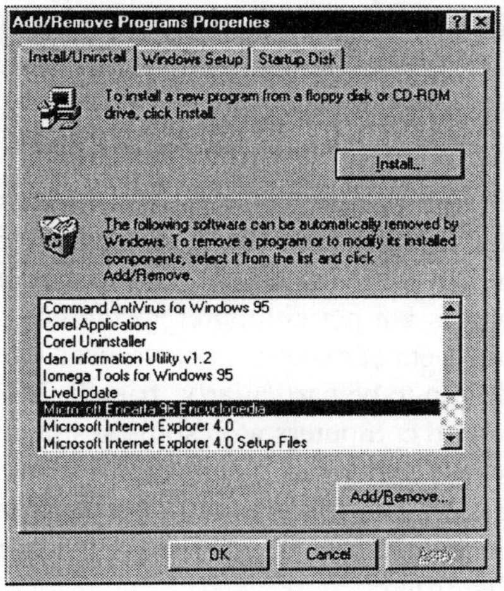

Figure 9.12. *Windows 9x uninstall utility*

✍️Exercises

1. (i)   What is the general function of a device *driver*?

   (ii) A device driver can often be selected from a library of drivers provided with the operating system. With reference to a particular device, such as a printer, video card or sound card, suggest what limitations this option may place on the performance of the device.

   (iii) Why may it be useful to obtain updated drivers from the device manufacturer's web site?

2. Trace the main stages in the installation of software.

3. What benefits may obtain from choosing to customise installation of a package and what pitfalls may this option present for the inexperienced user?

4. Identify a common technique used by manufacturers to discourage unauthorised, multiple installations of their software products.

5. Why is it important to use the uninstall utility to remove software, rather than simply deleting the files using, for example, Windows Explorer?

User interface design

The movement from centralised to distributed systems and the expansion in microcomputer usage has spawned the need for a variety of approaches to the design of *user interfaces* (UIs) which fulfil the requirements of an increasing population of computer users, the majority of whom are not computer specialists. When all computer processing was controlled by small numbers of experts, in centralised data processing departments, there was little pressure for UI design to be particularly 'friendly'. This is probably a major reason why many people used to regard computers with some suspicion and apprehension. UIs are also variously known as *human-computer* and *man-machine* interfaces. UI design is now recognised as being of critical importance and is usually the yardstick by which a system is judged; poor UI design can seriously affect a user's view of a system's functionality. Several design principles can be identified:

❑ it should be a product of collaboration between the designer and the users;

❑ user, not designer, convenience should be paramount;

❑ the interface should be of consistent design throughout the system;

❑ built-in help and advice should be accessible at different levels, depending on the degree of assistance required.

Interface metaphors

Through the use of metaphors, an interface can present a system's facilities in a form familiar to the user. A number of metaphors are commonly employed.

Desktop metaphor

As the term indicates, the UI relates everyday desktop or office facilities to routine computer tasks such as loading, saving or deleting files. The following representations are usual:

❑ filing cabinets for disc drives;

❑ documents for files;

❑ folders for directories;

❑ waste paper baskets for the deletion of files from backing storage.

Control panel metaphor

A screen control panel may include a variety of elements, such as: *buttons* for initiating actions, for example, print; *switches* for setting options on and off, for example, a grid on a spreadsheet; *radio buttons* for choosing from ESGs (exclusive selection groups), for example, A5/A4/A3 documents sizes; *sub-panel menu* of buttons or switches to select, for example, system default settings; *lights* to indicate some active event, for example, printing; *signs* displaying, for example, which file is currently active; *sliders*, to vary for example, RGB (red green blue) colour mixes.

WIMP interfaces

An acronym for Windows, Icons, Menus, Pointing (alternatively, Windows, Icons, Mice and Pull-down menus), the WIMP concept stems from original work by Xerox PARC Laboratories in the mid-1970s and was first employed on Apple Lisa and Macintosh computer systems. Since then a number of WIMP orientated UIs have been developed, notably, GEM, MS-Windows, ARC and Sun.

Such interfaces have a number of characteristics and features:

❑   the necessary skills are easy to grasp and the systems are easy to use;

❑   multiple windows for switching between tasks (multi-tasking);

❑   full-screen interaction allows quicker command execution than is usually possible through a *command line interpreter*;

❑   control panels (see previous section).

However, as a relatively new concept, there are no standards for the design of WIMP-based products. Certain difficulties in their design may be experienced:

❑   although multiple windows are useful for task switching, too many windows can be confusing;

❑   designing icons which unambiguously tell the user of specific functions can be difficult and some may need to be augmented with text support, perhaps in a help window.

The graphical user interface (GUI) used on modern operating systems uses the WIMP design principles.

Graphical user interface (GUI)

Figure 10.1 shows the graphical user interface (or GUI, pronounced GOOEY) for the Windows 98 operating system. The figure illustrates the following features of a GUI:

❑   a *pointer* on screen, moved by a pointing device, typically a *mouse*.

❑   *icons* (small pictures) representing, amongst other things, programs, which can be run by pointing and clicking the mouse. The recycle bin, browser and system icons are on the right hand side of the figure.

❑   *windows*. Applications run in their own self-contained areas called *windows*. There are two in the figure, one for CorelDRAW, a graphic design program and another for Microsoft's Word, a word processing package. These are all examples of *applications software*.

Most users are not really interested in the technical details of a computer's operation and simply want to use it. However, to do so effectively, a user must learn routine maintenance tasks, such as creating folders, copying files and formatting disks as well as the use of the particular applications they need. A GUI is designed to make these tasks easier as follows.

❑   Methods of doing things are more *intuitive*. This means that a user can often anticipate what certain actions with the mouse will do. For example, selecting a file with a mouse pointer and dragging it to an *icon* (small picture) of a dustbin has the effect of deleting the selected file.

❏   Applications running under a GUI have common features, so, for example, it is easier to transfer skills learned using a word processor to those needed for a spreadsheet.

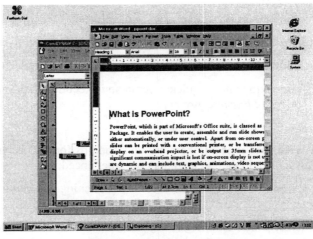

Figure 10.1. *Windows 98 GUI*

The hardware needed to run GUI systems needs to be of higher specification, in terms of disk space, RAM capacity, processor speed and screen resolution, than is the case for command line interpreter (CLI - see later) systems.

Menu systems

A menu of options is displayed, from which a user can make a selection. Menus are only appropriate where a limited range of options is available at any one time, although the selection of an item may cause the display of a further sub-menu. Commonly, each option is identified by a single letter or number which has to be keyed to select the option. Some packages, typically those running under the MS-DOS operating system, use a menu system which allows selection of an option either by highlighting the option with the cursor and pressing the 'enter' key or simply by keying the first letter of the option (without the need for confirmation). The problem for all such systems is to design each menu such that the first letter of each option is unique in that menu. The use of main menus which give access to sub-menus, each of which in turn may provide access to further sub-menus, follows a hierarchical structure.

A number of design principles may be employed:

❏   Provided a simple mechanism is available for the user to return to the main menu, then several levels of menu can be used without the user becoming 'lost'. Commonly, the Esc key allows the user to work backwards from lower level menus to the main menu. Alternatively, each sub-menu may include an option 'Return to Main Menu'.

❑ The designer of a menu structure should limit the number of options displayed in a menu to a maximum of about eight, at which point, a sub-menu should be considered for further options. An excessive number of options on screen at one time looks untidy and may be rather intimidating to the user.

Pull-down menus

This method generally displays the main menu along the top of the screen and is popularly associated with WIMP orientated systems. When an option is selected with the cursor or mouse pointer, the range of sub-options associated with it are 'pulled down' and displayed.

Menu systems provide a number of benefits:

❑ all possibilities are presented as a command list;

❑ minimal typing is required;

❑ error trapping is simple;

❑ inappropriate choices can be withheld from the user;

❑ context sensitive help can be provided.

The drawbacks are that:

❑ they can be tedious for experienced users;

❑ an extended hierarchy of menus can be difficult for the user to follow;

❑ a large number of choices may require the use of several screens, as is the case, for example, with viewdata systems.

Form-fill dialogue

This type of dialogue requires that the screen layout matches the associated input document as closely as possible. The operator is then able to make the entries in the same logical progression as the hand-filled form.

A number of features are usually evident:

❑ boxed in areas indicate fields for data entry;

❑ form headings are protected and cannot be overwritten by the user;

❑ cursor movement is restricted to the variable data entry points adjacent to each heading.

A number of design features can be applied to the data entry process:

❑ with fixed length data items, for example, a 6-digit account number, the cursor skips automatically to the next field as soon as the last character is entered;

❑ with variable length data items, the TAB key is pressed by the user when an entry is complete. This causes the cursor to skip to the next field;

❑ when all entries have been made, the user scans the screen to ensure all entries appear correct and the confirms them by pressing 'return';

❑   if errors are discovered before the 'return' key is pressed, a mechanism is available to enable corrections to be made.

The form-fill method is inappropriate when system responses are displayed which may obscure the screen headings or entries. Thus, if an invalid entry is made, the system should 'bleep' to indicate that a correction is required, without displaying an error message or display the message in a status line at the bottom of the screen; users should be well trained and aware of the valid data formats, so the need for help messages should be minimal.

Natural language dialogue

This type of dialogue is frequently used in database systems to allow users to specify their requirements in a 'natural' language style. The construction of the language is a complex process and many systems only allow the use of strictly limited syntax and sentence construction. Thus although the language can be described as 'natural', there is limited flexibility to allow different users to form requests in a way which is natural to each. As a result, the casual user may become frustrated by having to rephrase requests in attempts to resolve ambiguities. Queries tend to be verbose and speech recognition may provide useful support in the future.

Mnemonic driven dialogue

This design is suitable for highly trained users carrying out specialised tasks. Virtually no explanatory prompts are provided. A typical example can be found in airline reservation systems. The operator can carry out a variety of tasks relating to seat reservations using only brief mnemonic (memory aid) representations for the input. For example, in response to a customer enquiry, the operator requests a list of flights which may satisfy the customer's requirements. These may be:

```
Departure Date: 23rd June
Departure Time: 2.30pm
Departure From: London
Destination City: New York, USA
```

The operator's screen entry may appear as follows:

```
? A23JUNLHRNYCJFK1430
```

The string of characters is in strict sequence according to function. Thus: A = Available; 23JUN = 23rd June; LHR = London, Heathrow Airport; NYCJFK = New York City, John F. Kennedy Airport; 1430 = 2.30pm or up to one hour earlier or later. The system then displays any flights which satisfy these criteria, together with details of seats available, arrival times, type of aircraft etc. The operator can, if requested, immediately make a reservation for the customer with a similar mnemonic command.

Command line interface

The user enters a command to initiate action, to access information, or to call up a sequence of other commands. Still available with operating systems such as MS-DOS, a number of advantages and disadvantages are evident.

Advantages

☐   easy to implement with low resolution alphanumeric displays;

☐   the language processing techniques used with the command line interpreter (CLI) are well developed in the related area of compiler design and CLI's are thus cheap to produce;

☐   the power of the interface can be extended with macro commands;

☐   the brevity of commands, although not particularly user friendly, is ideally suited for rapid expert use.

☐   can be implemented on less powerful computer systems than is necessary for GUIs.

Disadvantages

☐   unsuitable for inexperienced users;

☐   the command language must be learned and remembered;

☐   system interaction is restricted to the keyboard.

Some design considerations

☐   When designing command mnemonics, trying to achieve clarity of meaning tends to conflict with the aim of making them brief enough for rapid use.

☐   It may be helpful to use a two-tier system, providing menus for novices, leaving the 'hot key' facilities for experiences users.

Figure 10.2 shows the command line interface for the MS-DOS operating system.

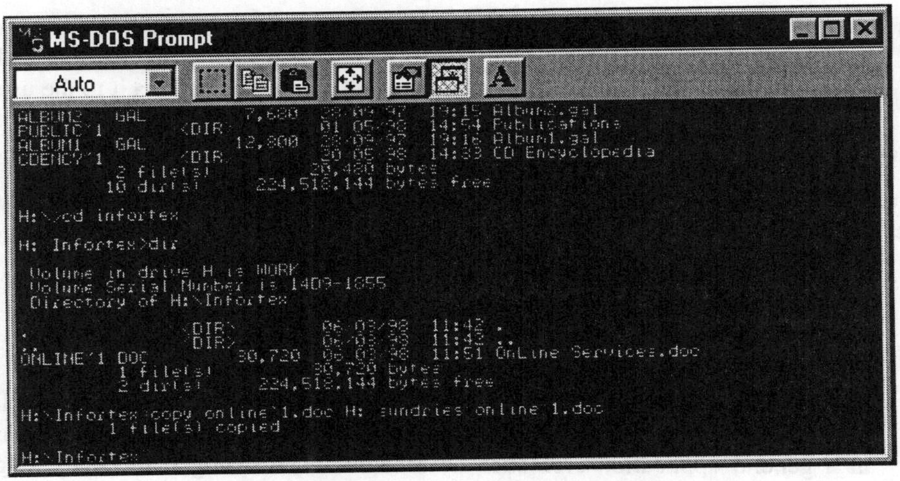

Figure 10.2. *MS-DOS command line interface*

At the bottom of Figure, there is a lengthy command sequence to copy a file from one directory to another. It is followed by the message "1 file(s) copied", which confirms that the command has been executed successfully.

Communication of errors

Where data validation is to be performed at the time of data entry, it is important that the interface facilitates error detection and correction. Before designing error dialogues, the following points should be noted.

❏   A screen which leaves error messages on screen and re-displays the prompt beneath is untidy and confusing to the user

❏   Repeated rejection of data without any explanation can be extremely frustrating. Such systems are only suitable for properly trained users who know the forms of input expected.

❏   Validation alone cannot ensure accuracy. Proper input document design, staff training and clerical checking are also vital. Users should be made aware of what validation is and its limitations, otherwise they may come to think of the system as infallible.

❏   It can save considerable frustration if the system is 'transparent' in terms of upper and lower case characters. In other words, entries are not made invalid simply because they are upper or lower case. Even if characters are to be output in only one case, the conversion can be carried out by the software.

❏   Where inexperienced users are involved, it may be useful if the system produces appropriate help messages from a file on disk. This facility is provided with many general-purpose packages.

❏   Error messages should be concise but detailed enough to allow the user to correct the error.

❏   Whilst using an application program, the user should not be presented with an error message directly from the operating system; as far as possible, all errors should be capable of being handled by the application and communicated via it to the user.

Other design considerations

It is important that the interface presents screen prompts and responses in a way which aids interpretation and to this end:

❏   any dialogue should follow a logical progression appropriate to the user, the activity and in the case of data entry, to the input document;

❏   spacing is important. Full use should be made of the screen space available;

❏   the interface should, as far as possible, be consistent across all applications in a given user area. This is particularly desirable when several packages are being used in a general application area such as accounts. The dialogue for sales ledger, purchase ledger, stock control and so on, should follow a similar structure. Many integrated packages allow the user to learn basic dialogue structure which allows rapid transfer of skills from one part of the package to another;

❏   techniques of highlighting such as brightness variation, blinking and colour coding should be used sparingly. Brightness variation should be limited to two levels, bold and normal as other variations will be difficult to detect. The blinking of a field on screen to attract the user's attention can be useful provided it does not continue once appropriate action has been taken.

Exercises

1. Study the graphical user interfaces (GUIs) of various software packages and identify examples of *control panel* metaphor elements, such as switches, buttons, lights and radio buttons.
2. With reference to a particular GUI, identify tasks which appear to use intuitive methods.
3. (i) Examine a range of GUI packages and note those task features, such as opening files which are common to all.
   (ii) What benefits does this use of common features have for users?
4. (i) Describe two important principles for the design of menu systems.
   (ii) Examine two versions of the same package and identify changes the manufacturer has made to the menu structure. New features will have been added and resulted in some menu changes, but others may have been made to improve usability of the package. Study the changes and judge whether they have made the package easier or more difficult to use.
5. Describe a suitable application for *form-fill* dialogue.
6. Describe an application which may benefit from the use of *natural language* and suggest major difficulties which inhibit the use of truly 'natural language'.
7. (i) Identify two disadvantages of a text-based, *command line interface* (CLI) for some users.
   (ii) Why may a CLI be more effective than a GUI for technical support staff and computer system administrators?
8. Why is it beneficial to use simple text displays for supermarket checkouts?
9. Input errors have to be communicated to the user in a way which is appropriate to the application and the experience of the user. Suggest the kind of on-line support which is appropriate for communicating input errors to the following users:
   (i) Supermarket checkout operator using a simple text display.
   (ii) System administrator communicating with the operating system through a command line interpreter.
   (iii) Airline booking clerk using an in-house booking system.
   (iv) Graphic designer using a general-purpose graphics package.
   (v) Accounts clerk using an off-the-shelf accounts package with a GUI.

If a computer system is viewed as a set of resources, comprising elements of both hardware and software, then it is the job of the collection of programs known as the *operating system* to manage these resources as efficiently as possible. In so doing, the operating system acts as a buffer between the user and the complexities of the computer itself. One way of regarding the operating system is to think of it as software which allows the user to deal with a simplified computer, but without losing any of the computational power of the machine. In this way, the computer system becomes a virtual system, its enormous complexity hidden and controlled by the operating system and through which the user communicates with the real system.

The central core of an operating system, which remains in memory permanently when the computer is running, is the *executive* (also known as the *supervisor* or *kernel*); as the terms suggest, it has a controlling function, its major function being to carry out system requests from applications programs in such a way that conflicts between them are avoided. The remainder of the operating system is normally held on a direct access medium, from where parts of it can be called as and when required.

Main functions of an operating system

The introduction states that the function of an operating system is to manage the resources of the computer system. These resources are described below.

Central processing unit (CPU) or processor

Since only one program can be executed at any one time, computer systems which allow several users simultaneous access (multi-user) must carefully control and monitor use of the processor. In a timesharing multi-user system each user receives a small time-slice from the processor before it passes on to the next user in a continually repeating sequence. Another common scheme is to assign priorities to users so that the system is able to determine which user should next have control of the processor.

Memory

Programs (or parts of programs) must be loaded into the memory before they can be executed, and moved out of the memory when no longer required there. Storage space must be provided for data generated by programs, and provision must be made for the temporary storage of data, caused by data transfer operations involving devices such as printers and disk drives.

Input/output (I/O) devices

Programs will request the use of these devices during the course of their execution and in a multi-user system, conflicts are bound to arise when a device being utilised by one program is requested by another. The operating system controls the allocation of I/O devices and attempts to resolve any conflicts which arise. It also monitors the state of each I/O device and signals any faults detected.

Backing storage

Programs and data files are usually held on mass storage devices such as magnetic disk and tape drives. The operating system supervises data transfers between these devices and memory, and deals with requests from programs for space on them.

Files

These may be regarded as a limited resource in the sense that several users may wish to share the same data file at the same time. The operating system facilitates access to files and ensures that only one updating program can retrieve a particular record at any one time.

The above is by no means an exhaustive list of the functions of an operating system. Other functions include:

❑   interpretation of the command language by which operators can communicate with it;

❑   error handling, such as detecting and reporting inoperative or malfunctioning peripherals;

❑   protection of data files and programs from corruption by other users;

❑   protection of data files and programs from unauthorised use;

❑   accounting and logging of the use of the computer resources.

Types of operating system

Single-stream

As the term suggests, single-stream operating systems are designed to handle only one job at a time. Today, the only operating systems which are likely fall into this category are those designed for microcomputer systems, for example MS-DOS (really, it is a *single-user* system- see also *multi-tasking*), but in the late 1950s the then state of the art mainframe systems could only handle jobs singly. These early systems automated the running of their jobs under customised *control programs* (initially punched onto cards), which were the forerunners of operating systems.

Batch processing systems

Batch processing improves early single-stream operating systems with the use of an *executive* which queues a number of separate jobs, *schedules them according to allocated priorities* and *executes* them, one after another. Jobs judged as being more urgently than others are allocated priority accordingly; jobs are loaded and executed according to their priority rating, not their position in the queue, so additional jobs can be added at any time.

Such systems are very inefficient for various reasons. Each job must be completed before commencement of the next; the fact that most jobs require a great deal of I/O and very little processing means that the processor is idle much of the time. This under use of the processor is worsened by the mismatch between the operating speed of the processor and the data transfer rate of system storage devices, and the imbalance is even greater where printed output is required. When the overall system's speed is dictated by the speed of the I/O peripheral, rather than the processor, the system is described as being *I/O bound*. The technique of *off-lining* was introduced in the late 1950s to help deal with the problem of very slow peripherals, such as card readers and printers.

Batch multi-programming systems

Optimisation of resource usage

Multi-programming is the term used to describe the running of several jobs in main memory, apparently simultaneously. In reality, however, the processor's attention is being repeatedly switched from one job to another under the control of the executive. This makes much better use of the processor's time than the single stream batch processing described previously. Thus, the objective of a batch multi-programming operating system is to *optimise the use of processor time and the rate of system throughput*.

Dynamic resource allocation

With single-stream processing, computer resources (processor time, main memory space, file storage and peripherals) can be allocated to each job and remain fixed for the duration of each job. In contrast, the concurrent processing of several jobs inherent in a multi-programming environment, with the likelihood that the mix of jobs will change as some are completed and new ones are initiated, requires an executive capable of allocating resources *dynamically* to each job.

Job priority

Jobs will vary according to:

- ❏ the amount of I/O involved;

- ❏ the types and speeds of I/O devices used;

- ❏ the amount of processor time needed.

After consideration of these factors, each job is given a *priority rating*, which will determine how frequently and how much processor time it receives. The allocation of priorities can be a complex process but simplistically:

- ❏ high priority will be given to a job requiring a large amount of I/O and a relatively small amount of processor time. When I/O operations are being carried out, processor attention is not required after the initial I/O command is given. Conversely, when it does require attention, a high priority will ensure that its small processing requirements are attended to promptly and fully, following which it can return to I/O;

- ❏ a low priority job will tend to be one which requires a large amount of processor time; a high priority would result in it using the processor too much, thus preventing largely I/O jobs from receiving what little attention they require.

Scheduling

High-level scheduler

It is a function of a high-level scheduler to determine which programs in the job queue should next be loaded into main memory. Before loading a job, the following criteria must be satisfied:

❑ there is sufficient room for it in main memory;

❑ all associated input files are on-line;

❑ the necessary peripherals are also on-line.

If priorities are allocated then, subject to fulfilment of the above criteria, these will be used by the high level scheduler to decide the order in which jobs are removed from the job queue.

Dispatcher or low-level scheduler

The dispatcher allocates the processor amongst the various processes in the system. To understand the operation of the dispatcher, it is useful to differentiate between the concept of a *program* and a *process*. A process is a sequence of actions produced through the execution of program instructions. Processes carried out within the system include, for example, interrupt handling, error handling, I/O control and so on; each process may involve one or more programs.

To do this the dispatcher must record the current *status* of each process selecting from the following possibilities:

❑ it is runnable, that is, free to run;

❑ it is running; in other words, it has the attention of the processor;

❑ it is unrunnable or suspended, perhaps because it is awaiting completion of an I/O operation.

A *process descriptor table* records the status of each process in the *processor queue*. The dispatcher must refer to it before deciding on re-allocation of the processor to a process in the queue; such a decision needs to be made each time there is an *interrupt* (see later). The dispatcher will choose the process with the highest priority, from those which are available to run, unless the process which was running at the time of the interrupt still outranks them.

The dispatcher is invoked under the following circumstances:

❑ whenever the current process cannot continue; this may result, for example, from a programming error or a switch to I/O, **or**

❑ when an external interrupt changes the status of a process, for example, following completion of data transfer; it thus becomes runnable.

Batch processing systems collect all input data in a file, from where it is loaded and processed to completion by the relevant application program, storing any output data in another on-line file; the executive then directs the printing program to print any hard copy results from the output file. Prominent features of such systems are:

❑ lack of any communication or interaction with the user;

❑   the delay in producing results of processing.

The following categories of operating system allow results of processing to be obtained, frequently on a VDU screen, directly after their entry. They are categorised according to the techniques used to manage the computer resources:

❑   time-sharing;

❑   multi-tasking;

❑   multi-user;

❑   real-time.

Time-sharing

The term time-sharing refers to the allocation of processor *time-slices* to a number of user programs in a multi-programming environment. The aim of a time-sharing operating system is to *keep the users busy*; this contrasts with the batch multi-programming system which aims to keep the processor occupied. The time slices are controlled and synchronised by a real-time clock which generates frequent, regularly timed pulses; each time-slice is extremely short, say 100 milliseconds.

Round robin system

With this method, the operating system works sequentially through the list of programs being run, giving each process an equal slice of processor time.

If all current programs can be accommodated in main memory at one time, users should not experience poor response times. Unfortunately, the total main memory requirements of all current users may exceed the capacity of main memory, making it necessary to swap programs or program segments in and out from backing storage as the processor switches its attention from one to another. The number of such data transfers can be reduced by extending the length of each time slice, but at the cost of reducing the frequency with which the processor transfers its attention from one process to another. Optimising system performance requires a balance to be struck between these two objectives. Unless the processor is overloaded, perhaps because there are too many users or because the applications require a large amount of processor time (for example, program compilation - see Programming Language Translators), each user should feel that he or she is the sole user of the system.

Priority system

Instead of giving single time-slices on a round robin basis, they are allocated according to a system of priorities. This means that some programs will receive a number of time slices in succession before another is attended to. The priority rating of each program will not normally remain static but will be adjusted in relation to the relative amount of processing time it receives in comparison with the other programs in operation.

Time-sharing systems are used *interactively* in that users communicate directly with the computer through VDU terminals. A common use of a time-sharing operating system is to provide *multi-access* to one or more programming languages for the purposes of program development. Other systems may provide users with access to various applications programs which can be run apparently simultaneously.

Multi-tasking

Multi-tasking is a technique which allows a computer to carry out tasks in a similar fashion to a human worker. For example, the Financial Director of a business may be composing a financial report which requires the use of a dictaphone, occasional reference to various financial summaries and telephone calls to other executive staff in the business. Although these tasks are not carried on at exactly the same time, the director is rapidly switching from one to another, and they all contribute to the completion of the financial report. At certain times, an unrelated task may have to be completed, for example, the answering of a brief query from a member of staff. This does not require complete abandonment of the other tasks in hand and the main work continues from the point at which it was left.

Computer multi-tasking requires that the system can accommodate several tasks in memory at one time and that these tasks can be run *concurrently* by rapidly switching the processor's attention between them. The principles of resource management are similar to those employed in *multi-programming*, except that they relate to a *single user*, are controlled interactively and must be executed in ways which maintain response times acceptable to the user.

Device drivers (disk controllers, screen and printer drivers) operate at a higher level of privilege within memory, because they have to remain accessible to all current applications.

Pre-emptive and co-operative multi-tasking

Pre-emptive multi-tasking means that the operating system controls the amount of processor time each application receives, giving each application a slice of time before switching activity to one of the others. Windows 9x, Windows NT, OS/2 and UNIX all operate pre-emptive multi-tasking.

An operating system which uses co-operative multi-tasking does not control the amount of time given to an application. Therefore, a processor intensive application will keep control of the processor for as long as it needs it, although when it terminates or switches to an input or output tasks, another application will gain access to the processor. For a co-operative multitasking operating system to be effective, programs must be designed so that they do not control the processor for long periods. Generally, this is achieved by splitting programs into small modules which individually require only short periods of processing before they release the processor.

Multi-user

A multi-user system is invariably multi-access (although it is possible to provide multi-user facilities within a single stand-alone microcomputer, but only one user at a time) in that it provides a number of users with concurrent access to shared computing resources, which may be part of a computer network or may comprise a centralised computer with multiplexed terminals. Additionally however, the multi-user operating system must protect each user's (or user group's) files from access and/or corruption by other users, either within memory or on backing storage. This is achieved through dynamic memory partitioning and directory-based file management respectively.

Real-time

A real-time system is one which reacts to inputs sufficiently rapidly to permit tight control of its environment. A computer system's environment can be defined as the application or activity it is controlling. Real-time operation is essential for computerised *process control*, for example, in chemical production. Such activities require continual control so that parameters of, say pressure and temperature, are adhered to. Inputs from the process, collected through *transducers*, are digitised, input and processed, to provide immediate feedback to the system's controllers, which for the previous example may be a heating mechanism and air pressure control.

Some business information systems also require real-time control. Typical examples include airline booking and some stock control systems where rapid turnover is the norm. The mechanisms used by a real-time operating system to control the system resources are beyond the scope of this text.

Further functions and facilities

Command language interpretation

An important function of the operating system is to interpret the command language which allows the user/operator to communicate with it. Two types of language are generally recognized:

- ❏ command language;
- ❏ job control language.

Command language

A *command line interpreter* (CLI) accepts command lines, checks them for syntax errors and passes on the relevant requests to the operating system. Such requests may be, for example, to display directory contents on screen, delete files from disk, or copy them from one disk to another. Simple, ad hoc requests will generally be made via a keyboard but lengthy, regularly used sequences of commands may be stored in a command or batch file. The MS-DOS operating system (see later) provides such a facility. Today, the *graphical user interface* (GUI) is preferred to the command line interpreter. Operating system utilities are selected, with a mouse, from representative icons on the screen; the GUI communicates these requests in the systems command language and the CLI interprets and passes them on to the operating system in the normal way. The GUI is another level of interface between the user and the CLI.

Job control language (JCL)

Associated with batch processing operating systems, JCLs allow details of job requirements to be specified to the operating system. An example JCL sequence is given below.

```
BEGIN
JOB 3367
COMPILE payroll.cbl (disk 1)
LOAD payroll.obj (disk 1)
RUN
END
```

This sequence of commands identifies the job, compiles a COBOL (cbl) source program, loads the resultant object program and executes it.

I/O handling

The executive part of the operating system controls data transfers to and from peripherals, normally through a system of interrupts (see Topic 14 on Input/Output Control). Other causes of interrupts are dealt with below.

Interrupt handling

Apart from I/O operations, interrupts are necessary to notify the operating system of a variety of other system events, including:

❑ hardware failure, for example, through power loss or a memory parity error;

❑ program termination;

❑ peripheral data transfer failure, for example, because a printer is out of paper or the directory on a disk has been damaged;

❑ an attempt to access a non-existent memory address;

❑ in a time-sharing or real-time system, a clock pulse indicates completion of time slices;

❑ program instruction error, for example, an attempted division by zero or an attempt to communicate with a non-existent device;

❑ an externally generated command from the operator.

When such events occur, the *interrupt handler* routine must establish the cause/source of the interrupt and call the appropriate *interrupt service routine*.

Error handling/trapping

It is important that events which would ordinarily upset or crash the computer system, are *trapped* and handled in an orderly way. Thus, for example, upon encountering an illegal application program instruction, an interrupt is generated, followed by entry to an appropriate interrupt service routine in the executive. The application program is aborted and the service routine displays an error message on screen, detailing the nature of the error. Arithmetic errors, such as an attempt to divide by zero, and I/O errors should also be trapped and treated in a similar fashion. Although data lost as a result of programming errors may not be recoverable by the operating system, any loss caused by abnormal operational interrupt of an I/O activity should be preventable by an appropriate routine to restore the data.

Of course, applications software should, wherever possible, anticipate possible system errors such as disk read errors and other peripheral faults, and protect the user from contact with the operating system by producing its own user friendly messages. Further, in the same way that the operating system prevents system crashes, applications software should, if the fault can be corrected, be robust enough to allow its continuance without loss of data.

Accounting and logging

An important part of system control is that the operator should have a record of all operator communications, error conditions and applications which have been run; the operating system keeps a log of such events and either outputs the relevant messages to the operator's console printer or records them on backing storage for later printing.

Multi-access and network operating systems normally provide an accounting facility which identifies and records terminal usage, including basic details such as user-id, time logged on and off, and processor time used; in this way, users or departments of an organization can be charged for computer time.

Memory management

Single user operating systems such as MS-DOS do not provide particularly sophisticated memory facilities, as only one application is *resident* at one time. There is one special case, that of the graphical user interface (GUI) which stays resident in memory; it must advise the operating system of its storage needs, in order that it is not corrupted by subsequent loading of applications.

Multi-programming and multi-tasking systems require quite complex memory management facilities in order to accommodate and maintain the *integrity* of the several programs and associated data which may be resident at any one time. Memory requirements do not remain static because the mix of programs being run may vary from moment to moment; the space left by a program swapped out of memory may not be large enough to accommodate an incoming program, requiring the *relocation* of programs already there.

Virtual memory

Although main memory and direct access backing storage are physically separate, it is possible to present their joint capacity as being available to run programs. Such virtual memory can be used to accommodate much larger programs, as well as expand the level of multi-programming. A programmer can regard the addressable memory space as being beyond the physical capacity of main memory. Programs are automatically divided into *pages* (a fixed unit of virtual storage) and when one is loaded, its virtual memory addresses are mapped to the absolute memory addresses by the executive. The addresses of each page are held in main memory and during program execution, they are paged-in and paged-out as required.

✍️Exercises

1. List the five computer *system resources* which are managed by the operating system.
2. In the context of single-stream, batch processing systems, what is the purpose of *scheduling*?
3. In the context of batch multiprogramming systems:
    (i)   What is meant by *dynamic resource allocation*?
    (ii) What factors may determine the *priority* rating of a job?
4. Distinguish between the *high-level scheduler* and the *low-level scheduler*, or *dispatcher*.
5. (i)   Suggest circumstances when a *time-sharing* operating system may be needed.
    (ii) Briefly describe two methods of allocating processor time to user applications.
6. *Multi-tasking* operating systems are now in common use. With the use of a suitable example, describe the benefits they bring to users.
7. Distinguish between *cooperative* and *pre-emptive* multi-tasking operating systems and suggest why the latter type is favoured for the general user market.
8. What is the primary function of a multi-user operating system?
9. (i)   Briefly describe two applications which make use of a real-time operating system.
    (ii) Why are real-time operating systems essential for systems which control processes or interact directly with their environment?
10. (i)   Define the term interrupt.
    (ii) Identify four events which may trigger an interrupt.
11. What role does memory management play in multi-programming and multi-tasking operating systems?
12. Why is virtual memory an important resource for a computer system?

Program development utilities

As part of the systems software provided with a computer system there are a number of utility programs specifically designed to aid program development and testing (language translators or processors are dealt with in Topic 15). These include the following.

Editors

These permit the creation and modification of source programs and data files. The facilities offered by these programs usually include such things as character, word and line insertion and deletion, automatic line numbering, line tabulation for languages which require program instructions to be spaced in a specific manner, the storage and retrieval of files from backing storage, and the printing of programs or other files.

Debugging aids

Programs in which the appropriate translator can find no fault will often contain errors in logic, known as bugs, which only become apparent when the program is run, producing results which are contrary to expectations, or even causing the computer to cease functioning. These bugs are often very difficult to detect and may lead to long delays in the implementation of the program. Debugging aids help programmers to isolate and identify the cause of bugs.

File managers

These simplify and facilitate a number of operations connected with program development and maintenance such as:

- keeping backup copies of important files;
- deleting files and creating space for new ones;
- merging files;
- providing details of current files held on backing storage;
- sorting file names into specified orders.

Without the help of such dedicated programs, operations such as these could be extremely time-consuming and consequently expensive.

System maintenance utilities

These are programs, usually included with the operating system, which carry out routine maintenance tasks on the computer system.

Disk defragmentation

This utility is extremely important for the efficient operation of the main hard drive(s) in a computer system because it optimises the use of disk space and helps to maintain drive performance. To describe its operation, a brief explanation of disk storage is needed.

Disk space is allocated in *clusters*, which are units of disk storage. For example, the cluster size may be 16 kilobytes (KB). When a file is stored on disk it takes up as many clusters as it needs. For example, if a document is of size 525 KB, it will need $525 \div 16 = 33$ clusters (to the nearest whole cluster). When a file is first stored on disk it is given, if possible, a *contiguous* (no gaps between) chain of clusters. Each time it is altered and made larger, it may not fit in its original place, so the extra has to be placed somewhere else. This *fragmentation* of files leads to slower disk performance, because the read/write heads may have to go to several different parts of the disk to retrieve a single file. The defragmentation utility rearranges the disk space so that each file is held in a contiguous set of clusters. The empty space is also organised into a contiguous block of clusters. The Windows 9x defragmentation utility is known as Disk Defragmenter.

Drive compression

This utility is used to increase the amount of disk space, by compressing some of the existing physical space. So, for example, using a compression ratio of 2:1, a disk can be made to hold twice as much data. The Windows 9x drive compression utility is called DriveSpace.

File compression

File compression utilities can be used to reduce the space taken by individual files or groups of files. The storage space taken by bitmap files can be radically reduced through compression by around 95%. Compression programs, such as WinZip allow the creation of *archives* which contain one or more compressed files. The compression program must be available to decompress the files before they can be used again. Compression standards include ZIP, LZH, ARJ, or ARC. Archiving files makes it possible to, for example, backup files to a medium such as floppy disk, which would otherwise have insufficient space. Compression can also reduce the time taken to transmit files over a data communications link, although there is no benefit to be gained if the process is also carried out by the transmitting modem. A compressed file cannot be further compressed.

Disk repair

This vital utility detects and repairs disk recording errors. Some locations on disk may not record data properly and if they are not found and repaired, data may be stored in those locations and be corrupted or lost. The utility also finds 'lost' files. When a program 'crashes', or more seriously, when the operating system crashes, corrupted files, or bits of files, may be left on disk. These lost files take up valuable disk space and often contain meaningless information or 'garbage'. The Windows 9x repair utility is called ScanDisk.

Other systems software

Device drivers

See Topic 9.

System configuration files

System configuration files contain operating system commands which tell the operating system such things as what hardware is available, what software is required for the hardware to operate correctly, and how to organise the internal memory. In other words, they contain programs to configure the computer system on startup.

config.sys and system.ini

Command	Meaning
DEVICE=C:\WINDOWS\ HIMEM.SYS	Load the upper memory manager
DOS=HIGH,UMB	Load DOS into the upper memory area and enables device drivers to be installed in the upper memory area
DEVICEHIGH=C:\CDROM\TORISAN.SYS /D:CD1 /P:SM	Load the CD-ROM driver into the upper memory area
DEVICEHIGH=C:\MOUSE\MOUSE.SYS	Load the mouse driver into the upper memory area
BUFFERS=30	Allocate memory for 30 disk buffers
FILES=30	Set the number of files that can be accessed at one time

Table 12.1. *config.sys*

The old MS-DOS operating system used a configuration file called config.sys. A sample configuration files is shown in Table 12.1. System.ini is the Windows 9x equivalent of the MS-DOS config.sys file. An extract of a system.ini file is shown below.

```
[boot]
oemfonts.fon=8514oem.fon
system.drv=system.drv
drivers=mmsystem.dll power.drv
shell=Explorer.exe
user.exe=user.exe
gdi.exe=gdi.exe
sound.drv=mmsound.drv
dibeng.drv=dibeng.dll
comm.drv=comm.drv
mouse.drv=mouse.drv
keyboard.drv=keyboard.drv
*DisplayFallback=0
fixedfon.fon=8514fix.fon
fonts.fon=8514sys.fon
386Grabber=vgafull.3gr
display.drv=pnpdrvr.drv
SCRNSAVE.EXE=C:\WINDOWS\SYSTEM\BLANKS~1.SCR

[keyboard]
keyboard.dll=
oemansi.bin=xlat850.bin
subtype=
type=4

[boot.description]
system.drv=Standard PC
keyboard.typ=Standard 101/102-Key or Microsoft Natural Keyboard
mouse.drv=Microsoft IntelliPoint
aspect=100,120,120
display.drv=ATI Rage 128 GL AGP (English)
```

✎Exercises

1. Study the operating system on a machine and produce a table of the system utilities you find there. The table should include the name of the utility and its function in the management of the computer system.

2. (i) Briefly describe the process of disk fragmentation and its causes.

   (ii) What are the effects of fragmentation on the performance of the computer system?

   (iii) What does the defragmentation utility do?

3. What is a disk repair utility and why is it important for the prevention of serious data loss?

4. (i) Distinguish between drive compression and file compression.

   (ii) To speed the transmission of a file to a colleague at another branch, through a modem link, an employee first uses a compression program to compress the file. Why may there be no benefit in doing this?

5. What is the purpose of a system configuration file?

BIOS (basic input | output system)

A computer system's BIOS holds details of what hardware is installed and settings for individual components. The settings are held in CMOS RAM. This is a special type of RAM, which can retains its contents with only a tiny amount of battery power - the battery is attached to the motherboard and recharged whenever the machine is switched on. The BIOS settings are used to control the *system start-up* and carry out diagnostic checks on the hardware.

System start-up

When a computer system is 'powered on' the BIOS starts the Power-On Self-Test (POST) routine. The POST routine is in two stages:

1. The *motherboard* (also known as the *system board*) and its components (processor, RAM etc.) are checked for their normal operation. The RAM test is visible on screen while it is being carried out.

2. The hardware actually installed is checked to see that it matches with the system's BIOS (Basic Input/Output System) settings.

If an error is identified, the system reports it, either with a 'beep' or an error message on screen. The POST sequence checks the hardware to see that the major components, including RAM, are present and working properly.

BIOS Setup utility

The BIOS Setup utility is held in ROM so that it is not lost when the machine is switched off. The program is used to enter details of the computer system's hardware, that is, the BIOS settings. When a computer is powered on and before the operating system starts to load, the operator has the opportunity to access the BIOS Setup utility, normally by pressing a designated key. Because settings entered through this program are then stored in CMOS RAM, the program menu includes the following two options: Standard CMOS setup; BIOS Features (or Advanced CMOS) setup.

Standard CMOS setup

Standard CMOS Setup is used to record details of the basic hardware in the computer system. The settings are recorded when the motherboard is installed, normally by the manufacturer. This is usually the first BIOS Setup menu option. An example of a Standard CMOS Setup screen is shown in Figure 13.1. The exact settings will vary according to the computer hardware, but note the following details labelled in the figure.

❑   The Primary Master is the main hard disk drive inside the system unit and in this example, it has a capacity of 2·5 GB.

❑   The Primary Slave, in this example, is a 100MB Zip drive, which uses removable disk cartridges.

❑   There is only one floppy disk drive, designed for 1·44 MB floppy disks.

❏ The 'Halt on' setting specifies that any hardware error will cause the powering up sequence to stop, until the error is corrected. The only other options are to ignore keyboard and/or floppy disk errors. Failure of RAM or the hard disk drive, for example, would always halt the system.

❏ The RAM total is 128 MB.

❏ The screen type is EGA or VGA, which are screen resolution standards. VGA is a minimum 800 × 600 resolution.

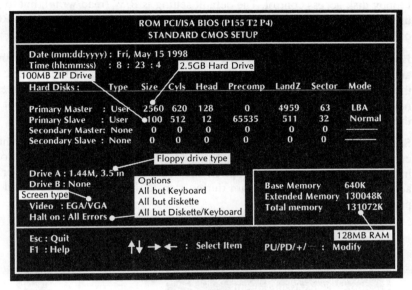

Figure 13.1. *Standard CMOS settings*

The Standard CMOS Settings option would only need to be used if:

(a) the CMOS contents are corrupted or lost, perhaps through battery failure (as can happen if a machine is switched off for a long period). It is important that the settings are written down, so that if the contents are lost or corrupted, they can be re-entered. Without the correct settings, the machine may not work properly or at all;

   or

(b) the system configuration is altered, perhaps through replacement of the hard disk or installation of a new motherboard.

BIOS Features setup

This option is used to 'fine tune' the hardware configuration, to improve performance and to set certain user preferences. Figure 13.2 shows an example BIOS Features screen. Four features in the previous figure are labelled with comments:

❏ Boot sequence. Following a successful Power-On Self-Test (POST) routine, the

BIOS loads the operating system, normally from the hard drive. The boot sequence dictates the order in which the BIOS checks the various disk drives to find the operating system. Setting the A: (floppy) drive as the first to be checked, allows for an emergency 'boot' if the operating system will not load from the hard drive. Windows 9x provides an option to create such a Startup Disk. To carry out the emergency boot, the Startup disk is placed in the floppy drive before the machine is powered up. As soon as the BIOS finds the Startup disk it boots the system from there, rather than trying to load the operating system from the hard drive.

❑ Floppy disk access control. The default setting is R/W (read/write), but to prevent users copying files from the hard drive onto floppy disk, it may be set to RO (read only). This may be done for security reasons.

❑ Boot-up NumLock status. Setting the NumLock key to 'On' ensures that it is automatically on when the system is powered up. The keys on the numeric keypad then operate as such. If set to 'Off' the numeric keys have an alternate use as navigational keys (cursor left, right, page up and so on). Whatever the boot setting, the user can switch the NumLock key on or off as necessary.

❑ Security option. As the earlier warning points out, altering BIOS settings has to be carried out with great care and only by someone who knows what they are doing and has the authority to do it. This option allows a password to be set. If a user tries to access the BIOS Setup program during startup, he or she will be asked for the password.

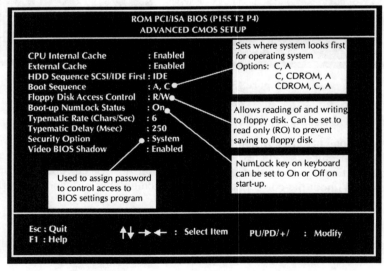

Figure 13.2. *BIOS features setup screen*

Plug and Play BIOS

Plug and Play operating systems use a BIOS which is automatically updated when a new device is added. On a Windows 98 machine, the BIOS details then appear in the System Properties window, as shown in Figure 13.3.

The Device Manager tab lists all the categories of device attached to the computer system. In the figure, three of the items are expanded, to show details of the actual attached device:

❑ The CD-ROM is identified as a TEAC CD-58E;

❑ The display adapter, or graphics card, is a Matrox Millennium;

❑ The monitor is identified as Plug and Play (VESA DDC). 'VESA' indicates that it meets the Video Electronics Standards Association requirements for monitors.

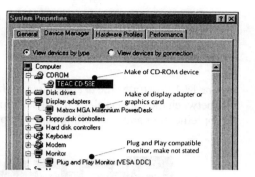

Figure 13.3. *Example BIOS details in Windows 9x system*

Once a new device, such as a disk drive, or extra RAM, has been connected, the BIOS detects it during the next startup. If the device is not Plug and Play compatible, the installation settings have to be made through the BIOS setup utility.

✎Exercises

1. Although a computer system without its operating system is of limited practical use, the various devices which make up the system will operate at a basic level. The BIOS (basic input output system) enables this basic operation. Access a machine's BIOS and note the settings for the various items of hardware.

   Draw up a machine hardware specification based on your findings.

   N.B. Do not alter any of the settings as this may prevent the machine from working.

2. What is meant by 'plug and play'?

3. What benefits does the facility provide for:

   (i) non-specialist users?

   (ii) technical support staff?

4. Under what circumstances may an operating system be unable to use its plug and play facility?

5. Identify reasons why users may wish to upgrade their machine and the kinds of hardware they may wish to add.

Input|output control

Figure 14.1 illustrates the *architecture* of the communication system which allows data transfers between the various elements of a computer system. This Topic examines various methods of implementing and controlling input/output (I/O) operations.

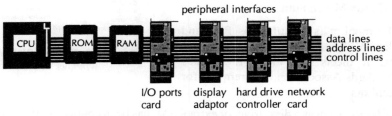

Figure 14.1. *Computer communication architecture*

A number of components can be identified:

❏ *Bus* or *highway*. A bus consists of a number of wires, one for each bit making up the unit of data transfer. A common I/O bus connects all I/O peripherals to the processor, so only one peripheral can use the bus at a time. This is not normally a restriction because the processor can only handle one instruction at a time, but most computers have an I/O bus which is independent of that used for processor/main memory transfers. Those machines using a common bus for I/O and processor/memory data movements are referred to as single bus systems;

❏ *Interface*. This is a hardware device containing electronic components, which connects an I/O peripheral to the computer. One of the functions of an interface is to carry out the conversion process between the internal and external codes for internal computer and external peripheral operations respectively, according to whether data is being transferred to or from the peripheral;

❏ *Device controller*. This device is fundamentally the same as the interface, except that it is associated with the control of data transfers to and from storage devices, such as magnetic disk and tape drives.

Methods of I/O control

The transfer of data to and from a peripheral device can take place either:

❏ under the control of the machine's processor - *programmed input/output* or *PIO*;

❏ or, under the autonomous control of the device; most commonly, this is *direct memory access* or *DMA*.

Programmed input/output (PIO)

PIO means that the computer's processor controls each stage of data transfer between, for example, the system's hard disk drive and itself. PIO can be effected in one of two ways: software polling; hardware interrupts.

Software polling

The operating system software regularly polls (checks) each device to see if it requires attention. To achieve I/O transfers by this method, instructions are needed:

- ❑ for input - to transfer data from peripheral to processor;

- ❑ for output - to transfer data from processor to peripheral;

- ❑ to set individual control flags in the I/O interface unit;

- ❑ to test individual flags in the I/O interface unit.

A peripheral device is attached to an interface unit by a cable. The interface unit (usually inside the computer) is connected to one of a number of I/O slots, each of which has a fixed address, by which a peripheral can be identified for input or output. There are 3 basic elements in an interface unit which is polled by software:

- ❑ a control bit or *busy* flag - used to signal a device to start input or output. This cannot be set by the device as it is under control of the processor;

- ❑ a flag bit or *done* flag - this is set by the device when the data transfer is complete and can be tested or cleared by program instructions;

- ❑ a *buffer* register for the storage of data transferred into (read by) or to be transferred from (written by) the device.

When a 'start read' instruction is given, one character is transferred between the interface buffer register and the device. A single character is transferred in the opposite direction if a 'start write' instruction is given. A processor instruction commands the device to operate by setting the busy flag and then repeatedly tests the done flag to discover when the transfer is complete. The major difficulty with software polling is that the repeated testing of the done flag is carried out at the same time as it continues with some other computation. This means that the program instructions currently being executed (probably the program that issued the I/O instruction) must be interleaved with the regular issue of instructions to test for completion of the transfer. The last operating system to use software polling was CP/M (Control Program/Microcomputer) which was used on some early microcomputer systems, but is now obsolete. An example instruction sequence for software polling may be as follows.

For *input* from a specific device:

- ❑ instruction to interface to set the busy flag for 'start transmit';

- ❑ send instruction to test done flag. If the flag indicates that the transfer is complete, skip next instruction;

- ❑ branch to previous instruction;

- ❑ issue instruction to transfer character from buffer register into accumulator;

❑   issue store instruction to transfer character from accumulator to main memory.

For *output* to a specific device:

❑   issue instruction to transfer character from processor accumulator into buffer register of interface device;

❑   issue instruction to set busy flag to start transfer;

❑   issue instruction to test done flag and if set, skip the next instruction;

❑   branch to previous instruction.

The repetitive flag-test loop is necessary to ensure that a character transfer is completed before the next one is transmitted. A more efficient method of PIO control is to use hardware interrupts.

I/O using hardware interrupts

An I/O interrupt is a signal from an I/O device to the processor to indicate that:

❑   data is waiting to be read;

❑   an I/O error has occurred;

❑   a previous I/O transfer is complete.

To enable I/O devices to initiate requests for service from the processor, an I/O bus includes interrupt request (IRQ) lines, typically 15. All the IRQ lines go to every expansion slot in the I/O bus, so when a device adapter card (for example, a disk drive controller) is plugged into a slot, the specific IRQ line it is to use can then be set, by configuring the card, either through utility software or by physical switches on the card. The device then uses that IRQ line to signal the processor that it requires service. A processor has only one interrupt pin, which is set when an I/O interrupt occurs, to indicate the presence of an interrupt, but not its source. An interrupt handler routine (part of the operating system software) is executed when an interrupt is detected, to establish its source. On a typical microcomputer, interrupts are used by the keyboard, mouse, disk and the COM (communication) ports.

Establishing the source of an interrupt

The source of the interrupt is determined by checking each IRQ line to see if it has been set. If more than one device has set its IRQ line, the handler routine will select the one with the highest priority. Once the source has been identified, the interrupt handler calls the relevant *interrupt service routine*. Following completion of the service, control of the processor must be returned to the original process. The checking of the processor's single I/O interrupt register is carried out at the start of each instruction, as part of the fetch-execute cycle.

Executing the interrupt

Before entry to the relevant interrupt service routine, the current state of the machine must be saved. This includes storing the state of the current process and the contents of the Program Counter or PC (the processor register which keeps track of the next program instruction to be executed) in a separate location; the PC value is then replaced by the starting address of the interrupt service routine and the routine is executed. Once the interrupt has been serviced, control of the processor must be returned to the appropriate point in the original program by copying its stored continuation address back into the PC. An interrupt-on/off flag in the processor must be set to off prior to acceptance of an interrupt and then cleared to on as soon as control has been returned to the original program, in order to prevent an interrupt from another device being accepted until the original program has resumed control.

Interrupt priority

Interrupts may emanate from a variety of sources (I/O and others) and for a number of different reasons (see Operating Systems); the operating system can be used to allocate different priority ratings to particular events and devices.

Nested interrupts

Some systems may leave the interrupt mechanism enabled so that an interrupt service routine may itself be interrupted by a higher priority request; this may happen repeatedly, requiring the nesting of interrupts. A LIFO (Last In First Out) stack can be used to store the return addresses and accumulator contents relating to these nested interrupts so that they can be retrieved in reverse order. If a higher priority interrupt occurs during I/O there is a danger of data being lost. Each peripheral is allocated a given priority rating which must be compared with that of the current process, before the interrupt routine is entered. As a general rule, low speed devices are given high priority, because frequent interruptions to relatively slow data input may result in there being insufficient data to continue processing. Where the interrupting peripheral has a priority rating lower than or equal to that of the current activity, it is kept waiting; otherwise the interrupt takes place.

Masking device interrupts

Where the interrupt mechanism is left enabled, it may be desirable to selectively mask out certain low priority devices from that facility. This can be achieved by using a register as an interrupt mask (Table 14.1), with bit positions corresponding to individual devices in the interrupt request register; devices are masked out by setting the relevant bits in the mask to 0 and carrying out a logical AND operation between the mask and the interrupt request register.

	interrupt request register						
device	1	2	3	4	5	6	
interrupt status	1	0	1	1	0	1	AND
interrupt mask	1	0	0	0	0	1	
device	1	2	3	4	5	6	
interrupt status	1	0	0	0	0	1	

Table 14.1. *Masking device interrupts*

With the current mask settings, only devices 1 and 6 are allowed to request interrupts.

A number of other system conditions, some with higher priority than I/O requests, may generate interrupts and these are examined in Topic 11 on Operating Systems.

Direct memory access (DMA)

Not all data transfers between peripheral devices and the processor are carried out under continual program control (programmed input/output or PIO). Other schemes such as DMA allow data transfer to or from high speed storage devices such as tape or disk to be effected without continual processor control.

Data is transferred in blocks, as opposed to character by character. DMA is possible because of the ability of peripheral devices to operate autonomously, that is, after the initial input or output instruction has been given by the processor, the peripheral is able to complete the data transfer independently. To allow the memory to be accessed directly by a peripheral, instead of via the processor, hardware known as a DMA controller is needed. For transfers from main memory to peripheral, the processor supplies the DMA controller with the start address in memory of the data block to be transferred and its length. A transfer from, for example, a disk pack to memory would require the processor to tell the DMA controller the relevant disk address and into which memory locations the data is to be copied.

The DMA controller 'steals' memory cycles from the processor while the data transfer is taking place. Meanwhile, the processor can continue execution of its current program, although its operation is slowed slightly by the cycle stealing. Under these circumstances, DMA is not as quick as PIO, but is an essential component to any computer system working in multi-programming mode.

Recently, the use of 'bus mastering' processors has removed the need for cycle stealing, thereby allowing the main processor to continue work at its normal rate. For this reason, DMA is now widely used.

✐Exercises

1. Distinguish between *programmed input/output* (PIO) and *direct memory access (DMA)*.
2. What is the main disadvantage of *software polling* to control input/output?
3. What is the function of an *IRQ line*?
4. Why is *interrupt priority* important for the efficient and reliable operation of a computer system?
5. Identify typical interrupt sources and suggest their relative priorities.
6. Define the terms:
   (i)   bus;
   (ii)   interface;
   (iii) device controller.

Programming language translators

The function of a *language processor*, or *translator*, is to convert a program written in a computer language (the *source code*) into a form which the computer can understand and execute (the *object* or *machine code*).

An *assembler* is a language processor for assembly language (low level language) programs and *compilers* and *interpreters* are required for translating high-level language programs, written in, for example, COBOL, Visual Basic, C and Pascal.

Assemblers

A program written in an assembly language is much more readable and understandable than its equivalent in machine code as the examples in Tables 15.1 and 15.2 show. The instructions in the assembly language version use mnemonic *opcodes* (for example, LDR, ADD, STR) which makes the purpose of instructions easier to remember than the hexadecimal codes (automatically converted to binary code on input to the machine) used in machine code. Assembly language also allows the use of *symbolic addresses* (for example, R1, HOURS, RATE) for more meaningful identification of memory locations.

Memory location	Contents (Hex)	Comments
1000	220F	Load R0 from ..
1001	2000	..memory location 2000
1002	221F	Load R1 from ..
1003	2001	..memory location 2001
1004	0901	Add R1 to R0
1005	351F	Store R0 in ..
1006	2002	..memory location 2002
1007	FFFF	Halt execution

Table 15.1. *Example machine code program to add two numbers*

Instruction	Comments
LDR R0, N1	;LoaD Register R0 with the contents of location N1
LDR R1, N2	;LoaD Register R1 with the contents of location N2
ADD R0, R1	;ADD Ro and R1 and store sum in R0
STR R0, N3	;STore Register R0 in location N3
HLT	;HaLT execution of program

Table 15.2. *Example assembly language program to add two numbers*

However, the assembly language code in Table 15.2 is not executable by the computer and an assembler is needed to carry out the necessary translation. The assembly process is illustrated in Figure 15.1.

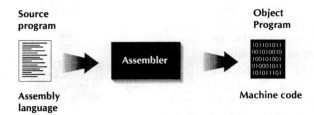

Figure 15.1. *Translation process with assembler*

The assembler accepts an assembly language program (the source code) as its data input, processes it and produces as output the required machine code program (the object code).

An assembler carries out a number of tasks during the process of assembly, including:

❑   Opcode (operation code) translation. The mnemonic op-codes must be replaced by the numeric opcodes which the computer uses to identify its various instructions;

❑   Absolute address allocation. Each instruction or data word in the source program must be allocated an absolute machine address (its physical location).

❑   Symbolic operand conversion. This refers to the assembly process of replacing any symbolic operands with numeric machine addresses.

Apart from sending the resulting object code to backing storage, an assembler will normally carry out a number of other tasks, including the generation of error messages and the output of source code listings.

Compilers and interpreters

There are two main types of high-level language translators (or *language processors* as they are often known):

❑   compilers;

❑   interpreters.

Since the choice of translator has implications regarding program development time, debugging and testing, memory requirements, execution speed and program security, it is important from a programming point of view to be quite clear about the difference between the two types.

Somewhat like an assembler, a *compiler* accepts a source program, that is, a program written in some high-level language, Pascal for instance, checks that it is correctly formed and, if so, generates the equivalent object program in a low-level language. The translated program may be in the form of an assembly language, in which case it must first be assembled before it is executed, or it may be in machine code, allowing it to be executed directly without further modification. If any errors are detected during compilation, they will be reported and, if serious enough, may prevent the compiler from completing the translation process. Figure 15.2 illustrates the compilation process.

A compiler will often have access to one or more *libraries* of pre-compiled procedures for performing commonly used tasks. Included in these libraries of machine code subprograms will be routines for performing arithmetic operations, input/output operations, backing storage data transfers and other commonly used functions. Whenever the source code refers to one of these routines specifically, or needs one to perform the operation specified, the compiler will ensure that the routine is added to the object program.

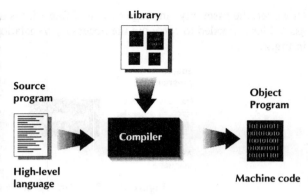

Figure 15.2. *Compilation process*

Note that the final object code is independent of both the source code and the compiler itself. That is, neither of these two programs needs to be resident in main store when the object code is being executed. However, any alterations to the program subsequent to its compilation will necessitate modification and re-compilation of the source code prior to executing the program again.

An *interpreter* uses a different method to translate a source program into a machine-sensible form. An object program is not generated in this form of translation, rather the source program, or an intermediate form of it, is scanned statement by statement, each in turn immediately being converted into the actions specified. Figure 15.3 illustrates the interpreter process.

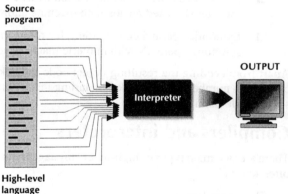

The source program statements are translated and executed separately, as they are encountered, while the source program is being processed by the interpreter. The object code actually

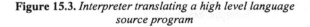

Figure 15.3. *Interpreter translating a high level language source program*

executed is held within the interpreter; the latter merely identifies from the source statement which piece of object code (*subroutine*) is relevant and causes it to be performed. On completion of a statement, control returns to the interpreter which then processes the next logical statement in the program sequence.

It might seem, therefore, that an interpreter has a big advantage over a compiler. In terms of the amount of effort required in obtaining an executable program, this is certainly true, but there are a number of other factors which favour the use of a compiler. For example, an interpreter must do a considerable amount of work before it can even begin to cause a source statement to be executed (error checking, for instance); on the other hand, a compiler has already done this work during compilation. Moreover, should a section of source code be repeated one or more times, an interpreter must re-interpret the section each time. Consequently, interpreted programs tend to run significantly slower than equivalent compiled programs, and for time-critical applications this might be a major concern. Furthermore, because the translation and execution phases are interwoven, the interpreter must be resident in memory at the same time as the source code. If memory space is at a premium, this can be a severe limitation of an interpreted language.

Languages designed for use by children or for teaching purposes are often interpreted. Logo, for example, originally designed as a language for children, is interpreted to facilitate its interactive nature. Similarly, BASIC is interpreted in order to simplify its use for programming novices.

A possible compromise is to provide both an interpreter and a compiler for the same language; this allows rapid development time using the interpreter, and fast execution obtained by compiling the code.

Linkers and loaders

Some programming languages allow a program to be developed in modules, which simplifies the task, but before the program can be executed the modules must be linked by a linker utility program. The process is the same as that illustrated in Figure 15.2 which shows the linking of machine code subprograms from a library into the main code during program compilation.

A loader is an operating system utility which loads a program from backing store into memory for execution. The process of converting symbolic addresses to absolute machine addresses, described in the earlier section on assemblers, is carried out by a loader within the assembler program.

Dynamic Link Libraries (DLLs)

A Dynamic Link Library is a collection of functions and procedures forming part of *the Application Programming Interface* (API) of the Microsoft Windows operating system. In the form of DLL files, the Windows API provides hundreds of functions and procedures for commonly required programming tasks. For instance, there are DLLs provided by Microsoft for displaying and processing common dialog boxes such as those that appear when a user selects the Open command from a File menu.

DLLs greatly simplify the task of creating Windows application programs. Windows programming languages such as Visual Basic take advantage of the Windows API by providing a convenient interface between the programmer and the hundreds of useful functions and procedures contained in DLLs. Moreover programmers can easily create their own DLLs, thereby providing a means of using the same functions and procedures in more than one application program. Note that although DLLs contain executable program code, they are not independently executable. The code within a DLL must be linked to an application program for it to be used.

When an application is launched, Windows checks any references it contains to DLL procedures or functions. If it finds a reference to a DLL, it first checks to see if it has already been loaded into memory by Windows. If not, the complete DLL is transferred into memory and linked to the application program. Note that this process is initiated only when a program is run, hence the term *Dynamic* Link Library. The word *Library* in Dynamic Link Library refers to the fact that a DLL is usually a collection of executable functions and procedures. This means that the complete DLL has to be loaded into memory even if only one function or procedure within it is required.

DLLs provide several benefits for the development and execution of application programs:

❑   Only one copy of a DLL needs to be loaded into memory even though several applications may be using it.

❑   All applications that use a particular DLL benefit from improvements to it without the applications themselves needing to be modified

❑   Programmers can re-use the same code in different applications. This can greatly improve programmer productivity.

❑   Because they are only loaded into memory when they are required, DLLs do not occupy memory unnecessarily.

🖎Exercises

1. Define the terms *source program* and *object program*.
2. Briefly describe the process of translating an *assembly* language program into *machine code*.
3. What is meant by the terms *mnemonic opcode* and *symbolic addressing*? Give an example of each.
4. Distinguish between *compilation* and *interpretation*.
5. List the relative benefits and drawbacks of compilation and interpretation for:
    (i)   the programmer;
    (ii)   the application.
6. What are *Dynamic Link Libraries* (DLL) and
    (i)   How do they simplify the task of application development?
    (ii)   How do they make efficient us of system resources?

Section 4

Files and file processing

Topics

Files

A *file*, in computer terms, refers to a collection of data stored on a backing storage device such as a magnetic disk or tape drive. This data, however, can be in numerous different forms. For instance, a file could contain:

❑ the output from a program such as a word processor, spreadsheet or drawing package;

❑ a database of personnel records or customer details, for example;

❑ a program written in a language such as BASIC or COBOL;

❑ an application program such as a word processor, spreadsheet, database package, DTP or CAD program.

The form of file is often indicated by the name under which it has been stored. In the operating system MS-DOS, three extra characters (*file extension*) are allowed in the file name for the purpose of identifying the type of file. If you were to view a list of files held on a disk you might see something like that shown in Figure 16.1. Files with the extension BAT or EXE can be executed by the operating system directly, but all the rest are used in conjunction with programs of various types. Many files have no particular structure. For instance, a picture file which contains colour information for the pixels comprising the picture is simply a list of colour codes in the order that they appear on a display screen; a text file from a word processor is a list of codes for letters and special characters such as tabs and paragraph marks; data files produced by other programs can contain mixtures of numbers and characters. Many files, for example those used in business and commercial processing, do have a common type of structure.

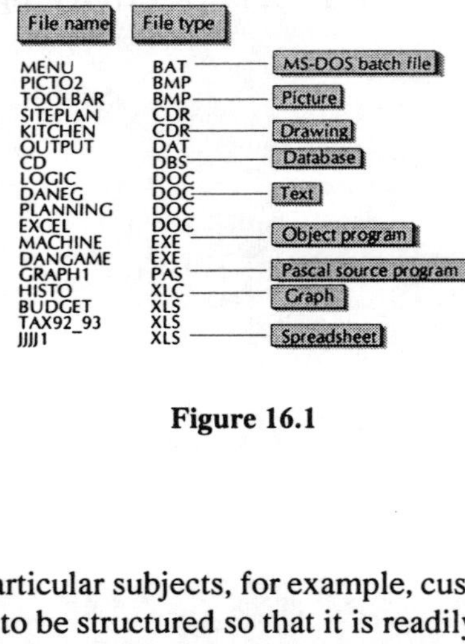

Figure 16.1

Structured files, records and fields

In data processing, it is necessary to store information on particular subjects, for example, customers, suppliers or personnel and such information needs to be structured so that it is readily controllable and accessible to the user. In traditional data processing systems, each of these 'topics' of information is allocated a file. Figure 16.2 illustrates the structure of a book file.

The *file* is a collection of *records*, one for each book. Each record contains details of the book's title, its author(s), ISBN number, publisher, date of publication and cost; each of these *data items* is allocated physical space, known as a *field*, within the record. Figure 16.2 shows a sample record, with the Title field (each one is identified by its *field name)* containing the value 'Turbo C++ for Windows' and the other fields containing values associated with that book.

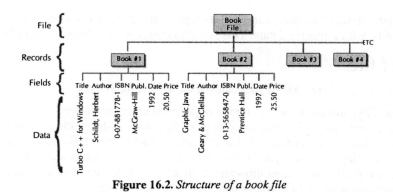

Figure 16.2. *Structure of a book file*

Data types

Each field is assigned a particular data type to suit the kind of data it is to hold and to assist in data validation. Database packages provide a number of built-in data types, but programming languages also allow the programmer to define new data types. The following types are typical of those available in database packages.

Character, text or alphanumeric

This is for a field which may contain text, or a mixture of text, symbols and numbers. Sometimes a field may only contain numeric digits, perhaps an account number or telephone number. If it is not treated numerically, but as text, character type is normally used. Because a character field can hold any kind of data, it is more difficult to control the format and validity of its contents. When the data values are unpredictable or wide ranging, as is usually the case for names and addresses, a character field is the only option. However, it is still possible to impose controls on the contents of some character fields. For example, a Part Code could be a mixture of letters and numbers but have a strict format such as AAA999, that is three letters followed by three digits. Character fields should not be used where other data types are more appropriate. For examples, dates may contain alphanumeric data but it is better to use a date field which restricts entries to a strict format.

Numeric

This type must be used for fields containing numerical values (such as money amounts or quantities) to be used in calculations. The number of decimal places and the range of values can also be set.

Logical (yes/no)

This type allows the entry of two possible values, indicated by *true* or *false*. Sometimes, *yes* and *no*, respectively, may be used instead. For example, the Student table in the academic database contains a field to record the sex of a student. Use of the field name Male means that Yes is entered for a male student and No for a female. If the field name Female is used, No is entered for a male and Yes for a female student. The name of the field determines whether an affirmative or a negative (Yes or No) is entered.

Date

Although character type may be used for the storage of dates, the *date* type allows the correct sorting of dates. Also, in defining queries, date type fields enable the database to compare dates held in records, with a specified date. This is not practical with a character type field.

Types of file

Structure data files fall into one of four categories, according to use.

Master files. They are used for the storage of *permanent*, or *semi-permanent*, data which is used in applications such as stock, sales or payroll. Some of the fields tend to contain data which is fairly static, for example, customer name and address, whilst data in some fields is continually changing, for example, customer balance, as transactions are applied to the file. Such *updating* is carried out, either through the direct entry (on-line) of individual transactions, or from an accumulated set of entries stored on a *transaction* file.

Transaction files. These are transient and only exist to allow the updating of master files. Each transaction record contains the *key field value* of the master record it is to update (to allow correct matching with its relevant master record), together with data gathered from source documents, for example, invoice amounts which update the balance field in customer accounts.

Reference files. These contain data used for reference or look-up purposes, such as price catalogue and customer name and address files.

Archival or historical files. These contain data which, for legal or organisational reasons, must be kept and tend to be used on an ad hoc basis and may be referred to only occasionally.

Fixed and variable length records

The extent to which the information in a particular file can be standardised and categorised will determine whether each record in the file can be fixed or variable in length. The length of the record is the number of character positions allocated to it within the file. In Figure 16.2 the file would probably contain *fixed* length records because:

❑ the number and types of data items required in this case are likely to be the same for each book;

❑ the number of character positions for each field can be fixed or at least set to a maximum. For example, the ISBN is fixed at 13 character positions and Title could be set to a maximum of 30, provided that no book title exceeded this length.

Variable length records may be used in files which have storage requirements markedly different from those referred to above, for instance:

❑ some records could have more fields than others. In a personnel file, for example, each record may contain details of previous jobs held and as the number of previous jobs may vary considerably from one employee to another, so the number of fields would be similarly varied;

or

❑ the number of character positions used for individual values within a field is variable. For example, in a library system each record may contain a field for data which describes the subject of the book and the amount of text needed to adequately describe this may vary from book to book.

Listed below are some of the advantages of *fixed length* records.

❑ Fixed length records are simpler to process, in that the start and end points of each record can be readily identified by the number of character positions. For instance, if a record has a fixed length of 80 character positions, a program reading the file from the start will assume that the second record starts at the 81st character position, the third at the 161st character position and so on, making easier the programming of file handling operations.

❑ Fixed length records allow an accurate estimation of file storage requirements. For example, a file containing 1000 records, each of fixed 80 characters length, will take approximately 80000 characters of storage.

❑ Where direct access files are being used, fixed length records can be readily updated 'in situ' (in other words the updated record overwrites the old version in the same position on the storage medium). As the new version will have the same number of characters as the old, any changes to a record will not change its physical length. On the other hand, a variable length record may increase in length after updating, preventing its return to its home location.

There are some instances when *variable* length records are more appropriate. For example:

❑ where records in a file contain highly variable quantities of information, variable length records may be more economical of storage space;

❑ when the saving in storage space makes the introduction of more complex file handling techniques worthwhile.

Locating records with primary and secondary keys

In most organisations, when an information system is operational it will be necessary to identify each record uniquely. In a Personnel File, for example, it might be thought that it is possible to identify each individual record simply by the employee's Surname and this would be satisfactory as long as no two employees had the same surname. In reality, many organisations will have several employees with, for example, the same surnames, dates of birth, job titles and grades, so to ensure uniqueness each employee is assigned a unique identifier, such as a Works Number. The <u>WorksNo</u> field is then used as the primary key in the filing system, with each staff member being assigned a unique Works Number, as illustrated in Table 16.1.

WorksNo	Surname	Forenames	Dept	Post	Grade	DateOfBirth
....	....	....	....	....	....	....
301011	Williams	Alun	Sales	Clerk	A	06/05/92
301012	Williams	Alun John	Sales	Supervisor	C	03/07/88
301013	Ginelli	Massimo	Accounts	Supervisor	C	09/11/94
....	....	....	....	....	....	....

Table 16.1

The remaining fields which cannot guarantee a unique value in each record are known as *secondary keys*. In Table 16.1, Surname, Forenames, Dept, Post, Grade and DateOfBirth are all examples of secondary keys. Some secondary keys will be used regularly as a means of extracting useful information from a file. For example, the secondary key Dept could be used to retrieve the records of all employees who work in Sales, or the Post and Grade fields could be used to list Grade B staff holding the post of Clerk.

Composite primary key

Sometimes, the primary key may be a *composite key*, that is, one made up of more than one field. The adjacent example in Table 16.2 shows how a pair of fields, which individually may not be unique, can be combined to provide a unique identifier for each record.

The file extract details suppliers' quotations for a number of different products. There is a need for a composite key because there may be a number of quotations from one supplier (in this case, SupplierNo 41192) and a number of quotations for the same part (in this instance, PartNo A112). It is necessary, therefore, to use both SupplierNo and PartNo to identify one quotation record uniquely.

SupplierNo	PartNo	Price	DeliveryDate
23783	A361	2.59	31/01/96
37463	B452	1.50	29/01/96
40923	A112	3.29	30/01/96
41192	A112	3.29	28/01/96
41192	C345	2.15	30/01/96

Table 16.2 *Extract from quotation file with composite primary key*

Indexing fields

Indexes are used to speed the retrieval of records. Table 16.3 illustrates an index for the job Grade field in a Personnel file. To find the records of Grade C staff, for example, without an index would require that all records are examined, a lengthy process if there are thousands of records. Using the index allows the immediate identification of all the relevant records for a particular Grade.

Grade	Primary keys or pointers to records
A	301011 301019 301023 301067 etc
B	301014 301015 301027 301033 etc
C	301012 301013 301065 301077 etc
D	301088 301090 301122 301133 etc
E	301001 301005 301186 301111 etc

Table 16.3. *A field index*

The principle is the same as that used for a book index which lists the page numbers on which a particular topic can be found. In this example, it is assumed that there are 5 job Grades, A, B, C, D and E. Each Grade letter in the table has a list of pointers to the records which contain that letter in the Grade field. In this example the pointer is the WorksNo, which is the primary key for each record. However, the precise mechanism for locating all the records for a particular indexed value depends on the filing system being used.

Logical and physical pointers

The WorksNo is an example of a *logical pointer*, that is one which does not directly represent a physical address on the storage medium. To retrieve a record, the logical pointer must be converted to a *physical pointer* which represents a location on the storage medium.

Exercises

1. Draw up a list of file types and provide an example of each type and the kind of application with which it is associated

2. (i) Referring to Figure 16.2, produce a similar structure for another application with which you are familiar.

   (ii) Modifying the structure if necessary, label each field with its relevant data type.

3. A holiday company's information systems make use of *master*, *transaction*, *reference* and *archive* files. The system contains files relating to holidays, ferry, airline, rail and coach companies, customers, hotels and other forms of accommodation and travel insurance offers.

   (i) Explain each of the italicised terms, identifying files within the holiday company's system which illustrate each definition.

   (ii) Distinguish between *fixed length* and *variable length* records and suggest circumstances when each may be appropriate in the holiday company's system.

   (iii) Define a structure for one of the files and include some sample records. Identify the *primary key* (including a *composite* key if appropriate) and state its purpose.

   (iv) For the file defined in (iii), suggest which *secondary keys* could be used to produce useful reports or summaries.

   (v) What is the purpose of an *index* and when is it beneficial to use one? Suggest one or more fields in your sample files which may benefit from indexing.

4. Distinguish between a *logical pointer* and a *physical pointer*.

Serial and direct access

There are two principal ways in which stored data can be accessed, serially or directly, as Figure 17.1 illustrates.

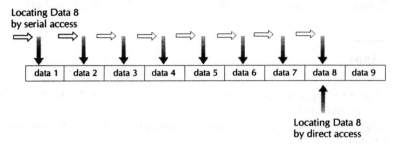

Figure 17.1. *Serial and direct access to stored data*

Serial access simply means that the data, usually records in a file, are accessed one after another, starting at the beginning. If the records are not in any particular order, like a shuffled pack of cards, then serial access cannot anticipate where any single record will be found. For this reason files which are to be accessed serially are normally held in sequence, according to a primary key, such as Item Code for a stock file and Works Number for a personnel file. When an ordered file is accessed serially it is also being accessed sequentially.

When a record is accessed directly, there need be no reference to other records in the file. Direct access is only possible if the storage medium has addressable physical locations. Most ICT storage systems provide direct access but one storage medium, magnetic tape, only allows serial/sequential access.

Serial access media

Serial access means that in order to identify and retrieve a particular record, it is necessary to 'read' all the records which precede it in the relevant file. The standard medium for serial access is magnetic tape. One of the difficulties with this medium is that there it has no readily identifiable physical areas which can be addressed. In other words, it is not possible to give a name or code and refer this to a particular location. It is said to be *non-addressable*. To find an individual record, the software needs to examine each record's *key field*, starting from the beginning of the file, until the required record is found.

Direct access media

Storage media such as floppy disks, hard disks and CD ROMs allow *direct* access to individual records, without reference to the rest of the relevant file. They have physical divisions which can be identified by computer software (and sometimes hardware) and are *addressable*, so that particular locations can be referred to by a name or code to retrieve a record which is stored at that location. Retrieval of an individual record stored on such a medium is achieved by specifying the relevant *primary key field value*, thus providing the software with a means of finding and retrieving the specific individual record directly.

Magnetic tape - a serial access medium

Because of the physical characteristics of magnetic tape it is necessary, when processing a file, that the tape unit (see Figure 17.2) starts to read the tape at the beginning of the reel.

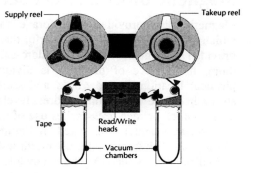

As there are no specific physical locations on the tape which the computer can address, the only way it can find a particular record is by reading the file up to the point where the specific record it is seeking is found. For this reason, it is generally used in applications such as payroll where the whole file is to be processed from beginning to end. As the tape is read, the computer will compare the key field value of each record which it comes to, with the specified key value, until the required record is found.

Figure 17.3. *Large magnetic tape unit*

Logical records and blocks

Figure 17.3 illustrates the way in which a file is arranged on tape both *logically* and *physically*.

Note that records R1, R2, R3 and R4 are instances of logical records. If this were a stock file, each logical record would relate to one commodity held in stock. On the other hand each *block* consists, in this illustration, of 4 logical records. Data is transferred between the computer's internal memory and the tape storage medium in manageable blocks (the physi-

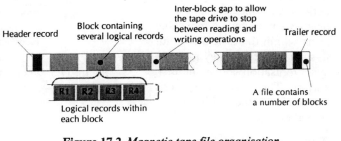

Figure 17.2. *Magnetic tape file organisation*

cal unit of transfer), the optimum size of each depending on factors such as the size of the computer's internal memory.

Between each block transfer, the tape has to stop while the previous one is processed by the computer. In order to give the tape time to stop and then restart for the next block, there is an *inter block gap* (IBG), a blank area of tape between each block. It is unlikely that the optimum block size will coincide with the actual length of a single logical record, so it is necessary to transfer a number of logical records between tape and internal memory at one time. Thus, a block often consists of a number of logical records.

The example of a stock file is used again to illustrate this point further. Assume that each block contains 3 logical stock records (in other words three individual commodities). If the first record to be processed is stored in the fifth block, then the first four blocks have to be read in sequence into memory and each logical stock record examined for its key field value, without any records actually being used. When the fifth block is eventually read into memory each of the three logical stock records is then examined for its key field value until the required key and thus logical record, is identified.

Magnetic disk - a direct access medium

Magnetic disk provides file storage facilities which are more flexible and powerful than those provided by magnetic tape. As an addressable medium, the surface of the disk is divided into physical locations called *tracks* and *sectors*, as shown in Figure 17.4. A third address level known as a *cylinder* or *seek area* makes use of multiple disk surfaces and is illustrated in Figure 17.5. Commonly, disk storage units use multiple disks to form disk packs, which may be removable or permanently sealed within the computer system.

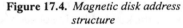

Figure 17.4. *Magnetic disk address structure*

To transfer data to or from the disk pack it is mounted on a disk drive unit which rotates the pack at high speed. Data is recorded magnetically on disk in a similar fashion to the recording on magnetic tape. Special read/write heads are mounted on moveable arms within the disk drive unit in such a way that they move in synchronisation across the disk surface. The software positions the heads for the writing or retrieval of records.

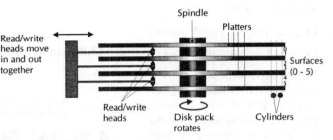

Figure 17.5. *Disk pack showing cylinder address level*

Tracks and sectors

The address of any one physical location on a single disk incorporates a *track* number, and within that track, a *sector* number. A sector is the smallest physical area on the disk which can be addressed, each addressable unit being referred to as a *block*. A block may contain a number of logical records which are transferred as a unit between disk and memory. The following example illustrates how the number of logical records in a block affects processing of a file. The size of the block is normally determined by the systems designer through the use of systems software, although some disk storage systems use *hard sectoring* (the block size cannot be altered). The number of logical records which can be accommodated in a particular block obviously depends upon the physical size of the block and the length of each logical record. The maximum number of logical records which can be fitted into a block is known as the *blocking factor*. Considerations regarding the determination of block size are beyond the scope of this text, but some of the design factors can be readily explained as follows.

Example

If a disk's block size approximates to the storage of 500 characters and a stock file has logical records, each with a fixed length of 110 characters, then the maximum number of records which can be stored in a block is 4. To retrieve one logical stock record requires the software to address and retrieve the relevant block. This means that it will retrieve all the logical stock records in the block. Therefore, the larger the number of logical records stored in any specific block, the less selective the software can be in fetching them but the faster the complete file is processed.

Cylinders

A *cylinder* or *seek area* is a logical grouping of tracks within a vertical plane. Thus, a two-sided disk with 80 tracks has 80 cylinders (0 to 79) with two tracks or surfaces in each cylinder. The disk pack illustrated in Figure 17.5 shows that each cylinder includes 6 surfaces, numbered 0 to 5.

An example disk address could be

```
cylinder 14; surface 3; track 4
```

This disk address structure supports direct access to records within a file, but the precise way in which this is achieved depends on the file organisation method which is used. Although disk storage supports direct access, there are occasions when file processing is still made more efficient when records are accessed serially/sequentially

Blocks and buckets

The minimum amount of data which can be transferred between the backing store of the computer and its internal store is the *block*. However, there are occasions when a larger unit of transfer is required and on such occasions the concept of the *bucket* is used. A bucket is a number of blocks (up to the maximum of one track) which is given the same disk address (this is usually the address of the first block in the bucket). Any logical records held within such a bucket are retrieved when that disk address is used.

✍️Exercises

1. A magnetic tape allows *serial* and *sequential access* to records. With reference to an application explain the terms in italics.
2. What prevents magnetic tape being used for *direct access* applications?
3. Why are logical records on magnetic tape grouped into *blocks*? Illustrate your answer with an example.
4. A magnetic disk pack provides up to three *levels* of address. What are they?
5. What are the maximum and mimimum amounts of data which can be transferred to or from magnetic disk?
6. Define the term *seek area*.

File organisation and access

The ways in which data can be accessed depends on the storage medium (see Topic 5) and which file organisation method is used. There are three principal methods of organisation.

- ❏ sequential
- ❏ indexed sequential;
- ❏ random.

All methods require use of a file's *primary* key, for example, WorksNo or ItemCode. The primary key provides a value which the computer software can use to assign each record's position within the file. The chosen file organisation method will dictate how individual records are assigned to particular logical positions within a file. As a non-addressable medium magnetic tape only provides serial access and sequential organisation is the only practical option. Disk media, such as floppy disks, hard disks and CD ROMs are addressable and so more versatile because they support all file organisation methods.

Sequential organisation on magnetic tape

Tape file processing can only be carried out satisfactorily if records are placed in sequence according to the primary key. Serial files, which are out of sequence, are only useful as an interim measure, prior to processing. For example, when customer orders are written to tape in the order in which they are received, a serial transaction file is created. This unsorted transaction file will then be used to update the information on another file, such as a Stock file. However, because the master file must be processed serially, the transaction file must first be sorted by computer into the same sequence as the master file. The processes are illustrated in Figure 18.1.

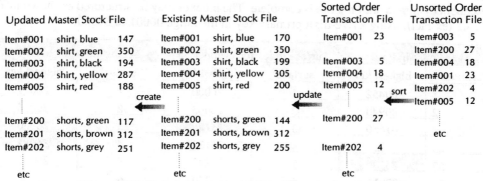

Figure 18.1. *Updating a sequential file with a sorted transaction file*

When a tape file is updated, a new master file must be created on a new reel of tape because the tape drive unit cannot guarantee to write an updated record to the exact position from which it was read (it is *non-addressable*). There is a danger, therefore, of adjacent records being corrupted or completely overwritten.

File organisation methods on magnetic disk

Magnetic disk supports all file organisation methods and the principles for serial and sequential organisation are the same as for magnetic tape.

Sequential

Sequential organisation is the most efficient method if records are always to be accessed sequentially. The fastest way of reading or writing records on disks is achieved by minimising the movement of the read/write arms between cylinders. This is achieved by writing records to the disk pack in the required sequence, such that track 0 on surface 0 is filled first, followed by track 0 on surface 1 and so on, until all number 0 tracks are filled (the first cylinder). Then, if the file requires more than one cylinder, further cylinders are filled until the file is complete.

Indexed sequential

Records are stored in sequence according to their primary keys and an *index* is produced when the file is created, allowing direct retrieval of individual records. If the file is to processed sequentially, there is no need for the index to be used. For direct access, the software searches different levels of the index (a *multi-level index*) in the following order:

1. Cylinder index - identifies to which cylinder the read/write mechanism moves;
2. Surface index - identifies the relevant surface within the cylinder;
3. Sector index - identifies the sector within the surface (track).

Constructing the indexes

The records are written sequentially (in primary key order) to the disk pack and at the same time, the indexes are built. As each sector is filled, the primary key of the last record to be placed in the sector (the highest key value) is recorded in the *sector index*. Once all sectors in a track have been filled, the last key to be entered is added to the surface index. Once a cylinder is filled the last key to be entered is added to the *cylinder index*. These stages are repeated with subsequent cylinders until the file is complete. The indexes may be structured as shown in Table 18.1 (extract), using a five-digit primary key in the range 00001 to 50000.

Cylinder index		Surface index for cylinder 55		Sector index for track 3	
cylinder	highest key	surface	highest key	sector	highest key
1	00452	1	26000	1	26071
2	00940	2	26063	2	26076
3	01650	3	*26120*	3	26080
......	......	4	26185	4	*26087*
55	*26500*	5	26242	5	26095
56	27015	6	26320	6	26104
......	......	7	26426	7	26112
115	50000	8	26500	8	26120

Table 18.1. *Extract from multi-level index*

Searching the indexes

The retrieval of records requires a *serial search* to be made of the cylinder, surface and sector indexes respectively, unless a complete track is to be read, in which case the sector index is not used. Referring to Table 18.1, suppose that the record with primary key 26085 is required; the indexes may be used as follows:

1.   A serial search of the cylinder index is made until a highest key entry is found which is equal to or greater than the required key. The entry which meets this requirement is 26500, indicating that a search of the track index for cylinder 55 is needed;

2.   A serial search of that track index, again looking for an entry greater than or equal to record key 26085, reveals that the record is to be found in track 3, where the highest key field is 26120;

3.   Searching the sector index for track 3 returns the entry of 26087, the highest key field entry for sector 4.

Unless record 26085 has been placed in an *overflow area*, owing to a full sector, it can be retrieved by reading in the block of data occupying the address - sector 4, track 3, cylinder 55.

Location of indexes

The cylinder index for a given file will normally be read into main memory when the file is first opened and held there until processing is complete. Each track index is normally held in the cylinder to which it relates and will be read into main memory as required. Similarly, the sector index is usually held within its relevant track.

The preceding procedures and mechanisms only illustrate the main principles of index construction and usage, as the detail is likely to vary considerably from one system to another. To facilitate updating, space will normally be left in sectors, tracks and cylinders to allow for the insertion of new records.

Sequential and direct access

This method allows the efficient sequential processing of the file as well as direct retrieval of records using the indexes. Indexes can become quite large and the file may need to be re-organised periodically so that new records can be inserted in the correct sequence. Records which are marked for deletion need to be removed from the file and the indexes then have to be reconstructed. The frequency with which such re-organisation is necessary depends on the level of file activity and the number of insertions and deletions. File re-organisation is a *house-keeping* activity.

Overflow

Where new records, or variable length records which have been extended by updating, cannot be inserted into their correct sequenced positions, they are assigned to overflow areas.

Local overflow areas include any located within the same cylinder as their associated home locations; thus, local overflow areas may be located within each track or sector of a cylinder, or at the end of the cylinder. These overflow areas have the advantage that access to them requires no head movement and therefore, no increase in seek time.

Global overflow areas may be formed from a separate cylinder or cylinders and will tend to be used when local overflow areas are full. The main disadvantage is that access to an overflow record requires additional head movement.

A file may use either local or global overflow areas, or a combination of the two; the use of global overflow only, tends to be less wasteful of space but with the disadvantage that the retrieval of any overflow record will require additional head movement. If frequent reference is required to overflow records, *performance degradation* (a worsening of the system's response times) is likely to be noted by users and file re-organization will be beneficial.

Random organisation

This is a method which is impractical in any non-computerised situation. However, in a computerised system it is feasible to place records on to disk at random. The procedure for placing specific records in a particular position on disk may simply relate the primary key *directly* to its disk address, for example,

> *disk address = primary key*
>
> *disk address = primary key + index value*

With absolute and *indexed addressing*, each record has a unique address and can be retrieved directly with its own primary key. A major disadvantage of this method is its orientation towards the needs of the computer; the values needed for disk addressing may well be inappropriate for use as meaningful (to the user) primary keys for logical records. Further, the unique link between a disk address and a particular logical record means that any vacated space cannot be used by another record unless it adopts the same key as the previous occupant record.

Hashing algorithms

A more usual method of addressing uses a mathematical formula called a *hashing algorithm*, which generates a disk address from the record's primary key. The hashing algorithm operates on the primary keys within a given range to produce pseudo-random numbers which may then be used as bucket addresses, to which the logical records are allocated. Each pseudo-random number could refer to an address where a single record is stored, but it is more economical for it to refer to an area where a group of records is stored; thus a *bucket* address will normally contain a number of logical records.

Example algorithm

Prime number division. The primary key is divided by the largest prime number which is less than the number of available buckets. The remainder of this calculation is taken as the *relative* bucket number, that is, the number of buckets after the first. For example:

> *available buckets 2000*
>
> *prime number 1999*
>
> *primary key 22316*
>
> *22316/1999 = 11 remainder 327*

The relative bucket number is thus 327. The same mathematical formula is used to subsequently retrieve records, which is ideal in situations where random enquiries are the norm and there is little need for sequential processing. Randomly organised files can be processed sequentially but with less efficiency than sequentially organised files. An advantage of this method is the lack of large indexes which tend to take up considerable storage space on the disk.

The aim of any randomizing or hashing algorithm is to achieve an even distribution of records over the disk space allocated to a file. Most random files allow more than one logical record to occupy a single bucket, as any given algorithm will normally generate the same disk address from several different primary keys; conversely, any hashing algorithm is likely to leave some buckets with no allocated records. Any record which is stored in the address allocated to it by an algorithm is referred to as a *home record*.

Overflow

An uneven distribution of records means that some buckets overflow and cannot accommodate all the logical records allocated to them, whilst others remain empty or are seriously un-der-used. Excessive overflow slows the access time for any record which cannot be allocated to its home address. To achieve a reasonably even spread, the selection of a particular algorithm requires consideration of the following factors:

❑   the pattern and range of the primary keys within the file;

❑   the size of each bucket and the number available;

❑   the *packing density* required (number of records, divided by the total record capacity of the available buckets).

Synonyms and collisions

If an address can only hold one record, the first one to be allocated to it, then subsequent records have to be stored elsewhere; such records are referred to as *synonyms* and the circumstances causing their re-allocation, as *collisions*. Synonyms increase access times for affected records, so one aim of an algorithm is to minimize their occurrence. Other factors to be considered by the file designer include, *bucket size* and *packing density* (see previous paragraph). A large bucket size (the maximum is one track) will obviously reduce the number of synonyms, but at the cost of reduced precision in the retrieval of individual logical records. It is fairly unlikely that, in a random file, more than one logical record from the same bucket will be required at the same time, so a number of records are read unnecessarily. In deciding on the packing density (the percentage of the file space occupied) for any particular file, the designer has to consider the *volatility* or activity of the file. It is generally recognized that 50 per cent is probably the minimum packing density and is appropriate only for highly volatile files where a large number of record additions is likely; most files are designed to be 75 to 80 per cent packed when they are set up. A low packing density will further reduce the likelihood of synonyms, but at a cost of increased storage space.

Accessing disk files

Serial files

As with magnetic tape, the only way to retrieve records is serially, in other words, one after an-other. The addressing facilities of disk are not needed.

Sequential files

The addressing features of disk are not used and the method is the same as that for sequential tape files.

Indexed sequential files

There are 3 methods of retrieving such records:

1.   *Sequentially*. Transactions are sorted into the same sequence as the master file. This is suitable when a large proportion of the records in the file are to be processed in one run, that is, when the *hit rate* (the percentage of master records in a file, for which there are transactions) is high. Minimal use is made of the index. The cylinder index and track index may be searched, then the whole track is read into memory, sector by sector, without reference to the sector index.

2.   *Selective* or *skip sequentially*. When records are sequentially organised by key, not every record need be read when scanning the file. The transactions are sorted into master file sequence and the indexes are used, so that only those blocks containing master records for which there is a transaction are read into memory. This is suitable when the hit rate is low.

3.   *Randomly*. Transactions are not sorted. They are processed in the order in which they occur, the indexes being used to find the relevant master records as they are required. The read/write heads have to move back and forth through the file and so head movement is greater than with sequential methods of processing. This method is appropriate when records are updated immediately after the transaction occurs or, for example, when there is a need for random enquiries of a stock file.

Random files

Transactions or enquiries need not be in any logical sequence. Records are retrieved by generating the physical address from the record key. The software uses the same hashing algorithm it used to assign the record to its address in the first place. Random files can be processed sequentially, but with less efficiency than sequential or indexed sequential files.

Choice of organisation method and storage medium

Choice should be based on the type and purpose of the system to be used. For example, an on-line enquiry system or stock control system needing frequent, rapid, direct access to individual records within large files will best be served by a randomly organised file, using hash addressing. Very large files, of an archival nature are probably best held off-line on magnetic tape; the medium's lack of an addressing facility would necessitate such files being maintained sequentially. It may be reasonable to hold sections of such archival data, those which are most in demand, on magnetic disk and organised as indexed sequential files. An illustration of this is provided by the Police National Computer system, which holds more recent data on magnetic disk, with older files held on magnetic tape. Systems which do not require direct access, for example, monthly payroll files, can be efficiently stored and processed on magnetic tape and even if the computer system only has disk storage, sequential organisation is still likely to be the chosen method. Applications which require both sequential and direct access are generally best served by indexed sequential files.

Typically, the only files which are held serially, are temporary files, such as transaction files prior to sorting for a sequential update run.

Exercises

1. (i) What is the benefit of *sorting* a transaction file before it updates the relevant master file?

   (ii) Under what circumstances is sorting of the transaction file essential?

2. Briefly describe an application for which an *indexed sequentially* organised file would be appropriate. Justify your answer.

3. With the use of a suitable example, outline the use of a *multi-level index* to retrieve a record according to its primary key value.

4. (i) In the context of an indexed sequential file, what is meant by *overflow*?

   (ii) What effect will excessive overflow have on file performance? Explain your answer.

   (iii) What needs to be done to restore a heavily overflowed, indexed file to its maximum efficiency?

5. In the context of random organisation, how is a record allocated its position in the file and subsequently retrieved?

6. What is the purpose of a *hashing algorithm*?

7. In the context of a random file, what is meant by *overflow*?

8. What are synonyms and collisions and what effect do they have on random file organisation performance?

9. Distinguish between the following methods for accessing an indexed sequential file.

   (i) sequentially;

   (ii) selective or skip sequentially;

   (iii) randomly.

Data control

Controls should be exerted over the *input*, *processing* and *output* stages of data processing. They can be implemented by both clerical and software procedures.

It is only through the combined application of both *clerical* and *software* controls that data errors can be minimised. Their entire exclusion can never be guaranteed.

Collection and input of data

Before describing the types of data controls, it is necessary to outline the activities which may be involved in the collection and input of data. Depending on the application, these may include the following.

❑ Source document preparation. To ensure standardisation of practice and to facilitate checking, data collected for input, for example, customer orders, are clerically transcribed onto specially designed source documents.

❑ Data transmission. If the computer centre is geographically remote from the collection point, data is transmitted through a telecommunications link.

❑ Data encoding and verification (see Verification and Validation). This involves the transcription, usually through a keyboard device, of the data onto a storage medium such as magnetic tape or disk. A process of machine verification, accompanied by a repeated keying operation, assists the checking of keying accuracy.

❑ Data input and validation (see Verification and Validation). Data validation is a computer-controlled process, which checks data for its validity, according to certain pre-defined parameters, so it must first be input to the computer. The topic of validation is examined in more detail later.

❑ Sorting. In order to improve the efficiency of processing, input data is sorted into a sequence determined by the primary key of each record in the relevant master file. This is always necessary for efficient sequential processing, but direct access files allow records to be processed by transactions in the order that they are received.

❑ Transcription of data from one medium to another, for example, from telephone notepad to customer order form, or from *source document* (for example, an order form or requisition) to magnetic disk, provides the greatest opportunity for error.

A number of strategies can be adopted to minimise input errors, including:

❑ Minimising transcription. This may involve the use of automated input methods, such as bar code reading and *turnaround documents*. These are forms which the information system produces as output and which can at a later date be returned to the system as input. For instance, a mail order book club might produce a combined invoice and statement for its customers and, at the same time, attach an order form. The customer completes the order form by entering the catalogue codes in the boxes provided and then returns the document together with the amount due in an addressed envelope provided by the club. Notice that the club member needs only to enter the catalogue code numbers for his or her book selections; even the membership number has been printed on the order form to prevent members from either forgetting about it or getting it wrong.

❑ Designing data collection and input documents in ways which encourage accurate completion.

❑ Using clerical checking procedures such as the re-calculation of totals or the visual comparison of document entries with the original sources of information;

❑ Using codes of a restricted format, for example, customer account numbers consisting of two alphabetic characters, followed by six digits. Such formatted codes can easily be checked for validity;

❑ Employing batch methods of input which allow the accumulation and checking of batch control totals, both by clerical and computerised methods (see Data Control in Batch Processing);

❑ Using screen *verification* (visual checking of input on screen) before input data are processed and applied to computer files.

❑ Checking input data with the use of batch or interactive screen validation (see Validation) techniques;

❑ Ensuring that staff are well trained and that clerical procedure manuals are available for newly trained staff;

❑ Controlling access to input documents. This is particularly important where documents are used for sensitive applications such as payroll.

Verification

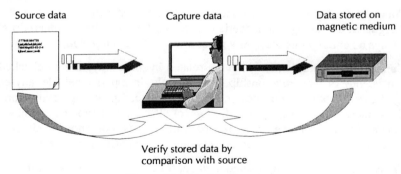

Source data   Capture data   Data stored on
                                       magnetic medium

Verify stored data by
comparison with source

Figure 19.1. *Verification process*

Figure 19.1 illustrates the verification process. When information is gathered using source documents such as forms, which cannot be read directly by the computer, it needs to be converted into a form which can be processed. A common method of performing this task is by means of *key-to-storage* devices such as *key-to tape* or *key-to-disk*.

The data is entered using a workstation consisting of a keyboard and monitor. As data is typed in it is displayed on the screen and stored on the magnetic storage medium (tape or disk). This process is error prone, in that workstation operators may easily omit characters or type them in the wrong order. To reduce the risk of data entry errors, before the computer processes the data, it is usual to verify them by re-typing the data, using the same source documents, but with the key-to-storage device in *verify mode*. In this mode, the data is typed in a second time and compared with that typed in originally, and any differences are signalled to the operator who is then able to make the appropriate corrections.

Validation

This process is carried out after the data has been encoded on to an input medium and involves a *data vet* or *validation program*. Its purpose is to check that data falls within certain parameters defined by the systems analyst. A judgement as to whether data is valid is made possible by the validation program, but it cannot ensure complete accuracy. This can only be achieved through the use of all the clerical and computer controls built into the system at the design stage. The difference between validity and accuracy can be illustrated with a simple example. A company has established a Personnel file and each record contains a field for the Job Grade. The permitted values are A, B, C, or D. An entry in a record may be *valid* and accepted by the system if it is one of these characters, but it may not be the *correct* grade for the individual worker concerned. Whether a grade is correct can only be established by clerical checks or by reference to other files. During systems design, therefore, *data definitions* should be established which place limits on what constitutes valid data. Using these data definitions, a range of software validation checks can be carried out. Some typical validation checks are outlined below.

❑ **Size**. The number of characters in a data item value is checked; for example, a stock code may consist of 8 characters only;

❑ **Range**. Data must lie within maximum and minimum values. For example, customer account numbers may be restricted within the values 00001 to 10000;

❑ **Format checks**. Data must conform to a specified format. Thus, a stock code designated as having 2 alphabetic characters, followed by 4 numeric digits must always be entered this way. Any other arrangement is rejected;

❑ **Consistency**. Data items, which are related in some way, can be checked for the consistency of their relationship. For example, in a personnel file, any employee aged 25 years or over must be contributing to the company superannuation scheme. Conversely, employees under the age of 25 years cannot be members of the superannuation scheme. Any record which does not show such consistency indicates that either the age or the superannuation entry is incorrect;

❑ **Check digit**. An extra digit calculated on, for example, an account number, can be used as a self-checking device. When the number is input to the computer, the validation program carries out a calculation similar to that used to generate the check digit originally and thus checks its validity. This kind of check will highlight transcription errors where two or more digits have been transposed or put in the wrong order. One of the commonest methods of producing a check digit is the *modulus 11* algorithm. The following example serves to illustrate its operation.

Consider a stock code consisting of six digits, for example 462137.

The additional check digit is calculated as follows:

1.   Each digit of the stock code is multiplied by its own *weight*. Each digit has a weight relative to its position, assuming the presence of a check digit in the rightmost position. Beginning from the check digit position, (x), the digits are weighted 1, 2, 3, 4, 5, 6 and 7 respectively as shown in Table 19.1.

Stock code	4	6	2	1	3	7	(x)
Multiplied by weight	7	6	5	4	3	2	(1)
Product	28	36	10	4	9	14	-

Table 19.1

2.   The products are totalled. In this example, the sum produces 101.

3.   Divide the sum by modulus 11. This produces 9, remainder 2.

4.   The check digit is produced by subtracting the remainder 2 from 11, giving 9. The new seven digit stock code is thus 4621379.

Whenever a code is entered with the relevant check digit, the validation software carries out the same algorithm, including the check digit in the calculation. Provided that the third stage produces a remainder of zero the code is accepted as valid. This is proved in Table 19.2, using the same example as above.

Stock code	4	6	2	1	3	7	9
Multiplied by weight	7	6	5	4	3	2	1
Product	28	36	10	4	9	14	9

Table 19.2

The sum of the products in Table 19.2 is 110, which when divided by 11, gives 10, remainder 0. Therefore, the number is valid.

If some of the digits are *transposed* (swapped around) the check digit is no longer applicable to the code and is rejected by the validation program because the results of the algorithm will not leave a remainder of zero. This is shown in Table 19.3.

The sum of the products in Table 19.3 equals 111, which when divided by 11, gives 10, remainder 1. The number is, therefore, invalid.

Stock code	6	4	1	2	3	7	9
Multiplied by weight	7	6	5	4	3	2	1
Product	42	24	5	8	9	14	9

Table 19.3

File processing controls

Once validated data has entered the computer system, checks have to be made to ensure that it is:

❑ applied to the correct files;

❑ consistent with the filed data.

Header records

Files can have header records, which identify the function, for example, Sales Ledger, the version number and the *purge date*. The purge date indicates the date after which the file is no longer required and can be overwritten. Thus, a file with a purge date after the current date should not be overwritten. The application program can check such details, to ensure that the correct file is used and that a current file is not accidentally overwritten.

File validation checks

Some validation checks can be made only after data input when reference can be made to the relevant master file data. Such checks include:

❑ new records. When a new record is to be added to a master file, a check can be made to ensure that a record does not already use the record key entered;

❑ deleted records. It may be that a transaction is entered, for which there is no longer a matching master record. For example, a customer may order a product which is no longer supplied;

❑ data consistency checks. A check is made that the transaction values are consistent with the values held on the master record which is to be updated. For instance, an entry to indicate maternity leave would obviously be inconsistent with a record for a male employee.

Data integrity

The printing of all master file changes allows the user department and auditors to check that all such changes are authorised and consistent with transaction documents. All data used by applications for *reference* purposes should be printed periodically. Price lists, for example, may be held as permanent data on master files, or in table form within computer programs.

Output controls

It might reasonably be supposed that input and file processing controls are sufficient to ensure accurate output. Nevertheless, a number of simple controls at the output stage can help to ensure that it is complete and is distributed to the relevant users on time. They include:

❑ comparison of filed control totals with run control totals. For example, when an entire sequential file is processed, the computer counts all records processed and compares the total with a stored record total held in a *trailer record* at the end of the file;

❑ reconciliation of control totals specific to the application with totals obtained from a related application. For example, the total sales transactions posted to the Sales Ledger in one day should agree with the total sales transactions recorded in the Sales Day book for that day;

❑ following of set procedures for the treatment of error reports;

❑ proper checking and re-submission of rejected transactions.

Data control in batch processing

Batch processing involves the processing of batches of input data at regular intervals. The data is generally of identical type. Examples include customer orders or payroll details. Although generally associated with large organisations using mainframe or minicomputer systems, the technique is equally applicable to microcomputer-based systems. The controls used combine both clerical and software methods and are briefly as described below.

Batch totals - clerical preparation

Batch totals allow the conciliation of clerically prepared totals for a batch of transactions, with comparable computer-produced totals. Following the arrangement of source documents into batches, totals are calculated on add-listing machines for each value it is required to control.

On an order form, for example, quantities and prices may be separately totalled to provide separate control totals. Totals may also be produced for each account number or item code, simply for purposes of control, although otherwise they are meaningless. For this reason, such totals are called 'hash' or 'nonsense' totals.

The totals are recorded on a *batch control record* (see Figure 19.2) attached to the batch, together with a value for the number of documents in the batch and a batch serial number. The batch serial number is kept in a register held by the originating department so that missing or delayed batches can be traced.

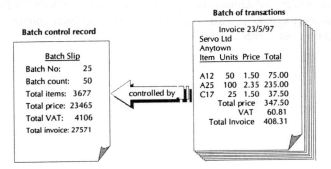

Figure 19.2. *Batch control record*

Batch totals - software checking

The details from each batch control record are encoded, with each batch of transactions, onto the storage medium. The resulting *transaction file* thus consists of a series of transactions, with each batch being preceded by the relevant batch totals. A *validation program* then reads the transaction file from beginning to end, accumulating its own comparable batch totals for each batch as it proceeds. At the end of each batch, the validation program checks its accumulated totals with the clerically prepared totals and reports those in error.

Rejected batches and associated batch totals must be re-checked and corrected where necessary, before re-submission. The originating user department should carry out the corrections. Where volumes of input are not particularly large, involving say, two staff for an hour each day, a modified version of the full-scale batch processing method may be used. Thus, when batch totals do not agree, only erroneous transactions are re-submitted.

A validation program should also check individual data items against pre-defined limits. Such validation can be carried out as part of the batch processing system described above, or *interactively* (through screen/keyboard dialogue between the computer and the data entry operator), as data is entered.

Exercises

1. A data entry operator is keying in a batch of customer orders. Order Numbers are 4 digits and range from 0001 to 5000. Old order numbers are re-used after completion. One of the Order Numbers is keyed as 3126, instead of 3216.The order entry system uses verification through a key-to-disk system.Once the orders are stored on disk, they are processed by a validation program.

   (i)   What type of error has the operator made with the Order Number?

   (ii)   Explain how the verification would work and how it may correct the mistake.

   (iii)   Describe how a check digit for the Order Number would be calculated and show how it would detect the keying error.

   (iv)   Apart from a check digit, suggest one character and one field validation check which could be made on the Order Number.

   (v)   Would either of the validation checks you suggested in (iv) pick up this particular error?

2. The same order entry system uses batch controls. What type of batch control is created if the Order Numbers in each batch are totalled?

Processing methods

Data handling systems make use of one or more processing methods, depending on the requirements of the application. The methods can be categorised according to the ways in which data is controlled, stored and passed through the system; the major categories are: *batch* processing; *on-line* processing, which includes *real-time* and *time-share* processing; *distributed* processing and *centralised* processing; *database* systems. To allow particular methods of processing a computer must have the necessary *operating system* software (Topic 11); thus any particular computer system is equipped with, for example, a batch processing or real-time operating system, or even a combination of types, depending on the needs of the user organisation.

Batch processing

Such systems process *batches* of data at regular intervals. The data is usually in large volumes and of identical type. Examples of such data are customer orders, current weekly payroll details and stock issues or receipts. The procedure can be illustrated with the example of payroll, which is a typical application for batch processing. Each pay date, whether it is every week or every month, the payroll details, such as hours worked, overtime earned or sickness days claimed, are gathered for each employee (these details are referred to as *transactions*) and processed in batches against the payroll *master file*. The computer then produces payslips for all employees in the company. A major feature of this and similar applications is that a large percentage of the payroll records in the master file are processed during the payroll 'run'. This percentage is known as the *hit rate*. Generally, high hit rate processing is suitable for batch processing and if, as is usual, the master file is organised sequentially, then the *transaction file* will be sorted into the same sequence as the master file. In the case of magnetic tape, transactions must be sorted because the medium only allows *serial* (one record after another in their physical order) access.

The batch processing method closely resembles manual methods of data handling, in that transactions are collected together into batches, sent to the computer centre, sorted into the order of the master file and processed. Such systems are known as traditional data processing systems. There is normally an intermediate stage in the process when the data must be encoded using a *key-to-tape* or *key-to-disk* system.

A disadvantage of batch processing is the delay, often of hours or days, between collecting the transactions and receiving the results of processing and this has to be remembered when an organisation is considering whether batch processing is suitable for a particular application. Conversely, batch processing has the advantage of providing many opportunities for controlling the accuracy of data and thus is commonly used when the immediate updating of files is not crucial.

On-line processing systems

If a peripheral, such as a Visual Display Unit or keyboard, is *on-line*, it is under the control of the computer's processor or Central Processing Unit (CPU). On-line processing systems therefore, are those where all peripherals in use are connected to the CPU of the main computer.

Transactions can be keyed in directly. The main advantage of an on-line system is the reduction in time between the collection and processing of data. There are two main methods of on-line processing: *real-time* processing; *time-share* processing.

Real-time processing

Process control in real-time

Real-time processing originally referred only to process control systems where, for example, the temperature of a gas furnace is monitored and controlled by a computer. The computer, through an appropriate sensing device, responds immediately to the boiler's variations outside pre-set temperature limits, by switching the boiler on and off to keep the temperature within those limits.

Real-time processing is now used in everyday consumer goods, such as video cameras, because of the development of the 'computer on a chip', more properly called the *microprocessor*. An important example of the use of the microprocessor is the engine management system, which is now standard on an increasing range of cars. A car's engine performance can be monitored and controlled, by sensing and immediately responding to, changes in such factors as air temperature, ignition timing or engine load. Microprocessors dedicated to particular functions are referred to as *embedded systems*. Further examples of the use of microprocessors can be found on the automated production lines of engineering works and car plants, where operations requiring fine engineering control can be carried out by *computer numerical controlled* (CNC) machines. The important feature common to all real-time applications is that the speed of the computer allows almost immediate response to external changes.

Information processing in real-time

To be acceptable as a real-time information processing system, the *response-time* (that is the time between the entry of a transaction or enquiry at a VDU terminal, the processing of the data and the computer's response) must meet the needs of the user. The delay or response time may vary from a fraction of a second to 2-3 seconds depending on the nature of the transaction and the size of the computer. Any delay beyond these times would generally be unacceptable and would indicate the need for the system to be updated. There are two types of information processing systems which can be operated in real-time: *transaction processing*; *information storage and retrieval*.

Transaction processing

This type of system handles clearly defined transactions one at a time, each transaction being processed completely, including the updating of files, before the next transaction is dealt with. The amount of data input for each transaction is small and is usually entered on an *interactive* basis through a VDU. In this way, the user can enter queries through the keyboard and receive a response, or the computer can display a prompt on the screen to which the user responds. Such 'conversations' are usually heavily structured and in a fixed format and so do not allow users to ask any question they wish. A typical example of transaction processing is provided by an *airline booking system* and the following may describe a client's enquiry for a seat reservation.

(i)   A prospective passenger provides the booking clerk with information regarding his/her flight requirements.

(ii)   Following prompts on a screen, the clerk keys the details into the system, so that a check can be made on the availability of seats.

(iii)   Vacancies appear on the screen and the client can confirm the booking.

(iv)   Confirmation of the reservation is keyed into the system, usually by a single key stroke and the flight seating records are immediately updated.

(v)   Passenger details (such as name, address, etc.) can now be entered.

Such a system needs to be real-time to enable reservations to be made at once, while the client is there (or on the telephone) and so that the seating records accurately reflect availability at all times.

Information storage and retrieval

This type of system differs from transaction processing in that, although the information is updated in real-time, the number of updates and the number of sources of updating is relatively small. Consider, for example, the medical records system in a hospital. A record is maintained for each patient currently undergoing treatment in the hospital. Medical staff require the patient's medical history to be available at any time and the system must also have a facility for entering new information as the patient undergoes treatment in hospital. Sources of information are likely to include a doctor, nurses and perhaps a surgeon, and new entries probably do not number more than one or two per day. This is an entirely different situation from an airline booking system where the number of entries for one flight record may be 200-300 and they could be made from many different booking offices throughout the world.

Time-share processing

The term *time sharing* refers to the activity of the computer's processor in allocating *time-slices* to a number of users who are given access through terminals to centralised computer resources. The aim of the system is to give each user a good *response time*. These systems are commonly used where a number of users require computer time for different information processing tasks. The processor time-slices are allocated and controlled by a time-share operating system. The CPU is able to operate at such speed that, provided the system is not overloaded by too many users, each user has the impression that he or she is the sole user of the system.

A particular computer system will be designed to support a maximum number of user terminals. If the number is exceeded or the applications being run on the system are 'heavy' on CPU time the response time will become lengthy and unacceptable. Time-share systems are possible because of the extreme speed of the CPU in comparison with peripheral devices such as keyboards, VDU screens and printers. Most information processing tasks consist largely of input and output operations which do not occupy the CPU, leaving it free to do any processing required on other users tasks.

Distributed processing

As the term suggests, a distributed processing system is one which spreads the processing tasks of an organisation across several computer systems; frequently, these systems are connected and *share resources* (this may relate to common access to files or programs, or even the processing of a single complex task) through a data communications system. Each computer system in the network must be able to process independently, so a central computer with a number of remote intelligent terminals cannot be classified as distributed, even though some limited validation of data may be carried out separately from the main computer. Examples of distributed systems include mini or mainframe computers interconnected by way of *wide area networks*, or a number of *local area networks* similarly linked.

Distributed systems provide a number of benefits:

❏ *Economy*. The transmission of data over telecommunications systems can be costly and local database storage and processing facilities can reduce costs. The radical reduction in computer hardware costs has favoured the expansion of distributed systems against centralised systems.

❏ *Minicomputers and microcomputers*. The availability of minicomputer and microcomputer systems with data transmission facilities has made distributed processing economically viable. An increasingly popular option, in large multi-sited organisations, is to set up local area networks of microcomputers at each site and connect them through communications networks to each other and/or to a central mainframe computer at the Head Office. This provides each site with the advantages of local processing power, local and inter-site communications through *electronic mail* and access to a central mainframe for the main filing and database systems.

❏ *Local management control*. It is not always convenient, particularly where an organisation controls diverse activities, to have all information processing centralised. Local management control means that the information systems will be developed by people with direct knowledge of their own information needs. Responsibility for the success or otherwise of their division of the organisation may be placed with local management, so it is desirable that they have control over the accuracy and reliability of the data they use.

Centralised systems

With this type of system, all processing is carried out centrally, generally by a mainframe computer. The continuing reduction in hardware costs and the increase in computer power has led the move towards distributed processing systems. This is achieved through computer networks.

✍️Exercises

1. Using the examples of a cinema booking system and a payroll system:
    (i)   Differentiate between *batch* and *transaction processing*.
    (ii) Why is batch processing unsuitable for the cinema booking system?
    (iii) If there are 850 records in the payroll master file and 810 will be updated by transactions, what is the *hit rate*?
    (iv) Why is hit rate considered when choosing a processing method for an application?

2. Agros uses *transaction processing* to enter stock issues and receipts into its stock control system. If the transactions are not entered until the end of each day, it is not a *real-time* system.
    (i)   Explain why this is so and what Agros would need to do to employ a real-time system.
    (ii) What factors would Agros need to take into account when deciding whether to change to a real-time system?

3. A library's computer system allows borrowers to enter key words or phrases to search for books on particular topics. The system displays a list of books which accord with the search criteria.

    Describe features of the library's 'book search' application which would categorise it as an *information storage and retrieval* system

4. (i)   Define the term *time-sharing* system.
    (ii) What circumstances may cause a time-sharing system's response time to be unsatisfactory?

5. The Acme group has three subsidiary companies, each involved in different market areas: car production; supermarket chain; transport and distribution.
    (i)   Write a list of brief arguments which would favour the use of *distributed* processing over *centralised* processing.
    (ii) Why would the Acme Group need to use *wide area network* facilities?

Security against data loss

The loss of *master files* can be an extremely serious occurrence for any organisation so properly organised security procedures need to be employed. Among commercial organisations that have lost the major part of their information store, a large percentage subsequently go out of business. The main causes of data loss are as follow:

❑ environmental hazards such as fire, flood and other natural accidents;

❑ mechanical problems, for example the danger of disk or tape damage caused by a drive unit malfunction;

❑ software errors resulting from programming error;

❑ human error. A wrong file may be loaded, the wrong program version used, a tape or disk mislaid, or physical damage caused to tape or disk;

❑ malicious damage. It is not unknown for staff to intentionally damage storage media or to misuse programs at a terminal.

The standard solution to such problems is to take regular copies of master files and to store the copies in a separate secure location. It is also necessary to maintain a record of transactions affecting a file since the last copy was taken, so that if necessary they can be used to reconstruct the latest version of the file.

Magnetic tape file security

When a tape master file is updated by a tape transaction file the physical nature of the medium makes it necessary for a new tape file to be produced. As Figure 21.1 illustrates, the updating procedure provides a built-in security system referred to as the Grandparent, Parent and Child (*generation*) system.

In the first run, Master File 1 is updated by the transactions file to produce Master File 2 as its Child. Master File 1 is the Parent. Should the Child file be damaged and the data lost, it can be re-created from the Parent master file and the relevant transactions. At the end of the second run, Master File 1 becomes the Grandparent, Master File 2 becomes the Parent and Master File 3, the Child. Each generation provides security for subsequent files. The number of generations used will

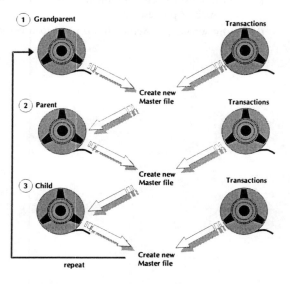

Figure 21.1. *Generation back-up system for sequential tape files*

depend on the policy of the organisation. Three generations are usually regarded as providing sufficient security and the oldest files are re-used by being overwritten as each cycle of generations is completed.

Internal header labels

Internal header labels are designed to deal with two major areas of concern:

❏   It is important that the correct file is used in a file processing operation to ensure correct results. Thus, the *subject* of the file and the *version* must be identifiable. For example, it is no good producing monthly payslips using information from a payroll master file three months out of date.

❏   A tape file must be protected against accidental erasure. This may occur because tapes are re-usable and when a file is no longer required it can be overwritten by new information.

To ensure that the correct file is used for any particular job, a tape file usually has an internal header label. The label appears at the beginning of the tape and identifies it. The identifying information in the label is usually recorded under program control or by a data encoding device.

A tape header label usually contains the following items of information:

❏   file name e.g. Payroll, Stock, Sales;

❏   date created;

❏   purge date - the date after which the tape is no longer required and may be re-used.

The label is checked by the program, before the file is processed, to ensure that the correct tape is being used.

File protection ring

A device called a file protection ring can be used to prevent accidental erasure. When tapes are stored off-line, the rings are not fitted. To write to a tape, the ring must first be fitted to the centre of the reel. A tape can be read by the computer whether or not a ring is fitted. The simple rule to remember is 'no ring, no write'.

Magnetic disk file security

Security back-ups

Disk files can be treated in the same way as tape files in that the updating procedure may produce a new master file leaving the original file intact. On the other hand, if the file is updated *in-situ* (which in so doing overwrites the existing data), then it will be necessary to take regular back-up copies as processing proceeds. The frequency with which copies are taken will depend on the volume of transactions affecting the master file. If the latest version of the master file is corrupted or lost, then it can be re-created using the previous back-up together with the transaction data received since the back-up.

Transaction logging

In an on-line system, transactions may enter the system from a number of terminals in different locations, thus making it difficult to re-enter transactions for the re-creation of a damaged master file. One solution is to log all the transactions onto a serial transaction file at the same time as the master file is updated. Thus, the re-creation process can be carried out without the need for keying in the transactions again. The systems flowchart in Figure 21.2 illustrates the procedure.

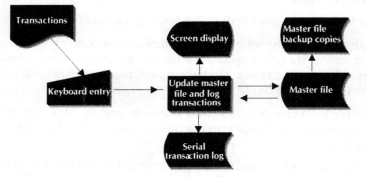

Figure 21.2. *Transaction logging and security back-up system*

✍ Exercises

1. A company holds its payroll files on magnetic tape. Name the file types used in the process.
2. Approximately 300 transactions update (in-situ) a stock master file every hour and a master file backup is taken every 3 hours. The last backup was taken at 1.30 pm. The current master file is corrupted at 4 pm. Describe what needs to be done.
3. How would transaction logging have improved the situation in 2?

Section 5

Databases

Topics

The traditional file has a flat, or two-dimensional, structure, as illustrated by the Customer Order file extract in Table 22.1. Each record contains the same categories of information, held in fields identified by the column headings. <u>OrderNo</u> is the primary key.

OrderNo	AcctID	Name	Address1	Address2	Order Total
0001	11003	The Red Lion	33 May Be	Nowhere	£1500.35
0002	11005	The Black Horse	45 Round About	Somewhere	£315.77
0003	11008	The Fat Ox	28 Just About	Anywhere	£425.66
etc	etc	etc	etc	etc	etc

Table 22.1. *Flat file structure*

Of course, not all information occurs in two-dimensional form. Figure 22.1 shows the three-dimensional structure which is created when there are repeated details for each order.

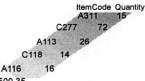

0001 11003 The Red Lion 33 May Be Nowhere £1500.35

Figure 22.1. *Three-dimensional data structure*

For an order of 5 items this would add 10 fields to the record length. Table 22.2 shows the addition of some of these repeated fields.

OrderNo		Order Total	ItemCode1	Quantity1	ItemCode2	Quantity2	etc
0001	....	£1500.35	A116	16	C118	14	
0002	....	£315.77					
0003	....	£425.66					
etc		etc					

Table 22.2. *Accommodating repeated fields in a single flat file*

The additional fields could be handled by using fixed or variable length records, but if customers could order any number of items, this would make for a very unwieldy structure. Alternatively, the details of each order could be held in an entirely separate file. To link orders with order details, the programmer would have to explicitly link them by including the OrderNo field in both files. However, the information is essentially three-dimensional and would be better accommodated in a database structure which is designed to handle it effectively. Some complex database structures are designed to accommodate information of the three-dimensional form shown in Figure 22.1. Databases of this type are based on *network* structures (see later). However, these more complicated file structures can still be broken down into groups of flat files and accommodated in simpler database structures, such as the tables used in *relational* databases (see Topic 23).

General definition of a database

A database can be defined as - *a collection of structured data, generally related to some subject or topic area and serving the needs of a number of different applications, but with a minimum of duplicated data items.*

From this definition it is possible to identify specific features of a database:

❑   A database contains data of use in a *variety* of applications.

❑   The data is *structured* to allow separate data items to be connected, to form different *logical* records according to the requirements of users and hence, to applications programs.

A database will normally be used for different applications, but those applications should have some *common interests* concerning the data items they use. For example, sales, purchasing, stock control and production control applications are likely to use common data in respect of raw materials or finished goods. On the other hand, a database containing data on both materials and personnel may be difficult to justify; even then connections between the separate databases can be facilitated if the information requirements so justify.

Basic database principles

Controlled redundancy

'Controlled redundancy' means reducing to a minimum the number of data items which are duplicated in a database. In traditional computerised filing systems, each department in an organisation may keep its own files, which results in a massive amount of duplication in the stored data. Although the removal of duplicated items is a desirable aim in terms of keeping database volume to a minimum, there are occasions when duplication is necessary to provide efficient access to the database.

Data independence

Periodically, the *physical* database needs to be changed to accommodate changes in user requirements. However, there is no need to alter all applications programs, because the way the data is *physically* stored on the storage medium is independent of the *logical* record structures required by applications programs. Figure 22.2 illustrates the use of a database by two separate applications with some common data requirements.

Programmers need have no knowledge of the way data is actually organised and each is given the 'data view' he or she needs for the particular application. If the database contents are rearranged or supplemented to accommodate the needs of a new application, existing applications will continue to operate correctly.

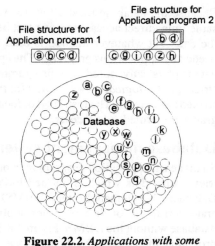

Figure 22.2. *Applications with some common data requirements*

In a database, records can be stored essentially in two different ways.

❑ Independently - the primary key is used to decide the physical location of a record; frequently this is effected through a *randomising* process to distribute records efficiently on the storage medium.

❑ In association - records are stored according to their relationship with other records and connections may be made between them with the use of *pointers*. A *physical pointer* gives the address where a record is stored and can be used to relate records anywhere in the database; a *logical pointer* is a value from which the physical address can be calculated.

The physical and logical database

A database has to satisfy the differing information needs of many users, generally through specially written applications programs. Therefore, it is often necessary to add further data items to satisfy changes in users needs. The software which controls the database must relate to the data at data item rather than at record level, because one programmer's logical record requirements may contain some data items which are also required for another programmer's logical record description. The physical database must allow for both. It must be possible for data items to be connected into a variety of logical record forms.

Creating and manipulating the database

A special language called a *data description language* (DDL) allows the database to be created and changed and the logical data structures to be defined.

A *data manipulation language* (DML) enables the contents of the database to be altered by adding, updating or deleting records. The language is used by programmers to develop applications programs for users of the database. The functions of both these languages are combined, together with a query language facility in *Structured Query Language* (SQL) - Topic 39.

Schemas and sub-schemas

Because the database must allow for various user applications programs accessing it at the same time, direct access storage must be used. There are many ways of physically organising the data, but whatever method is used it must allow for the variety of logical record forms needed by applications programs. The applications programmer does not need to know how the data is physically stored. The programmer's knowledge of the data held in the database is restricted to the *logical view* required for the program. The complete or global logical database is termed the *schema*. The restricted or local logical views provided for different applications programs are termed *subschemas*.

Database management systems (DBMS)

So that each application program may only access the data which it needs for processing or retrieval (that data which is defined in its subschema), a suite of programs referred to as the Database Management System (DBMS) controls the database and prevents accidental or deliberate corruption of data by other applications programs. An application cannot access the database without the DBMS. Figure 22.3 illustrates the relationship between users, application programs, the DBMS and the database.

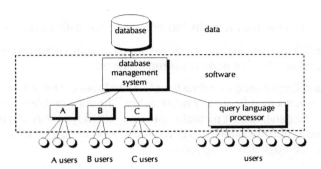

Figure 22.3. *Relationship between DBMS, applications and users*

A DBMS has the following functions.

❏ It is the common link between all applications programs and the database.

❏ It facilitates the use and organisation of a database and protects the database from accidental or deliberate corruption.

❏ It restricts a programmer's logical view of the database to those items of data which are to be used in the applications program being written.

Types of database

The logical structure of a database can be based upon one of a number of natural data structures which the Database Management System (DBMS) uses to establish links between separate data items. Physical pointers inform the DBMS where the next logical record is to be found. In certain types of database the logical organisation of the database is constrained by whatever data structure is used and can therefore be described as *formatted*. Two main categories of data structure are used in such databases:

❏ *hierarchical* or *tree* structure;

❏ *complex* and *simple plex* structure (often called *network* structures).

To avoid some of the restrictions inherent in formatted databases, a popular method of database management is to use a *relational* approach. To provide a basis for comparison with relational databases it is useful first to examine the data structures used in formatted databases.

Hierarchical or tree structure

A hierarchical or tree structure is illustrated in Figure 22.4. Each element is called a *node* and the only node which is not a *member* in any relationship is the *root* at the top of the tree. Three features of this structure need to be identified:

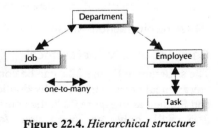

❏ only *one-to-many* relationships are supported;

Figure 22.4. *Hierarchical structure*

For example, in Figure 22.4, each Department can have many Employees, but each Employee can only belong to one Department. Similarly, each Employee may have more than one Task but each Task can only be carried out by one Employee.

❑ the highest level in the hierarchy has only one node called the *root;*

❑ each node is a member in exactly one *relationship* with a node on a level higher than itself, except for the root node at the top of the tree.

For example, Job and Employee each relate to only a single *parent node* (Department); the root node, Department, is not a member in any relationship. The main problem with the hierarchical structure is that not all databases fit naturally into it; a record type may require more than one parent. For example, a library database may require a book to be a member in more than one book category, say, Geology and Geography.

Network data structures

There are two types of network or plex data structures: *complex*; *simple*.

Complex plex structure

A complex plex structure is illustrated in Figure 22.5. This structure supports *many-to-many* (complex) relationships. Thus, a Student may be enrolled on one or more (many) Courses and each Course may have many Students.

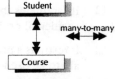

Figure 22.5. *Complex plex*

Whether or not such data structures can be used depends on the data description language (DDL) being used. IBM's DDL called DL/I supports any plex structure but the Codasyl DDL (described later) does not and cannot therefore, be used to describe complex plex structures.

Simple plex structure

A simple plex structure is illustrated in Figure 22.6. This structure supports *one-to-many* or simple relationships and unlike the tree structure, a node can have more than one parent. Thus, for example, a Quotation record may be owned by both one Builder and one Job record, but each Builder and Job record could own many Quotation records. A complex plex structure can be reconstructed if the available software does not support such a structure. For example, the complex plex structure in Figure 22.5 can be converted to a hierarchical structure or to a simple plex structure.

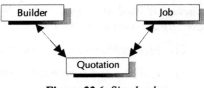

Figure 22.6. *Simple plex*

These reconstructions are shown in the Figures 22.7 and 22.8 respectively.

Complex plex to hierarchical

The structure in Figure 22.6 can be converted to two hierarchical or tree structures by duplicating Course and Student as in Figure 22.7; the course and student data will only be duplicated *logically*, not physically.

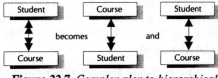

Figure 22.7. *Complex plex to hierarchical*

Complex plex to simple plex

Figure 22.8 shows the transformation from a complex plex to a simple plex structure, achieved through the creation of another record, which avoids the need to duplicate the Student and Course data. The relationships are now one-to-many rather than many-to-many.

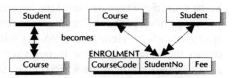

The new record Enrolment must contain the information necessary to establish the relationship between the original Course and Student records; as in this example, the record identifiers are generally used for this purpose.

Figure 22.8. *Complex plex to simple plex*

An example of a DBMS which supports *simple plex* structures is the CODASYL database management system. The Codasyl logical schema in Figure 22.9 serves to illustrate this method of database organisation.

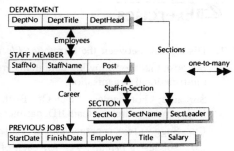

Codasyl schema for a large company

The schema can be explained in terms of *sets* as follows. There are 4 record types: DEPARTMENT; STAFFMEMBER; SECTION; PREVIOUS JOBS.

Figure 22.9. *Example Codasyl schema*

Each of 1, 2 and 3 can be retrieved directly by its *record key*, DeptNo, StaffNo and SectNo respectively. Record type 4 is only accessible through the STAFF MEMBER type record. This is reasonable as it would be unusual to search for a PREVIOUS JOBS record without first knowing the identity of the member of staff.

There are 4 *sets*, each of which has an *owner* record and one or more *member* records. For example, one DEPARTMENT will have a number of STAFFMEMBERs (a one-to-many relationship). The sets are:

> Employees (*owner*, DEPARTMENT/ *member*, STAFF MEMBER)
>
> Sections (*owner*, DEPARTMENT/ *member*, SECTION)
>
> Staff-in-Section (*owner*, SECTION/ *member*, STAFF MEMBER)
>
> Career (*owner*, STAFF MEMBER/ *member*, PREVIOUS JOBS)

Diagrammatically, a set can be pictured as shown in Figure 22.10. Referring to Figure 22.9, Department 4 (an owner record) may have a number of Section (member) records.

Data Manipulation Language statements could be used to retrieve a Section record directly using its SectNo or through its Sections Set (owned by Department Record). For example, if the section is in Department No 12, it may be found through the following steps.

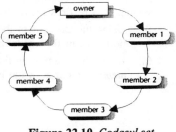

Figure 22.10. *Codasyl set*

```
1  move 12 to DeptNo
2  find any Department
3  show Section
4  find next Section
5  show Section
```

Steps *4* and *5* are repeated until the correct Section record is found or the end of set is reached. It should be noticed that a PreviousJobs record can *only* be found through the Career set and the appropriate StaffMember record. As with any database, a Codasyl DBMS organises and accesses the logical database through the schema description. In all formatted databases, the structure defines the route which can be taken through the database, but to be aware of how and what data can be accessed the programmer/user must know what linkages exist.

✍️Exercises

1. Distinguish between the terms *flat file* and *database*.
2. Suppose that the following data items are amongst those held in the personnel database of a multi-national organisation.

   Surname; Forename;   DateOf Birth, Salary; Qualifications; JobTitle; Department; DepartmentAddress; HeadOfDepartment; Country.

   (i)   Suggest two, separate *logical record* structures (list the fields in each) which may be useful.

   (ii) Suggest a *primary key* for each of the logical record structures you described in (i).

   (iii) What is the role of the database management system (DBMS) in relating the physical database to the logical record structures used by applications?

3. Distinguish between the terms *schema* and a *sub-schema*.
4. A database provides *data independence*. What does data independence mean and how is it beneficial for maintaining applications programs?
5. A particular company has separate departments to handle payroll and personnel information. The company operates a traditional file processing system, with each department maintaining its own files.

   (i)   Give examples of data in these systems which may be duplicated

   (ii) Briefly explain how the feature of *controlled redundancy*, provided by a database system, would help reduce such duplication.

6. Suggest a database application for which a tree structure would not be suitable.
7. An academic database maintains the following information concerning students, departments, courses and tutors. Each student is assigned to a particular course and has one personal tutor. A tutor will be responsible for a number of students. Each course operates in one of the five departments within the college and each department runs many courses. The system also records previous qualifications obtained by students.

   (i)   Using the example in the Topic as a guide, draw a *Codasyl schema* to reflect the information held in the academic database.

   (ii) Using the example in the Topic as a guide, draw a diagram to illustrate an *owner* and its *member* records in the academic database.

Relational databases

RDBMS (Relational Database Management System) software packages are designed for the construction and control of *databases*. Packages, such as dBase, Paradox and Access, are often loosely referred to as databases. Strictly, they are database management systems (DBMS) and their function is to store, manage and process information held in a database.

Tables, records and fields

A relational DBMS is designed to handle data in two-dimensional, *table* form and a single database is likely to contain a number of separate, but related, tables. This tabular view of data is easy to understand; everyday examples include telephone directories, train timetables and product price lists. An example of tabular data is given in Table 23.1. The table is labelled as PART_SUPPLIER and its purpose is to hold price and supplier information on all the parts stocked by a business.

PART_SUPPLIER		
PartCode	Price	SupplierNo
012	3.25	14
015	0.76	07
016	1.26	14
018	7.84	05

Table 23.1. *Tabular data*

- ❑ Each column in the table is identified by its *field name*, namely PartCode, Price and SupplierNo.

- ❑ Each of the four rows beneath the field name represents a *record*. The table would contain one record for each part stocked by the business.

Establishing relationships

The power of a relational DBMS lies in its facility to allow separate tables to be manipulated and combined in a variety of ways to establish new tables. Thus, for example, a table containing details such as the names and addresses of a firm's employees can be combined with a table detailing the make and registration numbers of cars owned by the employees, to produce a new table containing the names of employees owning, say, Ford cars.

When setting up a relational database it is often necessary, or simply desirable for the efficient management of the database, to divide the information logically into separate tables. Consider the example file in Figure 23.1.

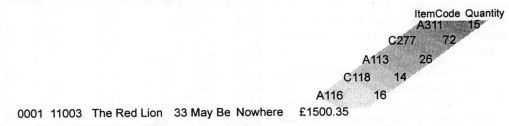

```
                                              ItemCode  Quantity
                                         A311        15
                                  C277        72
                            A113        26
                       C118      14
                  A116      16
0001  11003  The Red Lion   33 May Be Nowhere   £1500.35
```

Figure 23.1. *Three-dimensional file resulting from repeated values for ItemCode and Quantity*

The ItemCode and Quantity values are repeated and such a structure cannot be accommodated directly in a relational database table. It must be divided into two separate tables as shown in Tables 23.2 and 23.3.

ORDERS					
OrderNo	AcctID	Name	Address1	Address2	Order Total
0001	11003	The Red Lion	33 May Be	Nowhere	£1500.35
0002	11005	The Black Horse	45 Round About	Somewhere	£315.77
0003	11008	The Fat Ox	28 Just About	Anywhere	£425.66
etc	etc	etc	etc	etc	etc

Table 23.2. *Order table*

ORDER DETAILS		
OrderNo	ItemCode	Quantity
0001	A116	16
0001	C118	14
0001	A113	26
0001	C277	72
0001	A311	15
0002	C345	10
etc	etc	etc

Table 23.3. *Order details table with OrderNo as foreign key to link with Orders table*

In the ORDER DETAILS table, both OrderNo and ItemCode are needed to identify uniquely each record. Such a combination is known as a *composite* primary key. The OrderNo field in the ORDER DETAILS table also acts as a *foreign key* (see later) and is used to maintain the relationship with the records in the ORDERS table. The need for common values to establish relationships requires some duplication of data and thus some *controlled redundancy* (see Topic 22).

An attraction of the relational database is that its tabular representation of information can be clearly understood by programmers and non-programmers alike. This is in contrast to the complex structures which may arise in network structured databases. Through a process of *normalisation* (Topic 39), complex information structures can be simplified and divided into the tables used by the relational database.

As explained in the previous example, the division of related information into tables requires that the relationships between them are maintained. Here is a further example.

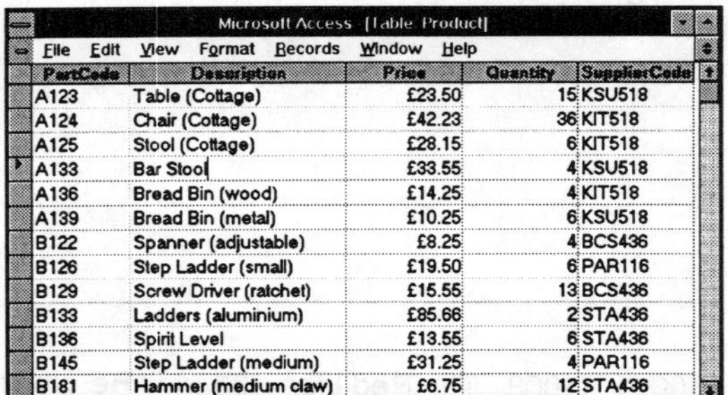

Consider the Product table in Figure 23.2. It is assumed that each product is supplied by only one supplier, but that each supplier provides many of the products. Additional fields could be included in the Product table for suppliers' names and addresses, but

Figure 23.2. *Product table*

much data would be needlessly repeated. It is more useful to create a separate table for the suppliers' names and addresses, as shown in Figure 23.3.

Note that the use of two tables in the first example was <u>essential</u> because of the repeated ItemCode and Quantity values for each record. In this example, the Supplier details <u>could</u> be held in the Product table, but to avoid unnecessary data duplication, they are placed in a separate table.

Figure 23.3. *Product and Supplier tables*

PartCode	Description	Price	Quantity	SupplierCode
A123	Table (Cottage)	£23.50	15	KSU518
A124	Chair (Cottage)	£42.23	36	KIT518
A125	Stool (Cottage)	£28.15	6	KIT518
A133	Bar Stool	£33.55	4	KSU518

Table: supplier

SupplierCode	SupplierName	SupplierAddress
ABC123	ABC Supplies	Transit Row, Darlington
KIT518	Kitchen Systems	28 Holmeside, Sunderland, SR3 4ST
KSU518	Kitchen Supplies	112 High Street, Darlington, DL1 4SJ
PAR116	Parsons Ltd	Parsons House, Market Place, York YO4 3NS
STA436	Stapleton	36 Warwick Place, Darlington, DL4 6AJ

To maintain the relationship with the Supplier table, the Product table also contains a Supplier Code field; this is the *foreign key* (see later) which links each Product record with a particular Supplier record.

The *degree of the relationship* (see later) between the tables has practical implications for the RDBMS and in this case there is a one-to-many relationship Supplier and Product - each supplier supplies many products, but each product is supplied by a single supplier.

Apart from the necessity of removing repeated fields and avoiding unnecessary data duplication, logical division of topics into separate tables can make a database simpler to manage and maintain. This benefit can be illustrated with the example of an academic database.

Suppose that a database for the maintenance of student records contains a single table consisting of twenty or thirty data items ranging from student name, address, and date of entry, to all assignment and exam grades for all subjects studied within a given course. Clearly, such a database would be unwieldy when, for example, a list of student names and addresses is all that is required by a particular user.

The following sections describe some important concepts relating to proper database design.

Entities

As illustrated by the earlier examples, a database should contain a number of logically separate tables, each corresponding to a given subject or part-subject (an *entity*). In the example of the product database (Figure 23.3), two logically separate tables (one for the Product entity and the other for the Supplier entity) are constructed. *Entities* are the objects of the real world which are relevant to a particular information system.

Attributes

An entity has a number of related *attributes*, which are of interest to users. Consider, as an example, a Personnel database. An entity, StaffMember, may have the attributes of StaffCode, Name, JobCode, JobTitle, DeptCode, DepartmentName. These attributes determine the *fields* which are associated with the StaffMember *table*. Some attributes may be kept in a separate table. For example, JobTitle and DepartmentName are likely to contain the same values in numerous records in the StaffMember table. In other words, some employees work in the same department and some have the same job title. With an RDBMS, it is more efficient to separate these attributes, through the creation of separate tables (one for Department and the other for Job). Although an employee has a given job title and works in a particular department, these attributes are also of separate interest; each is a separate *entity*. For example, a new job title may be identified before an employee has been assigned to it. Figure 23.4 shows the tables which represent these entities.

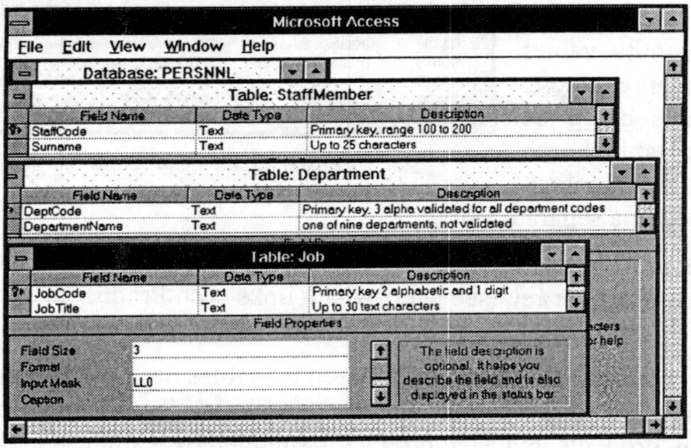

Figure 23.4. *Tables for StaffMember, Department and Job entities*

Identifying and non-identifying attributes

'Identifying attributes' and 'non-identifying attributes' are the equivalent database terms for primary and secondary keys, respectively (Topic 16).

Some attributes, for example, Name and JobTitle, are descriptive and serve as secondary keys. Another (StaffCode) may serve as a unique identifier (or primary key). Attributes can be classified, therefore, as being either *identifying* or *non-identifying*. In Figure 23.4, StaffCode acts as the unique identifier (or *primary key field*) for a StaffMember record. The Department and Job records use DeptCode and JobCode, respectively, as their unique identifiers.

These entity and attribute structures can be expressed in the form shown below. Unique identifiers are underlined.

```
StaffMember(StaffCode, Name, JobCode, DeptCode)
Job(JobCode, JobTitle)
Department(DeptCode, DepartmentName)
```

Sometimes, more than one attribute is needed to uniquely identify an individual record; such attributes form a composite identifier or key. An example of such a key is given below.

```
OrderLine (OrderNo, ItemNo, Description, Price, Quantity)
```

An order form usually has several lines, each relating to a separate item which a customer wants. The same item may be ordered by other customers, so the OrderNo and ItemNo are needed to identify a particular order line, relating to a particular customer order.

Relationships, link fields and foreign keys

The JobCode and DeptCode fields must also remain in the StaffMember table to allow relationships, or links, to be established between the tables. Suppose, for example, that a user wishes to view a list of employee details, which includes Name, DepartmentName and JobTitle.

To process the necessary query, the RDBMS needs to extract information from more than one table. An examination of the entity structures in Figure 23.5 reveals that all three are needed (StaffMember, Job and Department). The user must specify which fields are used to link the tables to one another. Figure 23.5 illustrates these links.

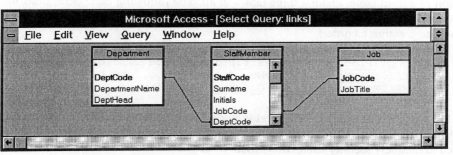

Figure 23.5. *Link fields to establish relationships between tables*

DeptCode is the primary key for the Department table, but the same attribute also appears in the StaffMember table. When the two are linked, DeptCode in the StaffMember table is acting as a *foreign key*. A foreign key is a field in one table which links to the primary key in another table. JobCode in the StaffMember table also serves as a foreign key to link with the Job table.

Degree of relationship

The degree of relationship that exists between a pair of tables in a relational database has practical implications for the way that tables are handled by the RDBMS. The degree of relationship may be: one-to-one; one-to-many; many-to-one; many-to-many.

One-to-one relationship

Figure 23.6 provides an example of a one-to-one relationship. Each hospital patient develops a unique medical history and each medical history can only relate to one hospital patient.

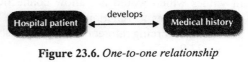

Figure 23.6. *One-to-one relationship*

One-to-many relationship

Figure 23.7 could illustrate a business which uses many suppliers, but buys each of its products from a particular supplier. More formally, a supplier supplies one or many products, but each product is unique to one supplier. The double arrow head indicates the *many* side of the relationship.

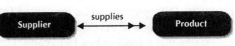
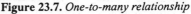

Figure 23.7. *One-to-many relationship*

By many, we mean one or more, whereas one means one only.

Of course, Purchase to Supplier reverses the relationship and is expressed as many-to-one relationship.

Many-to-many relationship

A Product may appear in many different Orders and a single Order may include a number of Products. This is symbolised in Figure 23.8.

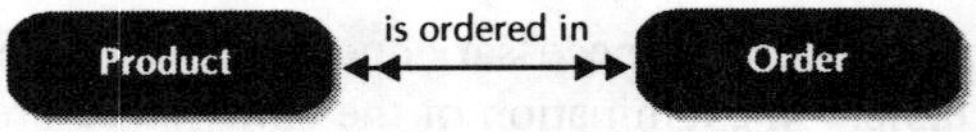

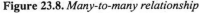

Figure 23.8. *Many-to-many relationship*

This many-to-many relationship could not be handled directly by the RDBMS without the creation of a third table, making three tables in all. The following table definitions (or entity structures) illustrate how this could be achieved. ORDERLINE represents the information held on each item within an order).

```
PRODUCT(ProductCode, Description, Price .....etc)
ORDER(OrderNo, CustomerNo, TotalCost.....etc)
ORDERLINE(ProductCode, OrderNo, Quantity, ......etc)
```

The PRODUCT table and ORDER table each have a one-to-many relationship with the ORDERLINE table. A composite primary key formed from <u>ProductCode</u> and <u>OrderNo</u> is needed to uniquely identify each ORDERLINE record.

ProductCode in the PRODUCT table acts as the foreign key to link with the ORDERLINE table. Similarly, OrderNo in the ORDER table is the foreign key which links it to the ORDERLINE table. The converse is also true in that ProductCode and OrderNo in the ORDERLINE table are the foreign keys linking it with the PRODUCT and ORDER tables, respectively.

Referential integrity

Referential integrity is a phrase used by the Microsoft Access RDBMS and refers to the maintenance of valid relationships between tables. Referential integrity between pairs of tables can be enforced to prevent accidental deletion or insertion of values which would not allow connections between the tables to function properly. The Access setting for enforcing referential integrity is shown in Figure 23.9.

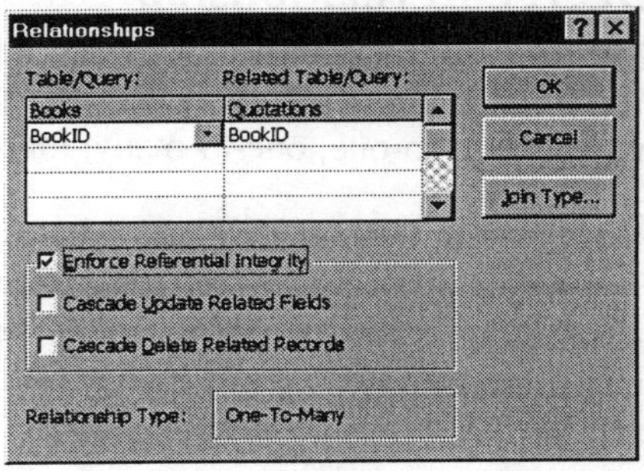

Figure 23.9. *Setting referential integrity*

For example, in a one to many relationship, such as exists in the previous example of PRODUCT and ORDERLINE, you would be prevented from entering a ProductCode in the ORDERLINE table which does not exist in the PRODUCT table. The rule states that a foreign key field cannot hold a value which does not occur in the primary key of the table to which is connects. However, if an order included an item which was not normally stocked, the RDBMS would allow entry of a Null value in the ProductCode field of the ORDERLINE table.

Using the same example, referential integrity would also prevent deletion of a PRODUCT record, the primary key of which exists in an ORDERLINE record. The rules also prevent the alteration, for example, of a ProductCode in the PRODUCT table if an ORDERLINE record included that ProductCode value.

Data analysis

The process of data analysis is concerned with establishing what the entities, attributes and links (or relationships), for any given database, should be. To make such an analysis, it is obviously necessary to have knowledge of the organisation to which the information relates, because there will be certain items of information which only have significance to that particular organisation. For example, in an Academic database, the following entities may be identified and a table established for each.

Student; Course; Tutor; EducationHistory; ExamGrade

Benefits of a relational DBMS

❏ Logical record structures and connections between them are not constrained by pointers using rigid formats such as those provided by the hierarchical and plex structures described earlier.

❏ The relational DBMS allows use of implicit relationships between tables through the presence of foreign keys and does not require the programmer to explicitly link tables (although this can be done). When linking flat files, the programmer must establish an explicit relationship which cannot be changed without modification of the program code.

❏ New tables can be added or existing relations modified as user requirements change.

Levels of database access

A fundamental principle of security is that access is limited to those persons who require it and that the degree of access is limited to that which is necessary to their jobs. For example, authorisation to alter schema or sub-schema descriptions may be limited to the Database Administrator. User A may be given access to particular data for enquiry, but not for alteration purposes, whilst User B may be the only person authorised to change prices in the Stock File.

Access controls include the use of passwords and the assignment of appropriate access levels and user rights . The controls may be implemented within the database or through the operating system software.

In SUPERVISOR mode, the person assigned to the role of Supervisor has unrestricted access to the network, or in the case of a database, to the RDBMS. The Supervisor is likely to be the Database Administrator who, apart from having unrestricted access to the database, can assign rights to users in respect of particular applications or files within the database. Such rights determine what a user can do. For example, within an application area, such as Sales, the Sales manager may be able to create, copy, delete and modify the contents of Sales records. In contrast, clerical staff may have restricted rights to view and perhaps add new Sales record. The access rights of each user are defined in a User Account. When a user enters his or her user-id and password, the particular rights and restrictions set in the user account will apply.

✍️Exercises

1. Consider the following record structure for a library loan record.

   (MemberNo, Surname, Forename....etc, BookRef, DateIssued).

   A member can borrow up to 12 books at any one time.

   (i)   Why is the structure not suitable for storage in a relational database?

   (ii) Suggest a suitable structure for a relational database, adding any fields you need to produce an efficient structure and identifying the relationships between the tables.

   (iii) Use the example to define the terms *entity*, *attribute* (identifying and non-identifying) and *foreign key*.

2. Give examples of entities which have a:

   (i)   one-to-one relationship;

   (ii) one-to-many or many-to-one relationship;

   (iii) many-to-many relationship.

3. What is meant by *referential integrity* and what is it designed to prevent?

4. How can security be improved by using access controls at different levels? Illustrate your answer with a suitable example.

Section 6

Networking

Topics

The word *telecommunications* can be applied to any system capable of transmitting text, sounds, graphical images or indeed, data of any kind, in electronic form. The signals may travel along wires or they may be radio signals, which require no wires, but can travel through the atmosphere and space. The term *data communications* refers to the transmission of data in digital form. In the developed world digital communication is becoming the norm. Analogue communication systems which transmit information in sine wave form are still widely available, notably in the fields of television and radio, but these will be obsolete within the next few years.

Computer networks

Computer data is represented in *digital* form, so communication channels between computers in a network must also be able to support the transmission of digital data. When computers are networked over a small area, such as within a single room or building (Local Area Network), they are linked by a dedicated digital transmission medium such as co-axial or optical fibre cable.

The cost of linking computers in this way over larger distances (Wide Area Network) soon becomes prohibitive, so existing public and private communications networks have to be used. Some parts of these networks include analogue sections which do not directly support digital transmissions. Although all UK telephone exchanges are now digital the links to most domestic and small business telephone users are still analogue. In these cases, a special device called a *modem* must be used to interface a computer with the standard telephone socket. A modem adapts the computers digital signals for transmission over the analogue section on the network.

Data generated by a computer is already in digital form, but other data (the term is used in its broadest sense), such as sounds of human speech, or a photograph, need to be digitally encoded before transmission over a digital network.

Although not all transmissions of digital data involve general-purpose computers, they are generated and controlled by digital computer technology. A wide range of dedicated devices is used to support, monitor and control communications between computers, including hubs, routers, bridges and multiplexers, all of which are described in Topic 49.

Local and wide area networks

Computer networks can be classified according to their geographical spread.

❑ A network confined to, say, one building, with microcomputer workstations distributed in different rooms, is known as a *local area network* (LAN). One particular type, known as a ring network can extend over a diameter of around five miles.

❑ A computer network distributed nationally or even internationally makes use of telephone and sometimes, satellite links, and is referred to as a *wide area network* (WAN). In large organisations with several branches, it is common practice to maintain a LAN at each branch for local processing requirements and to link each

LAN into a WAN covering the whole organisation. In this way, branches of an organisation can have control over their own processing and yet have access to the organisation's main database at headquarters. In addition, inter-branch communication is possible.

LAN architecture

It is important that the components are combined in such a way that the LAN can be:

❑ *extended*. The LAN must be capable of providing for new users and new equipment, as the need arises;

❑ *upgraded* to take advantage of new technologies which can improve network performance;

❑ *connected* to other LANs, both local and remote and Wide Area Networks.

LAN architecture comprises hardware and software, both for the control of the LAN communications and as an interface between the LAN and its users. In order that all components are compatible and operate as a coherent system, it is important that they conform to agreed standards. This means that LAN producers have to take account of generally agreed standards for equipment linking and data communications so that, as new products come onto the market, the user is not left with a system which cannot take advantage of them. Unfortunately, a number of different standards exist and this means that the decision on which type of LAN to purchase is not always straightforward.

Hardware components

Figure 24.1 shows a simple *client-server* LAN and identifies the main hardware components: *workstation*; *file server*; *printer server*; network *cabling*. The way in which they are connected defines its general *topology* (Topic 25) or shape.

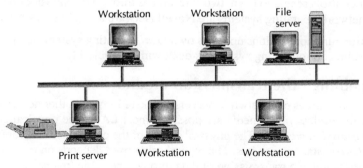

Figure 24.1. *Main components of a LAN*

LAN Workstation

A *workstation* gives a user access to a LAN and its facilities. A workstation comprises a *micro-computer* with a *network card*, which fits into an *expansion slot* inside its system casing. The network card enables workstations to communicate across the network, and with the *file server*. The card converts computer-generated data into a form suitable for transmission over the LAN and as such is an *interface*. The card is operated with a network card driver.

Servers

The general function of servers is to allocate shared resources to other nodes on the network. There are a number of different types of server, which can be categorised according to the resources they control.

File server

The file server is usually a specially configured microcomputer, with a network card, more memory and disk storage, as well as a more powerful processor than is needed for a workstation. It has to control access to shared storage, directories and files. In addition, it controls the exchange of files between network users. Most network software provides *multiple device* support. This means that file servers can support several disks, allowing file storage capacity on the LAN to be increased beyond that of the file server's integral hard disk. A LAN can also consist of several file servers; indeed except for the smallest of networks, this is normally the case.

Print server

A print server (there may be several) accepts and queues jobs from workstations; the user may be informed when printing is complete. The print server may also provide certain print management functions, for example, to attach priorities to different print jobs so that certain jobs are printed before others, no matter what their positions in the queue. A print server will be configured to support the use of particular printers and service particular printer *queues*; users with the right to use a particular print queue can then place their jobs in that queue.

Communications server

If a LAN is to have access to external networks or databases, a communications server is required. Generally, the communications server can establish a temporary link with remote computers or users on other networks.

LAN software

The file server controls access to the network resources through the *network operating system*. Examples of network operating systems are Novell Netware and Windows NT.

Each workstation runs applications under its own *local* operating system, such as Windows 98 or OS/2. The subject of operating systems is dealt with in Topic 11.

Network cabling - the transmission medium

In order to share resources on a network, servers, workstations and other devices must be connected; although wireless radio media are possible, most LANs use physical cabling, which acts as the *transmission medium*. The physical layout of the cabling should conform to one of the basic *topologies*: star, ring or bus. The type of cable used depends on the chosen topology and the rules governing the transmission of data through the cable (the *protocol*). The cabling standards of Ethernet and Token Ring, described below, are also LAN protocols. Which type to use for a given situation largely depends on the bandwidth requirements of the network.

Ethernet cabling

Ethernet is one the two most widely accepted standards (the other is Token Ring) for specifying how data is placed on and retrieved from a LAN. An Ethernet-equivalent standard is IEEE 802.3 (see Topic 48), which also uses Ethernet cable, but packets data slightly differently for transmission through the cable. Ethernet cable falls into three main categories:

❏ *Thick Ethernet* coaxial cable, with a diameter of 10mm has a solid copper core conductor. A single network segment can be 500 metres and supports the attachment of 100 devices. The cabling conforms to the IEEE 802.3 Type 10Base5 standard. The bandwidth is 10 megabits (1024^2 bits) per second (Mb/s).

❏ *Thin Ethernet*, which is 10 millimetres in diameter, has a core of stranded cable. The maximum length of cable which can be used in a single network segment is around 180 metres and the maximum number of workstations is around 30. The cabling conforms to the IEEE 802.3 Type 10Base2 standard. The cable supports a maximum bandwidth of 2 Mb/s.

❏ *10BaseT* Standard Ethernet. The T stands for *twisted pair*. This cable is much cheaper than the thick Ethernet cabling, but provides the same bandwidth of 10 Mb/s; being the same as most telephone cabling, it is easier to install.

Token ring cabling

Used in *IBM token ring* networks use twisted pair cabling, either two pairs or four, depending on data transmission requirements. A single IBM Token Ring network will support up to 260 network devices at rates of 4 Mb/s or 16 Mb/s. Up to eight rings can be connected using *bridges*.

Fibre-optic cabling

Cable of this type is available for use with any of the network types, but provides greater *bandwidth* and permits transmission over greater distances, without the use of *repeaters* (Topic 49). Fibre Distributed Data Interface (FDDI) is a fibre optic standard with bandwidth of over a Gigabit (1024^3) per second. FDDI is also a token ring standard, but operates with two counter rotating rings and workstations may be attached to one or both rings. FDDI is used widely for network backbones. A *backbone* is the part of a network which carries the main traffic and connects, for example, the LANs in different departments of an organisation.

Connecting to a wide area network (WAN)

The first consideration when linking to a WAN is the type of connection, which can be dial-up or permanent.

❏ Leased lines. Permanent connections can be leased from British Telecom and increasingly commonly from Internet Service Provider companies. A leased line provides a permanent connection for devices in a network, with a choice of transmission rates. Obviously, the higher the rate, the greater will be the cost. Leased lines are cost-effective for high volume data transmission, or when a permanent link is vital to the users, perhaps for retrieval of orders from an Internet store. Charging is by a flat rate rather than when calls are made.

❏ Dial-up or switched lines. These are cheaper, but cannot support the higher transmission rates available with leased lines. They are more cost effective than leased lines for low-volume work and allow the operator to choose the destination of transmissions. Dial-up connections can be made with a modem or an ISDN (see Topic 51) terminal adapter. If an ISDN adapter is used, there is virtually no dialing delay.

Another consideration is the hardware, software and protocol (see later) requirements of the remote computer to which connection is being made. We will use the Internet to illustrate these requirements.

Connecting to the Internet

The Internet is a world-wide network composed of thousands of smaller regional networks scattered throughout the globe. A common set of communication protocols enables every computer connected to the Internet to interchange information with every other computer so connected. All types of computers make up the hardware connected on the Internet. They vary from PCs, Macintoshes and UNIX workstations to minicomputers, mainframes and supercomputers. Figure 24.2 shows a PC connected to the Internet via a remote service provider which is itself a LAN (Local Area Network).

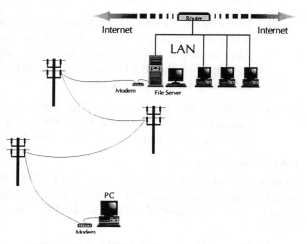

Figure 24.2. *A PC linked to a service provider for connection to the Internet*

The PC connects to the service provider using a modem (or ISDN adapter) and the telephone system. The Internet Service Provider (ISP) is directly connected to the Internet by means of a *router,* a computer which provides the link to special data transmission lines required to access the Internet. A large organisation might have its own direct link to the Internet, but many private and small business users rely on commercial service providers for the connection, for which they may have to pay a subscription. Many service providers do not charge a subscription but generate revenue from advertising and a percentage of telephone call charges received from subscribers who take advantage of the telephone help lines they run for their clients.

Modems, analogue and digital signals

Figure 24.3 illustrates the role of the modem in a data telecommunications link.

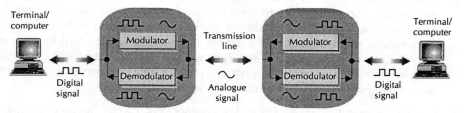

Figure 24.3. *Modems in data communications link*

Even though much of the public switched telephone network (pstn) uses digital transmission techniques, most local connections to homes and businesses still use analogue signals. To allow transmission of computer data (which is digital) over these analogue links, a device called a *modem* is needed to *modulate* and *demodulate* the computer's signals. The modem for the transmitter device has to modulate the digital signal into the corresponding analogue form for transmission along the telephone line. The modem at the receiver device has to carry out the reverse operation. Modems are capable of both functions, so that two way communications are supported.

Computer-modem connection

To make use of a modem, the microcomputer should have a serial communication (RS232) port. However, there are two possible alternatives; an adapter card with a serial port capability; a communications board (this fits in an expansion slot, located inside the computer's system casing), which combines the functions of the serial port and the modem.

Software requirements

Modern operating systems include utility programs for some types of WAN communications. The Windows operating system includes Hyperterminal, a program which allows connection to any remote computer to which the user has authorised access and the sending or receiving of files. Before sending or receiving a file, the user must specify whether the file is text or binary (such as an image or program file) and if the latter, the communications protocol to be used; this must be one that is recognised by the remote computer.

A Dialup Networking 'wizard' guides the user through the process of setting up a connection to a WAN such as the Internet. The settings needed to establish a connection with a Service Provider's Internet server include: telephone number, communication device (modem or ISDN adapter), the type of server (e.g. Internet, Windows 98 etc or Unix), Internet server address and the communication protocol (see Topic 26 - TCP/IP).

Apart from built-in utilities, there exist a number of application packages that provide more sophisticated communications facilities. These include Web browsers, graphical interface client programs to help users to navigate through the World Wide Web, to transmit and to receive information from other users or information providers. Examples of commercially available browsers are Netscape's *Communicator*, Microsoft's *Explorer*.

There are also communication packages specially designed for communication with FTP (File Transfer Protocol) sites. Internet Service Providers use these sites to allow the remote management of client web sites hosted by them. The site owner uses the FTP package to connect to the Provider's FTP server and is then able to download web pages, modify them and then upload the amendments. The changes to the web site are immediate.

The importance of bandwidth

Digital bandwidth is measured in bits per second and indicates the volume of data which can be transmitted over a communications link in a fixed time. Bandwidth is important because is determines the practicability of using remote communications for modern user applications. High bandwidth is not a crucial consideration for users who wish to exchange the occasional text email, but it is fundamental to the success of businesses with more complex and high volume communication needs. For example, a multi-sited organisation may need use its communications links to the Internet for the transmission of complex documents containing high quality images, voice communications and video conferencing. To meet these requirements the organisation would need dedicated, high speed links from each site to a 'backbone' (a major communications link) in the Internet In summary, bandwidth can be:

❏   Baseband. In a baseband network, a transmitting device uses the whole bandwidth so only one signal can be carried at any one time. This means that, for a brief moment, a transmitting device has exclusive use of the transmission medium. In general, broadband networks are suitable for small networks with low data volumes..

❏   Wideband. Wideband networks provide a number of channels within the total bandwidth and thus allow simultaneous use by different devices on the network.

Controlling user access to networks

Access to networks needs to be controlled because unauthorised access may:

❏   provide vital information for business competitors;

❏   result in the deliberate or accidental corruption of data;

❏   allow fraudulent changes to be made to data;

❏   result in loss of privacy for individuals or organisations.

To control access, a network operating system provides facilities for setting up user accounts and the assignment of a user-id and password for each user. To restrict each user to the level of access he or she needs, access rights can be assigned to the user account. For example, a clerk in the Personnel Department may need to view the names and addresses of employees to address correspondence and may be prevented from viewing other personal details or making any alterations to records. The Personnel manager is likely to be assigned rights which allow viewing and alteration of, for example, job grades, salaries or training details.

Assignment of a user-id and password, therefore, allows:

❏   the allocation of a level of access to information and the assignment of rights, for example, to view, alter or create records;

❏   identification and authentication of each user. The user can be identified by the user-id and authenticated by the password.

To detect unauthorised attempts at access, the system should log all unsuccessful attempts and perhaps 'lock out' the user after a certain number of failures. If a genuine user is locked out, perhaps because of keying errors, he or she can contact technical support, have the account unlocked and make a fresh attempt.

Password features

Passwords should be carefully chosen, kept secure (memorised and not divulged) and changed frequently. Using people's names, for example, may allow entry by trial and error. Characters should not be echoed on screen as the password is entered.

Handshaking is a technique which requires more than a simple password and may be used between two computers or a computer and a user, as a means of access control. In the latter case, the user would be given a pseudo-random number by the computer and the expected response would be a transform, of that random number. The transform may be to multiply the first and last digits of the number and add the product to a value equal to the day of the month plus 1. Provided the transform is kept secret, handshaking provides more security than simple passwords.

One-time passwords. The computer will only accept a password for *one access occasion*; subsequently, it will expect the user to provide a different password for each additional access, in a pre-defined sequence. Provided the password list and their expected sequence list are kept separate, then possession of one list only will not be of any assistance. The number of attempts at logging-on should be controlled, so, for example, after three unsuccessful attempts, the user should be locked out and a record kept of the time and nature of the attempt.

✍️Exercises

1. Distinguish between a *local area network* (LAN) and a *wide area network* (WAN) and suggest how each may be used by a large organisation.
2. List the main hardware components of a local area network and briefly state the function of each.
3. Research LAN *cabling* products and draw up a specification table, detailing the standard and performance data for each.
4. Suggest organisations and applications which would be likely to use:
   (i)   leased lines
   (ii) dial-up connections.
   to access external networks. Justify your choice in each case, indicating how the link would be used.
5. Produce a simple, step-by-step guide for gaining access to the Internet, detailing hardware, software and any service requirements. Research the latest options.
6. Describe the function of a modem, distinguishing between *analogue* and *digital* signals.
7. List and define the purposes of the various types of communications software used to access the Internet and its services and for each type give a commercial example.
8. Define the term bandwidth and say why it is important for the expansion of network services.
9. List a range of security measures which can be used to control access to computer networks.

Computer networks can be categorised according to their physical shape or topology. Each terminal in a network is known as a *node*. If a central computer controls the network it is known as the *host* computer. The topology of a network is the *arrangement* of the nodes and the ways they are interconnected. The communication system within a network is known as the *subnet*. Data can be transmitted around the subnet either on a *point-to-point* basis or through a *broadcast* channel. If point-to-point transmission is used, the data passes through each device in the network. Thus, if two devices wish to communicate, they must do it indirectly, via any intervening devices. Each device must have the facility to store the entire message and forward it when the output channel is free. If a broadcast channel is used, a common communication channel is shared by all devices in the network. This means that any message sent by a device is received by all devices. The message contains the address of the device intended to receive it, so that the other devices can ignore it. There are a number of recognised network topologies and some of the most common are described below.

Star network

A star topology means that each node is connected, by separate connections to a computer at the centre, known as the *hub*. Figure 25.1 shows a LAN in a star topology. It is also a popular topology for a WAN. In this structure, all messages pass through the host (probably a mainframe or minicomputer) computer, which interconnects the different devices on the network. So, in this topology the host computer at the hub has a *message switching* function. Messages are transmitted point-to-point. The topology is particularly useful for intercommunications between pairs of users on the network

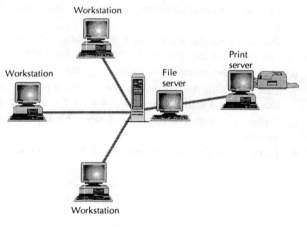

Figure 25.1. *Star network topology*

(via the host). The network may consist of numerous computer systems (the nodes), connected to a larger host computer which switches data and programs between them.

The star computer network is by far the most popular for WANs, because most large organisations start with a central computer at the head office, from which branch computer facilities are provided through the telephone network. The main aim is to provide computer communication between the branches and head office. Most other network topologies aim to provide communication between all devices on a network. The star topology can also be used for a LAN.

Ring network

The ring topology is specifically designed for use with a LAN and is not suitable for a WAN. A ring network connects all the nodes in a ring, as illustrated in Figure 25.2. The *Cambridge Ring*, developed at Cambridge University, has no host computer and none of the nodes need have overall control of access to the network. In practice, a monitoring station is used for the control of data transmission in the network. Messages in a ring network flow in one direction, from node to node.

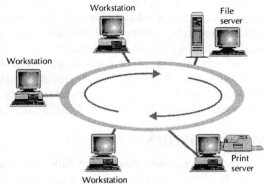

Figure 25.2. *Ring network topology*

The ring consists of a series of repeaters, which are joined by the physical transmission medium (twisted pair, co-axial, or fibre-optic cable). The choice of medium depends on the distances to be covered and the desired transmission rates. Fibre-optic cable allows the greatest distances to be covered and the highest transmission rates. Repeaters are used to regenerate messages as they pass around the network. The use of repeaters allows a ring network to cover larger distances than is possible for other topologies. In fact, recent developments using fibre optic cable allow a ring with a range of about 100 kilometres, which makes it a *metropolitan area network* (MAN). The user devices are connected to the repeaters. A message from one node, addressed to another, is passed continually around the ring until the receiving node flags that it is ready to accept it. Acceptance of a message is determined by its *destination address*, which is examined by each node it passes. If the destination address matches the node's own address, the node takes the message; otherwise, the node repeater regenerates the signal to be passed to the next node in the ring. Data is transmitted in mini-packets of about 40 bits and contains the address of the sending node, the address of the destination node and some control bits.

Bus network

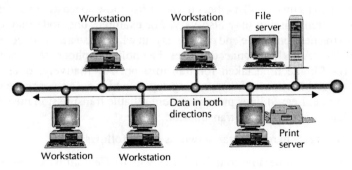

Figure 25.3. *Bus network topology*

With a bus topology (Figure 25.3), the workstations are connected to a main cable (known as the *bus* or trunk), along which data travels. The ends of a bus are not connected, so that data has to travel in both directions to reach the various nodes on the network. The bus topology makes the addition of new devices straightforward, either by attachment to the existing cable or to cable which can be added at either end. The main bus standard is known as *Ethernet*. The term *station* tends to be used rather than node for this type of network. The communications subnet uses a *broadcast* channel, so all attached stations can hear every transmission. As is the case in the ring network, there is no host computer and all stations have equal priority in using the network to transmit. The maximum length of a single bus *segment* is 500 metres and 100 stations can be attached to it. Segments can be specially linked to form larger configurations, up to a maximum of about 12 kilometres. Transmission speeds of 10 megabits/second are obtainable.

Mesh network

The nodes of a mesh network are fully interconnected. The mesh topology is not found in LANs, but is typical of the public switched telephone network (pstn) and WANs. Its complexity requires the use of switching techniques to route data through the network (see Packet Switching in Topic 51).

Each topology has its own benefits and drawbacks in the context of any particular application.

Advantages and disadvantages of topologies

Star topology

The *advantages* of a star network topology are as follows:

❏ It is suitable for WANs where organisations rely on a central computer for the bulk of processing tasks, perhaps limiting the nodes to their local processing needs and the validation of data, prior to transmission to the central computer;

❏ Centralised control of message switching allows a high degree of security control;

❏ Each spoke in the star is independent of the rest and a fault in a link or device in one spoke, can be identified by the computer at the hub;

❏ The data transmission speeds used can vary from one *spoke* (a link from the hub to a node) to another. This is important if some spokes transmit using high speed devices, such as disk, whilst others transmit from low speed keyboard devices. The method of transmission may also vary. For example, one node may only require access to the network at the end of each day, in which case a *dial-up* connection may be sufficient. A dial-up connection uses the public telephone network and the user only pays for the time taken for transmission. Alternatively, other nodes may require the link for most of the working day, in which case a permanent *leased line* is appropriate. Leased lines provide a more reliable transmission medium and also allow higher speeds of data transmission.

The main *disadvantages* inherent in star networks are as follows:

❏ The network is vulnerable to hub failures which affect all users. As a distributed processing system, some processing is still possible at the nodes but inter-node communication is lost when the host computer fails;

For a WAN, the control of communications in the network requires expensive technology at the hub, probably a mini or mainframe computer. Complex operating and communications software is needed to control the network.

Ring topology

The ring network presents advantages:

❑ There is no dependence on a central host computer as data transmission around the network is supported by all the devices in the ring. Each node device has sufficient intelligence to control the transmission of data from and to its own node;

❑ Very high transmission rates are possible; 10 megabits/sec is typical;

❑ Routing between devices is relatively simple because messages normally travel in one direction only around the ring;

❑ The transmission facility is shared equally amongst the users.

The main disadvantages are as follows:

❑ The system depends on the reliability of the whole ring and the repeaters, although it can be designed to bypass any failed node;

❑ It may be difficult to extend the length of the ring because the physical installation of any new cable must ensure that the ring topology is preserved.

Star/ring network - IBM token ring

The *IBM Token Ring* Network is a star-based topology, with a hub or *multiple access unit* (MAU) to which all the workstations are connected. The movement of data is, however, in a *logical ring*. All signals between workstations are through the MAU. The star/ring structure has a major advantage over the basic ring. If one workstation breaks down, or the connection with the MAU is broken, other workstations are not affected (except that they cannot communicate with the damaged workstation).

Bus topology

The bus network provides certain benefits:

❑ If a node malfunctions, it simply stops communicating; it doesn't prevent the rest of the network from working;

❑ The attachment of devices is straightforward and the cable can be extended, if necessary; additional *segments* can be linked to extend the network.

The main drawback is that:

If a part of the Ethernet cabling develops a fault, the whole network (assuming it consists of a single segment) fails.

✍️Exercises

1. (i)   Name the *network topology* which features a central computer for message switching between the attached nodes.

    (ii) What is the topology's main weakness?

2. (i)   Which weakness of the *Cambridge ring* topology is the *IBM Token Ring* network designed to overcome?

    (ii) Name the device used to overcome the weakness.

3. Name the topology for which *Ethernet* is the main standard.

4. Compare and contrast the topologies described in the Topic, with particular reference to the movement of data around the network and communication between attached devices.

A protocol is a set of rules for the transmission of data devices. Without these rules, devices would not 'understand' one another and the extent of computer networks would be severely restricted. There are numerous protocols for wide area networks which, by definition, may involve communication between computers of many different types and *platforms* (hardware and operating system). There are LAN communication protocols which are specific to particular network operating systems, such as IPX for Novell networks; these protocols drive the network card inside the LAN workstation and allow it to communicate with other stations on the network. There are also *access protocols* which determine how an attached device communicates with the network transmission medium (often cabling).

Wide Area Network protocols

We begin by looking at the protocols which are used for modem communications, typically between a home or small business user and an Internet Service Provider's server. Sending and receiving computers must use the same modem protocols and settings if they are to communicate reliably. Protocols are, essentially, sets of rules about how the two devices are to communicate. So, for example, if a modem is set to use 8 data bits, no parity bit and 1 stop bit (see later), the other modem will not be able to interpret the data unless it uses the same settings.

Also, both modems must operate at the same speed. This is why, for example, when connecting to the Internet, the connect speed may vary, up to the maximum of the user's modem. The connect speed depends on the modem speed at the Internet Service Provider's site, when the dial-up connection is made.

For communication between two devices, the protocol must establish as a minimum:

❑ the data transmission rate (measured in bits per second). If the devices have different maximum transmission rates, the rate is dictated by the slower of the two.

❑ whether both devices may transmit to each other simultaneously (in *full-duplex* mode) or one direction at a time (in *half-duplex* mode). In the latter case, the protocol must also allow determination of which device currently has *control of the communications link*.

❑ whether *synchronous* (data is sent in a stream with sender and receiver synchronised to identify when one character ends and another starts) or *asynchronous* (characters are sent at irregularly timed intervals, with start and stop bits to separate characters) transmission is to be used.

A protocol may also specify:

❑ The method by which each device will indicate that it has finished sending or receiving a message.

❑ The method of *data flow control*. This is to ensure that data transmission flows smoothly, that the communications channel is not overloaded and that the transmitting device does not send data more quickly than the receiver can handle.

❑ The method for *error detection and correction*. Although digital signals are infinitely more stable than their analogue equivalent, errors will occur and the communicating devices must have a means of detecting and re-transmitting them correctly. For transmission over analogue links (which are the norm for local connections to the public telephone network) error detection and correction is even more important and all modem error protocols are built in to the hardware.

❑ *Data compression* method; through encoding data is reduced in volume, allowing its speedier transmission.

Protocols can be implemented by software or hardware. Typically, dedicated network devices such as modems use hardware implementation, but general-purpose computers which have not been designed for connection to a particular network may have to set up transmission protocols through the communications software. Figure 26.1 shows the protocol settings in Windows 98 for a dial-up connection to the Internet.

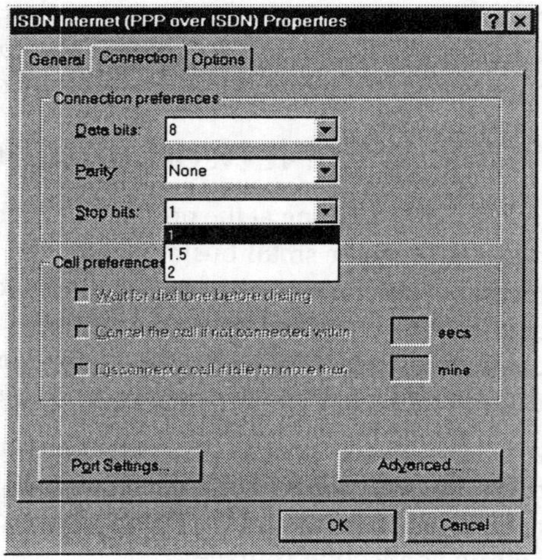

The following settings are shown.

Data bits. This is the number of binary digits used to represent each character in a data stream. For example, in a widely used 7-bit code called ASCII, the binary pattern 1000011 represents the capital letter 'C'.

Figure 26.1. *Modem protocol settings*

Parity bit. A parity bit is an extra bit which is used to help control errors in transmission. For example, with *even* parity, a 1 is attached if the number of 1s in the data bits is odd. Otherwise, a 0 is attached. Either way, the number of 1s, including the parity bit must be even. When each character is received, the receiver checks that the number of 1s is still even. If not the character is re-transmitted. This is illustrated below.

data bits	parity bit	reason
1001001	1	number of 1s odd so parity bit = 1
0101000	0	number of 1s even so parity bit = 0

This is a simple technique and will only detect single bit errors - if an even number is altered, the parity will still be maintained. Modems include sophisticated error checking and correction features, so the parity bit is not normally used.

Stop bits. These are used to mark the end of each character in asynchronous transmissions. In the Figure, 1 stop bit is used. The alternatives of 1·5 or 2 stop bits are also shown.

Example WAN protocols

See also Topics on The Internet and Internet Security for HTTP and S-HTTP protocols, respectively.

TCP/IP

TCP/IP (Transmission Control Protocol/Internet Protocol) is the standard for communication between Internet host computers and is probably the most well known. It is actually a suite of several protocols. The importance of the Internet for network communications means that all modern operating systems provide support for TCP/IP, including those PC and Macintosh computer systems and network operating systems such as Novell Netware. Unix, as the standard operating system for most Internet host computers, has the TCP/IP protocol built in.

SMTP

SMTP stands for Simple Mail Transfer Protocol and is the standard for e-mail transmissions between servers and between clients (user e-mail software) and servers on the Internet.

UDP

UDP or User Datagram Protocol is used for the broadcast of data over IP (Internet Protocol) networks but unlike TCP, does not require that a connection is first established between sender and receiver (point to point). In other words, the data is transmitted without any guarantee that it will reach its destination. For this reason, UDP is referred to as a *connectionless* protocol (TCP is a *connection-orientated* protocol. Ethernet local area networks (Topic 24) also operate on a connectionless, broadcast principle.

X.25

This is a CCITT protocol for packet switching networks (Topic 51). X.25 Packet Switched networks allow remote devices to communicate with each other across high speed digital links without the expense of individual leased lines. Packet Switching is a technique whereby the network routes individual packets of data between different destinations based on addressing within each packet.

FTP

File Transfer Protocol (FTP) allows large amounts of information to be transferred between two computers very conveniently. FTP originated with the UNIX operating system and was used to transfer files of all types between remote computer systems. A popular application of FTP is for the uploading and downloading of Web site pages.

ASCII

This is only appropriate for *text* files, which contain no control characters. Thus it cannot be used to transfer files produced with a word processor, spreadsheet or graphics package. Neither can it transfer command (COM) or executable (EXE) files, or files in compressed (ZIP, for example) form. Apart from this, the protocol is not good at controlling errors.

Xmodem

This is a file-transfer protocol used for asynchronous communications. It is commonly used in communications packages. Its ability to find and correct errors makes it suitable for the transfer of files which must retain their integrity, such as program files.

Zmodem

This is one of the most advanced protocols, being much faster than Xmodem. Its error correction controls are absolutely reliable.

CCITT V42bis

This protocol includes a *data compression* (through encoding, data is reduced in volume) technique and error detection and correction. Both the sending and receiving modem must possess the error correction facility.

Local area network access protocols

Empty slot technique

This system is appropriate for networks in the shape of rings or loops, where messages are passed point-to-point in one direction. One or more empty *slots* or *packets* circulate continuously around the ring. When a device has information to transmit, it loads it into the slot, which carries it to its destination. At the time of loading, the destination address is placed in the slot and a full-empty flag is set to full. As the slot is passed from one repeater to another, no attempt will be made to load the slot as long as the flag is set to full. When the slot reaches the destination device, the devices repeater reads the information without clearing the slot. Before passing it on, the repeater sets a received message flag in the slot. When the slot again reaches the sending device, the flag is set to empty. The destination device can check that the message was received by checking the received flag. If the message was not successfully received, perhaps because the destination device was not listening, the sender device can check the acknowledgement flag and re-transmit in the next slot.

Token passing technique

This technique is also used for ring networks. An imaginary *token* is passed continuously around the ring. The token is recognised as such by the devices, as a unique character sequence. If a device is waiting to transmit, it catches the token and with it, the authority to send data. As long as one device has the token, no other device can send data. A receiving device acknowledges the receipt of a message by inverting a 1-bit field. Token Ring (IEEE 802.5 Standard) employs this access method.

Carrier sense multiple access (CSMA)

This method of access control is used on broadcast systems such as the bus network. Each device is theoretically free to transmit data to any other device at any time. Before attempting to transmit, a device's network card polls the network path to ensure that the destination device is free to receive data and that the communications channel is free. A device wishing to transmit must wait until both conditions exist. Generally such delay will be no more than a few millionths of a second.

❑   CSMA *Collision Detection* (CSMA-CD). Because of the possibility of collision through simultaneous transmission, a collision detection mechanism is used. When collision does occur, the devices involved cease transmission and try again some time later. In order to avoid the same collision, each device involved is made to wait a different time. If a number of retries prove unsuccessful, an error will be reported to the user. Ethernet (IEEE 802.3 Standard) networks use a form of CSMA/CD.

❏   CSMA *Collision Avoidance* (CSMA-CA). This strategy attempts to improve on that of CSMA-CD, which allows a device to place a packet onto the network path as soon as its network card detects it as being free. In the time between the test (measured in fractions of a microsecond) and the placing of the packet onto the path, another device's network card may have detected the path as free and be about to place another packet onto it. CSMA-CA seeks to remedy this problem by requiring a device's network card to test the path *twice*, once to see if the path is free and a second time, after alerting the device that it may use the network, but before the packet is placed onto the path.

✍Exercises

1. (i)   Give an example of a protocol that may be used for modem communications with the Internet and indicate typical values for the protocol. You may find it helpful to examine the settings on a typical PC with a modem connection.

   (ii)   Why is it necessary to set protocol values?

   (iii) What is the function of a parity pit?

2. (i)   Distinguish between synchronous and asynchronous transmission.

   (ii)   Why do most modems use asynchronous transmission?

3. If a computer uses a 56Kb/s modem to connect to the Internet, why may the this connection speed not always be achieved?

4. Which protocol is only appropriate for the transmission of simple text?

5. Name a protocol associated with packet switching networks.

6. Why is the TCP/IP protocol so important?

7. (i)   What does CSMA-CA stand for?

   (ii)   What is CSMA-CA?

   (iii) Which network topology uses CSMA?

Many networks, both private and public, provide additional services which give them the collective name of *value-added networks* or VANs. Megastream (see Topic 51) is a VAN provided by British Telecom. Other VANs provide specific services, such as *videotext* (see later), electronic mail, facsimile transmission, bulletin boards and bibliographic databases, for use by academics and researchers.

Bibliographic databases

These databases provide information on specialised or widely ranging subjects. For example, BLAISE, which is provided by the British Library, gives information on British book publications. Euronet Diane (Direct Information Access Network in Europe) provides information extracted from publications, research documents and so on, which may be of interest to specialists, such as scientists, engineers, economists and lawyers. Each extract provides the relevant bibliographic references to allow users to access the original sources more fully.

Bulletin boards

A bulletin board (BB) is simply a means by which users can, for example, exchange ideas, pass on information and buy or sell items to one another. Frequently, no charge is made. Chat lines are often included; this means that two users can carry on a conversation, through the use of screen and keyboard.

Teleconferencing

This service allows users to support a discussion over the telephone with a shared computer application, such as a word processor, spreadsheet or drawing package and a common whiteboard (an area of the display screen) visible to the conference users. The whiteboard is a comment or drawing area which users can use to illustrate points they wish to make. Each user has the ability to control the application, allowing co-operative development of, for example, a drawing or a spreadsheet model. Of course, such application sharing needs to be carefully managed and controlled to avoid inefficiency and time-wasting, which may result if users have different views on how the drawing or model should develop. The voice communications may be carried out over a conventional telephone network or over the Internet as part of the teleconferencing package. Microsoft's NetMeeting is built into the Explorer browser and supports all these facilities.

Video conferencing

Using computers with attached video cameras, microphones and speakers, conference participants are able to see and hear one another. The audio and video signals are carried over the Internet for real-time display as the conference takes place. The availability of cheap mini video cameras has radically increased the popularity of this service. Both tele and video conferencing have the potential to make significant savings for organisations in staffing, travel and accommodation costs. The main cost derives from local rate telephone charges.

Telex

Telex is a well established communications system which, rather like the public telephone network, allows subscribers to communicate with one another. There are over a million subscribers in this country at present. Each subscriber is given a telex code (you will often see it at the top of business letter headings next to the telephone number) and must have a teleprinter which is a combination of keyboard and printer. There is no screen, so all messages sent or received are printed onto hard copy.

The transmission rate of approximately 6 characters per second is slow compared with more modern telecommunications systems, but the limitations of keyboard entry and printer speed on the teleprinter, make any faster speed unnecessary. The main benefit of telex is that a permanent record of communications is kept and the receiver does not have to be on the spot when the message arrives. Its main disadvantage is that there is no storage facility for messages. Any transmission has to be printed as soon as it is transmitted so that if the receiver is faulty, the system comes to a halt. Although it is inferior to e-mail (see next paragraph), it is still the only method (apart from telephone) of instant communication with less developed countries, where Telex machines are still widely used.

Electronic mail (e-mail) services

E-mail systems based on computer networks are paper-less (except when a user requires hard copy). A major advantage is the facility for message storage if a destination terminal is busy, or has a temporary fault. When it is free, the message can be transmitted. Certain basic features can be identified as being common to all e-mail systems:

☐ a terminal for preparing, entering and storing messages. The terminal will be intelligent, possibly a microcomputer, mainframe terminal or dedicated word processor. In any event, it should have some word processing or text editing facilities to allow messages to be changed on screen before transmission. A printer may also be available for printing out messages received over the system;

☐ an electronic communication link with other workstations in the network and with the central computer controlling the system;

☐ a directory containing the electronic addresses of all network users;

☐ a central mailbox facility (usually the controlling computer) for the storage of messages in transit or waiting to be retrieved.

Ideally, the following facilities are available to e-mail users:

☐ messages are automatically dated upon transmission;

☐ messages are automatically acknowledged as being received when the recipient first accesses it from the terminal;

☐ multiple addressing, that is the facility to address a message to an identified group, without addressing each member of the group individually;

☐ priority rating to allow messages to be allocated different priorities according to their importance.

Networks require two particular features in order to support e-mail:

❑ a message storage facility to allow messages to be forwarded when the recipient is available;

❑ compatibility with a wide range of manufacturers' equipment. Devices attached to a network have to be able to talk to the communications network using protocols or standards of communication.

Benefits of e-mail

The following major benefits are generally claimed for e-mail systems:

❑ savings in stationery and telephone costs;

❑ more rapid transmission than is possible with conventional mail;

❑ e-mail can be integrated with other computer-based systems used in an organisation;

❑ all transmissions are recorded, so costs can be carefully controlled;

❑ e-mail allows staff to telework, that is, to work from home via a terminal;

❑ the recipient does not have to be present when a message is sent. Messages can be retrieved from the central mailbox when convenient.

Teletex

Teletex is nothing to do with teletext systems, such as Ceefax and Oracle (see Videotex). Teletex is similar to Telex, except that transmissions are quicker and cheaper and text is not restricted to upper case characters. It uses the pstn, but can also access packet switching networks and the Telex system through *gateways*. Teletex standards have been internationally agreed through the CCITT (International Consultative Committee on Telegraph and Telephone) and Teletex is now used in many countries throughout the world.

Electronic data interchange (EDI)

Similar to E-mail, EDI allows users to exchange business documents, such as invoices, delivery notes, orders and receipts over the telephone network. EDI can drastically reduce the volume of paperwork and business can be transacted much more quickly than is possible through the normal postal system. UK examples of EDI systems are:

❑ Tradanet, linking manufacturers, wholesalers, distributors and retailers;

❑ Brokernet, which links insurance companies and brokers;

❑ Drugnet, linking medical practices to pharmaceutical companies, allowing the provision of current information on various products;

❑ Factornet allows firms to deal with *factors* who buy outstanding customer bills at a discount; the factors then obtain payment from the debtor. Small firms find this service particularly useful as it enables them to improve their cash flow.

EFTPOS (electronic funds transfer at point-of-sale)

This service provides for the automatic debiting of customers' bank accounts at the checkout or point of sale. Many garages now have a device for reading the magnetic strip details on bank and credit cards. The system saves considerable time when contrasted with payments by cheque and as an alternative to cash, reduces the likelihood of theft. The retailer also has the assurance that the payment is authorised before the sale is made. Usually, a retailer will have a floor limit, or amount above which a telephone call needs to be made to the credit card company for authorisation of payment.

EFT (electronic funds transfer)

This system is used to transfer money between the branches of the same bank and between different banks. In the UK, the system is known as the Bankers Automated Clearing Service (BACS). The service is not restricted to bank use; organisations can pay their employees salaries directly into their bank or building society accounts. Business accounts can also be settled through this EFT system. Apart from the banks, other users usually link into the pstn through a dial-up connection (unless the volume of data justifies a leased line).

Facsimile transmission (FAX)

This service allows the transmission of facsimiles or exact copies of documents or pictures through a data communications network. Using a fax machine connected to a telephone line, the user simply dials the fax number of the recipient, waits for the correct signal and the document is fed though the fax machine and transmitted. The fax machine sends picture elements or pixels obtained by scanning the document in a series of parallel lines; a synchronised fax machine at the other end prints a facsimile from those pixels. Fax/modems allow computer communication by fax with other fax modems or with conventional fax machines.

Teletext

Teletext systems, such as Ceefax and Oracle, provide a public service based on a central computer database, which users can access via an ordinary television set with special adapter and keypad. The database consists of thousands of pages or frames of information which are kept up to date by Information Providers. Pages can be accessed and displayed on the television screen through the use of the keypad, directly via page number or through a series of hierarchical indexes. Major subject areas include Sport, News, Business, Leisure and Entertainment, Finance and Travel. Pages are transmitted using spare bandwidth unused by television pictures, in carousels or groups. The user may have to wait some time while the carousel containing the required page is transmitted. Its major drawback is that communication is *one-way*. The user cannot send messages to the database, only receive.

Viewdata or videotex

A viewdata system is based on a central computer database, which provides pages of information on a variety of subjects, including sport, travel and business, for access by subscribers. As an *interactive* system, users typically access services using simple, low cost, viewdata terminals, or microcomputer systems equipped with special software. Users connect with a viewdata *gateway* through the public telephone network. The major public viewdata system in the UK is

Prestel. It uses the Teletext *alpha mosaic* character set. The graphics it produces appear similar to Lego building blocks. Developed by British Telecom, Prestel is now technologically out of date and is used, mainly, as a *gateway* to third party databases, for example, Electronic Yellow Pages, and CitiService (a financial database). Apart from information provision, the following services may be available through a viewdata system:

❑ Electronic mail. Viewdata users can transmit electronic messages to other users in the system, using such things as bulletin boards and chat lines. The British Campus 2000, which links together schools in Britain and other countries is an example of a viewdata electronic mail system.

❑ Paying bills, purchasing tickets, ordering goods and other such transactions.

❑ The distribution of computer programs. Centrally stored computer programs can be transferred to users' microcomputer systems so that they can later be used independently of the viewdata system. This is sometimes referred to as *telesoftware*.

In France, a combined teletext and viewdata system is called Antiope, and another viewdata system, available since 1984, is called Teletel. The latter system is very widely used, with more than eight million terminals attached to the system. The US service is called Prodigy and in Japan it is called Captain.

✍️Exercises

1. Research a range of network services, including bulletin boards, e-mail, teleconferencing and video conferencing and find commercial examples of each. Produce a simple brochure describing these services and their application and potential benefits for a business or other type of organisation.

2. Telex is an outdated technology but still widely used. Why?

3. Briefly describe the main applications of EFTPOS and EFT.

4. Distinguish between videotex and teletext services and indicate the relative benefits and drawbacks of each.

Networks - benefits and drawbacks

Benefits

Computer networks allow:

- ❑ sharing of appropriate *software, hardware resources;*

- ❑ sharing of common *data*;

- ❑ sharing of *processing* activity;

- ❑ electronic communication, including e-mail and video conferencing

Sharing hardware and software

In a LAN, particularly, there are opportunities to share hardware and software. This is because resources tend to be distributed over a small area; it is reasonable to ask users to share a printing resource if the printers serving them are within the same room, or perhaps in an adjacent room. It could be argued that the rapid fall in hardware costs has, to a certain extent, reduced the need for sharing peripherals, such as hard disk drives and printers.

A number of factors concerning computer usage, storage and printing confirm that resource sharing remains a major benefit of a LAN.

- ❑ Applications. The range of computer applications and the number of users is continually increasing.

- ❑ Software packages. The increasing sophistication of software means that large amounts of disk space are needed for each package. Network versions of a package are cheaper (per user) than those for stand-alone systems.

- ❑ Storage technologies. Although the costs of high capacity hard drives have fallen dramatically, there are still savings to be made through sharing. A shared, large volume hard drive can satisfy the storage needs of all users on a network

- ❑ Printers. Most users require only occasional use of a printer, so there is little point in providing one for each. This is particularly the case for colour printers. A laser printer can produce the high quality output demanded by many applications and it operates at speeds which allow sharing to take place, without unreasonable delay for users.

- ❑ Other devices, such as scanners and plotters are likely to be used only occasionally and sharing makes good economic sense.

Sharing data

A major benefit of all types of network concerns the sharing of data, frequently from central-ised databases. Data can also be regarded as a resource, so sharing it can bring similar benefits to those available from sharing hardware. For example, a common data store supports the use of a *database* system (Topic 22), which itself reduces the need for data duplication.

Traditional computer processing methods require that each application has its own files and this results in the duplication of many data items and the updating process. For example, in a retail business both the stock control and purchasing departments make use of commodity details such as Stock Codes, Descriptions and Prices; if separate files are maintained by each department, a change in, for example, the Price of a commodity requires more than one input.

A database system allows these details (a single copy of each commodity's Stock Code, Description and Price) to be shared by all departments that need them. Even if database methods are not used, the storage of the various application files in a common disk store, means that they can, if desired, be made available to all users on a network. For an organisation with numerous branches, each with its own processing facility, there needs to be a central resource, where the results of processing at branches can be merged (and possibly re-distributed) to give corporate (across the organisation, as a whole) information.

Sharing processing activity

Host computer with intelligent terminals

A host computer with intelligent terminals allows processing to be carried out at remote sites; as such it comes under the heading of WAN. The distribution of processing work may be very limited, such that the majority is processed by a central computer. For example, terminals connected to a remote host computer often have their own processing power, file storage and printing facilities. Usually, before being transmitted to the host computer for the updating of files, *transaction* data will require some *validation* and other accuracy checks and this can be done at the terminal. Microcomputers equipped with suitable software are often used to *emulate* mainframe intelligent terminals, with the added advantage of being useable as stand-alone systems, when not communicating with the mainframe.

Alternatively, the work may be equally shared amongst a number of powerful computer systems, which then merge the results of their separate efforts.

Client-server network

A *client-server* LAN aims to exploit the full processing power of each computer in the network, including the *file server* and the user workstations or *clients*. This is effected by dividing the processing tasks between a client and a server. The client, a microcomputer in its own right (as opposed to the *dumb* terminal found in older mainframe systems) provides the user with a completely separate facility for running applications. The file server which could be a microcomputer, minicomputer, or mainframe, enhances the client component by providing additional services.

These services are traditionally offered by minicomputer and mainframe systems operating a *time-sharing* operating system; they include shared file management, data sharing between users, network administration and security.

The major benefit of a client-server network is that the power of the client and server machines is used jointly to carry out the processing of an application. Interactive activities, for example, construction of a spreadsheet or the word processing of a report, are carried out by the client machine; having logged onto the network, the user can load the required applications software from the file server.

Electronic communication

E-mail is made possible by computer networks and is the most widely used and important form of electronic communication. Its use can bring great benefits to business and other organisations. For example, a business can communicate with its clients, other businesses and external agencies more flexibly and effectively than is possible through conventional means.

Staff can be away from the office and still have access to their e-mail and the business systems which are essential to their work. For example, sales staff can have access to central database files and keep up to date on price or specification changes. Electronic communication allows the provision of high standards of customer service. For example, orders received through an on-line store can be acknowledged quickly and even automatically.

Drawbacks of networks

Potential loss of shared resources

The main disadvantage of the computer network arises from its major advantage of resource sharing. When a resource is shared, its breakdown or failure affects all users who share it. The significance of any loss will depend on the structure of the network and the function of the resource that fails. For example, failure of a central computer which holds all the programs and data will be more catastrophic than the breakdown of a shared printer. Some networks will break down entirely if there is a single break in the cabling that connects network devices to one another, but others reduce the potential for total failure by providing alternative routes by which data can travel.

Increased security risk

A network increases the number of points at which unauthorised users can gain access. In the case of a LAN occupying a single room, physical security is quite straightforward and user activity can be controlled through administrative procedures and software controls, such as passwords.

In the case of a WAN, control can be more difficult when users can gain access from remote locations. Software controls play a major part, but physical security can be more difficult. Private networks which can be accessed through the Internet (*extranets*) are particularly vulnerable when the possible entry points are so numerous. To protect private networks from unauthorised access through public networks, 'firewalls' and encryption may be used. A firewall is a combination of hardware and software systems which monitor attempts to gain entry and restrict access to authorised users. Encryption is the scrambling of data so that it cannot be deciphered by electronic 'eavesdropping'.

Slowed response from network overload

In any particular network, a shared resource such as a file server has the processing power and capacity to handle a given maximum workload. When this maximum is exceeded, perhaps through the attachment of more workstations to the network, or an increased number of requests from workstations, the response time will be degraded. The response time is the length of time a user has to wait, for example, for a file to download or a document to print. Ideally, a network user should have to wait no longer than would be the case with a stand-alone machine.

✍ Exercises

1. (i) List the four main resource-sharing benefits of computer networks, illustrating each benefit with an example from an organisation with which you are familiar.

   (ii) Identify and explain circumstances when certain resources may be difficult to share.

   (iii) Research prices of single user and network versions of a range of software packages.

2. (i) Identify and briefly describe a variety of computer network configurations which allow sharing of processing activity and distinguish between them.

   (ii) For each configuration described in (i), suggest an appropriate application or user organisation.

3. With the use of examples, identify benefits of electronic communication in comparison with conventional methods.

4. A small organisation is changing its present stand-alone, PC-based information systems to a client-server network. What is the main risk posed by this move?

5. To simplify staff access, a company has set up a Web site to provide Internet access to those information systems. Access to company resources will be through a login name and password. Name and briefly explain the function of two other methods to enforce security against unauthorised access.

6. Under what circumstances may a network's performance deteriorate?

Section 7

Social and legal issues

Topics

Although the agricultural and industrial revolutions of the 19th century transformed the way people lived and worked, the changes occurred over many decades. The ICT revolution is also creating massive changes, but at a speed which makes it more difficult for many people and organisations to adapt sufficiently quickly. Prediction of change is difficult, but it may be helpful to consider some of the predictions that were being made a decade ago. The major benefits of computer technology were seen as:

- ❑ increased productivity;
- ❑ higher standards of living;
- ❑ cleaner and safer working conditions;
- ❑ shorter working hours and more leisure time.

The last of these have proved to be completely inaccurate in that most employed people in the UK are now working longer hours and often under greater pressure than used to be the case. Causal factors may be scarcity of resources, increased consumer expectations, an ageing population and global competition. Possible negative consequences of computerisation were considered to be:

- ❑ polarisation of people into two groups - the technologically advantaged and disadvantaged;
- ❑ increased crime and delinquency rates;
- ❑ threat of a totalitarian state;
- ❑ loss of personal privacy.

It is the first and last of these concerns which stem directly from the ICT revolution. It is reasonable to say that the totalitarian state is not considered to be a present threat in Western societies, although personal privacy and freedom of information continue to be issues of concern. The impact of ICT on personal privacy and legislation to protect it are discussed in Topic 31. Division of society into the technologically skilled and unskilled is already a reality and removing this division is thought to be important for the success of an industrial economy and the welfare of its society.

Although computers have been part of everyday life for decades, the advent of the personal computer, the exponential growth of the Internet and other communication networks have produced the most significant changes in the way we live, work and play. The impact of ICT on employment is dealt with in Topic 30. Some of the other major social changes are briefly described below.

E-commerce

Many businesses including, for example, supermarkets, travel agents, wine merchants, booksellers and car sales companies now sell their products through e-commerce web sites. With a computer, Internet connection and Web browser, consumers can visit these virtual stores and view, select and pay for goods which can often be delivered within 24 to 48 hours. Until the 1960s it was common practice for shops to make home deliveries on orders taken over the telephone and Internet shopping has the potential to reduce the volume of traffic visiting, for example, out of town shopping centres. It is extremely unlikely that demand for conventional 'bricks and mortar' will disappear because Internet shopping provides no social interaction and many consumers will wish to view and handle many types of goods before buying.

More formally, e-commerce can be defined as *"conducting business transactions over electronic networks"*. E-commerce is fundamentally changing the way business operates. Because of e-commerce, businesses of all sizes are changing their internal operations and their relationships with suppliers and customers. When properly implemented, e-commerce can improve the efficiency of all stages of the business process, from design and manufacture to retailing and distribution.

E-commerce is playing a major role in the establishment of a global economy. The major catalyst for the expansion of international electronic retailing is the Internet. Its users, the number of which is rapidly increasing, can communicate with the Web sites of countless organisations all over the world, and it is through these *World Wide Web* sites that companies can provide 'on-line stores'. The Web-based on-line stores are accessible by Web browsers, such as Microsoft Explorer and Netscape Communicator and a standard feature of all modern home computers. An Internet store provides all the facilities that the customer needs, including a product catalogue, a 'virtual shopping basket' and a secure credit card payment system (see Topic 53 on Internet Security).

Business to business e-commerce

Business to business e-commerce is well established and one of the fastest growing areas. Many office equipment and consumables suppliers, for example, are able to take orders on-line and provide direct delivery to business customers. Because transactions such as the submission and settlement of invoices are all conducted electronically, the participating businesses enjoy significant cost savings.

Benefits of e-commerce for business

Businesses can benefit tremendously from e-commerce in many important ways, reducing costs and improving efficiency. For instance, expensive printed catalogues and service guides can be replaced by a single, up-to-date electronic product database that is accessible at all times. Many businesses use mail shots to inform customers of new products or special offers, a time consuming and expensive exercise. Instead the latest information can be held on the company web site and existing customers can obtain up-to-date information on new products or services at any time. A business can maintain closer contact with its customers and suppliers, and direct communication allows improved pre- and post-sales support.

Direct selling shortens the supply chain so delivery times and costs are reduced. Staffing costs can be a fraction of those for conventional sales outlets. For example, Web site software can handle routine sales transactions automatically, leaving sales staff to deal with more complex orders.

E-commerce also provides opportunities for entirely new products and services. These include network supply and support services, web site design and hosting, and various types of on-line information services.

Business to consumer e-commerce

Business to consumer e-commerce, or electronic retailing, is expanding rapidly as businesses become informed of the new opportunities it presents for market expansion. Physical products, information and various services are all available for purchase over the Internet. For example, consumers can buy cars, books, CDs, wine, stock market information and computer software from numerous Internet shops.

Benefits of e-commerce for consumers

Consumers can gain considerable benefits from electronic commerce. The range of products that can be bought on-line is continually being extended. There are virtual stores all over the Internet offering a wide range of goods, including books, wine, newspapers, cakes, computer hardware, software and even cars. Similarly, numerous services are available on-line. These include education, entertainment and information services.

There is the convenience of 24-hour home shopping and access to a wider range of goods and services than is conventionally available within their locality. A conventional shopping chain rarely offers its full product range at every shop, whereas a virtual shop can make its full product range available globally. The consumer is given global choice. If a product or service is available from a number of suppliers, the consumer can choose without regard to geographical location.

Consumers may benefit from lower prices because electronic commerce drastically reduces transaction costs. A transaction involving human interaction may be measured in £s, but the same transaction carried out electronically can cost a few pence.

Orders may be fulfilled more quickly. Direct supply from manufacturer to customer can also be effected with mail order or telephone order catalogues, but the human and paper-based transactions are more costly and involve longer delays than is possible with e-commerce. For products that can be delivered electronically, such as software, video and newspapers, the time delay between order and delivery can be reduced to an absolute minimum, and intermediaries in the traditional supply chain are entirely redundant.

By bringing products and services to the home, electronic commerce also has the potential to benefit the disabled, the elderly and those living in remote areas.

Social and employment costs of e-commerce

Clearly, some of the above benefits will not apply to all consumers and there will be social costs as well.

❏   If residents of rural communities choose to shop on the Internet local stores may be unable to compete and have to close. Not everyone will have, or wish to have, access to the Internet and such closures will bring serious social deprivation to some.

❏   Many aspects of electronic shopping are automated and fewer staff are needed to process orders. Much customer support can be provided through the Web site, which further reduces staff requirements. Of course, e-commerce will also create jobs, but the skills and working practices are very different from those in many traditional businesses.

❑ E-commerce businesses may have access to global markets, but they may also be subject to global competition. This means that the business must be able to respond much more quickly to changes in consumer demand and to the activities of its competitors. Working practices, therefore, tend to demand a much more flexible and multi-skilled approach than is usual in traditional business.

❑ E-commerce relies entirely on the operation and effectiveness of electronic systems and there are greater demands for people with suitable technical skills. Rapid delivery is considered to be a vital requirement if an e-commerce business is to keep its customers so jobs in distribution are likely to increase.

Video conferencing

Video conferencing has the potential to make significant savings for organisations in staffing, travel and accommodation costs. Working practices in 'virtual meetings' have to be significantly different and require much clearer and guided discussion for them to be effective. Some retraining may be necessary, not only to use the equipment, but also to adopt the particular etiquette and techniques which are needed for effective use of the medium.

Meeting people electronically does not allow the same degree of social interaction and it could be argued that, taken to extreme, such social separation would be a significant cost. On the other hand, video conferencing allows higher quality interaction between people who would otherwise not meet. For example, small schools in remote areas may lack specialist teaching in some subjects and video conferencing allows that teaching to be provided.

New employment opportunities will be in the production, sale and installation of video conferencing systems, as well as in support and training services.

E-mail

Conventional postal service, or 'snail mail', deliveries take at least 24 hours, whereas e-mail messages can be delivered in a few seconds, even to the other side of the world. More detailed information can be given in an e-mail than is possible with a telephone call and document, image and other files can be attached for viewing by the recipient. Although communication may be easier, it could be argued that electronic communications are not a substitute for real, face-to-face, discussion. In part, video conferencing allows participants to see one another as well as communicate electronically, but subtle facial expressions and changes in body language are more difficult to detect.

The majority of the population in the UK now own a mobile phone and the development of e-mail and Internet communications through the cellular telephone networks will increase the use of those services.

Automated and Internet banking services

An increasingly popular service is telephone banking which uses an interactive voice response (IVR) system. Customers can obtain account balances, order statements or cheque books and make money transfers by spoken commands or more reliably by tone entry with the telephone keypad. Interaction is very carefully controlled by the system and callers are interrogated for precise information, such as their account number. By using a highly structured series of questions and answers, IVR systems only need to recognise key values such as the digits from 0 to 9 and the words 'yes' and 'no'. A caller's spoken request for information is digitised and sent to the host computer; the response is converted into synthesised speech and read out to the caller. IVR systems speak by forming pre-recorded words and phrases into sentences and playing them. For example, a request for an account balance may bring the response "Your balance is", followed by a series of digits which were recorded separately, interspersed by the word "pounds" and "credit" or "debit", as appropriate.

The move towards automated services such as telephone banking, Internet banking, ATMs (automated teller machines) and the closure of many bank branches has serious implications for some sections of society and areas of the country where access to ICT systems is limited or non-existent.

As more and more people opt for the convenience of conducting their banking business by telephone or through the Internet, the major banks are undertaking a branch closure programme which could have devastating effects on many rural and urban communities. It is generally recognised that when branch banking services are withdrawn from a small town or village, local businesses find it difficult to survive. If people have to visit another town to go to the bank, it is likely that they will do their shopping at the same time and local businesses lose their custom. Elderly people and those without private transport also experience increased hardship. In poorer urban communities, loss of a branch banking facility can have similar effects and prevent economic and social regeneration. In some states of the USA, the problem is recognised and bank branches are seen as an important social facility and key to the survival and recovery of otherwise deprived communities.

Booking systems

If you go to a travel agent to book a seat on a major international airline, the travel agent will need to check the airline for the availability of the flight that you require. This normally involves communicating with the airlines computer to obtain up-to-date flight information. Remember that the same thing can be happening from all over the world: numerous travel agents could be accessing the same airlines computer at the same time, several of them even trying to book seats on the same flight that you want.

To cope with this type of demand, the airline will use a mainframe computer allowing on-line communication with each travel agent via the public telephone network. Each travel agency will have one or more terminals connected by modem to the airlines computer. Flight reservations will be performed in *real-time*, that is, the mainframe's flight and passenger information will be updated immediately to prevent the possibility of double-booking a seat on a particular flight. This ensures that the information that the travel agent obtains will be completely accurate and reliable. This form of processing, where a master file is updated immediately, is called *transaction processing*.

The process of reserving a seat on a flight is further complicated by the fact that several airlines might have scheduled flights to your destination, each offering different flight times, facilities and costs. Rather than contacting each one separately, a process that could take a considerable amount of time, the travel agent links into a wide area network(WAN) which connects the main computers of the different airlines. This allows the agent to choose the most appropriate flight for you and book it immediately. Though each airline in the system might have a different passenger reservation information system, the network software presents the same information format to the travel agents and takes care of transferring data in the correct format to the individual computer systems of the airlines.

When you have decided on your choice of airline and flight, your details are entered at the travel agent's terminal. While this is happening, other travel agents are prevented from accessing that particular flight record. On completion of the reservation, the flight record becomes available again. Booking cancellations and changes are handled in the same way. Your ticket, which will have been produced by the airline's computer, is usually sent out to you a few days prior to the departure date. Individual airline's computers also produce passenger lists automatically for use at the departure airports.

An airline's master passenger reservation and flight information file will be held on a high-capacity magnetic disk drive. For backup purposes, in case the master file is in some way lost or partly erased, or the disk drive fails, a separate disk drive will be used to hold an exact duplicate of the master file, and this duplicate file will be updated at the same time as the other master file. This duplication is necessary because the master file will be in constant use, night and day, and there will be no opportunity to stop updating it in order to make a backup on magnetic tape. For the same reasons of security, there will also be a duplicate main computer immediately ready to be used if the other one fails for some reason. Because of the importance of the fast response time required of the system, it will almost certainly be used exclusively for passenger booking purposes, and it will have been designed to operate without break, 24 hours a day, every day of the year.

Similar real-time systems are used by holiday firms, some of which are able to offer thousands of holidays all over the world. Travel agents must have access to accurate information regarding the availability of all the holidays on offer. Again it is important to ensure that exactly the same holiday is not sold to more than one customer, so the booking file held on the holiday company's main computer must be completely up-to-date.

ICT in medicine

Computer-controlled life support systems can monitor a patient's condition via a number of sensor devices checking on, for example, pulse rate, body temperature and blood pressure. This frees nursing staff for other duties and has the benefit of providing a continuous monitoring facility. Computer-assisted diagnosis systems make use of artificial intelligence to assist a physician in diagnosing a patient's condition. This raises the question of how much reliance should be placed on computers with artificial intelligence. It seems reasonable that a doctor should use an expert system as an aid to diagnosis, but less reasonable that a treatment decision should be made on the basis of computer diagnosis alone.

A particularly exciting development involves the use of computers to assist the plastic surgeon in the repair of facial injuries or deformities. The patient's face is scanned by a camera and the image digitised for display on a computer screen in three-dimensional form. This image can be rotated or tilted on screen by the surgeon and experimental 'cuts' made, the results of which can then be viewed on screen from any angle. In this way, a plastic surgeon can study the results of a variety of strategies before making a single mark on the patient.

Video conferencing facilities allow the conduct of operations to be monitored and guided remotely. For example, a specialist in one hospital could assist and guide a surgeon who is carrying out an emergency operation in another. Micro-surgical techniques (keyhole surgery) are made possible with the use of a tiny camera and wire-guided instruments, which can be inserted through tiny incisions or the normal orifices in a patient's body.

ICT in education

Computers have provided many educational opportunities in a wide variety of areas. A good example of the application of the computer in education is the use of the computer language, Logo. Turtle graphics in Logo allows children to experiment with and understand mathematical concepts in an enjoyable way. The Logo programmer, for example, "shows" the computer how to draw geometrical shapes, and thus acquires an understanding of geometry as well as certain types of problem solving. Writing a computer program involves careful analysis of the problem and careful planning of the proposed solution to the problem.

Another approach is to provide repetitive drills designed to allow a student to practise certain concepts. For young children this could be spelling simple words, or doing simple additions and subtractions, with correct answers being rewarded with a pleasing noise or by a graphics character doing something amusing. Learning foreign language vocabulary can be assisted with this type of program. The student may be asked by the computer program to provide the French word when given the equivalent English word, or vice versa. In geography, a map might be provided and the student must provide the names of marked cities or mountain ranges, or a biology student may be asked to name or position internal organs, muscles and bones on a picture of the human body. Such programs provide the correct answers so that a student can learn by his or her mistakes.

Graphics programs which allow pictures to be "painted" on the screen using a mouse allow students to experiment with design using colour and shapes. The advantage of using a computer for this type of activity is that mistakes can be corrected very easily and there is no real limit to the supply of paper and paint. Word processors and DTP packages also encourage the development of design skills, this time with text layout and styles.

Self-study material can use a microcomputer system to present textual and pictorial information. This type of software is often produced using authoring languages which are designed to present information and allow progress tests to be included in the course. Authoring systems usually allow the progress of the student to be monitored using test scores and prevent the student from going on to more advanced stages until previous stages have been mastered. This form of program is often termed computer-based training (CBT). The Internet has increased opportunities for remote delivery of education, which is particularly useful for mature students who may have to combine their education with a job or running a home.

ICT in the home

ICT has had a dramatic effect on devices used in the home. An increasing number of electrical appliances and gadgets contain microprocessors. The list includes: telephones and answering machines with a wide variety of functions, such as storing numbers, automatically dialing or re-dialing numbers and using voice synthesis to tell you how many messages you have and at what time they were recorded; washing machines that can be set to automatically wash and dry clothes according to a number of different washing programmes; dish washers, also with many different computer-controlled programmes; cookers with digital timers and time displays; microwave ovens with programmable cooking times and cooking intensities; video cameras with numerous automatic functions; stereo music systems with computer control of different types of sound reproduction, selectable CD track programmes, preset radio stations, timers and automatic recording facilities; mobile phones with digital displays; televisions with videotex; video recorders with slow-motion control and automatic, timed recording features and still cameras with digital storage; digitally controlled sewing machines; calculators, often with hundreds of scientific and mathematical functions; PCs with enormous computing power and a wide variety of software ranging from complex engineering design programs to adventure games; games consoles which rival the graphics quality of arcade machines; door chimes that can play a variety of different popular tunes; burglar alarms and other sophisticated home security systems; wrist watches that can store telephone numbers or short memos, or contain a built-in electronic calculator; chess-playing computers that play at good club level or even better.

The list is almost endless and it is growing all the time. Many of these microprocessor-controlled applications are labour-saving devices, while others are for leisure and other purposes. Home entertainment features high on the list of applications, but cheap personal computers have also allowed more people to use the home as an office. Communication equipment, such as modems and fax machines, mean that many occupations are possible from the home. Computer programmers, writers, graphic designers and architects for example can all gain access to more powerful computers via networks if necessary, or just use a PC if appropriate software is available. Working from home has obvious benefits for single parents or disabled people who find it difficult to commute to a place of employment.

✍️Exercises

1. (i) Briefly describe the components of e-commerce and types of organisations and individuals who use it
   (ii) Draw up a table of what you judge to be the benefits and drawbacks for (a) businesses and (b) society in general.
2. Commercial banking has changed radically in the way it offers its services. Describe the major changes which have occurred over the last few years and discuss the consequences (winners and losers) these changes have had for
   (i) bank employees
   (ii) customers.
3. Research and document the development of ICT in different areas of society, including medicine, the home and education, noting the potential impact of these developments on society or sections of it.

The rapid advances in computer and communications technologies have occurred during periods of considerable change in the industrialised economies and although many different factors have conspired towards the generally higher levels of unemployment, ICT has undoubtedly played a major role. No attempt is made in this text to relate particular numbers of employed or unemployed directly to the influence of ICT but its effects on and implications for employment patterns and prospects are considered. In general, introduction of new ICT systems into organisations may result in: a need for staff re-training; re-deployment; de-skilling; re-grading and changes in career prospects; redundancy; changes in job satisfaction; new job opportunities; introduction of teleworking.

ICT is in common use in most areas of work, but the effects on some are more radical than on others. For example, skills requirements for secretarial staff have increased quickly, but steadily, over the last few years. So, word processing skills have been a universal qualification for secretarial work for several years but job specifications may now include, for example, e-mail, Internet browsing and desktop publishing.

In some specialised areas such as banking, automatic teller machines (ATMs), telephone and Internet banking have drastically reduced staffing requirements. On the other hand, many new job opportunities have been created in call centres, set up by a variety of organisations to provide customer support .

Re-training

Obviously, the amount and type of re-training that is needed will vary with current skill and knowledge levels. Staff who already make daily use of ICT will learn to use new systems much more rapidly than those whose involvement with ICT has been minimal or non-existent.

Familiarity with computers in general and expertise in the use of some software, provides an individual with the confidence to quickly pick up skills for new applications as they arise.

Re-deployment

ICT generally reduces manpower requirements but increases the opportunities for business expansion. Unless new job specifications cannot be met by existing staff, perhaps because they require radically different aptitudes and skills, it generally makes more sense for an organisation to redeploy staff. Furthermore, rigid job demarcations have largely disappeared and staff in many organisations are expected to be multi-skilled and able to fulfil a variety of roles.

De-skilling

The judgement as to whether or not a job is de-skilled by the introduction of ICT is a rather subjective one. However, if ICT is being used as a tool and is not the primary skill, such as when an architect uses a computer-aided design system, then it cannot really be viewed as de-skilling. Where a job's primary skills are largely taken over by technology and the employee takes on a monitoring role, real de-skilling has resulted. For example, when a car is serviced electronic testing systems provide the mechanic with information on faults; the skills of deductive fault-finding are largely lost. Global positioning systems (GPS) use satellite communications to monitor a ship's position and although the captain and certain officers need to retain their navigation skills (if the GPS system breaks down), much of the time the skills are not needed.

Re-grading and career prospects

Sometimes, improvements in job gradings are introduced in order to encourage staff to accept the use of more ICT. At the same time, career prospects in many areas of office work are generally diminished. In the banking industry, the prospects for managerial jobs have fallen dramatically in the last two decades and currently, few clerical staff who did not enter the job with a degree have prospects for managerial posts.

Redundancy

A business may need to make staff redundant because ICT has, for example:

❏   radically changed job skill requirements and re-training is not considered viable;

❏   improved efficiency (output is maintained or increased with fewer staff);

❏   been introduced by competitors who have then taken some or all of the business's market share;

❏   been poorly implemented and created inefficiencies or administrative breakdowns that have caused the business to fail;

❏   removed the need for the business's products or services. For example, wholesalers and other 'middle men' in supply chains are vulnerable to direct selling by manufacturers over the Internet.

Changes in job satisfaction

Whether a job is made more or less satisfying by the introduction of ICT has to be a highly subjective judgement, but it is reasonable to assume that a reduction in task variety and the redundancy of experience and skill may well result in a less satisfying job.

For example, if a traditionally skilled tool machinist has to retrain as a CNC (computer numerical control) machine operator who supervises and services the machines, he would have a cleaner, less dangerous job, but it is fair to suggest that he may gain less satisfaction from his work. Conversely, young people without the experience of the old skills will suffer no such loss of job satisfaction.

Some jobs are made more interesting and demanding by the use of ICT. Graphic designers, for example, continue to use their primary skills but are able to use the technology to extend design possibilities and use them in print and electronic media, perhaps branching into Web design and multimedia..

New job opportunities

In the last few years, the accelerated expansion of the Internet and associated computer technologies that we now refer to as ICT has resulted in the creation of many new job opportunities for:

- ❑ computer hardware and software engineers;

- ❑ network designers and developers;

- ❑ graphic designers;

- ❑ Web designers;

- ❑ multimedia designers.

Internet Service Providers (ISPs) and wholly Internet-based e-commerce traders are examples of the entirely new kinds of business that have helped to create these jobs. The computer and networking industries have been major creators of 'high tech' jobs for many years and other areas of employment opportunity are found in computer engineering, systems software development, computer sales and support services, computer science research and education.

Teleworking

At present, millions of office workers travel by car or public transport to their respective places of work. Nearly all organisations carry out their business from centralised offices because information needs to be exchanged, usually on paper documents and decisions need to be made, which requires consultation between individuals. Through the use of telecommunications (most importantly, the Internet) and centrally available computer databases, some forward-looking organisations allow their staff to work from home, using a computer terminal. There are a number of advantages to be gained from home-based work.

Advantages of tele-working:

- ❑ savings in travel costs;

- ❑ no necessity to live within travelling distance;

- ❑ flexible hours of work;

- ❑ equality between men and women. Bringing up children can be a shared activity;

- ❑ savings for the organisation in terms of expensive city-centre offices;

- ❑ opportunities for the disabled, who may otherwise find it difficult to find employment in conventional work places.

Disadvantages of tele-working:

- ❑ loss of social contact;

- ❑ need for quiet workroom at home. This can be difficult in a small flat;

- ❑ the difficulty of office accommodation is compounded when two or three members of a family all work from home;

- ❑ blurring of boundary between work and home life. Self-discipline is vital if each is not to interfere with the other.

- ❑ loss of visible status for senior staff in terms of an office and other staff to command.

✍️Exercises

The first two exercises are designed to be group exercises.

1. Research and draw up a list of industries, service and manufacturing, which have been involved in radical changes in patterns of work and employment in recent years.

   Read the news regularly and monitor the performance of some of the new high-tec businesses, including .com companies. Note job gains or losses in these and more traditional industries and the reasons given by the industry and government commentators for their occurrence. In the case of job losses, there will be reasons given, such as lack of productivity (which may be owing to lack of investment in ICT) or cheaper competition from developing countries. Clearly it is difficult to attribute such changes to one particular cause, but it may be clear, for example, that the opening of a new customer service centre, or an electronics component factory can be attributed to the growth in ICT usage.

2. Discuss some of the difficulties of developing and sustaining the ICT skill levels needed for a modern economy, when the technology changes so quickly and continually, particularly in a society with an ageing population.

3. A former office worker has decided to work from home, which she shares with her husband and two children; they are both at secondary school. She is to work as a *teleworker,* for her present employer and her working hours will be from 9.00 to 5.00, Monday to Friday. She is to use a spare bedroom as a small office and this will accommodate the computer system, linked to the company offices. They are located in a city centre, 5 miles from her home.

   Identify three benefits and two drawbacks which she is likely to experience from the new arrangement.

Legislation relating to ICT

This section describes the purposes of the following UK laws:

❑   Computer Misuse Act (1990)

❑   Data Protection Act (1984 and 1998)

❑   Copyright, Designs and Patents Act (1988)

Computer Misuse Act (1990)

The Act identifies three categories of offence:

❑   Unauthorised access to computer material.

❑   Unauthorised access with intent to commit or facilitate commission of further offences.

❑   Unauthorised modification of computer material.

The Act deals with the general crime of 'hacking'. The first category of offence deals with un-authorised access to a computer system, its programs and data. An offence is committed if a person performs any computer function with the intent of securing unauthorised access to any program or data held in any computer. The second category covers the offence of persistent hacking. The third category covers the alteration of data to which a hacker has gained access.

These crimes are punishable by prison sentences.

Computer fraud and protection measures

Computer fraud is invariably committed for financial gain, but unlike some forms of fraud, the perpetrator(s) will make considerable efforts to prevent discovery of any loss by the victim. The rewards for such efforts may be complete freedom from prosecution, or at least a delay in discovery of the fraud and a consequent chance of escape. Unless proper controls and checks are implemented, computer systems are particularly vulnerable to fraudulent activity, because much of the time processing and its results are hidden. The following section examines some methods for committing fraud and the measures which can be taken to foil them.

To extract money from a financial accounting system requires its diversion into fictitious, but accessible accounts. To avoid detection, appropriate adjustments must be made to ensure that the accounts still balance. Sometimes, fraudulent activity may involve the misappropriation of goods rather than cash. Frequently, the collusion of several people is necessary to effect a fraud, because responsibility for different stages of the processing cycle is likely to be shared. Some common methods of fraud are given below.

❑   Bogus data entry. This may involve entering additional, unauthorised data, modifying valid data or preventing its entry altogether. Such activity may take place during the data preparation or data entry stages.

❏ Bogus output. Output may be destroyed or altered to prevent discovery of fraudulent data entry or processing.

❏ Alteration of files. For example, an employee may alter his salary grading in the payroll file or adjust the amount owing in a colluding customers account.

❏ Program patching. This method requires access to program coding and a detailed knowledge of the functioning of the program in question, as well as the necessary programming skill. By introducing additional code, in the form of a conditional subroutine, certain circumstances determined by the perpetrator can trigger entry to the subroutine, which may, for example, channel funds to a fictitious account.

❏ Suspense accounts. Rejected and unreconciled transactions tend to be allocated to suspense accounts until they can be dealt with; fraud may be effected by directing such transactions to the account of someone colluding in the crime. Transactions can be tampered with at the input stage to ensure their rejection and allocation to the suspense/personal account.

An organisation can minimise the risk of computer fraud by:

❏ controlling access to computer hardware; in centralised systems with a limited number of specialist staff access can be readily controlled. On the other hand, if power is concentrated in the hands of few staff, then the opportunities for undetected fraud are increased. Distributed systems or centralised systems with remote access, for example through the Internet, may increase the number of locations where fraud can be perpetrated;

❏ auditing of data and procedures; until hard copy is produced the contents of files remain invisible and a number of auditing techniques can be used to detect fraudulent entries or changes.

❏ careful monitoring of the programming function; program patching can be controlled by division of the programming task, so that an individual programmer does not have complete responsibility for one application program. Unauthorised alterations to existing software can be detected by auditing utilities which compare the object code of an operational program with an original and authorised copy.

Copyright, Designs and Patents Act (1988)

A computer program can now obtain the status of literary work and as such, retains protection for 50 years from the first publishing date. Computer software is now covered by the Copyright Designs and Patents Act 1988 and infringements include:

❏ the pirating of copyright protected software;

❏ the running of pirated software, in that a copy is created in memory;

❏ transmitting software over telecommunications links, thereby producing a copy.

The major software producers have funded an organisation called FAST (Federation Against Software Theft) which successfully lobbied for the inclusion of computer software into the above-mentioned Act.

The law also covers material published on the World Wide Web, including images and materials used as part of a Web site's design. For example, you would be committing an offence if you copied images of products from a manufacturer's on-line brochure. An offence is also committed if you place a link in your own Web site to another site which contains copyright material, without the copyright holder's permission. It is wise to assume that material is copyright protected unless there is a statement to the contrary.

Data Protection Acts (1984 and 1998)

The Data Protection Act of 1984 states that a business or other organisation which holds personal information on their computer system must register with the Data Protection Registrar, the body that administers the act. The registration process requires identification of the classes of data held and the purposes for which they are to be used. For example, a business may hold personal data which includes information on lifestyle and income which it uses to target its marketing campaigns.

A new UK Data Protection Act, passed in 1998 and which came into force on 1 March 2000, specifically concerns the processing of personal data on the Internet. The main provisions of each Act are given in the following sections.

Data Protection Act (1984)

Since the 1960s, there has been growing public concern about the threat that computers pose to personal privacy. Most countries, including the UK, have introduced legislation to safeguard the privacy of the individual. The Younger Report of 1972 identified ten principles which were intended as guidelines to computer users in the private sector. A Government White Paper was published in 1975 in response to the Younger Report, but no legislation followed. The Lindop Report of 1978 was followed by a White Paper in 1982 and this resulted in the 1984 Data Protection Act. Apart from public pressure concerning the protection of personal privacy, a major incentive for the Government to introduce the Act stemmed from the need to ratify the Council of Europe Data Protection Convention. In the absence of this ratification, firms within the UK could have been considerably disadvantaged in trading terms through the Conventions provision to allow participating countries to refuse the transfer of personal information to non-participating countries. The principles detailed in the Younger Report formed the foundation for future reports and the Data Protection Act. They are listed below.

❑ Information should be regarded as being held for a specific purpose and should not be used, without appropriate authorisation, for other purposes.

❑ Access to information should be confined to those authorised to have it for the purpose for which it was supplied.

❑ The amount of information collected and held should be the minimum necessary for the achievement of a specified purpose.

❑ In computerised systems which handle information for statistical purposes, adequate provision should be made in their design for separating identities from the rest of the data.

❑ There should be arrangements whereby a subject could be told about the information held concerning him or her.

❑ The level of security to be achieved by a system should be specified in advance by the user and should include precautions against the deliberate abuse or misuse of information.

❑ A monitoring system should be provided to facilitate the detection of any violation of the security system.

❑ In the design of information systems, periods should be specified beyond which information should not be retained.

❑ Data held should be accurate. There should be machinery for the correction of inaccuracy and updating of information.

❑ Care should be taken in coding value judgements.

The White Paper which followed the Younger Report identified certain features of computerised information systems which could be a threat to personal privacy:

❑ The facility for storing vast quantities of data.

❑ The speed and power of computers make it possible for data to be retrieved quickly and easily from many access points;

❑ Data can be rapidly transferred between interconnected systems.

❑ Computers make it possible for data to be combined in ways which might otherwise not be practicable.

❑ Data is often transferred in a form not directly intelligible.

The 1984 Data Protection Act sets boundaries for the gathering and use of personal data. It requires all holders of computerised personal files to register with a Registrar appointed by the Home Secretary. The holder of personal data is required to keep to both the general terms of the Act, and to the specific purposes declared in the application for registration.

Terminology

The Act uses a number of terms which require some explanation:

❑ Data. Information held in a form which can be processed automatically. By this definition, manual information systems are not covered by the Act.

❑ Personal data. That which relates to a living individual who is identifiable from the information, including any which is based on fact or opinion.

❑ Data subject. The living individual who is the subject of the data.

❑ Data user. A person who processes or intends to process the data concerning a data subject.

Implications

The requirements of the Act may result in an organisation having to pay more attention to the question of security against unauthorised access than would otherwise be the case; appropriate education and training of employees are also needed to ensure that they are aware of their responsibilities and are fully conversant with their roles in the security systems. The Act also provides the right of a data subject (with some exceptions) to obtain access to information concerning him or her. Normally, a data user must provide such information free of charge or for a nominal charge of around £10.

From the individuals point of view, the Act can be said to have a number of weaknesses:

❑   Penalties for infringement of the rules are thought to be weak and ineffective.

❑   There are a number of exemptions from the Act. Some holders do not need to register and there are exceptions to the right of access to ones own file. There are also limits to confidentiality.

The Registrar is appointed by the Home Secretary and cannot therefore, be wholly independent.

Data Protection Act (1998)

"An Act to make new provision for the regulation of the processing of information relating to individuals, including the obtaining, holding, use or disclosure of such information." [16th July 1998 Data Protection Act].

The Act defines 'data' as information which is automatically processed, or is gathered with that intention, or is held in a structured filing system which is not automatically controlled. In other words, the Act covers manual filing systems which were not covered in the 1984 Act.

The Act also refers to:

❑   the "data controller" as the person or persons who determine the purposes to which the personal data is put and the manner in which it is processed;

❑   the "data processor", meaning any person (other than an employee of the data controller) who processes the personal data;

The terms "data subject" and "personal data" retain the same meanings as stated in the 1984 Act.

The 1998 Act additionally refers to "sensitive personal data", meaning personal information relating to racial or ethnic origin, political opinions, religious or similar beliefs, trade union membership, physical and mental health, sexual life, offences or alleged offences and court proceedings for such offences.

There are a number of exemptions to registration, for example, when the data is held for national security, crime prevention or detection and certain tax purposes.

Ethics and Professional Codes of Conduct

The ethics, or moral principles, governing the use of ICT are of concern to society and general public concern is frequently expressed on the dangers presented by the Internet, in particular, its use for the distribution of pornography and the promotion of racial prejudice and hatred. There are other ethical concerns which relate to, for example, the protection of copyright and personal privacy. Professional bodies play an important part in providing informed views on these and other ethical issues relating to the use of ICT. They also act as an education resource for their professional members and the wider public, as well as contributing to the development of Government legislation.

Two of the most important professional bodies are the British Computer Society (BCS) and the Association of Computing Machinery (ACM), founded in the USA in 1947. The professional bodies undertakes a number of activities on behalf of its members and society in general. For example, the BCS promotes and maintains standards of professional competence, sets out disciplinary procedures, advises Government and its agencies on ICT legislative matters, such as the Computer Misuse Act, sets standards for education and training, informs debate on issues such as software certification and intellectual property rights (copyright, patents etc) and consults with overseas professional bodies on European and global ICT matters.

BCS Code of Practice

The BCS Code of Practice sets out the professional standards of competence, conduct and ethical practice for computing in the United Kingdom. The Code prescribes minimum standards of performance for its members in the following areas:

❑ Personal competence and performance. For example, members should keep themselves informed of technological and legal developments, seek advice where necessary, train subordinates and seek to meet the needs of clients efficiently.

❑ Organisation and management. Members are expected to meet deadlines, organise task completion efficiently through good communication with colleagues and subordinates and by allocating tasks to those competent to complete them.

❑ Contracting. Members should seek professional advice in drawing up formal contracts and ensure that responsibilities of the contracting parties are clearly defined.

❑ Privacy, security and integrity. This deals with the assessment of risks, such as potential for injury to people, the loss of data or equipment, the taking of measures to secure against the risks and confidentiality and personal privacy.

BCS Code of Conduct

The BCS Code of Conduct sets out the duties which members should discharge in the pursuit of their profession. These duties concern:

❑ The public interest. These duties relate to the safeguard of health and safety, protection of the environment, awareness and compliance with relevant legislation, attention to the legitimate rights of third parties, and the avoidance of damage to basic human rights.

❑ Duty to employers and clients. These duties concern, for example, quality of work, adherence to deadlines and budgets and the avoidance of corrupt practice (such as the taking of inducements or the selling of confidential information).

❑ Duty to the profession. Members are expected, for example, to uphold the reputation of the profession, promote public awareness of ICT issues and support fellow members and new entrants.

❑ Professional competence and integrity. These duties require members to advance their ICT knowledge and skills, maintain good practice and encourage their subordinates to do the same.

ACM Code of Ethics and Professional Conduct

The ACM Code sets out professional standards and the duties of members in its Code of Ethics and Professional Conduct. The issues are similar to those dealt with in the BCS Codes of Conduct and Practice. In the execution of professional practice, members are expected to attend to a number of issues relating to, for example, the well-being of society, honesty and trustworthiness, fairness and avoidance of discrimination, respect for intellectual property rights, personal privacy, high standards of work, knowledge and respect for the relevant laws, professional review, evaluation and risk analysis of ICT systems and the promotion of public awareness.

✍️Exercises

1. A DIY retailer is launching a new e-commerce service to provide on-line shopping to its customers. The directors are concerned about the new service's vulnerability to crime.

    (i)   Give two examples of crime which may damage the company.

    (ii)   Describe a legislative deterrent which may help to combat the threat.

    (iii) Describe any measures the company can take to protect themselves from electronic crime.

2. The ICT Services Manager of the DIY company is a member of a relevant professional organisation. Outline the benefits this may provide for the Manager and the obligations which arise from membership.

3. The DIY company aims to gather marketing information from customers through the Web site. Identify the company's obligations under the Data Protection Acts (1984 and 1998).

4. Identify aspects of the DIY company's operations which will require careful attention to the Copyright, Designs and Patents Act (1988).

Although a computer is not inherently dangerous, users should be aware of a number of potential risks to their safety and general health. Most employers have obligations (under Section 2 of the Health and Safety at Work Act, 1974) to protect the health, safety and welfare of their employees, by ensuring safe equipment, work systems and working environment. This legislative protection applies to work with a computer *workstation* (a visual display unit and its associated equipment and furniture), as it does to other work. In 1993, specific legislation was introduced to implement European Directive 90/270/EEC, "on the minimum safety and health requirements for work with display screen equipment".

This section examines the potential hazards of using a computer workstation and the steps that can be taken to avoid them. The 1993 legislation recognises that good work organisation and job design, and the application of established *ergonomic* principles, can largely avoid the hazards to health and safety.

Ergonomics

Ergonomics is the "study of efficiency of workers and working arrangements" (Oxford English Dictionary). Although a separate science in its own right, certain aspects of ergonomics are being applied increasingly to the design of:

❏ furniture associated with office computer systems;

❏ computer equipment for person/machine interfacing, for example, screen displays and keyboards;

❏ office and workstation layout.

It is generally recognised that, if workstation facilities and the working environment are inadequate, computer users will tend to be inefficient and may suffer from general fatigue and boredom. The increased emphasis on ergonomic design has come about because of the large increase in the number of computer users. The term *user* includes not only computer specialists, but also non-specialist users, such as data entry operators, clerks, accountants and managers.

Hazards to operator health and efficiency

In designing a suitable workstation, the designer needs to be aware of a number of potential hazards, which are described in the following paragraphs.

Visual fatigue

Various symptoms may indicate the onset of visual fatigue: sore eyes; hazy vision; difficulty in focusing when switching vision between near and distant objects; aching behind the eyes.

Certain workstation features and user behaviour can contribute to visual fatigue. The screen display and the positioning of documents that are being transcribed, typically contribute to this fatigue. More specifically, the fatigue may be caused by one or more of the following.

❑   screen glare;

❑   poor character-definition on screen;

❑   excessive periods of screen viewing and consequent short distance focusing;

❑   screen flicker;

❑   screen reflection;

❑   insufficient or excessive ambient (surrounding) lighting;

❑   frequent, excessive eye movement when switching between screen and document.

Bodily fatigue

Tense and aching muscles or inflamed nerves, generally in the shoulders, neck, back, wrists or hands may result from:

❑   adopting a poor seating posture;

❑   bending frequently to reach various parts of the workstation;

❑   using a keyboard which is not at a comfortable height. *Repetitive strain injury* (RSI), or *carpal tunnel syndrome*, is now recognised as a disabling condition, which can result from intensive keyboard work. Products are available to support wrists and help users to avoid the injury. The nerves which lie down the edge of the hand can also become inflamed and painful, a condition known as *ulnar neuritis*.

❑   holding the head at an awkward angle to view the screen or a document.

Other hazards to health and safety

The proper design and positioning of a workstation can help prevent a number of potential hazards, generally relating to the use of equipment. The hazards may include:

❑   *electric shock*. A person may receive a live electric shock, from faulty equipment (such as incorrect earthing of the power supply), and from incorrect use of equipment (such as the removal of the machine's casing, without first isolating the machine from mains power). This form of electric shock will persist until the person breaks contact with the machine, or else the power is cut. Clearly, this hazard is life threatening, and although this is the primary concern, it will probably also cause damage to the machine.

❑   *static electric shock*. This is caused by the sudden discharge through any conducting material of static electricity, which may have built up in the body. The equipment earths the static electricity which the person has accumulated. A person may build up static electricity by walking on a nylon carpet. Sometimes, static electricity accumulates on the computer screen and a shock may be received when it is touched (the person acts as the earth). If the screen is cleaned with special anti-static wipes, this problem should be avoided. Static electric shock is momentary and, whilst in exceptional circumstances it may injure someone, it is more likely to damage the equipment and, possibly, the stored data.

❏   *injury from impact*. For example, someone may bump against the sharp corner of a desk, be injured by dropping equipment when attempting to move it or be cut by sharp edges on equipment;

❏   *muscular or spinal strain*. Lifting heavy equipment may cause strained or torn muscles, or spinal injuries such as a 'slipped' disc;

❏   *burns, cuts or poisoning caused by equipment breakdown*. These injuries may result from fire or overheating of equipment.

Analysis of workstation requirements

There is no single standard for workstation design. The type of equipment and its layout will depend on, amongst other things, who is going to use it and how it is going to be used. Therefore, before choosing an appropriate workstation design, information should be gathered on the following topics.

Users

The physical characteristics and abilities of potential users should, if possible, be identified. User features may include: gender; physical or mental handicap; age range; height; build.

Obviously, it may not be possible to identify personally all members of a user group, in which case, information may be more generalised. Questions to ask may be as follow.

❏   Does the user group include males only, females only or both?

❏   What is the age range?

❏   Are there any handicapped users and if so, what are the handicaps?

❏   Are the physical characteristics of users similar or highly varied?

In addition to identifying the features of current users, it is important to allow for possible changes. For example, there may be no wheelchair users at present, but business policy may result in their inclusion in the future.

Existing workstations

If there are workstations already in use within the organisation, then it is useful to determine if there are any good features to include, or bad features to avoid, in any new workstations. The general physical state of the old workstations should be determined. Questions to pose may include:

❏   have screen displays lost some clarity or steadiness?

❏   is the seating still clean and serviceable?

❏   are keyboards still fully operable?

The opinions of users should also yield useful information on the suitability of the existing workstations concerning, for example, seating comfort, positioning of equipment and reliability of hardware.

The location of the workstation

The size of the room in which the workstation is to be located and the layout of existing furniture may place constraints on any design features.

Workstation usage

The various kinds of work to be carried out at a workstation may involve:

- ❏   data entry involving transcription from source documents;

- ❏   use of large reference manuals;

- ❏   storage of file media;

- ❏   customer enquiries which involve customers viewing the screen display;

- ❏   side-by-side working with another member of staff;

- ❏   use of a mouse which requires a flat surface area for its movement;

- ❏   some activities which do not involve the use of a computer. There may be no other available work areas in the office, so sufficient space should be available at each workstation.

It is also important to know how often particular activities are likely to be carried out and how long they will last.

Designing an appropriate workstation

A number of workstation features are considered in the overall design and together can contribute to a good working environment.

Work surface

Height. A user should have thigh clearance amounting to at least 180mm, measured from the front surface of the seat, to the underside of the work surface. Obviously, this measurement can be obtained if the chair is adjustable in height and the work surface height does not require seat adjustment below its minimum height. The minimum clearance may be insufficient for someone to sit cross-legged, a position which he or she may wish to adopt for short periods, so some extra thigh clearance may be desirable.

Typical heights of manufactured workstations are either 710mm for fixed or between 520mm and 750mm when adjustable. The standard 710mm which manufacturers use for a fixed height desk is based on the ideal writing height for an average male and does not take account of keyboard thickness.

Area. The work surface area required obviously depends on the nature of the work being carried out at the workstation. If transcription work is to be carried out, a *document holder* can be attached to one corner of the mobile workstation. Where more space is available, users may prefer that the document holder is positioned between the keyboard and the screen to reduce the amount of eye movement when alternately viewing the screen and the document. As with all computer equipment, a *matt surface* is desirable to avoid screen reflection and possible eye strain.

Chair

Where a fixed height desk of, say, 710mm is bought, then it is particularly important that the chair's height is *adjustable* and that a footrest is available for persons of small stature. This is obviously necessary for a comfortable keying height. At the same time, support is provided for the feet (if they are not supported, blood circulation in the legs may be impaired as pressure is exerted by the edge of the seat on the back lower thighs). The footrest should allow the thighs to be slightly raised above the front edge of the chair, thus avoiding 'pins and needles' in the legs and feet. An adjustable chair should be variable in height from 340mm to 520mm. Invariably, manufacturers produce computer workstation chairs which are adjustable for height and back, particularly lower back, support. A good seating posture is illustrated below.

Screen display

In workstation design, the screen display has to be judged for its *quality* and its *position* in relation to the operator.

Screen quality is measured for the clarity and steadiness of the images it displays. A high *resolution* screen is generally desirable, even for word processing work, but is of paramount importance if it is used for detailed design work. Several precautions can be taken to minimise eye strain if a poorer quality display is being used:

❑ appropriate lighting; this is examined in the next subsection;

❑ comparisons can be made with other screen displays (the clarity may deteriorate with age) and any deterioration reported;

❑ the use of a higher resolution screen, appropriate to the application and colour where graphical work is involved;

❑ the correct adjustment of contrast and brightness controls. Filters can cut glare and improve character definition by preventing screen reflection from inappropriate lighting. However, their quality is highly variable and a good quality screen should avoid the problem of glare.

There are two major concerns regarding the *positioning* of the screen. First, there is an optimum viewing range. Second, its location should be aimed at minimising excessive head and eye movement. The distance between the user's eyes and the screen should, ideally, fall somewhere between 450mm and 500mm and the design should try to achieve a viewing distance within this range. However, eye strain is more likely to result from repeated re-focusing for lengthy periods, whilst attention is switched from the screen to a document on the desk top. This can be avoided by attempting to position documents approximately the same distance away as the screen. A document holder can be useful in achieving this aim, even if it is positioned to one side and thus requires some head movement to view the document. Some head movement helps to keep the neck and shoulder muscle loosened and avoids stiffness and aching in those areas. A user should try to look away from the screen occasionally, perhaps to the other side of the office, to avoid eye strain which stems from constant focusing at one distance.

Lighting

Natural light falling through office windows may, at times, be adequate for healthy and efficient working but there will be many occasions when it is either too dark or too bright. It is generally necessary to supplement the natural light with artificial lighting and control the entry of bright sunshine with window blinds. The detailed study of lighting is beyond the scope of this text but the following points provide some basic guidelines as to the artificial lighting requirements for a workstation;

❑   attempt to avoid glare. This can result if there is insufficient lighting and the screen's brightness contrasts sharply with the ambient level of brightness;

❑   reflection on screen can make it difficult to see the displayed characters and cause eye strain. The use of window blinds and non-reflective work surfaces and equipment can help.

Cabling

Cabling is needed to power individual systems, connect the component parts of system unit, printer, keyboard and screen and for communications purposes when separate systems are networked. Loose cable trailing beneath desks or across the floor can result in injury to staff who trip over it. If, in the process, hardware is pulled from a desk onto the floor, it is likely to be damaged and may result in loss of data and temporary loss of system use. Cabling should be channelled through conduit or specially designed channels in the workstation. Cable 'bridge' conduit is specially designed to channel cable safely across floor areas.

Floor covering

It is important to choose the right type of floor covering and a number of considerations concerning choice are given below.

Noise. Staff generally prefer an office floor to be carpeted because it makes the room feel more 'comfortable'. Carpet also serves to absorb some office noise and results in a quieter environment than would prevail with a tiled floor.

Chair movement. If operator chairs are on casters then the carpets should be sufficiently firm and smooth to allow the operator to move easily while still seated. Movement should not be so easy that the operator has difficulty in maintaining position. A chair with casters is difficult to control on a tiled floor.

Static electricity. Carpets made with a large percentage of man-made fibre tend to cause rapid build-up in body static. The static is caused through friction as a person walks across the carpet. Woollen carpets produce less static electricity but are more expensive than the synthetic variety. An alternative is to use anti-static mats to cover carpet areas around workstations. An anti-static mat is earthed and designed to drain away body static when a person stands on it. Another way of preventing static is to spray a special chemical solution onto the carpet every six months.

Office layout

If the designer has the luxury of starting from 'scratch', then the simplest approach to designing the layout is to make a scale drawing of the office on which the location of equipment and furniture can then be marked. Designated work positions should also be indicated. Numerous drawing and computer aided design packages make experimentation easy. Libraries of standard symbols (representing office equipment and furniture) are available, which the designer can select and locate on screen. The designer has to take into account a number of constraints which will dictate the location of some furniture and equipment. Fixed items should be placed on the drawing first so that those with fewer constraints can be tried in different locations until an optimum layout is achieved. Ideally, the designer should present two or three alternatives for consideration by management and office staff, whose opinions ought to be paramount. A number of factors should be taken into account when choosing the location of workstations:

❏   staff should not be obliged to work in areas which are subject to extremes of temperature, for example, next to radiators or near a frequently used door which creates a draught each time it is opened;

❏   computer equipment should not be placed next to a radiator as overheating may cause the system to malfunction;

❏   computer screens should be protected from direct sun-light which causes screen reflection and glare;

❏   there should be sufficient space for staff to move around the office without moving equipment or furniture;

❏   workstations should have sufficient space to allow routine maintenance and cleaning to be carried out;

❏   there should always be easy access to fire fighting equipment and fire exits should be kept clear.

✍ Exercises

1. Name two pieces of legislation that are of particular importance regarding health and safety issues when working with computers.

2. List the health hazards which have been associated with the use of computers and identify commercial products or working practices which can be used to protect computer users from those hazards.

Section 8

Applications software

Topics

Generic software

Microsoft's Word, Excel and Access software packages are *generic* or *general-purpose*, meaning that they can be used for a range of different purposes. Microsoft's Word and Corel's WordPerfect are word processors and can be used to produce any kind of document, for example, letters and reports or magazines and books with colour graphics. Excel is a spreadsheet package and can be used for any number-based work, such as a sales forecast or a statistical analysis of the health of a population. It can also produce graphs or charts, to present the information in different ways. Other examples of generic software packages include: Microsoft Access, a relational database (Topic 39), Corel Ventura and QuarkXpress, for DTP (desktop publishing), CorelDRAW and Corel PhotoPaint, drawing and paint packages, respectively, Microsoft PowerPoint, for slideshow presentations and Macromedia's Director, for multimedia presentations. Although each package has a primary general purpose, its feature set is often extended to include secondary facilities (usually less sophisticated) which are the primary purpose of another package. For example, a spreadsheet is designed for the manipulation of numeric data, but it also offers database-like functions to allow sorting and searching of records. Similarly, word processing, DTP, presentation and spreadsheet packages provide drawing tools which for many users will be perfectly adequate and remove the need for a separate, specialist drawing package.

Choosing the most appropriate package

Despite some features overlap, choosing the most appropriate package for a particular task is not generally difficult. The following paragraphs provide examples of packages which share features and suggest ways in which they can be used for a variety of applications.

Word processors and spreadsheets

If, for example, you are required to calculate sales commission for a number of sales staff, or calculate wages it is clear that the problems are mainly numerical and best solved with a spreadsheet. If, on the other hand, you are writing a report and it includes a table of figures, you could use the table and formula facility in the word processor, rather than preparing the table separately in a spreadsheet.

Spreadsheets and databases

Similar feature overlap occurs between spreadsheets and databases. Data held in a spreadsheet can be sorted and extracted in much the same way as data held in a database and choosing between the two again depends on the problem to be solved. Suppose, for example, that you already hold sales staff records in a spreadsheet, for the purpose of calculating sales commission. The records can sorted on any column, such as surname, starting date, or commission earned and records can be filtered by criteria, such as, staff who have earned more than £350 commission and have been employed by the company for more than 2 years. However, if the main requirement is to store, retrieve, sort, print and generally manage staff records, a database would be a better choice as it also includes the facilities for commission and other calculations. If numerical data needs to be charted, this can also be done within the database. For a more complete description of database facilities, such as the structuring of data into separate tables, indexed sorts and searches, sophisticated query and report generation facilities, see Topic 39.

Drawing and paint packages

Other examples of feature overlap occur between computer-aided drawing (CAD) and graphic design (paint) packages. CorelDRAW is primarily a drawing package with powerful tools for producing geometric shapes and Corel PhotoPaint is primarily an image editing package, with extensive facilities for editing bitmaps, such as photographs, but each package contains some of the facilities provided by the other. Of course there are many differences as well. For example, the paint package includes tools such as a spray can, brush and eraser, which are of particular use to the artist or graphic designer. If, for example, you needed to produce a poster advertising a party, with text and some clip art you could do so with a word processor, a desktop publisher, a drawing or a paint package. If, on the other hand, you needed to produce a technical drawing with scaled dimensions a drawing package would be the best choice.

HTML editors and Web page generators

Web pages can be produced using specialist HTML (Topics 40 and 41) editors, such as Allaire Homesite, which are designed for use by experts in that language, or with packages such as Microsoft FrontPage which avoid the need for a knowledge of HTML, but the latter will tend to produce page designs which have a particular 'look'. An HTML editor, on the other hand, gives the Web author greater flexibility in design. Web pages can also be generated automatically from content in other packages, such as Microsoft Word (using File | Save as HTML), but unless the HTML code is subsequently altered in a suitable editor, their appearance will be determined by the automatic generation features of the package. A professional Web page designer would need to use an HTML editor to fulfil the varied design requirements of clients, but a small business may produce its own Web site quite cheaply using a package such as FrontPage or with the Web authoring tools within Microsoft Word. Generation of HTML pages directly from, for example, a word processor is probably not be a suitable option for the development of a Web site but it may be adequate for, say, the publication of research findings within a university's intranet (private network with Web features - Topic 52) Web site.

Automated package facilities

To make generic software easier to use and to allow the rapid execution of what would otherwise be complex tasks, every new version of a package includes more automation facilities than the last. Automation can enable the novice to produce sophisticated and complex document layouts, execute statistical analyses of data, generate complex charts and graphs, create and execute complex queries on the contents of a database, create presentations with sound and animation and undertake many other tasks without lengthy training or detailed knowledge of the underlying processes. Of course, to make effective use of an automated output, the user must understand its purpose. For example, calculating standard deviation from a range of figures in a spreadsheet without an understanding of statistics, or generating an invoice without understanding its contents and purpose, would be pointless. Automation facilities include, wizards, style sheets, templates and macros.

Style sheets

A style sheet supports the maintenance of a consistent appearance throughout a document or other form of displayed information, such as a Web page or slide. Templates have a similar function but may also make available, for example, particular toolbars and macros, when the document or other file type is loaded into the package. The style sheet facility used to be primarily associated with DTP software. Figure 33.1 shows the Column settings for pages in a document called 'Contents'. This is a style sheet but referred to as Page Tag Properties in the Corel Ventura package. Figure 33.2 shows paragraph tags in a style sheet labelled as 'generic'.

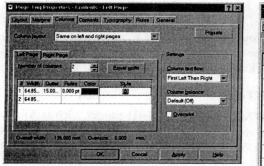

Figure 33.1. *Page tag properties*

Name	Font	Font..	Style	Ali
TableTextLt	Tim...	9.50 pt	Normal	Left
TableTextRt	Tim...	9.50 pt	Normal	Right
TableTextSmall	Tim...	9.00 pt	Normal	Center
TableTxtSmallLt	Tim...	9.50 pt	Normal	Left
TableTxtSmallRt	Tim...	9.50 pt	Normal	Right
TabProgInd00	Cour...	9.50 pt	Normal	Left
TabProgInd01	Cour...	9.50 pt	Normal	Left
TabProgInd02	Cour...	9.50 pt	Normal	Left
TabProgInd03	Cour...	9.50 pt	Normal	Left
TabProgInd04	Cour...	9.50 pt	Normal	Left

Figure 33.2. *Paragraph tags*

Thus, any Ventura publication document can be given the page style 'Contents' and within the document 'generic', the appearance of individual paragraphs set by application of a chosen style. For example, the style TableTxtLt uses the Times New Roman font, 10.5 point size, Normal style and the paragraph is left aligned (straight left and ragged right margins); other settings, such as paragraph indentation are not shown in the Figure.

The contents of a *cascading style sheet* used for HTML Web pages is shown in Figure 33.3 and an HTML page with the particular style sheet reference included is shown in Figure 33.4.

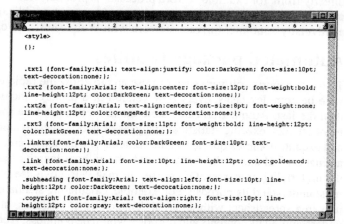

```
<style>
{};

.txt1 {font-family:Arial; text-align:justify; color:DarkGreen; font-size:10pt;
text-decoration:none;};
.txt2 {font-family:Arial; text-align:center; font-size:12pt; font-weight:bold;
line-height:12pt; color:DarkGreen; text-decoration:none;};
.txt2a {font-family:Arial; text-align:center; font-size:8pt; font-weight:none;
line-height:12pt; color:OrangeRed; text-decoration:none;};
.txt3 {font-family:Arial; font-size:11pt; font-weight:bold; line-height:12pt;
color:DarkGreen; text-decoration:none;};
.linktxt{font-family:Arial; color:DarkGreen; font-size:10pt; text-
decoration:none;};
.link {font-family:Arial; font-size:10pt; line-height:12pt; color:goldenrod;
text-decoration:none;};
.subheading {font-family:Arial; text-align:left; font-size:10pt; line-
height:12pt; color:DarkGreen; text-decoration:none;};
.copyright {font-family:Arial; text-align:right; font-size:10pt; line-
height:12pt; color:gray; text-decoration:none;};
```

Figure 33.3. *Cascading style sheet used for HTML Web pages*

```
index - Notepad
File  Edit  Search  Help
<HTML>
<LINK REL=STYLESHEET HREF=infortex.css TYPE=text/css>


<HEAD>
        <TITLE>Infortex Internet Services</TITLE>
```

Figure 33.4. *HTML page source code with style sheet 'Infortex.css' referenced*

Templates

Templates contain the features of styles sheets, plus additional tools to support development of, for example, documents of various types, including invoices, reports and memos and slide presentations. Other packages, such as spreadsheets and drawing packages also contain template facilities. Figure 33.5 shows the dialogue box for template selection in Microsoft Word, with separate tabs for each category of document and the Memo tab currently selected.

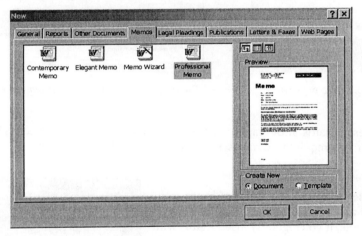

Figure 33.5. *Template selection in Microsoft Word*

Effectively, a template provides pre-defined entry points for the various parts of a standard document and standard styles, although these can be modified. The style list associated with the Memo template is shown in Figure 33.6.

Standard templates provided with a package are useful for generating standard documents quickly, but it is unlikely that such documents would meet the precise 'in-house' style requirements of an organisation without some modification.

However, once a document has been created in the particular in-house style, it can be

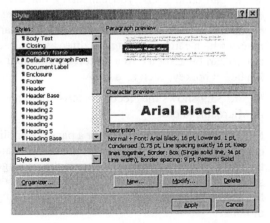

Figure 33.6. *Style list for Memo template*

saved as a template and used to ensure consistent presentation of that particular document throughout the organisation.

Wizards

Through a series of questions, a wizard prompts the user for the information needed to produce a document. Figure 33.7 shows a stage within a Web Page Wizard and Figure 33.8 shows the result.

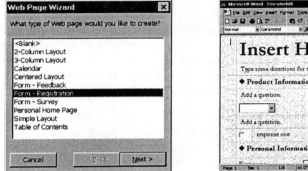

Figure 33.7. *Web page wizard* 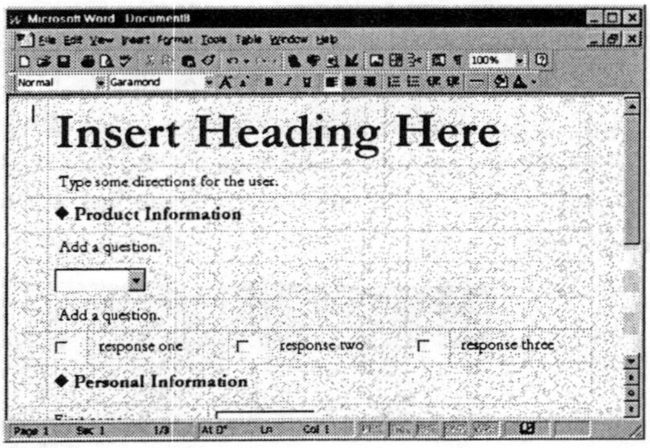   **Figure 33.8.** *Form Web page produced with wizard*

Like templates, wizards allow rapid creation of standard layouts, but rarely produce output which is exactly as required, so the user must have the skills to modify it.

Macros

Macros are used to automate a series of instructions or commands and allow their execution as a single task. For example, if you regularly insert a table with standard headings and then format the borders and shade particular cells, you can carry out the task once whilst running the macro recorder. The entire sequence of your actions is then stored as a named macro which can be executed as often as required. A macro can be assigned to a button on a toolbar or a keyboard hotkey, such as alt A.

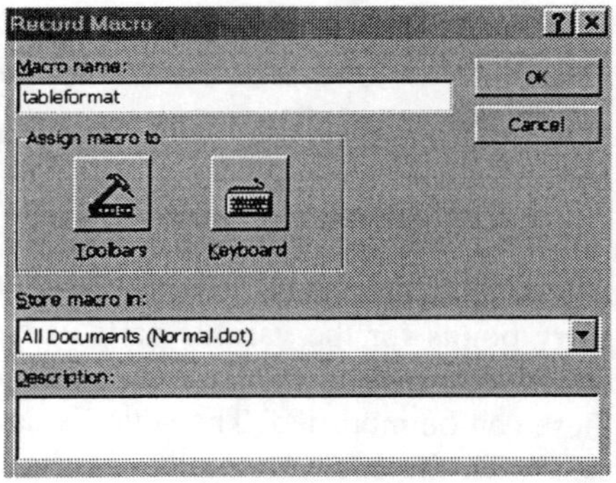

Figure 33.9 shows the 'record macro' dialogue box in Microsoft Word.

Figure 33.9. *Macro recorder*

Macros can also be used to tailor a package application for another user. For example, a macro could load a standard form, insert the current date and then place the cursor in the first data entry point. Some macros are built into the package and can be used to complete common tasks, such as summing a column of figures in a spreadsheet. Figure 33.10 shows such a macro in the Microsoft Works spreadsheet, with the user being prompted to accept the highlighted selection of cells.

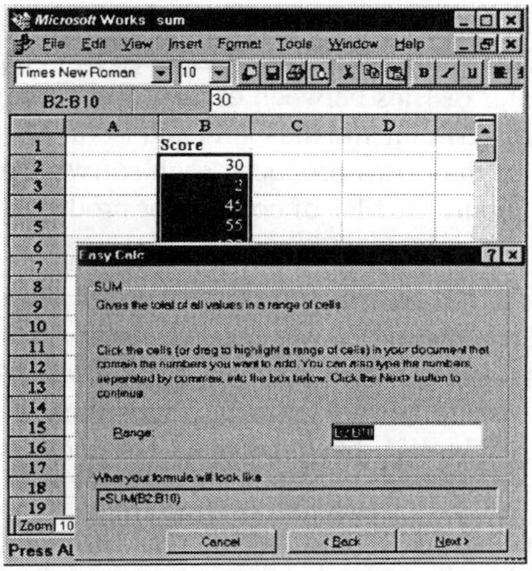

Figure 33.10. *Built-in macro so assist user with summing a column of figures*

Tailoring the user interface

The purpose of an interface is to protect the user from the complexities of package operation and protect the application or the data it manages from accidental or deliberate corruption. For example, if a spreadsheet is used to develop a break even analysis model (Topic 61), it is important that users only enter data into the cells assigned to variable data, for example, the values which make up the variable costs, such as wages and raw materials and not into cells occupied by labels or formulae. Limited protection can be achieved by using the spreadsheet's facility to 'lock' selected cells against alteration, but anyone with sufficient knowledge can simply remove the protection

A database has facilities for the creation of menus which give access to the various parts of an application and command buttons to add or delete a record and carry out other standard tasks, but the application can still be vulnerable to accidental or deliberate damage unless sophisticated security measures are used. To achieve a proper level of security some aspects of the application must be programmed, generally using Visual Basic which forms part of all the major generic software packages, including word processors, spreadsheets and databases. Programming also allows the development of more sophisticated applications than is possible if only built-in facilities, such as report wizards and command buttons are used.

Transferring files between applications

This is a frequent requirement in most organisations primarily, because of the decentralisation of computer processing and the expansion of personal computer use. For example, although a personnel system may be managed through a central database, the Sales manager may hold some staff details in a PC spreadsheet for analysing sales and allocating commission. The staff details could be typed into the spreadsheet manually, but it is much simpler if the relevant data can be transferred directly from the database. To do this, the database must be able to *export* the records as a file type (using a file converter) which can be handled by the spreadsheet, or the spreadsheet must be able to *import* the database file type directly. Generally, each generic software package includes all the necessary file convertors or filters to handle files from other generic software packages, even those which are produced by competitors. Microsoft Office is designed to allow the transfer of files between each of the packages in the suite, that is, the Word, Excel, Access and PowerPoint and the Corel and Lotus Office suites offer similar integration. To encourage use of their own products, each software manufacturer tries to ensure that their applications can import the files of competitor products.

Packages which form part of a suite will normally recognise the file type from an associated application and open it directly. For example, PowerPoint will open a Word document file and convert it to a PowerPoint Presentation. Sometimes it is necessary to load the file into its source application and positively save it, or export it as the file type which can be handled by the destination package. When a file is being exported to an earlier version of a package, for example, a Word 7 document is to be used by Word 6, the document must be saved as a Word 6 file within Word 7.

For text files, Rich Text Format (RTF) and .txt file types are universally acceptable by word processors. RTF files have the advantage that they retain the majority of their formatting when they are imported. Amongst graphics files, .bmp, .gif and .jpg are accepted by most packages. Topic 41 on Multimedia describes the major file types in more detail and the applications which use them.

✍️Exercises

1. A squash club uses a PC to record membership details, subscription payments, organise league tables, record match results and occasionally produce sorted and calculated summary reports.
    - (i)   Explain the options the club has in the choice of *generic software* which could be used for all these applications.
    - (ii) Provide further explanation of the options by detailing examples of text, numeric, calculated and graphical information which each package could produce.
    - (iii) Make judgements on the relative benefits and drawbacks of using each package, or a combination of packages.
    - (iv) Suggest what automated features could be used in the packages to ease the squash club's task.
2. Distinguish between a drawing and paint packages and with reference to commercial packages identify some of the major features which are unique to each package.
3. What is the function of a style sheet and what benefits does it provide for team working on document production?
4. Distinguish between a template and a wizard and suggest circumstances when each is appropriate.
5. With the use of an example, explain how macros can be used to tailor a package for other users.
6. Explain the limitations of using the standard features of a generic package to tailor it for a specific application.
7. Explain the requirements for effective data transfer between packages.

Word processing and DTP

Word processing describes the activity of writing with the aid of a computer. The term 'writing' is used in its widest sense and includes, for example, the production of personal or business documentation, such as letters, reports and memoranda, legal documents, posters, articles, books and even the addressing of envelopes. Most word processors include tools for the production of columns and tables, as well as the inclusion of graphics, all of which play an important role in modern document production. Any situation that requires communication by the *printed* word (including graphical images) may be appropriate for word processing. The word 'printed' normally means that the products of word processing activity are printed onto paper (*hard copy*), which is then sent or given to the intended recipient for him or her to read. Although this is usually what happens, word processed documents can be sent via e-mail or generated as HTML Web pages for publication on the Internet without the need for hard copy.

DTP packages are designed for the production of posters, magazines and books and include all the features you would expect for sophisticated text and graphics layouts, automatic hyphenation, precision control of text size, spacing and paragraph alignments and the automatic generation of contents and index pages. This book was published with Corel Ventura, a professional DTP package, but it could also have been produced with a word processing package such as Microsoft Word, which has all the main features of a DTP package. There are slight differences, however. For example, the point size for this book is 10.25, but Word would only have allowed 10, which would have been more difficult to read, or 10.5, which would have increased the page count and have looked slightly too large. Corel Ventura also provides finer character and line spacing control. Word limits line spacing to the nearest point, but Ventura allows setting to a precision of 2 decimal places. Ventura provides features which are not generally available in standard word processors, such as the rotation of standard text paragraphs.

Document layout

There are a number of components which can be used to determine the layout of a documents.

Page size, orientation and margin settings

Page size and orientation (landscape or portrait) and margin settings. The *top margin* sets the amount of space the printer leaves at the top of the page before printing text. The *bottom margin* determines the amount of space that the printer will leave at the end of a full page. The *left margin* and *right margins* are the offsets from the left and right sides of the paper and determine the limits of the print line. Printer margins are usually measured in inches or centimetres. Figure 34.1 shows the Page Setup tabs in Word, with the page size tab visible.

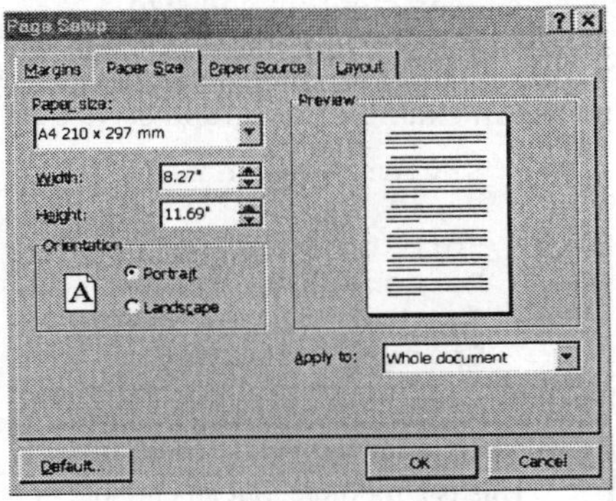

Figure 34.1. *Page setup tabs*

Headers and footers

A *header* is descriptive text which appears above the top margin on every page. For example, a header may include the page number, date, report title and the author's name. A *footer* serves a similar function except that it is located beneath the bottom margin on each page. You only have to enter a header or footer once and the word processor automatically places it on each page when the document is printed. Creating a header or footer is a separate operation from normal text entry and you can only create, edit or remove one through the relevant package commands. If you do not wish to place a header or footer on every page, there is normally a facility, for example, to exempt the first page or assign a different header or footer to the odd or even pages.

Footnotes and endnotes

Footnotes are useful if you want to briefly explain a word or phrase, without including the explanation within the main body of the text. Instead, a reference number is placed next to the relevant word or phrase and the explanation is put at the foot of the page, identified by the same reference number. Here is an example, to explain the word *endnote*[1].

Columns

Although you can use tabulation for column work, the technique is only suitable for lists of, for example, product descriptions or prices on an order form. For continuous prose, such as appears in a newspaper, you need a column facility. Typically, when you start your word processor you will be presented with a default page with a single column, spanning the width available between the left and right margins.

Usually, columns can be created before or after the entry of text and be altered at will. You can choose to have the columns the same width and equally spaced, or vary the column widths and spacing according to preference.

Paragraph styles

In preparing a more lengthy document, such as a booklet, or magazine article, it is advisable to make use of styles, which may be pre-defined, or which you have defined yourself. A style defines a number of features concerning text, including paragraph alignment (left, right, centred and justified - straight left and right margins), paragraph indent, bullets or numbering, line spacing, character font and size.

Styles can be applied, not only to headings and paragraphs, but also to *tables* and *frames* (see later). An example paragraph style definition is detailed below.

```
Style: Heading 2
Font: Arial, 16 pt
Format: bold
Paragraph alignment: flush left
Spacing before:10 pt
Spacing after: 6 pt
```

1   This is a footnote, but an endnote normally appears at the end of a document

See also Style sheets and Templates in Topic 33.

There follows examples of various paragraphs styles.

Left aligned

In preparing a more lengthy document, such as a booklet, or magazine article, it is advisable to make use of styles, which may be pre-defined, or which you have defined yourself. A style defines ....

Right aligned

In preparing a more lengthy document, such as a booklet, or magazine article, it is advisable to make use of styles, which may be pre-defined, or which you have defined yourself. A style defines ....

Justified

In preparing a more lengthy document, such as a booklet, or magazine article, it is advisable to make use of styles, which may be pre-defined, or which you have defined yourself. A style defines ....

Centred

In preparing a more lengthy document, such as a booklet, or magazine article, it is advisable to make use of styles, which may be pre-defined, or which you have defined yourself. A style defines ....

Bulleted

❑ In preparing a more lengthy document, such as a booklet, or magazine article, it is advisable to make use of styles, which may be pre-defined, or which you have defined yourself. A style defines ....

Tables

If you need to present text in a tabular way, you can use tabulation, but a *table* tool allows much greater control over layout. It may also provide extra features to enhance presentation and even allow simple calculations on numeric items. To define a basic table, you need to specify the number of *rows* and *columns*.

Each entry point in the table is known as a cell. The table can also be formatted by defining individual border widths and colours and cell shading or by using an *autoformat* facility.

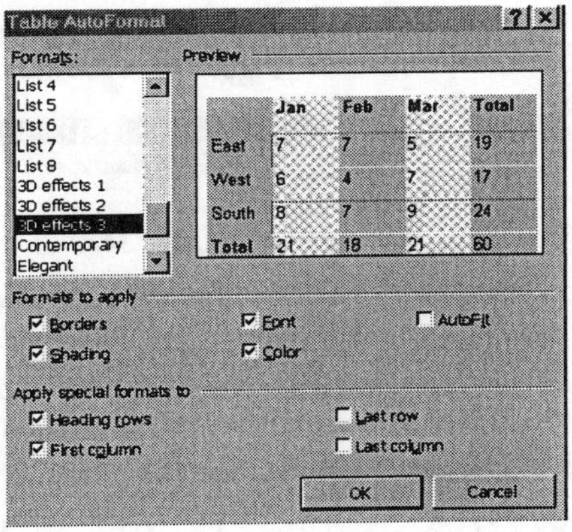

Figure 34.2. *Table autoformat dialogue*

Calculating and sorting with tables

If you have used a spreadsheet package, you should be familiar with the idea of carrying out calculations automatically, with the use of formulae. Word processor tables provide a number of simple functions, such as SUM, to add the contents of a range of cells and PRODUCT, to multiply the contents of cells.

A word processor or DTP package may also allow you to treat the table as a simple database and sort rows, as if they were records, using a single column as a sort key.

Frames

Frames are the basis of DTP package work and define where text and graphics will appear on a page. A master document which defines the basic layout of a page will, by default, have a single frame to define the limits within which the text will flow. Adding columns will create further frames and text will flow from one to another as each column fills. Further frames can be placed on the page, although these need not necessarily sit within the main text frame. For example, you may wish to include graphics in the margin. A frame can be used to position an item on a page, independently of any accompanying text. An item can consist of text or graphics, which may be produced within the package or they may be obtained from other sources, such as a drawing package or a 'clip art' file and then pasted into the frame. Normal paragraph text can be made to flow around the frame, through it, or it can be split by it. Frames are used to position most of the diagrams and tables in this book. Once you have positioned a frame within the paragraph text, you can assign it an exact position on the page (set an *anchor*), or allow it to move with the text. In the latter case, inserting new text above the frame will normally move the frame accordingly. Frames can be grouped or can overlay one another.

Graphics in documents

Both word processing and DTP packages include facilities for handling graphics. Figures 34.3 and 34.4 show the toolbars in Ventura and Word, respectively.

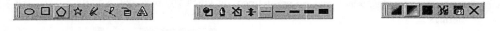

Figure 34.3. *Drawing, fill, line and text tools in Corel Ventura*

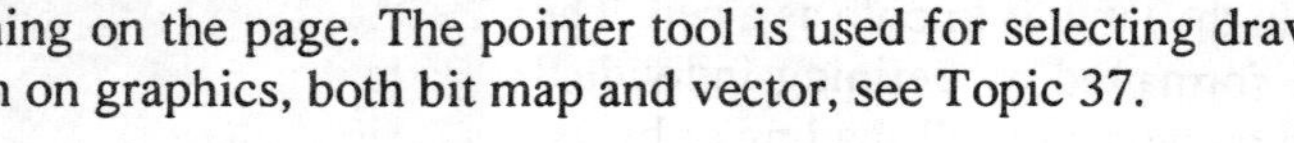

Figure 34.4. *Drawing, fill, line and text tools in Word*

The Figures also show tools concerned with text annotation (text and call out boxes), colour fill and line styles. Drawing tools produce drawing objects, which are manipulated separately from any surrounding text. Unlike imported graphics objects, they do not have to be in a *frame* to allow free positioning on the page. The pointer tool is used for selecting drawing objects. For more information on graphics, both bit map and vector, see Topic 37.

Mail merge and address labels

A *mail merge* facility allows the printing of multiple copies of a standard letter, with the automatic insertion of addressees' names and addresses and other personal details. It requires access to a file containing the relevant personal details of the intended addressees; alternatively, the file can be created within the word processor. Using the same data, an address labelling facility allows you to print labels of your own design or address envelopes of a given size. The process involves several stages:

❑   creation of the *main document*, for example, the standard letter;

❑   identification of a *data* source containing the merge data, for example, names and addresses in a database file or spreadsheet, or another document

❏ labelling of merge data fields as, for example, 'Title', 'Initials', 'Surname' etc.

❏ insertion of merge field labels at the appropriate points in the main document. Each merge field is associated with a particular field in the data source, such as a column in a spreadsheet or a field in a database table.

Example merge field «labels» are shown in Figure 34.5.

<<Title>> <<Initials>> <<Surname>>
<<Address1>>
<<Address2>>
<<County>>
<<Postcode>>

Dear <<Title>> <<Surname>>,

I am delighted to inform you have won £50,000 in our Prize Draw. Imagine, <<Title>> <<Surname>> what you can do with all this money. You could buy a luxury car and drive through <<County>>, to the envy of your neighbours, or take a holiday away from your dull <<County>>.

Yours faithfully,

Ivar Fortune
MoneyBags International plc

Figure 34.5. *Mail merge document showing field labels*

When the merge is executed, a copy of the letter is produced for each record in the merge data file.

Controlling the merge process

The merge can be restricted to addressees living, for example, within a particular county, or those whose surnames begin with a particular letter. Figure 34.6 shows the list of controls which can be used to filter records for a mail merge using Word.

Figure 34.6. *Options for selecting records for mail merge*

The ASK and FILL-IN fields can be used to prompt a user for information during the mail merge. This is useful for variable information which is not available in the data source. You can use IF ...THEN...ELSE fields to set conditions to limit which records are printed. For example, you can restrict the merge to people living within a particular county. NEXT merges the next data record into the current merged document, rather than creating a new merged document. This is useful if you wish to include a number of record details in one document, such as names and addresses. NEXTIF is the same as NEXT except it can be made conditional on the IF statement. SKIPIF ignores the current merge document and skips to the next data record IF a specified condition is met.

Spell checker

If your word processor includes a *spell checking* facility, you may find that, for example, it throws up words like 'organization' as being incorrectly spelled and indicates that only 'organisation' is correct. This does not mean that you cannot use the 'z' form. It simply means that the spellchecker's rules have not allowed for it. Spell checkers will identify as misspelled any word that does not appear in its *dictionary* (stored on disk). Thus, you may find that proper names, such as 'Wilkinson', or abbreviations like 'GNVQ', as well as many specialist technical terms, are highlighted as being incorrect. Most spell checkers allow you to add words to the dictionary, so that they are not identified as misspellings. If you misspell a word and it happens to be the correct spelling for another word, then the computer will not detect it. For example, 'stationery' and 'stationary' are both correctly spelled but have entirely different meanings. Such errors can only be found by careful proofing.

Apart from the standard dictionary, specialist dictionaries can be obtained or created by a user to cater for his or her particular requirements. So, for example, a research chemist would use a dictionary which included the specialist terminology for the subject. Similarly, a secretary may add words which relate specifically to the employer's business.

Thesaurus

Apart from a built-in spell checker, a word processor may also have a *Thesaurus*, which allows you to check the meanings of words and suggests alternatives. This facility should be used with great care, to avoid the use of unusual words which may obscure what you are trying to say. Further, it should only be used to jog your memory for an alternative word. If you use a word with which you are not familiar, you may discover that the word has a similar, but not identical, meaning to the original.

Grammar checker

The rules of grammar are too numerous to mention here, but your word processor may have a grammar checking facility which should accurately identify obvious errors and point out any grammatical constructions which it considers you should check. Use the facility with care and ensure that any suggestions it gives are valid before you accept them.

✍Exercises

1. This book was produced using a commercial DTP package, but a word processor could have been used instead. Look at the various layout techniques used and list the features of either package type that you would expect to be used by the:

   (i)   author;

   (ii) publisher.

2. Produce a document which illustrates the features which you identified in 1(i).

3. Produce a document which illustrates the features which you identified in 1(ii).

4. Which package features do you think a secretary would use for communications with customers and the production of standard business documents?

5. The proprietor of a small business uses a *mail-merge* process to produce marketing mail shots to customers.

   (i)   What is mail-merge?

   (ii) Briefly explain the principles of mail-merge.

   (iii) Explain how a single package or two packages can be used in the mail-merge process.

   (iv) Explain the alternatives for controlling the output from a mail-merge.

Spreadsheet packages are designed, primarily, for the manipulation of numerical information. The term *spreadsheet* is not new and has long been used to describe the computerised system's manual equivalent, commonly used by accountants to prepare, for example, budgets and financial forecasts. A manual spreadsheet is a large sheet of paper with a grid of intersecting rows and columns; a computerised spreadsheet adopts the same layout. Apart from financial applications, spreadsheets are used for statistical analysis and data modelling. Spreadsheet packages provide a graphics facility for the construction of graphs and charts (see Topic 36).

Rows, columns and cells

When you load a spreadsheet program, the screen displays a *worksheet*, from which a number of functional features can be identified. *Cells* are formed in a *grid*, each one being identified by a *column letter* (sometimes, columns may be numbered) and a *row number*. A worksheet provides hundreds of columns and thousands of rows, typically 256 and 16,384 (2^7) respectively, so more than the 26 letters of the alphabet are needed to uniquely identify each column. The problem is overcome by using two letters (AA, AB, AC ... AZ and then BA, BB, BC ... BZ and so on), from column Z onwards. The grid of cells is marked out by *gridlines* and your package may allow you to hide or display them. Each cell is a separate data entry point.

Types of cell entry

Figure 35.1 identifies three main types of cell entry.

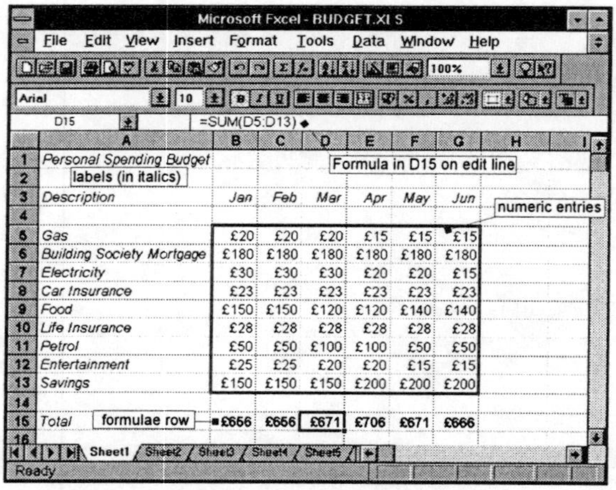

❑ a *label* or *text* entry consisting of alphanumeric characters. Labels are used for headings which identify numeric contents of another cell or group of cells. The italicised entries in Figure 35.1 are all textual. Text entries cannot be used in any numerical calculation;

❑ a *numeric value*, used in calculations and sometimes, for other special types of entry, such as dates.

Figure 35.1. *Types of cell entry*

❑ a *formula*, which normally makes reference to and performs calculations on other cells. A formula can comprise a single cell reference (this point is explained later, in the Cash Flow example) or refer to several, interspersed by arithmetic operators. Thus, for example, to multiply the contents of cell B6 by those of B7 and B8 and place the result in B9, you would enter the formula =B6*B7*B8 into cell B9 (the active cell). Figure 35.1 shows a formula, on the edit line, which makes use of a *function*. The formula in the active cell, D15 (shown on the edit line) uses the SUM function to add together the contents of cells D5 to D13, inclusive. The same function is used to total the adjacent columns, B, C, E, F and G.

Using formulae

The main power of the spreadsheet lies in its ability to use formulae which cause values contained in individual cells to be made dependent on values held in other cells. Any changes in cells referred to in a formula are reflected in the cell containing the formula. For example, if you look at the worksheet in Figure , you should see that any changes in the contents of cells within the *range* D5 to D13 would result in a change to the value displayed in cell D15, which contains the formula =SUM(D5:D13). This formula automatically totals the contents of cells D5 to D13 and displays the result in cell D15 where the formula is located. Similar formulae are contained in the adjacent cells, A15, B15, C15, E15, F15 and G15.

Whenever changes are made to *numeric* values (which may themselves be generated by formulae) in the worksheet, any dependent formulae reflect these changes in the values they display. This automatic calculation is usually referred to as the spreadsheet's *'what if'* facility. It is possible to set up complex combinations of inter-dependent factors and see 'what' happens to the final results 'if' one or more of the factors is changed. More complex examples are provided later, to illustrate the power of the spreadsheet for the solution of *predictive modelling* problems (see Topic 61, Spreadsheet Modelling).

Using functions

Functions provide you with in-built facilities, which allow you to execute a range of processes. A function requires one or more *arguments*, normally bracketed after the function name. For example, the =SUM function requires a cell range to be specified. Thus, to add the contents of cells F23 to F36, requires the function =SUM(F23:F36). The function =AVERAGE (A3:K3) calculates the average of the values stored in cells A3 to K3.

Other functions require different arguments. The function =PMT requires three arguments, *principal*, *interest* and *term* and calculates the periodic payment required to pay off a loan, given a particular periodic interest rate and number of payment periods. For example, the function =PMT(30000, 15%, 25) relates to a loan (the principal) of £30000, with interest charged at 15% per annum, repayable over a 25 year term.

Typically, a spreadsheet package will provide *statistical, mathematical, financial, lookup* and *logical* functions. The function names used here are not necessarily the same as you may find in the package you use, but you should be able to identify related functions from the examples which follow.

Statistical functions

=AVERAGE(*range*) which averages the values in a range of cells.

=MAX(*range*) which finds the largest value in a range of cells.

=MIN(*range*) which finds the smallest value in a range of cells.

=STDEV(*range*) calculates the population standard deviation of the values in a range of cells.

=SUM(*range*) sums the values in a range of cells.

Mathematical functions

The arguments symbolised by *x, y* and *n* may be cell references or fixed values.

=SQRT(*x*) calculates the square root of *x*.

=SIN(*x*) calculates the sine of angle *x*.

=TAN(*x*) calculates the tangent of angle *x*.

=ROUND(*x,n*) rounds the number *x* to *n* places.

=MOD(*x,y*) calculates the remainder (*modulus*) of *x* divided by *y*.

Financial functions

=NPV(*interest, range*) gives the net present value of a series of future cash flows, discounted at a fixed interest rate.

=FV(*payments, interest, term*) computes the future value of money invested in equal periodic payments, at a given interest rate, over a given term.

Lookup and reference

=HLOOKUP(*lookup_value, array, row_index*) Looks up a search value in a table (array) and returns an associated value from another row in the array. The function is described later, with an example.

=VLOOKUP(*lookup_value, array, column_index*). This is the same as HLOOKUP, except that the array is organised in columns (vertically as opposed to horizontally).

=CHOOSE(*index_no, value1, value2,...*), uses an index number to choose a value from a list of values.

Logical

=IF(*logical_test, value_if_true, value_if_false*). Alternative values are returnable depending on whether the result of a logical test is true or false. Examples of logical tests are: B3>25; Salary<15000 ('Salary' would be a *named* cell). The function is described in detail later.

=AND(*logical_test1, logical_test2,...*). Returns logical *true*, if all logical tests are true. It can be used in combination with IF. The function is used as part of examples illustrating the IF function, later.

=OR(*logical_test1, logical_test2,...*). Returns logical *true*, if any of the logical tests are true. Forms part of the group of logical functions, commonly used in combination with the IF function, which include, AND, OR, NOT.

Absolute and relative cell replication

You can copy or replicate numbers or labels to other cells. The contents are copied without change. You can also replicate a formula, *relatively*, to another cell or range of cells. This is necessary if you want the same calculation to be carried out in a different row or column, by referencing a different group of cells. Thus, for example, the formula in Figure 35.2, =SUM(B4:B7), which totals a group of values for the month of January can be copied to succeeding columns to the right for February as =SUM(C4:C7), for March as =SUM(D4:D7) and so on. The formula is logically the same but the column references change according to the position of the formula.

If you wish part of a formula to remain unchanged, you must make the relevant cell reference *absolute*. Typically, the software prefixes the row and column reference with a $ sign when you make it absolute. Thus, for example, the formula =(B3+C3)*$A$6 would add the contents of B3 and C3 (because the brackets give the expression precedence) and then multiply the resulting sum by the contents of A6. The $ prefixes will ensure that when the formula is copied, the reference to A6 remains constant. Thus when copied to, for example, rows 4 and 5 the formula becomes =(B4+C4)*$A$6 and =(B5+C5)*$A$6 respectively. An absolute cell reference (by naming) could be used, for example, to refer to a single price, which is multiplied by a series of sales figures. The replication process may require a series of operations which identify what is being replicated (which may be a single cell or range of cells), and the cell or range of cells to which the copy is directed; this is similar to the *copy* and *paste* operation in a word processor. The process may be simplified and allow you simply to drag a 'handle' on the cell (or highlighted group of cells) being copied, over the group of adjacent cells, where you wish the copy to be directed. An example of the process is illustrated in Figure 35.2.

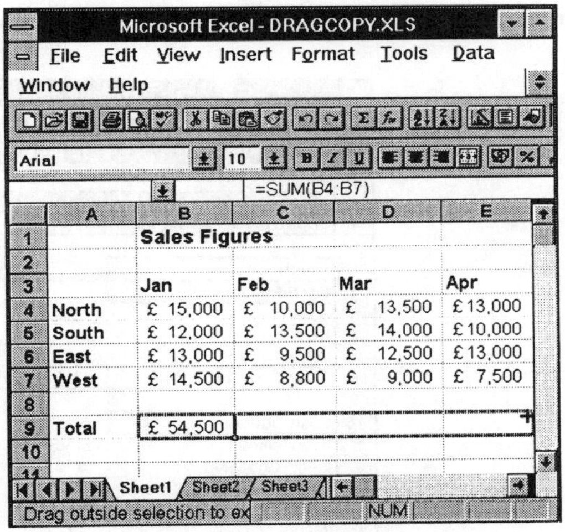

Figure 35.2. *Replication by dragging*

Documenting a worksheet

Even if a spreadsheet application is only to be used by the person who developed it, the worksheet should be fully documented. Documentation is particularly important if others are to use it or if it needs to be modified at some future date. The volume of documentation should depend on the complexity of the model; a few brief notes is probably sufficient for a simple personal cash budget model. As a general guide, the documentation should include the following elements:

- ❑ full print-out of the worksheet, including sample data;

- ❑ print-out of worksheet, showing formulae displayed, or a list of cell references with associated cell formulae;

- ❑ user notes on the operation of the model, including data entry requirements and expected forms of output;

❏   where explanation is needed, annotation of cells containing formulae.

A cashflow model

Although you should find that some applications, such as a simple spending budget, are relatively simple to develop, the main problem for the spreadsheet user lies in the development of more useful and often more complex models. Learning the basic skills of worksheet construction will not, in itself, help you to see its applications. Model building to allow 'what if' projections on, for example, a *cash flow forecast*, requires an understanding of the concepts behind the application, not simply an understanding of spreadsheet package operation. Figure 35.3 shows a model, which can assist a business in predicting its *cash flow* over a number of months.

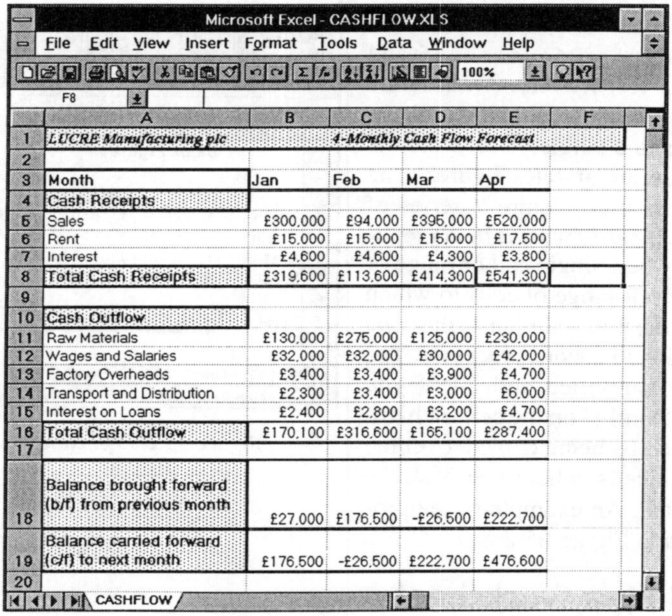

Figure 35.3. *Cashflow model*

By cash flow, we mean the cash surplus or deficit the business has at the end of each sub-period (in this case each month). Once developed, the only entries which need to be made are those concerning anticipated income and expenditure under a variety of itemised headings. The formulae built into the model automatically calculate new cash balances at the end of each month. The balance at the end of any particular month is carried forward and taken into account in the calculation of the next month's balance. This means that changes in anticipated income or expenditure, at any point before the end of the cycle, are reflected in the figures which follow. In other words, the model will allow 'what if' predictions to be made on what happens to the cash flow, when certain income or spending alternatives are placed into it.

Explanation of model entries

It is assumed that the model is being used at the beginning of January and that apart from the opening cash balance (which is known), all other figures are estimated. The accuracy of such figures depends on the stability of the company's business and their future sales orders. The model can be used to cover any period, for which future income and expenditure figures can be estimated. The various model entries are detailed in Table 35.1.

Cell References/Range	Explanation
B5 to E5	sales income
B6 to E6	rent income
B7 to E7	interest on investments
B8 to E8	total cash receipts
B11 to E11	raw materials costs
B12 to E12	wages and salaries costs
B13 to E13	factory overheads
B14 to E14	transport (sales distribution) costs
B15 to E15	interest payable on a loans
B16 to E16	total cash outflows
C18 to E18	closing cash balance brought forward from previous month
B18	opening cash balance for first month of model
B19 to E19	balance carried forward to next month. This formula calculates: Total Cash Receipts plus Balance b/f, minus Total Cash Outflow.

Table 35.1. *Explanation of cashflow model entries*

Figure 35.4 shows the worksheet with all the formulae displayed. The only formula that may need explanation appears first in cell C18. Note that it consists of a single cell reference, B19. This ensures that the 'balance c/f' figure is displayed in the next month's 'balance b/f' cell. Like all formulae in the worksheet example, this formula has been replicated (relatively) to the other relevant cells.

Worksheet layout

Although, you will sometimes need to make use of the spreadsheet's facilities, to insert and delete rows and columns, or to move the contents of cells elsewhere, you will save a great deal of time and effort if you plan the layout before you start. For a simple model, you probably don't need to write it down. For more complex models, you need to work out fairly precisely where everything should go. Most importantly, you need to decide what formulae you are going to use. Remember, if you need to use the same value (that is with the same purpose, such as a product price) more than once, only enter it once in the worksheet. If you need to use it elsewhere, reference it by formula. If the value needs to be changed, you only need to make one cell alteration and any formula which uses that cell then uses the new value.

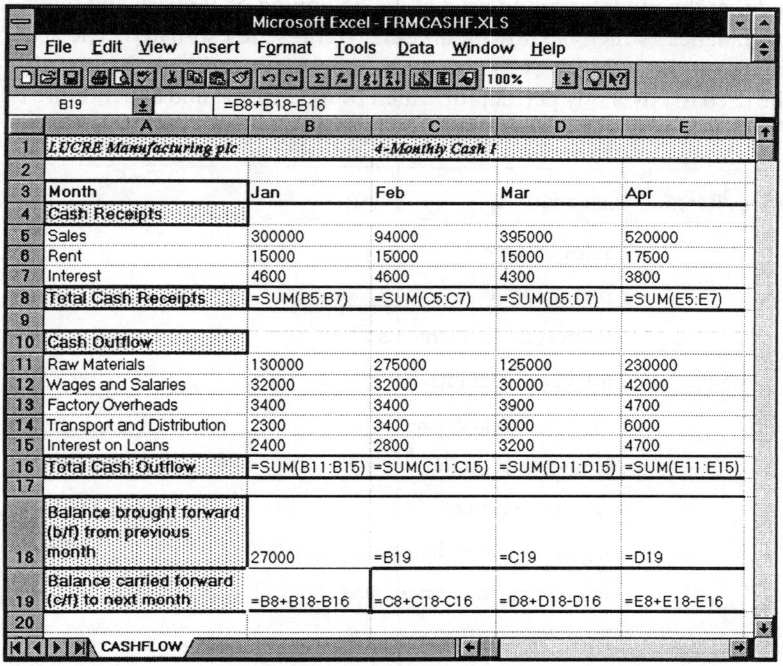

Microsoft Excel - FRMCASHF.XLS				
File Edit View Insert Format Tools Data Window Help				

B19 =B8+B18-B16

	A	B	C	D	E
1	*LUCRE Manufacturing plc*		*4-Monthly Cash F*		
2					
3	Month	Jan	Feb	Mar	Apr
4	Cash Receipts				
5	Sales	300000	94000	395000	520000
6	Rent	15000	15000	15000	17500
7	Interest	4600	4600	4300	3800
8	Total Cash Receipts	=SUM(B5:B7)	=SUM(C5:C7)	=SUM(D5:D7)	=SUM(E5:E7)
9					
10	Cash Outflow				
11	Raw Materials	130000	275000	125000	230000
12	Wages and Salaries	32000	32000	30000	42000
13	Factory Overheads	3400	3400	3900	4700
14	Transport and Distribution	2300	3400	3000	6000
15	Interest on Loans	2400	2800	3200	4700
16	Total Cash Outflow	=SUM(B11:B15)	=SUM(C11:C15)	=SUM(D11:D15)	=SUM(E11:E15)
17					
18	Balance brought forward (b/f) from previous month	27000	=B19	=C19	=D19
19	Balance carried forward (c/f) to next month	=B8+B18-B16	=C8+C18-C16	=D8+D18-D16	=E8+E18-E16
20					

CASHFLOW

Figure 35.4. *Cashflow model with formulae displayed*

Using the logical IF function

Your spreadsheet package provides a set of *logical* functions, which allow you to test the contents of cells against defined *logical tests*. The result of the test is either *true* or *false*. The idea can be illustrated without reference to a spreadsheet. Suppose, for example, that you are asked if you are over 25 years of age; your answer will be 'yes' or 'no'. If you answer 'yes', this equates to 'true'; you are over 25. A 'no' will confirm that you are 25 or less. The same question can be put to anyone, the answer being true (yes) or false (no), in each case. If you receive a 'no' answer, there is no need then to ask if a person is 25 or less, because the negative answer to the original question provides the information you want. Similarly, if you wish to know if someone subscribes to a superannuation scheme, you only need to ask one question, which can be phrased positively or negatively, thus: 'Do you subscribe to the superannuation scheme?' or 'Do you *not* subscribe to the superannuation scheme?'. Concerning your spreadsheet's logical functions, you should view such questions as logical tests.

The IF function has the following format. It has three arguments, separated by commas.

```
=IF(logical_test, value_if_true, value_if_false)
```

A simple example

Now consider the simple example in Figure 35.5. Column D is used to display a status message, indicating acceptance or rejection of each applicant for 'The Over 25 Club'. Only those aged over 25 are accepted. The `IF` formula in cell `D5` (shown on the edit line) tests the value in cell `C5` (the applicant's age), to determine if it is greater than 25. The first argument is, therefore, `C5>25`. The value in cell `C5` is 22, which means that the logical test returns *false* and that the word 'reject' is displayed. Cells `D6`, `D7` and `D8` contain the same formula, but testing the contents of cells `C6`, `C7`, and `C8`, respectively. The tests on `C6` and `C8` are found to be *true*, so the word 'accept' is displayed in the adjacent cells. The applicant Kerr, P is 25, so the logical test returns *false* and 'reject' is shown in the relevant Status cell.

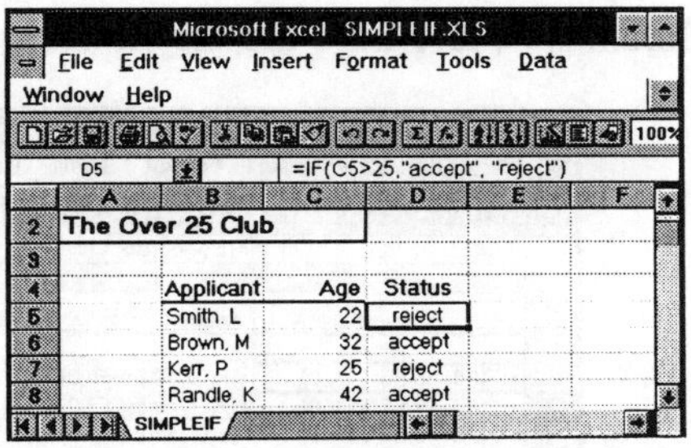

	A	B	C	D
2	The Over 25 Club			
3				
4		Applicant	Age	Status
5		Smith, L	22	reject
6		Brown, M	32	accept
7		Kerr, P	25	reject
8		Randle, K	42	accept

Figure 35.5. *Example use of IF*

A sales target model

Suppose that you are Sales Manager for the Target Corporation and wish to monitor the sales performance of your sales representatives.

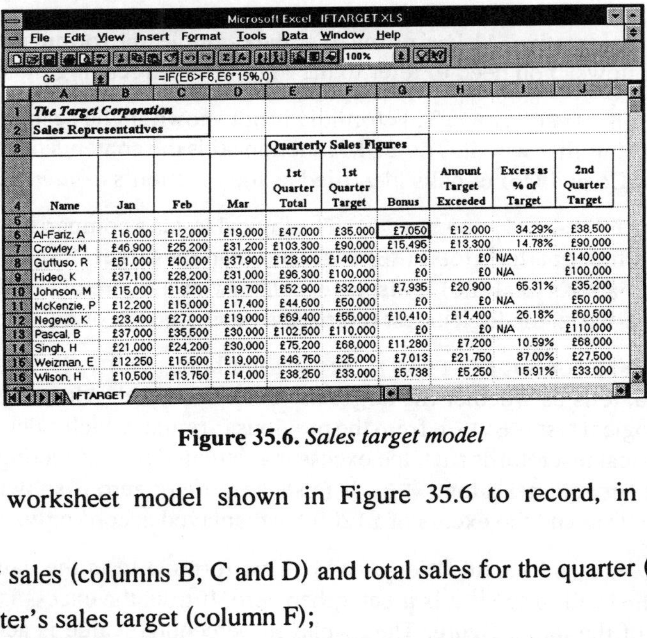

	A	B	C	D	E	F	G	H	I	J
1	*The Target Corporation*									
2	**Sales Representatives**									
3					**Quarterly Sales Figures**					
4	**Name**	**Jan**	**Feb**	**Mar**	**1st Quarter Total**	**1st Quarter Target**	**Bonus**	**Amount Target Exceeded**	**Excess as % of Target**	**2nd Quarter Target**
5										
6	Al-Fariz, A	£16,000	£12,000	£19,000	£47,000	£35,000	£7,050	£12,000	34.29%	£38,500
7	Crowley, M	£46,900	£25,200	£31,200	£103,300	£90,000	£15,495	£13,300	14.78%	£90,000
8	Guttuso, R	£51,000	£40,000	£37,900	£128,900	£140,000	£0	£0	N/A	£140,000
9	Hideo, K	£37,100	£28,200	£31,000	£96,300	£100,000	£0	£0	N/A	£100,000
10	Johnson, M	£15,000	£18,200	£19,700	£52,900	£32,000	£7,935	£20,900	65.31%	£35,200
11	McKenzie, P	£12,200	£15,000	£17,400	£44,600	£50,000	£0	£0	N/A	£50,000
12	Negewo, K	£23,400	£27,000	£19,000	£69,400	£55,000	£10,410	£14,400	26.18%	£60,500
13	Pascal, B	£37,000	£35,500	£30,000	£102,500	£110,000	£0	£0	N/A	£110,000
14	Singh, H	£21,000	£24,200	£30,000	£75,200	£68,000	£11,280	£7,200	10.59%	£68,000
15	Weizman, E	£12,250	£15,500	£19,000	£46,750	£25,000	£7,013	£21,750	87.00%	£27,500
16	Wilson, H	£10,500	£13,750	£14,000	£38,250	£33,000	£5,738	£5,250	15.91%	£33,000

Figure 35.6. *Sales target model*

You set up the worksheet model shown in Figure 35.6 to record, in respect of each representative:

1. monthly sales (columns B, C and D) and total sales for the quarter (column E);
2. the quarter's sales target (column F);
3. a bonus of 15% of the quarter's sales total, if the target has been beaten. Otherwise, the bonus is £0 (column G).
4. the amount by which the target has been exceeded (column H);
5. the target excess, as a percentage of the target (column I);
6. a new target for the next quarter (column J). If the 1st quarter's target has been exceeded by more than 20%, the new target should be set at 10% more than the 1st quarter's target. Otherwise, the new target is to remain the same as that of the 1st quarter.

Columns G, H, I and J are shown in Figure 35.7, with the formulae displayed.

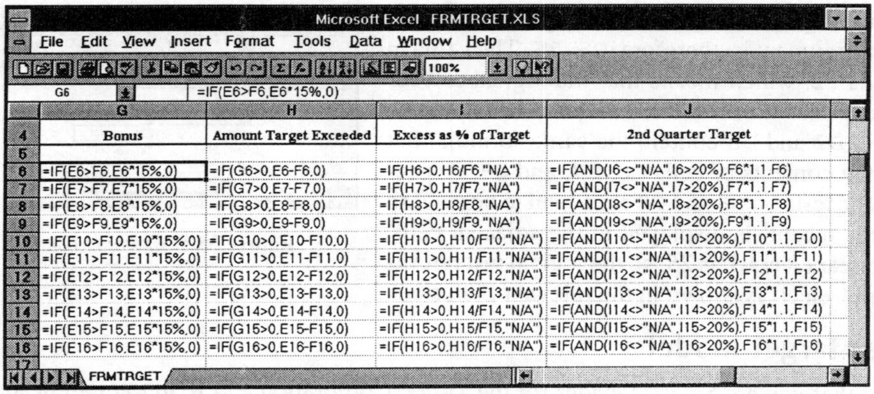

Figure 35.7. *Sales target model with formulae displayed*

Using the sales representative, Al-Fariz (row 6) as the example, the formula in each column can be explained as follows. You need to refer to the Figures when reading the explanations.

❑ Cell E6. =SUM(B6..D6). This formula is not shown in the second figure, but you should be familiar with it. The SUM function adds the contents of the *range* (in this case, B6, C6 and D6) of cells identified as the function's *argument*.

❑ Cell G6. =IF(E6>F6,E6*15%,0). The logical test is a comparison of cells E6 and F6. If the first quarter's total (E6) is greater than the target (F6) a bonus of 15% of the first quarter's total (E6) is displayed. Otherwise a figure of zero is shown. In the case of Al-Fariz, the logical test returns *true* and a bonus of £7050 is displayed.

❑ Cell H6. =IF(G6>0,E6-F6,0). Testing the bonus cell (G6) for a value greater than zero, tells us whether the target has been exceeded. Alternatively, you could use the logical test (E6>F6), from the previous formula, which calculated the bonus. If the logical test returns true, the excess is calculated by subtracting the target (F6) from the first quarter's total (E6). If false, a figure of zero is shown. For Al-Fariz, the test is true and the excess of £12000 is displayed accordingly.

❑ Cell I6. =IF(H6>0,H6/F6,'N/A'). This formula tests the value in the target excess (H6) cell to see if it is greater than zero. If true, the excess is calculated as a fraction of the target figure. The displayed percentage value is achieved with the *formatting* facility, which multiplies the fraction by 100. If false, the N/A (meaning 'not applicable') message is displayed. Note that you must enclose this non-numeric data in quotation marks. In the case of Al-Fariz, the test is true and the figure of 34.29% appears.

❑ Cell J6. =IF(AND(I6'N/A',I6>20%),F6*1.1,F6). This is an example of a *complex condition*. In other words, it tests the value in cell I6 to check that it is not equal to 'N/A' AND that it is greater than 20%. There is no point in checking for a percentage value if the cell contains the letters 'N/A', so both conditions must be satisfied before the value for true is returned. This is the case for Al-Fariz and the target is increased by 10% (F6*1.1) from £35000 to £38500. There is another reason for testing for both conditions. It so happens that, for the computer, 'N/A' is greater than the value 20%. If you did not test for the 'N/A' value, you would find that the target is still increased for those cells containing the 'N/A' value. If either test returns false, the new target remains the same as the old (it displays the same value as F6). Crowley (row 7) has beaten the target, but not by 20%, so the new target remains the same as the old. The excess percentage cell for Guttoso (row 8) shows 'N/A', so the new target is not increased.

Using the LOOKUP function

This function is used to extract a value from a table by reference to another value. It is likely that you already use *lookup tables*, but not necessarily in the context of a spreadsheet package. For example, when you want the price of an item in a catalogue, you scan the product list for the relevant item and thereby find the price. Thus the product name or code is the *lookup value* and the associated price is the *extracted value*. Similarly, banks often display a table of currency exchange rates. By scanning the list of countries, you can find the appropriate exchange rate, from one of the adjacent columns. Usually, there are four rate columns, to separately identify the rates at which the bank buys and sells notes and travellers' cheques. Once you have found the right country, you have to scan across to the appropriate column to extract the rate you want. There are two forms of the function, VLOOKUP for tables organised vertically, or in column form and HLOOKUP for tables which are set out horizontally or in rows. Table 35.2 shows the horizontal format, using rates of pay as an example.

Job grade	A	B	C	D
Hourly rate of pay	£5.00	£7.50	£8.50	£12.00

Table 35.2. *Pay rates in a horizontal table*

To identify a particular rate of pay, you need to identify the Job Grade (the lookup value is a letter in this case) from the top row and then look at the second row for the Hourly Rate, which appears beneath the letter.

Format of the LOOKUP function

The arguments for the two LOOKUP forms are shown below.

```
=VLOOKUP(lookup value, table array, column index)
=HLOOKUP(lookup value, table array, row index)
```

Note that they only differ in respect of the third argument; one refers to column and the other to row. The purposes of these arguments are given below.

1. *lookup value*. This will normally be a cell reference, which contains the value to be used to search the table. It may contain, for example, a product code to search a price table.

2. *table array*. This identifies the location of the table in the worksheet. The range of cells will be identified by the top left and bottom right cell references.

3. *column/row index*. This identifies the column or row in the table array, from which the

value is to be taken. In the earlier exchange rate example, you would use this argument to specify which exchange rate column was to be used. The Excel spreadsheet refers to the leftmost column in a table as 1 and columns to the right are identified as 2, 3 and so on. For a horizontal table, the top row is 1 and rows beneath are similarly incremented. Other packages may refer to the leftmost column as 0 and adjacent columns are referred to as *offset* column 1, 2 and so on. An equivalent pattern is used in horizontal tables. It is important to note that column and row indexes, or offsets, refer to the table array and not to the worksheet as a whole.

Note that the values in the leftmost column (for a vertical table) or the top row (for a horizontal table) must be in *ascending* sequence. Thus, alphabetic values must be in ascending alphabetical order and numeric values in ascending numerical order. Remember that the lookup value (the first argument) is compared with these values and if they are not in ascending sequence, the formula will not work properly.

A pay rates example

This example uses a table of pay rates, referenced by job grade, to calculate some simplified payroll details. Figure 35.8 shows some example output for this worksheet. The worksheet is repeated in Figure 35.9, with the formulae displayed.

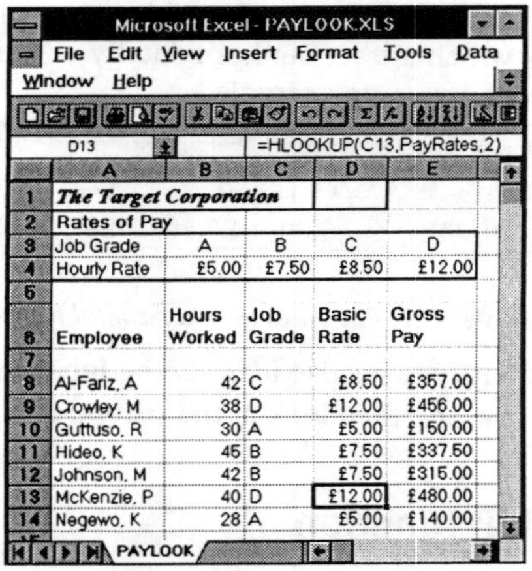

	A	B	C	D	E
1	***The Target Corporation***				
2	Rates of Pay				
3	Job Grade	A	B	C	D
4	Hourly Rate	£5.00	£7.50	£8.50	£12.00
6					
8	Employee	Hours Worked	Job Grade	Basic Rate	Gross Pay
7					
8	Al-Fariz, A	42	C	£8.50	£357.00
9	Crowley, M	38	D	£12.00	£456.00
10	Guttuso, R	30	A	£5.00	£150.00
11	Hideo, K	45	B	£7.50	£337.50
12	Johnson, M	42	B	£7.50	£315.00
13	McKenzie, P	40	D	£12.00	£480.00
14	Negewo, K	28	A	£5.00	£140.00

Figure 35.8. *LOOKUP table*

Using the Employee McKenzie (row 13) as the example, the formulae can be explained as follows.

- Cell `D13`. `=HLOOKUP(C13,PayRates,2)`. The `HLOOKUP` function ensures that the table is referenced horizontally, by row. The first argument, `C13`, contains the lookup value. In this case it is job grade D. The lookup value is compared with the entries in the top row of the table. The second argument identifies the lookup table as the range of cells named `PayRates` (array `B3:E4`). The third argument ensures that the value associated with this grade (in this case, £12.00) is taken from the second row of the table.

- Cell E13. =B13*D13. This simply multiplies the hours worked figure (in B13) by the rate of pay extracted from the lookup table, to give the gross pay for McKenzie.

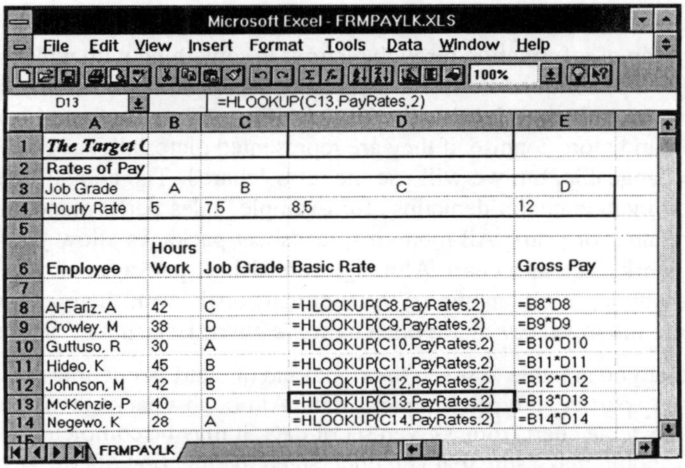

	A	B	C	D	E
1	*The Target C*				
2	Rates of Pay				
3	Job Grade	A	B	C	D
4	Hourly Rate	5	7.5	8.5	12
5					
6	Employee	Hours Work	Job Grade	Basic Rate	Gross Pay
7					
8	Al-Fariz, A	42	C	=HLOOKUP(C8,PayRates,2)	=B8*D8
9	Crowley, M	38	D	=HLOOKUP(C9,PayRates,2)	=B9*D9
10	Guttuso, R	30	A	=HLOOKUP(C10,PayRates,2)	=B10*D10
11	Hideo, K	45	B	=HLOOKUP(C11,PayRates,2)	=B11*D11
12	Johnson, M	42	B	=HLOOKUP(C12,PayRates,2)	=B12*D12
13	McKenzie, P	40	D	=HLOOKUP(C13,PayRates,2)	=B13*D13
14	Negewo, K	28	A	=HLOOKUP(C14,PayRates,2)	=B14*D14

Figure 35.9. *Pay calculation example with formulae displayed*

Exercises

See end of Topic 36.

Spreadsheet graphics

The communication of information through pictures is something with which we are all familiar. For example, a pictorial advertisement in a magazine can often convey information that, without a picture, would take a few hundred words of text. The meaning of numeric data is often made clearer and more concise, if they are represented pictorially, as *graphs* or *charts* (the terms are interchangeable, but we will use the term 'chart'). The annual financial reports of companies often include charts depicting, for example, sales performance over the year, or profits over a number of years. All modern spreadsheet packages allow you to represent numeric data in a worksheet, as a chart. Although spreadsheet packages allow you to produce a large variety of charts, in either two or three-dimensional form, there are four basic types, which are common to most: *bar* chart; *line* chart; *pie* chart; *xy (scatter)* diagram.

It is important that you are able to select the right kind of chart (sometimes more than one may be suitable) for any particular type of numeric data. Although a package may allow you to produce, for example, a pie chart from a given set of data, it may be completely meaningless. For this reason, you should make sure that you understand the function of any particular chart, and how to construct one manually, before you attempt spreadsheet graphics. Spreadsheet packages include many automated functions which you can use to make chart production simpler. It is common to provide a utility (Excel refers to it as a 'Chart Wizard') to take you, step by step, through the chart production process. It even displays the current state of the chart at each stage. This is particularly useful if you are required to make a selection, perhaps of the type of chart you want, and are unsure which to choose. You can simply try one, and if it is not what you want, select another.

Linking data to a chart

A set of numeric values which you want to use in a chart, is commonly known as a *data range* or *data series*. Various examples of such data series are shown in the figures which follow. Before you start the charting process, you should have decided (although you can change your mind later) on the type of chart you want. If you decide to produce a bar chart, then the data series you choose can also be used for a line graph (and vice versa). The following sections describe the component parts of each chart type listed in the introductory paragraph, and the procedures used to produce them.

Bar charts

A basic bar chart consists of a series of bars with lengths proportional to the quantities they represent. Bar charts are useful for depicting a series of changes in figures of interest.

Figure 36.1 shows an example *bar* chart, embedded in a worksheet which calculates the costs of various holidays. The chart's *axes* are generated from cells A3:B6. The Y-axis uses the costs in cells B3, B4, B5 and B6. The maximum value on the *Y-axis scale* has been set at £5000; the default maximum would be £4000, because the largest value in the data series is £3,505 and the scale is in divisions of £1000. The *X-axis labels* are taken from the holiday destinations of Vienna, Prague, Paris and Siena, in cells A3 to A6. *Data labels* can be used to show the precise figure represented by each bar, although the main purpose of the bar chart is to compare costs, as measured against the Y-axis scale. If data labels are not used and more precise comparison is wanted, then the Y-axis scale can be divided into £500 intervals. To generate the chart in Figure 36.1, the adjacent cells containing the X-axis labels and the Y-axis data series are highlighted. From this highlighted information, the spreadsheet can generate the basic chart, showing an X-axis with labels, a Y-axis suitably scaled to cover the range of values in the data series and bars representing each value. Other detail, such as chart title, axes titles and data labels can then be added. In Figure 36.1, the Y-axis title is 'Costs' and the X-axis title is 'Destination'.

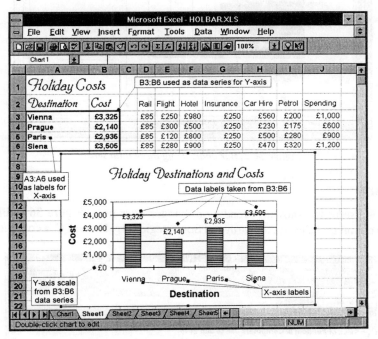

Figure 36.1. *Bar chart of holiday destinations and costs*

Bar chart with multiple data series

The chart in Figure 36.1 has only one data series. In other words, each bar relates to the cost of holidays. Figure 36.2 shows a worksheet and chart, which represent the sales figures (units sold) of three products, namely dishwashers, washing machines and cookers. This means that there are three sets of values, or data series, to represent. The process of chart construction is the same as that for the chart in Figure 36.1. The range of cells from D2 to G6 is highlighted and used by the program to generate the chart.

One feature of the chart in Figure 36.2, which is not present in Figure 36.1, is a *data legend*. This identifies each bar with the relevant product. If there is only one data series, then a legend is not necessary. You will also note that Figure 36.2 shows a bar chart, with a vertical X-axis and a horizontal Y-axis. The basic form of chart is, however, the same as that represented in Figure 36.1. Multiple bar charts are not recommended for more than four sets of figures, because more than this number of adjacent components detracts from the clarity and usefulness of the diagram.

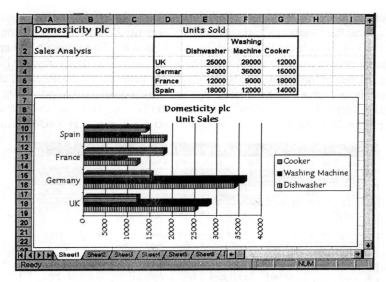

Figure 36.2. *Bar chart using three data series*

Line chart

A *line* chart is useful for showing trends, or changes over time. Figure 36.3 illustrates the movement in computer sales in the North and South regions by Home PC, a computer supplier.

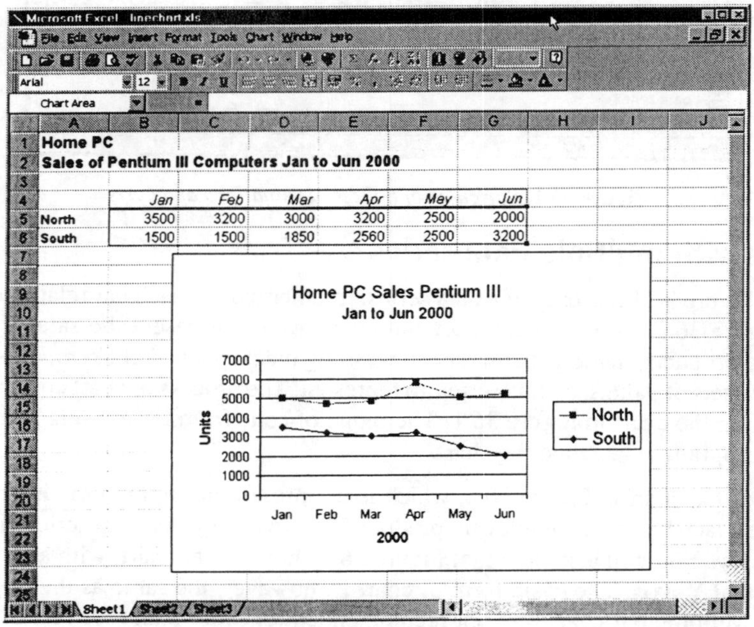

Figure 36.3. *Line chart using two data series*

Although a bar chart could have been used, the comparison of these two sets of sales figures (the data series) is more clearly illustrated with a line chart. The line joining the points marked with the diamond and square symbols help to emphasise trends, so that it is quite easy to compare the two sets of sales figures. It should be noted, however, that the connecting lines cannot be used to interpolate intermediate values; the horizontal scale does not represent a continuous quantity with meaningful values between those marked.

Pie chart

A pie chart is a circle divided into segments. The area of each segment is proportional to the size of the figure represented, and the complete 'pie' represents the overall total of all component parts. It is therefore, a convenient way of illustrating the sizes of quantities in relation to one another and the overall total.

Figure 36.4 shows a typical *pie* chart, together with the data series represented in the chart. A pie chart always contains just one data series and shows each value as a percentage of the total for the series. Each 'slice' or 'wedge' represents one value and colour or cross hatching is used to differentiate one slice from another.

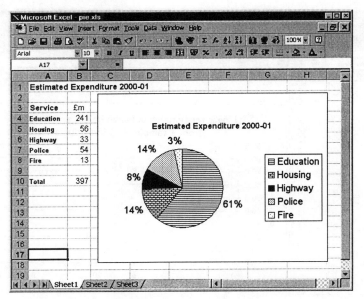

Figure 36.4. *3D pie chart showing distribution of expenditure items*

XY (scatter) diagram

A scatter diagram is particularly appropriate when two measurements are taken from some common *unit if association*, that is some common element on which the two measurements are taken, such as persons, places, or points in time. When each pair of points is plotted, the resulting graph is called a scatter diagram, or *scattergram*. For example, suppose that we have measured the height and weight of 20 subjects and the results are as shown in Table 36.1.

Subject	Height (cm)	Weight (kg)	Subject	Height (cm)	Weight (kg
1	178	85.1	11	176	79.0
2	162	73.6	12	166	75.0
3	173	78.5	13	161	72.2
4	179	79.1	14	169	81.6
5	160	62.5	15	165	71.1
6	168	72.3	16	176	85.6
7	179	82.6	17	167	75.1
8	153	63.1	18	168	75.5
9	159	74.3	19	166	79.0
10	167	73.0	20	166	72.7

Table 36.1. *Data for scatter diagram*

The scatter diagram based on this data and generated in a spreadsheet is shown in Figure 36.5.

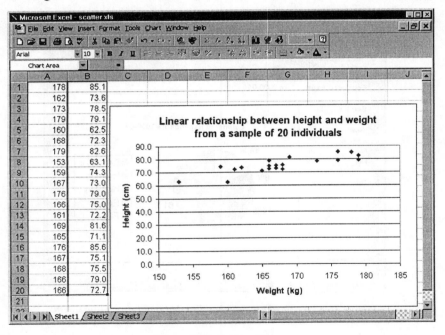

Figure 36.5. *Scatter diagram*

The scatter diagram appears to show that there is a simple linear relationship between the two measurements - there is a tendency for tall people to be heavy and short people to be light.

✍️Exercises

1. An extract of a sales record spreadsheet is shown below.

	A	B	C	D	E	F	G	H
1	Sales records					Unit Price	3.50	
2	Name		Units sold	Sales value				
3		Jones	500	=C3*$G1				
4		Guttoso	300					
5		Fariz	420					
6		McDonald	180					
7		Total						
8								

(i) The formula in cell D3 calculates the value of goods sold by Jones, what value will be shown here?

(ii) The $ sign indicates that the reference to cell G1 is absolute. What values would appear in cells D4, D5 and D6 if the formula in C3 was replicated to those cells?

(iii) If the absolute cell reference was not used, how would this effect the replication of the formula to cells D4, D5 an D6?

(iv) Referring to your answer to (iii), distinguish between an absolute and relative cell reference.

(v) Write a formula (using a function) which would calculate a total for column C.

(vi) Should the formula you enter in C6 be copied relatively or absolutely to D6?

(vii) Explain how a chart is created to compare and show the total sales value achieved by each salesperson.

(viii) State, with reasons, which chart type would be most appropriate to display the information detailed in (vii)

This Topic looks at three types of software, all designed for graphical work:

❑   'paint' packages for bit mapped images;

❑   computer-aided drawing packages for vector graphics.

Although drawing packages are designed primarily for vector graphics, they also make use of bit maps and the reverse is true of graphic design packages, such as Corel PhotoPaint and Adobe Photoshop. CorelDRAW is a good example of an illustrator's package, with sophisticated facilities for the manipulation of all types of image. Before you use a graphics package, you need to be clear about what is meant by 'bit map' and 'vector' graphics. We examine Bit maps first.

Bit maps

Bit maps include clip art, drawings produced with 'paint' software and other digital images, such as scanned pictures, photographs taken with a digital camera and individual frames captured from a video sequence. Also, graphics produced with a *vector-based* (see later) drawing package, such as CorelDRAW, can be *exported* as bit maps. A bit map comprises a fixed number of *pixels* (or picture elements), and the computer sets each one to a particular colour, to form the image. In the case of greyscale images, each pixel is set to a black, white or one of a number of shades of grey. For more information on bit map file formats see Topic 41 on Multimedia.

Processing bit maps

There are various ways in which bit maps can be edited, manipulated and processed.

Magnifying and editing

Alterations in the detail of the image can only be achieved at the pixel level, so paint software allows the user to *magnify* ('zoom in') the image, to enable the editing of individual or groups of pixels. The magnification does not enlarge the image, so the file size and the number of pixels remains unaltered. Figure 37.1 shows an unmagnified photograph and a section magnified 8 times.

Re-sizing and re-sampling

When an image is enlarged it is beneficial to maintain the pixel density (dots per inch or dpi), otherwise, depending on the scale of the enlargement, the image may appear 'grainy', or at worst, have a 'Lego block' appearance. Fortunately, image processing packages allow an image to be enlarged and through a process of re-sampling, maintain the number of pixels per inch (or other unit of measurement).

Figure 37.1. *Magnification*

For example, if an image has a pixel density of 96 dpi and dimensions of 2 x 1.333 inches, it can be calculated that the image is comprised of 192 columns of pixels (2 x 96) and 128 rows of pixels (1.333 x 96) vertically, giving a total of 24,576 pixels (196 x 128) over the whole image. If the image is enlarged four times to dimensions of 8 x 5.333 inches by re-sampling, the re-sampled image has 393,216 pixels – 768 x 512 - compared with the original image's 24,576. Note, however, that the re-sampled image is not as well defined or 'sharp'. This is because the additional pixels have been generated by averaging the existing areas of pixel colours and adding intermediary ones, where they did not previously exist; this process is called *interpolation*. Another process, known as *anti-aliasing*, smooths out sharp edges which appear when newly inserted pixels create sharp divisions between colours. Unfortunately, the anti-aliasing process can lead to a blurring of the image. Enlargement, without anti-aliasing, produces jagged edges where new pixels create sharp divisions instead of a smooth transition between colours.

Other image transformations

A number of effects can be used to transform the appearance of bit map images. Figures 37.2, 37.3 and 37.4 show some examples.

Figure 37.2. *Posterised image*   **Figure 37.3.** *Negative image*   **Figure 37.4.** *Edge detect*

Other image transformations include the adjustment of:

❑ Brightness and contrast. The brightness of all colours in the image are adjusted equally, which can result in the lighter colours appearing washed out and loss of detail. Adjusting contrast can bring the detail back.

❑ Gamma. This allows detail to be retained even when the image is brightened or darkened and is a useful alternative to adjustment of brightness and contrast. Shadows and highlights are not lost, as they tend to be when simple brightness adjustment is used.

❑ Hue, saturation and lightness. Hue means colour, saturation is the depth or richness of colour and adjustment of lightness affects the amount of white in the image.

❑ Colour balance allows adjustment of the amount of red, green or blue (RGB colour model) towards cyan, magenta and yellow respectively (CYM colour model).

Paint tools

Figure 37.5. *Tool box in Corel PhotoPaint*

The tools in Figure 37.5 are, from left to right: *object picker* for selecting, moving and resizing objects, such as text and shapes; *mask* tool for selecting areas of an image for copying or cutting. There are several mask types, including an ellipse, freehand and 'magic wand'. The wand automatically selects areas with pixels of similar colour to that selected with the wand; a colour tolerance bar allows the range of pixels which will be selected to be reduced or increased; *path* tool for creating paths which can be used to guide a brush stroke or create a masked area; *crop* tool for removing areas of the image outside of the crop selection; *magnifying* tool; *eyedropper* used to select a paint, paper, or fill colour from an open image. The colour is picked up from a pixel when it is selected; *eraser* tools for changing brushed areas to the paper colour or restoring a previously erased area; *shape* tool; *text* tool; *fill* tool; *transparency* tool which allows the background to show through a selected object to varying degrees; *paint* tool, with various brush styles and sizes. The toolbar shown in the Figure include a number of *flyouts* which gives access to additional tools.

Vector graphics

Vectored images are drawn by setting coordinate points, or vectors. A two-dimensional (2-D) drawing requires the setting of y-coordinates (the vertical position) and x-coordinates (the horizontal position). A three-dimensional image (3-D) needs a third vector for the depth, a z-coordinate. An image consists of a number of lines drawn between a number of x, y and, in the case of 3-D, z coordinates. By altering vector values, an image can be re-scaled and for animation purposes, moved around the screen.

When a vector image is enlarged, there is no loss of definition, as happens with bit maps (see later). For example, if you draw a 2cm square and fill it with a colour, there will be a particular number of pixels forming the image; the number will depend on the software used and the resolution capability of the screen. If you then re-scale the image to a 4cm square, it will be formed with proportionally more pixels, thus giving the same density and clarity to the enlarged image.

Computer aided drawing

Line drawings

A graphics program provides a range of tools which you can use to draw geometric figures, as well as freeform shapes. Figure 37.6 shows a simple line drawing.

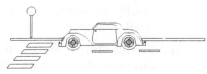

Figure 37.6. *Simple line drawing*

Freeform

Freeform drawing is the most difficult, because it requires a very steady and confident hand to produce smooth, flowing lines. If, as is likely, you are using a mouse (rather than a light pen or graphics tablet), you need to use the drag function to draw freeform lines. This means positioning the *pencil tool* pointer (typically, a cross) at your chosen starting point and then holding the appropriate mouse button down, while *dragging* the tool pointer through the required outline. To signal the end of the line may simply require that you release, or *double click*, the mouse button. You can smooth out any curves that are a little ragged by using control points to manipulate selected nodes on the line. Figure 37.7 shows a line being manipulated in this way.

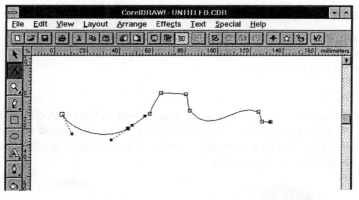

Figure 37.7. *Node manipulation of freeform line*

Regular shapes

There are tools for drawing rectangles, circles, ellipses and polygons, stars and polylines.

Line styles

The *default line style* is a solid, with a thickness approximating to that drawn with a sharp pencil. You may wish to vary the thickness of a line, make it dotted, or dashed, or place an arrow head on either, or both ends (some packages do not include arrow head symbols).

Colour and shade

If you are not using a colour printer, then you need to make use of shading to differentiate between various aspects of an image. The microcomputer image on the right makes use of such shading to produce a three-dimensional appearance. Five shades are shown in Figure 37.8, as percentages of black.

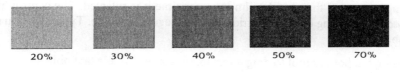

| 20% | 30% | 40% | 50% | 70% |

Figure 37.8.

Handling objects

An object is any graphical figure that can be handled as a unit. Thus, when you use any drawing tool, or key in some text (in one completed operation) you are creating an object. Some tools always produce an easily defined object. These include the ellipse (or circle), the rectangle (or square), the curve and single straight line tools, which all produce precise geometric forms. The freeform and polygon tools can be use to produce graphics that may be simple or complex. The completion of such a graphic object is determined by the point at which you indicate its completion (usually by double clicking the mouse button).

Selecting and re-sizing

Once you complete an object, *control handles* appear around it, or you may have to *select* the object with the pointer tool. These handles can be used to alter the size and proportions (by varying its overall length or height).

Object fill

Figure 37.9 shows two objects, a rectangle with no fill and, behind it an ellipse filled with 70% black. In other words, the rectangle is transparent, allowing the ellipse behind it to be seen (apart from the areas covered by the rectangle border. If the rectangle is filled, for example with white, then the result is as in Figure 37.10.

Figure 37.9   **Figure 37.10**

Magnifying

Generally known as a 'zoom' facility, it is usually represented in the toolbox by a magnifying glass symbol. You can use the tool to alter the amount of detail you have in view at any one time. If you want to see the whole page, you can reduce the magnification. To view a small part of an object in detail (for precise working), you can select the area to be magnified and then, a level of magnification. Often, these magnification levels are measured in percentages.

Grouping

As explained earlier, each separate drawing operation produces a separate object. As you build up a drawing, you may want to treat several objects as a group, for separate manipulation. For example, having completed a drawing consisting of say, 25 objects, you may want to alter its size. By selecting all the objects and then using the *group objects* option, a rectangular control box will appear around the complete image, each time it is selected. The control handles can then be used for re-sizing or re-proportioning the image as a whole. Typically, you may select multiple objects by:

❑   using the pointer tool to drag a rectangle around the relevant objects;

❑   clicking on each object separately, whilst holding down the shift key.

If you wish to edit a grouped object, you must first *ungroup* (separate into the original discrete objects) it. This may be an iterative (repeated an unspecified number of times) process, since you might have built up a group as a series of hierarchical sub-groups. Sometimes, objects may be selected and edited separately without ungrouping, typically by holding down the Control key whilst selecting the relevant object.

Layering

There will be many occasions when you want to superimpose one image onto another. In fact, you may end up with several objects stacked one on top of another. In such cases, you may need to alter the order of the objects in the pile. If, for example, you want to place some text inside a filled ellipse, you need to make sure that the text is on top, or it will be hidden by the ellipse. Depending on which you do first, you may have to place the ellipse at the back, or the text at the front.

Packages vary widely in the amount of flexibility they provide for changing the stacked order of objects. The simplest packages provide only two options - 'bring to the front' and 'take to the back'. If you are working with several stacked objects, you need to plan their stacking order carefully, or you will forget where a particular object is in the stack. Also complex reshuffling is impossible without separating all the objects and starting the stacking procedure again. More sophisticated packages allow more flexibility, by including additional options to bring an object 'one forward' or take it 'one back', and to reverse the stacking order.

Rotation

This facility can be used to alter the angle at which an object lies. Typically, an object (or several if they have been grouped) can be *rotated* 90 degrees to the left or to the right. The operation may be repeated if rotations of 180 or 270 degrees are required. *Flipping* an object allows you to turn it through 180 degrees about a vertical or horizontal axis. Examples of rotation and flipping are shown in the Graphics section of Word Processing. Some packages allow more precise rotations, using single degrees, or even tenths of degrees.

Duplicating

By selecting an object or group of object you can duplicate an image. This is useful if you want exactly the same image, or to modify it slightly, leaving the original intact. If for example, you want a series of squares, all the same size, duplication is the only sensible option to use.

Aligning

To align objects, you can use the *grid* (an arrangement of intersecting vertical and horizontal lines), which (if switched on) *snaps* any new or moved object to it. The density of the grid (the number of lines per inch) dictates the precision with which you can position objects. The grid is very useful if you need to arrange groups of objects in rows or columns. If the grid is switched on, any object you create, or one that you move, will snap to the nearest pair of intersecting grid lines (horizontal and vertical). With a density of, say, 8 lines per inch, you will notice a slight jerkiness of movement as you move an object around and it snaps to various points on the grid.

To position objects precisely, without the constraints of the grid, you may be able to use *guidelines* or some other alignment facility. Two guidelines are normally available, one for vertical alignment and the other for horizontal. The difference from the grid is that you can move the guideline to any desired position. An object brought near to a guideline automatically attaches to it. Objects can be attached to either side of either guideline (aligned left, right, top or bottom) or be centred on it. By using the intersection of both guidelines, you can, for example, align a group of circles (of various sizes) concentrically (all have the same centre).

Copying, cutting and pasting

You have probably come across these facilities in your word processor or desktop publishing package. In a graphics package, however, the facilities are used more for the transfer of images to other applications (see Using Multiple Applications). Both the *copy* and *cut* operations create a copy of the selected object(s) in a memory buffer (*clipboard*). As the terms suggest, 'copy' leaves the original intact, whilst 'cut' removes it. You may need to use the copy facility to duplicate objects, although there may be a separate 'duplicate' option.

Deleting or clearing

This option has the same effect as the cutting operation, except that no clipboard copy is created. This may be useful if you want to preserve the existing contents of the clipboard (another cut operation would destroy its existing contents).

Setting dimensions

If you are producing a technical drawing, you will probably want to draw images to scale, so you need to be able to set precise dimensions. Figure 37.11 shows an example.

There are a variety of facilities you can use to set dimensions, the most common being:

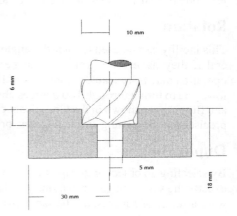

- ❏ a grid of horizontal and vertical lines (perhaps invisible), a set distance apart, to which you can 'snap' the limits of an object;

- ❏ rulers along the top and down the side of the drawing area, which you can use to size an image.

- ❏ specify the dimensions of each object through a dialogue.

Figure 37.11. *Dimensioned engineering part*

- ❏ an automatic dimension tool such as that used to produce the engineering drawing shown in Figure 37.11.

The drawing of small engineering part in the Figure is dimensioned. If the drawing is to scale, then other measurements can be taken directly from the drawing and multiplied by the scaling factor. For example, if a scale of 1:50 is used, then a measurement taken from the drawing must be multiplied by 50 to determine the actual figure.

Text

The text tool is usually represented by a letter 'A' and the pointer is a short, vertical line, similar to the insertion point cursor in a word processor. Like sophisticated word processors, CAD packages provide you with a wide variety of fonts, which can be varied in size and style. Entry of a text string produces an object, which like other graphics objects, can be selected for moving, copying, cutting or deleting. Although some sophisticated CAD packages allow you to use the control handles (see earlier section on Handling Objects) to vary the size of the text, most require that you select the appropriate menu option. You may also be able to rotate text objects, which is useful if you want to label a drawing.

Graphics libraries

Graphics software for a specialist application, such as architecture, kitchen design or circuit design will provide libraries of graphical symbols and images which are commonly used in the application. So, for example, a kitchen design package has standard symbols for cupboards, washing machines and cookers of various sizes for use in planned layouts. Similarly, an architect has symbols for doors and windows, cavity walls, drainage components and so on. The use of library images ensures consistent appearance across all designs and brings great improvements in application efficiency. Professional and industry standards bodies can provide updates on CD-ROM to their members or to the suppliers of the software and ensure the use of current symbol standards.

Exercises

1. An architect uses a vector graphics drawing program to produce dimensioned building plans to scale.
   (i) Explain the term *vector graphics* and explain why the architect uses this kind of package.
   (ii) The package also includes facilities for handling bit maps. Suggest examples of how these facilities may be put to use by the architect.
   (iii) What is a graphics library and how may the architect make use of one?
2. A graphic designer uses a graphics package which specialises in the processing of bitmap images, but also has vector graphics features.
   (i) A photograph is to be enlarged to 4 times the original size. What package features should enable the designer to produce the larger image whilst retaining much of the image quality?
   (ii) Some detailed editing of the image is also necessary. Explain the process.
   (iii) Research the facilities in a 'paint' package and note the types of special effects it can produce.

A slide presentation package, such as Microsoft PowerPoint, enables the user to create, assemble and run slide shows on a computer screen, either automatically, or under user control. Apart from on-screen presentations, individual slides can be printed with a conventional printer, or be transferred to acetate sheets for display on an overhead projector, or be output as 35mm slides. It has to be said that significant communication impact is lost if on-screen display is not used. On-screen displays are dynamic and can include text, graphics, animations, video sequences and sound, as well as hyperlinks (text or images which can be mouse clicked to jump to another part of the presentation, to a different presentation or indeed, to other sources of information, such as a Web site). A presentation can be viewed passively or with user interaction. Colour, movement and sound can all contribute to get your message across. Facilities also include various screen 'wipes', 'zooms' and 'dissolves' (commonly available with camcorders). Images can be produced or taken from a library within the package, or they may be produced in another application and then imported. The three Figures show some of the features of a sample slide show.

Figure 38.1. Opening slide

Figure 38.2. Second slide

Figure 38.3. Closing slide

The main facilities you need are:

❑ *Backgrounds.* You can select a background from a library provided with the package, or create your own. Most of the backgrounds in the library are only suitable for screen presentation, because, that is the way they are meant to be used. If you do want to print them, you should probably design one of your own, using only limited shading; heavy use of colour and shading does not print well in monochrome. A colour printer, on the other hand, should produce satisfactory results. The package may provide in-built facilities for you to create your own backgrounds, or you may have to create them in another graphics package and then import them using OLE (Object Linking and Embedding), to allow access to the source package and editing of the image.

- ❑ *Graphics objects from other packages.* This includes clip art and other images created with other software. The appropriate import filters must be available to convert one form of image to another.

- ❑ *Text entered within the package.* The usual text formatting facilities are available, including the facility to add bullets to listed items.

- ❑ *Sound and animation.* The package may allow the inclusion of sound objects and animation sequences created with a package, such as CorelMOVE.

- ❑ *Slide sorter.* This facility allows you to insert or delete slides and change their sequence.

- ❑ *Run screen show.* This starts the display, one after another, of the slides you have included in your show. You can set a standard time for the display of each slide or use a *timeline* to set individual timings for each slide.

- ❑ *Transition effects.* These are commonly available with camcorders and provide various screen 'wipe' or 'dissolve' modes to smooth the transition between slides.

The following features are specific to PowerPoint, but illustrates the ways in which presentations can be developed.

- ❑ PowerPoint provides a number of standard slide layouts, with text boxes and places to insert pictures. These can be altered or you can create your own. Alternatively, a slide can be set up with preset entry points for text and graphics, using an AutoLayout. A standard layout can be altered by moving, resizing, deleting or inserting text boxes or graphics frames.

- ❑ Animations can be applied to both text and picture objects.

- ❑ When you insert a blank slide, it will use the same template as the others and have the same background, thus ensuring consistency across the presentation.

- ❑ Clip art, photographs, sounds and video sequences are all accessible through the Insert | Picture menu.

Slide presentation design

A presentation needs to be carefully designed to take into account its content and the target audience. It is helpful to consider the following questions and guidelines.

1. Is the user going to browse through and control the flow of the presentation or will the show be controlled by a presenter with spoken commentary? The answer to this question will affect the content of slides - if there is spoken commentary, supplementary information can be provided without cluttering up the slide with too much information.

2. Is the information provided in the presentation regarded as important or of real interest to the audience? Careful use of animation and where possible, sound can provide impact and prevent the audience from slipping into a deep sleep. On the other hand, fancy effects can distract the audience from the content of a message.

3.   Images should be carefully chosen to suit the subject and the target audience. Car-
     toon images can add a little humour, but <u>may</u> distract from a serious message. On
     the other hand effective use of cartoon images can 'lighten' the presentation of what
     is otherwise a serious subject.

4.   Text font styles and sizes should be consistent and appropriate to the presentation.
     A wild array of several font styles will simply make the text more difficult to read.

5.   Don't pack too much information onto one slide and keep the font size large enough
     for the audience to read, taking into account the distance that they will be from the
     screen.

6.   Good use of colour is more difficult for some, but provided colours are not too gar-
     ish and text fonts contrast sufficiently with the background to make text legible,
     then the effect should never be too objectionable.

7.   Timing of slide changes and animations within slides is also important if the user is
     not controlling its progress. You will need to check time delays to give the audience
     time to absorb the message on each slide. Excessive delays between slide changes
     are likely to be irritating.

Exercises

1. A company uses a presentation package to produce slide shows for use in its training
    programmes. The package includes many features to aid the construction and running of a
    show, including *master slide*, *transitions*; *buttons*, *hotspots*, *backgrounds*, *templates*, *text*,
    graphics and *animations*.

    (i)   Evaluate how these features may be used to produce an effective presentation.

    (ii) Produce a list of guidelines for the production of a well-designed presentation.

This Tutorial guides you through the process of designing, creating and using a Personnel database with Microsoft Access, a relational database management system (see also Topic 23 for an introduction to the subject). The aim of this Tutorial is to show you the main practical steps (it is not a step-by-step guide to using Access) that you need to follow and use them to explain some important relational database concepts. With a proper understanding of these concepts you will be better able to design, create and use databases for other applications. Pilcon Electronics is a manufacturer with a traditional hierarchical staffing structure. The Personnel department is setting up a database to hold personal staff details which are currently stored manually. Each staff member's details are held on a single sheet as shown in Figure 39.1.

Pilcon Electronics Staff Record						
Staff Code	**Surname**	**Initials**	**Job Title**	**Salary**	**Start Date**	**Pension Scheme**
108	Winkle	R.V.	Supervisor	£18,000	1 Sep 85	Yes
Dept Head	**Dept Name**					
I. Lostem	Warehousing					
Course Date	**Course Title**	**Duration**	**Certificated**			
8 Jul 99	Excel SS 2	4	No			
8 Dec 99	Excel SS 3	4	No			
5 Mar 00	Access 1	3	No			

Figure 39.1. *Manual staff record in Pilcon Electronics*

Data normalisation

Converting this information into a suitable form for entry to a relational database requires the application on data normalisation rules. Normalisation is a technique established by E.F. Codd to simplify the structure of data as it is *logically viewed* by the programmer or user. With the relatively simple information structure shown in Figure 39.1, it is not difficult to identify the separate subjects or *entities* which exist within it. There are the personal details of Mr. Winkle, the name of his Department, his Job title and the Courses he has attended. So, without any consideration of normalisation rules, we could suggest that four tables (one for each entity) should be created:

```
STAFFMEMBER    DEPARTMENT    JOB    TRAINING
```

However, when the information is split into these separate tables, the relationship between each staff member and the associated department, job title and training record must be maintained. The application of three normalisation rules will help us to do this and for more complex structures, the process is essential. We begin by considering the first rule of normalisation - the removal of repeating groups.

First Normal Form (1NF)

Notice that Mr. Winkle has attended three training courses; using standard computer file terminology, Course Date, Course Title, Duration and Certificated are *repeating groups*. Table 39.1 shows that a relational database table cannot accommodate repeating groups because it results in repetition of the same primary key value for multiple records, when the primary key for each record must remain unique.

Staff Code	Surname	etc	Course Date	Course Title	Duration	Certificated
108	Winkle	......	8 Jul 99	Excel SS 2	4	No
108	Winkle	....	8 Dec 99	Excel SS 3	4	No
108	Winkle	....	5 Mar 00	Access 1	3	No

Table 39.1. *Illegal duplicated primary key value*

The first stage of normalisation demands

❑   removal of any repeating groups.

This is the only normalisation rule that <u>must</u> be satisfied for data to be stored in a relational database. It <u>may</u> be desirable to apply the second and third stages but it is not essential. The original data structure can be expressed formally as follows.

```
StaffMember(Staff Code, Surname, Initials, Job Title, Salary, Start
Date, Pension, Dept Name, DeptHead [Course Date, Course Title,
Duration, Certificated])
```

Figure 39.2. *Personnel data structure before normalisation*

The fields bounded by square [brackets] identify the repeating groups which are to be placed in a separate entity called TRAINING, as follows. The entity names have the suffix 1 for 1NF.

```
STAFFMEMBER-1(StaffCode, Surname, Initials, JobCode, JobTitle, Salary,
StartDate, Pension, DeptCode, DeptName, DeptHead)

TRAINING-1(CourseDate, StaffCode, CourseTitle, Duration, Certificated)
```

Figure 39.3. *Personnel entity structures in First Normal Form (1NF)*

Note the addition of two attributes, JobCode to associate with JobTitle and DeptCode, to associate with DeptName and DeptHead. They are not needed in the manual system, but we will need them when defining the relational database structure.

Relationships and foreign keys

Figure 39.3 shows that to retain the link between a staff member and his or her training details, StaffCode (primary key for STAFFMEMBER-1) is included in TRAINING-1 as a *foreign key*. Some necessary *data redundancy* is created by including StaffCode in both entities. However, such duplication of data does not necessarily mean an increased use of storage because normalisation is concerned with the *logical structure* of the data and not with the ways in which the data is physically organised.

Composite primary keys

To ensure the uniqueness of each TRAINING-1 record, the CourseDate and StaffCode form a composite primary key. CourseDate on its own cannot ensure a unique value because there may be several members of staff attending the same course or other courses which start on the same day. Equally, StaffCode could not guarantee uniqueness because a member of staff may attend several courses (but not on the same day).

Second Normal Form (2NF)

The second rule of normalisation requires that

❑   all non-identifying attributes are *functionally dependent* on the unique identifier (the primary key).

If the identifier is composite (comprising more that one attribute), then non-identifying attributes must be functionally dependent on the whole of the identifier.

Referring back to Figure 39.3 showing the 1-NF entities, it can be seen that in the TRAINING-1 entity the non-identifying attributes of CourseTitle, Duration and Certificated do depend on the entire composite key. Put simply, to obtain details of a particular course you would need to specify a date an a staff code value, for example, 3/4/99 and 103. Entering 3/4/99 on its own may bring up several records for courses which started on the same day. If the staff member 103 had attended several courses, this value would also result in the retrieval of multiple records.

In this case, the 1-NF structures also satisfy the 2-NF rules and can be given the suffix-2 as shown in Figure 39.4.

STAFFMEMBER-2 (StaffCode, Surname, Initials, JobCode, JobTitle, Salary, StartDate, Pension, DeptCode, DeptName, DeptHead)

TRAINING-2 (CourseDate, StaffCode, CourseTitle, Duration, Certificated)

Figure 39.4. *Unmodified Personnel entity structures in Second Normal Form (2NF)*

An alternative structure

To show what would happen if the 2NF rules did require the modification of a structure, consider the slightly modified Personnel 1NF entities in Figure 39.5.

STAFFMEMBER-1 (StaffCode, Surname, Initials, JobCode, JobTitle, Salary, StartDate, Pension, DeptCode, DeptName, DeptHead)

TRAINING-1 (CourseCode, StaffCode, CourseTitle, Duration, Certificated)

Figure 39.5. *Modified structure which does not meet the Second Normal Form rule*

Figure 39.5 shows that CourseDate has been replaced by a CourseCode, which identifies a particular course which is not dependent on a date, but exists in its own right. In this case, CourseTitle, Duration and Certificated are only dependent on CourseCode.

To convert the structure to 2NF requires that the Course details are made a separate entity, as shown in Figure 39.6.

```
STAFFMEMBER-2(StaffCode, Surname, Initials, JobCode, JobTitle, Salary,
StartDate, Pension, DeptCode, DeptName, DeptHead)

TRAINING-2(CourseCode, StaffCode)

COURSE-2(CourseCode, CourseTitle, Duration, Certificated)
```

Figure 39.6 *Application of 2NF rules to create separate COURSE entity*

The relationship between the Training record and Course record is maintained through CourseCode. The potential benefit of having a separate entity COURSE-2 is that new Course records could be created before any staff had attended the courses that they detail. This would be appropriate, if for example, an organisation (such as a college) ran numerous internal courses. This is not the case in Pilcon where Course details are only associated with staff attendance, that is, particular course details do not appear in the database unless a staff member attends it. However, it has to be recognised that the arrangement does lead to some duplication of course details. Our original structure could be modified to allow the use of a separate Course entity, but this does not suit the requirements of Pilcon.

Third Normal Form (3NF)

For convenience, the 2NF structures are repeated below.

```
STAFFMEMBER-2(StaffCode, Surname, Initials, JobCode, JobTitle, Salary,
StartDate, Pension, DeptCode, DeptName, DeptHead)

TRAINING-2(CourseDate, StaffCode, CourseTitle, Duration, Certificated)
```

The third stage of normalisation requires:

❏   the removal of any *functional dependencies* between non-identifying attributes.

A simple test is to ask "Are there any non-identifying attributes which would act as the unique identifier in a separate table?" STAFFMEMBER-2 contains two such attributes, namely, JobCode and DeptCode. Clearly, JobTitle is dependent on JobCode and DeptName is dependent on DeptCode and in their present form the entities do not satisfy the 3NF rule. We can satisfy the rule by creating an entity for each. Figure 39.7 shows the structure in 3NF.

```
STAFFMEMBER-3(StaffCode, Surname, Initials, JobCode, Salary,
StartDate, Pension, DeptCode)

TRAINING-3(CourseDate, StaffCode, CourseTitle, Duration, Certificated)

JOB-3 (JobCode, JobTitle)

DEPARTMENT-3 (DeptCode, DeptName, DeptHead)
```

Figure 39.7. *Personnel structure in Third Normal Form (3NF)*

In STAFFMEMBER-3, JobCode and DeptCode are foreign keys to maintain the relationships with the JOB-3 and DEPARTMENT-3 entities respectively.

Defining the database dictionary

A data dictionary (Topic 54) system is a data processing department's own information system, with the database administrator, systems analysts and programmers as the main users.

A dictionary for the Personnel database is shown in Tables 39.2, 39.3, 39.4 and 39.5. It is good practice to prepare it before setting up the database.

STAFFMEMBER				
Field name	StaffCode	Surname	Initials	JobCode
Data type	text	text	text	text
Field size	3	25	4	3
Input mask	000			LL0
Validation rule	>=100 and <=200			
Validation text	Range 100 to 200			
Required	Yes	No	No	No
Indexed	Yes (no duplicates)	No	No	No
Field name	DeptCode	Salary	StartDate	Pension
Data type	text	currency	date	yes/no
Field size	3	0 decimal places		
Input mask	LLL			
Validation rule	ACC or GOS or MIS or PER or PRO or PUR or RAD or SAL or WAR	<=8000 and <=45000	<=now()	
Validation text	Invalid Code	Range 8000 to 45000	Invalid date	
Required	No	No	No	No
Indexed	Yes (duplicates OK)	No	No	No

Table 39.2. *STAFFMEMBER data dictionary definition*

TRAINING		
Field name	CourseDate	StaffCode	CourseTitle
Data type	date	text	text
Field size		3	30
Input mask		000	
Validation rule		>=100 and <=200	
Validation text		Range 100 to 200	
Required	Yes	Yes	No
Indexed	Yes (Duplicates OK)	Yes (Duplicates OK)	No
Field name	Duration	Certificated	
Data type	number	yes/no	
Field size	integer 0 decimal places		

Input mask			
Validation rule	>=1 and <=10	<=8000 and <=45000	
Validation text	Range 1 to 10	Range 8000 to 45000	
Required	No	No	No
Indexed	No	No	No

Table 39.3. *TRAINING data dictionary definition*

JOB		
Field name	JobCode	JobTitle
Data type	text	text
Field size	3	35
Input mask	LL0	
Validation rule		
Validation text		
Required	Yes	No
Indexed	Yes (No duplicates)	No

Table 39.4. *JOB data dictionary definition*

DEPARTMENT			
Field name	DeptCode	DeptTitle	DeptHead
Data type	text	text	Synonym for StaffCode
Field size	3	35	
Input mask	LLL		
Validation rule	same as in STAFFMEMBER		
Validation text	Invalid code		
Required	Yes	No	
Indexed	Yes (No duplicates)	No	

Table 39.5. *DEPARTMENT data dictionary definition*

Setting up the Personnel database

Having set up a new blank database in Access, you need to define a table for each entity. Refer to the data dictionary definitions shown on the previous two pages. The four completed table definitions are shown in Figures 39.8, 39.9, 39.10 and 39.11. Note the use of the Description column to further clarify the nature of each field.

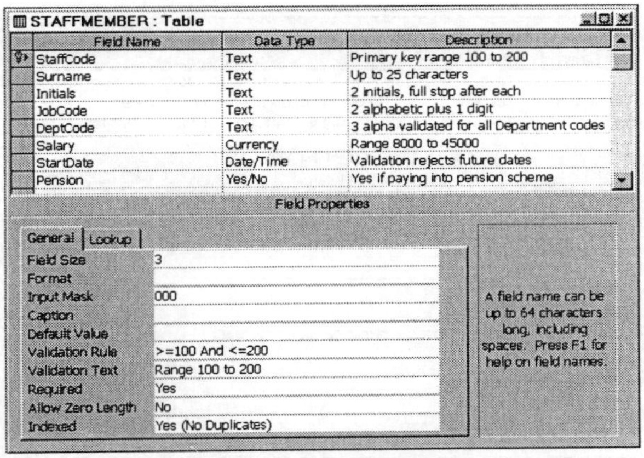

Figure 39.8. *Access definition of STAFFMEMBER table*

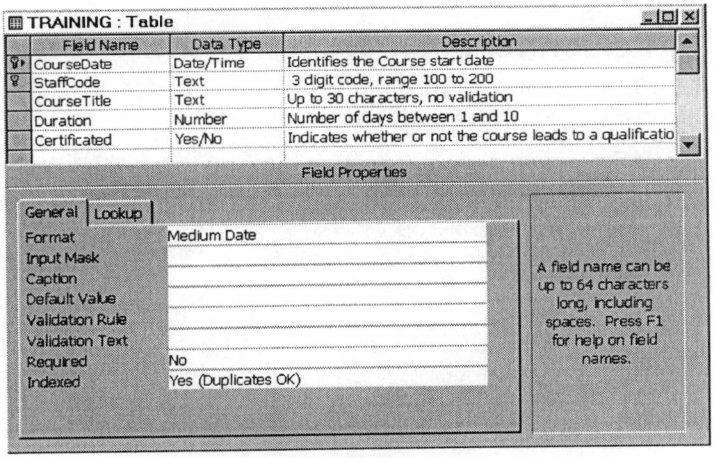

Figure 39.9. *Access definition of TRAINING table*

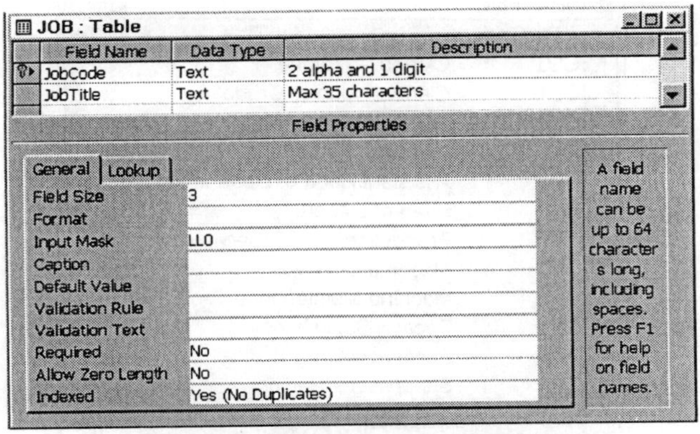

Figure 39.10. *Access definition of JOB table*

DEPARTMENT : Table

Field Name	Data Type	Description
DeptCode	Text	Primary key. 3 alpha validated for all department codes
DepartmentName	Text	One of nine departments, not validated
DeptHead	Text	Synonym for StaffCode in StaffMember table

Field Properties

General | Lookup

Field Size	3
Format	
Input Mask	LLL
Caption	
Default Value	
Validation Rule	"ACC" Or "GOS" Or "MIS" Or "PER" Or "PRO
Validation Text	
Required	No
Allow Zero Length	No
Indexed	Yes (No Duplicates)

A field name can be up to 64 characters long, including spaces. Press F1 for help on field names.

Figure 39.11. *Access definition of DEPARTMENT table*

Contents of Personnel database

Figures 39.12, 39.13, 39.14, and 39.15 show sample contents for the `DEPARTMENT`, `JOB`, `STAFFMEMBER` and `TRAINING` tables, respectively.

DEPARTMENT : Table

DeptCode	DeptName	DeptHead
ACC	Accounting and Finance	128
GOS	General Office Services	155
MIS	Management Information Services	160
PER	Personnel	168
PRO	Production	149
PUR	Purchasing	136
RAD	Research and Development	172
SAL	Sales and Marketing	180
WAR	Warehousing	187

Record: 1 of 9

Figure 39.12. *Sample contents for DEPARTMENT table*

JOB : Table

JobCode	JobTitle
CL0	Clerical - Trainee
CL1	Clerical - Junior Grade
CL2	Clerical - Middle Grade
CL3	Clerical - Senior
HD1	Assistant Head of Department
HD2	Head of Department
LS1	Production Line Supervisor
OP1	Machine Operator
OP2	Machine Maintenance Technician
SS1	Section Supervisor
SU1	Supervisor
SU2	Supervisor - Senior

Record: 1 of 12

Figure 39.13. *Sample contents for JOB table*

STAFFMEMBER : Table

StaffCode	Surname	Initials	JobCode	DeptCode	Salary	StartDate	Pension
100	Picket	W.	CL2	ACC	£15,000	23-Jan-77	☑
101	Ringwood	K.	HD1	PRO	£33,000	14-May-95	☑
103	Clacket	D.	CL0	GOS	£13,500	01-Jan-85	☐
106	Boreham	L.	SS1	ACC	£23,000	23-Sep-72	☑
108	Winkle	R.V.	SU1	WAR	£18,000	01-Sep-85	☑
110	Dickens	C.	OP1	PRO	£8,000	14-May-95	☐
115	Cratchit	B.	CL2	ACC	£8,500	01-May-94	☐
118	Boffin	C.	HD1	RAD	£38,000	01-Sep-66	☑
123	Heap	U.	HD1	SAL	£37,500	31-Oct-93	☑
124	Miggins	M.	SU1	GOS	£14,500	31-Oct-93	☑
126	Squeers	W.	SS1	PER	£37,500	13-Jun-88	☑
128	Chiseller	M.	HD2	ACC	£43,000	01-Apr-83	☑
131	Marley	J.	OP1	PRO	£8,600	16-Jun-91	☐
133	Server	I.	HD1	WAR	£32,000	01-Sep-60	☑
136	Grabbit	U.	HD2	PUR	£45,000	12-Apr-66	☑
138	Stackit	I.	OP1	WAR	£9,200	03-Apr-68	☐
139	Broaket	H.E.	OP2	PRO	£13,000	17-Apr-85	☑
145	Ramidos	Z.	SU1	MIS	£17,900	12-Jun-88	☑
149	Machem	I.	HD2	PRO	£40,000	01-Apr-90	☑
155	Pusher	P.	HD2	GOS	£44,000	01-Feb-60	☑
159	Nervey	M.	OP1	WAR	£10,000	01-Apr-95	☐
160	Surcoat	I.	HD2	MIS	£40,000	02-May-66	☑
168	Sached	U.R.	HD2	PER	£37,000	02-Mar-66	☑
172	Tefal	B.	HD2	RAD	£37,000	02-Mar-85	☑
180	Leavmey	B.	HD2	SAL	£42,000	01-Oct-72	☑
187	Lostem	I.	HD2	WAR	£32,500	31-Oct-88	☑
190	Fezziwig	M.	CL1	SAL	£9,000	14-Jun-85	☑
195	Swidger	F.	CL1	SAL	£10,000	10-May-74	☑
197	Dilber	C.	CL2	MIS	£11,400	09-Sep-82	☐

Record: 1 of 29

Figure 39.14. *Sample contents for STAFFMEMBER table*

TRAINING : Table

CourseDate	StaffCode	CourseTitle	Duration	Certificat
02-Mar-99	103	Pegasus Accounts 1	5	☑
09-Mar-99	110	CAD 3 Circuit Design	3	☑
09-Mar-99	118	Neural Networks Advanced	10	☐
16-Mar-99	145	Oracle Server Concepts 1	1	☑
04-Apr-99	103	Pegasus Accounts 2	5	☑
07-Jun-99	115	Pegasus Advanced	4	☑
07-Jun-99	168	Access Database 1	3	☐
08-Jul-99	108	Excel Spreadsheet 2	4	☐
14-Jul-99	106	Pegasus Advanced	4	☑
18-Jul-99	131	CAD 2 Circuit Design	3	☑
15-Sep-99	197	Oracle Server Concepts 1	1	☑
20-Oct-99	197	Oracle Server Concepts 2	3	☐
13-Nov-99	139	CAD 1 Circuit Design	4	☑
08-Dec-99	108	Excel Spreadsheet 3	4	☐
08-Jan-00	145	Oracle Server Concepts 2	3	☐
05-Mar-00	108	Access Database 1	3	☐

Record: 1 of 16

Figure 39.15. *Sample contents for TRAINING table*

Forms

You can use a form to tailor your view of information held in a table. A form is always associated with a particular table (or query - see later) and allows you to enter, edit and view the data held within it. A form is not a separate store of data, but simply an alternative view of its associated table. A benefit of a form is that it allows you to view or edit one record at a time; the standard *datasheet* view (see previous screen shots of sample table contents) in Access displays as many records as can be accommodated within its window. Figure 39.16 shows a form associated with the STAFFMEMBER. It has a column layout and was created with Form Wizard.

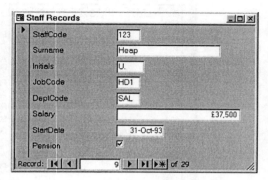

Figure 39.16. *Form view of STAFFMEMBER table*

You can begin with a blank form and design your layout, or more easily, you can produce one with a wizard and then modify it to your requirements. Figure 39.17 shows the Staff Records Form in design mode, with the Surname field label selected and the Toolbox used for, amongst other things, inserting *command buttons* and *list boxes*. You can see from the Figure that a form consists of a number of objects, including *field labels* and *data entry* points. Each data entry point uses the field name defined in the table definition and ensures that each entry point on the form is as-

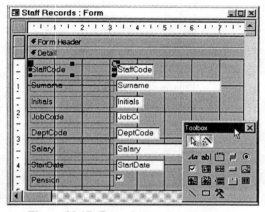

Figure 39.17. *Form design view and toolbox*

sociated with the correct field in a record. As a consequence, field names should not be altered on the form (unless they are also altered in the table definition). Field labels, on the other hand can be altered; the field names are used by default, unless you specify otherwise. The form design is divided into sections: *header* (for titles); *detail* (for the field names and data entry points); *footer* (for additional comments, perhaps to guide the data entry process).

Reports

Report facilities allow you to decide what information from a table (or query) is visible when you view it or print it. Reports are usually categorised as:

❑ *Single column*. Records are displayed in full down the side of the page or screen, rather than across the page in columns.

❑ *Multiple column*. A column is provided for each field you specify and records are placed one after another. You can allow the field names to be used as column headings, or design your own.

❑ *Grouped*. If the information can be grouped into different levels, then the report can be presented in this way, with sub-totals or other calculations on numeric or currency fields, at the end of each group or subgroup.

Figure 39.18 shows a report on screen, generated with a 'report wizard', using the `TRAINING` table . The sequence is by StaffCode and this was specified as part of the report construction process. As with *forms*, you can design a report from scratch or use a wizard and then switch to Design view and modify the design as necessary. The headings in the report have been changed using design view.

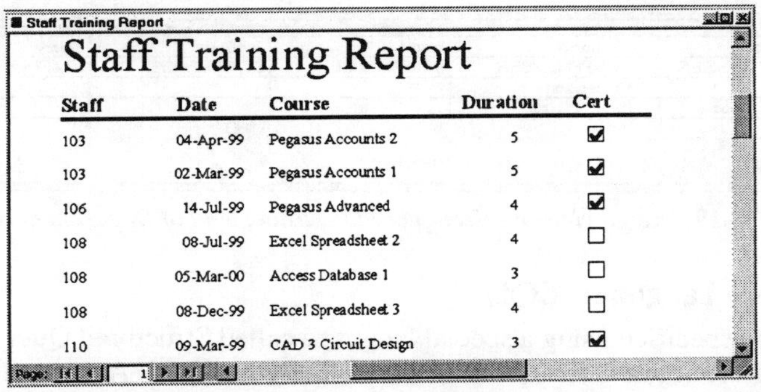
Staff Training Report

Staff Training Report

Staff	Date	Course	Duration	Cert
103	04-Apr-99	Pegasus Accounts 2	5	☑
103	02-Mar-99	Pegasus Accounts 1	5	☑
106	14-Jul-99	Pegasus Advanced	4	☑
108	08-Jul-99	Excel Spreadsheet 2	4	☐
108	05-Mar-00	Access Database 1	3	☐
108	08-Dec-99	Excel Spreadsheet 3	4	☐
110	09-Mar-99	CAD 3 Circuit Design	3	☑

Page: 1

Figure 39.18. *Column report on contents of TRAINING table with modified headings*

To include, for example, staff names in the Report would require that it be based on a query which used the STAFFMEMBER and TRAINING tables. We will look at such a query next.

Queries

A query is a request for information from a database. You can use a query to:

(i) display information from several tables by *joining* them (see later);

(ii) display limited information by specifying that only certain fields are displayed;

(iii) use *criteria* to *filter* records from one table or from several joined together.

Select query

To illustrate (iii) and (iv), we will specify that records are to be filtered from the `STAFFMEMBER` table if the `JobCode` field contains "HD2", which according to the Pilcon coding system means Heads of Department. Although the JobCode field must be used in the query, we can choose not to display its contents, which would simply be a repetition of "HD2". Also we will specify that the records are listed in ascending `StaffCode` order. Figure 39.19 shows the *select* query design to meet these requirements.

The Figure shows the query design grid with the criterion ="HD2" in the `JobCode` column, the 'Show' box deselected and 'Ascending' in the `StaffCode` column to dictate the sequence. `DeptCode` has been left out of the query.

This form of specifying queries is often referred to a query by example (QBE).

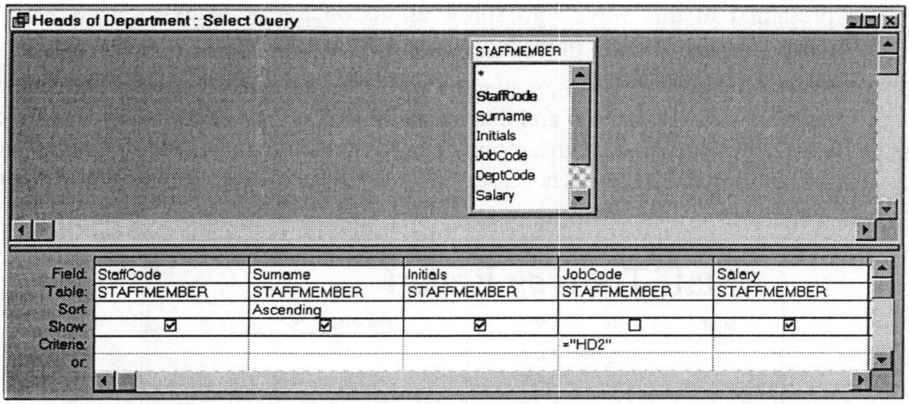

Figure 39.19. *Design view of select query to extract Head of Department records*

Structured Query Language (SQL)

Queries can also be specified using a special language called Structured Query Language. The SQL equivalent of the above select query is shown in Figure 39.20. Access allows you to view the SQL equivalent of any query you create.

```
SELECT STAFFMEMBER.StaffCode, STAFFMEMBER.Surname,
STAFFMEMBER.Initials, STAFFMEMBER.JobCode, STAFFMEMBER.Salary
FROM STAFFMEMBER
WHERE (((STAFFMEMBER.JobCode)="HD2"))
ORDER BY STAFFMEMBER.Surname;
```

Figure 39.20. *An example of Structured Query Language*

We are not concerned with the details of this language at present, but you should be able to see that it is a rather stilted form of natural language. Many new RDBMS packages provide SQL Developed by IBM, SQL is a *non-procedural* language and as such belongs to the group of programming languages known as 4th Generation Languages (4GLs); this means that programmers and trained users can specify what they want from a database without having to specify how to do it. Procedural languages such as COBOL, Pascal and C, require the programmer to detail, explicitly, how a program must navigate through a file or database to obtain the necessary output. The programmer must, for example, code procedures such as read the first master record, process it, read the next, process it and so on until the end of the file is reached.

Relationships

For a query to extract information from more than one table requires that relationships exist between them, through the use of primary and foreign keys. If the keys which relate two tables use the same name, for example, JobCode, the primary key in JOB and JobCode, the foreign key in STAFFMEMBER, then Access will detect and establish the relationship when you first use the tables in a query. Otherwise, if one key is a *synonym* for the other, for example, DeptHead in DEPARTMENT is a synonym for StaffCode in STAFFMEMBER, the relationship will not be automatically detected. Figure 39.21 shows a query design with the four Personnel database tables, with all relationships detected save for the one between DeptHead and StaffCode.

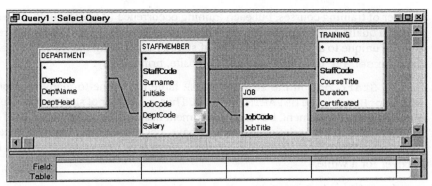

Figure 39.21. *Relationships can be automatically detected, except for synonyms*

Establishing relationships explicitly

Relationships can be established explicitly as shown in Figure 39.22, by dragging the foreign key from its table to the relevant primary key field in the related table.

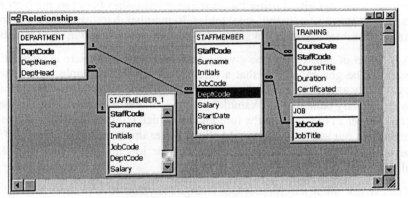

Figure 39.22. *Explicitly establishing relationships*

The lines between the tables in Figure 39.22 indicate the one-to-many degree of the relationship between each pair, as follows (the extra copy of the STAFFMEMBER(-1) table in the Figure because StaffCode is connected in two relationships).

❏ DeptCode in DEPARTMENT (the *primary* table) has a one-to-many relationship with DeptCode in STAFFMEMBER (the *related* table); that is, each department can have many staff, but each member of staff can only belong to one department. For the database, this means that each record in the DEPARTMENT table has a unique value for DeptCode (the primary key), but a DeptCode value in the STAFFMEMBER table may occur many times.

❏ JobCode in the JOB table has a one-to-many relationship with JobCode in the STAFFMEMBER table, which fits with the fact that each Job title may be held by many staff, but each member of staff only has one job title.

❏ StaffCode in the STAFFMEMBER table has a one-to-many relationship with StaffCode in the TRAINING table; that is, each member of staff may take a number of training courses, but each training occurrence (it may be helpful to think of it as a qualification) relates to only one member of staff. Each TRAINING record is made unique to a particular member of staff by combining the StaffCode with the CourseDate to form a unique, composite, primary key.

❑ Finally, StaffCode in the STAFFMEMBER table has a one-to-many relationship with DeptHead in the DEPARTMENT table. Thus, a member of staff may be Head of more than one department, but each department has only one member of staff as its Head. A one-to-one relationship could have been specified, but if a Head of Department leaves or is absent through illness, it may be necessary for another Head to cover for a while.

Enforcing referential integrity

Figure 39.22 identifies the one and the many side of relationships with the symbols '1' and '00', respectively. In Access this indicates that *referential integrity* has been enforced when the relationship was set. If you choose to apply referential integrity to a relationship, you need to be aware of a number of restrictions this places on the operation of the database.

These restrictions are described using the example relationship between the JOB (the 'one' side) and STAFFMEMBER (the 'many' side) tables. Remember that JobCode is the foreign key in the STAFFMEMBER table which links records to the relevant record in the JOB table.

❑ A member of staff can not be given a Job Code for which there is no existing JOB record. The general rule is that a foreign key (in this example, JobCode in the STAFFMEMBER table) can not be given a value which does not exist as a primary key in the primary table (in this example, JobCode in the JOB table). Access does allow you to enter a Null value in the foreign key, which indicates that the records are not related. In our scenario this would allow, for example, entry of a new staff record before they had been assigned to a particular job (the JobCode would be left blank).

❑ You can not delete a JOB record, or change the value of its primary key, if there are any members of staff who are still recorded as holding that type of job. The general rule is that you are not allowed to delete a record from a primary table, or change the value of its primary key, if matching records exist in a related table.

Query using multiple tables

This multiple table example uses the STAFFMEMBER and JOB tables to list the Surname, Salary, JobTitle and StartDate of each employee who is a member of the pension scheme. Heads of Department are excluded from the list.

Figure 39.23 show the design of this select query.

JobCode is needed in the query to allow use of the criterion <>"HD2" which filters out any non-Heads of Department and Pension is needed to filter out non-pension scheme members. To exclude both fields from the query results, their 'Show' boxes are deselected. The results of the query are shown in Figure 39.24.

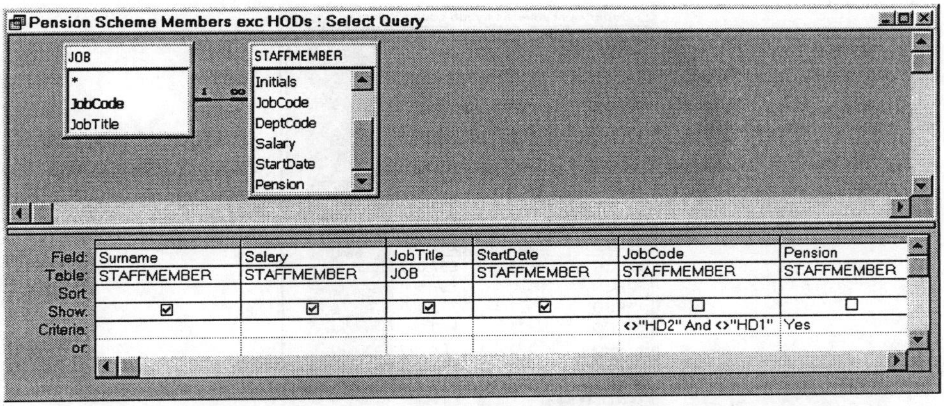

Figure 39.23. *Query to list pension scheme members, excluding Heads of Department*

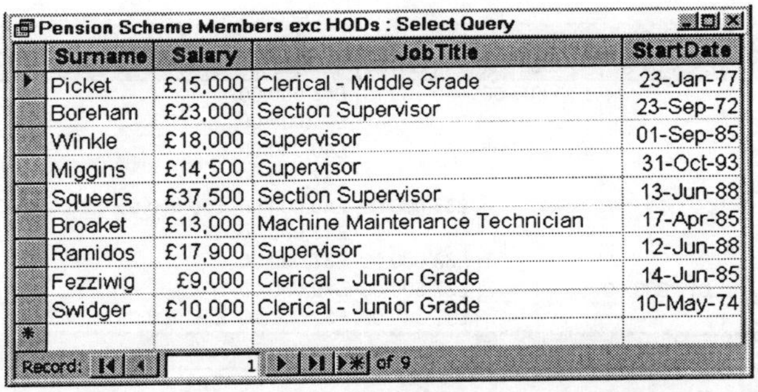
Pension Scheme Members exc HODs : Select Query

Surname	Salary	JobTitle	StartDate
Picket	£15,000	Clerical - Middle Grade	23-Jan-77
Boreham	£23,000	Section Supervisor	23-Sep-72
Winkle	£18,000	Supervisor	01-Sep-85
Miggins	£14,500	Supervisor	31-Oct-93
Squeers	£37,500	Section Supervisor	13-Jun-88
Broaket	£13,000	Machine Maintenance Technician	17-Apr-85
Ramidos	£17,900	Supervisor	12-Jun-88
Fezziwig	£9,000	Clerical - Junior Grade	14-Jun-85
Swidger	£10,000	Clerical - Junior Grade	10-May-74

Record: 1 of 9

Figure 39.24. *List of pension scheme members, excluding Heads of Department*

Cross tab query

A cross-tab query uses row and column headings to display results in a more compact form. Figure 39.25 is a conventional select query which displays the salaries received by staff in each department, according to `JobCode`. Figure 39.26 shows the cross-tab query equivalent with row and column headings and salaries summed according to `JobCode`, to present the information in a more compact form.

The design of the cross-tab query is shown in Figure 39.27.

The design has three elements, which must be included in a cross-tab query:

- one field selected as a Row heading;
- one field selected as a Column heading;
- one field with a Value option. The Total row for this field must have an aggregate function, such as Sum, Avg with which to summarise this numeric field. In the example, the Sum function is used to calculate sub totals for each Job category within each Department.

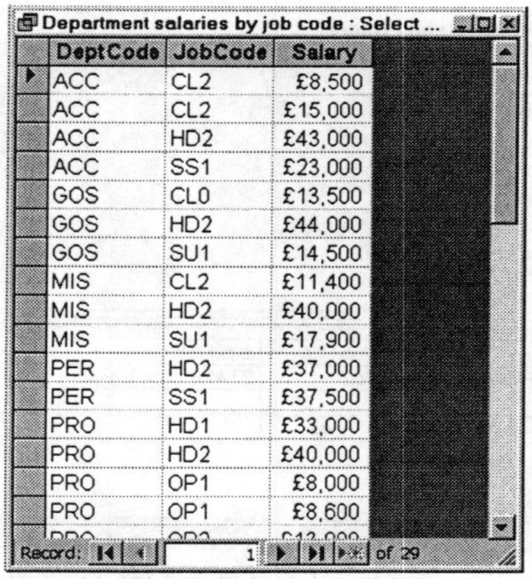

Department salaries by job code : Select ...

DeptCode	JobCode	Salary
ACC	CL2	£8,500
ACC	CL2	£15,000
ACC	HD2	£43,000
ACC	SS1	£23,000
GOS	CL0	£13,500
GOS	HD2	£44,000
GOS	SU1	£14,500
MIS	CL2	£11,400
MIS	HD2	£40,000
MIS	SU1	£17,900
PER	HD2	£37,000
PER	SS1	£37,500
PRO	HD1	£33,000
PRO	HD2	£40,000
PRO	OP1	£8,000
PRO	OP1	£8,600

Record: 1 of 29

Figure 39.25. *Extract of select query results (29 records in all)*

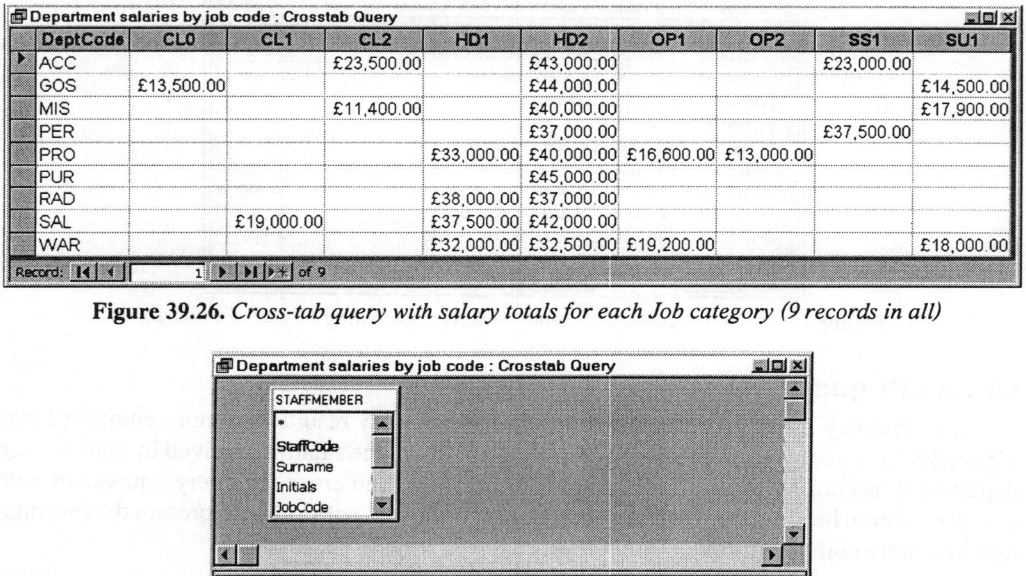

Department salaries by job code : Crosstab Query

DeptCode	CL0	CL1	CL2	HD1	HD2	OP1	OP2	SS1	SU1
ACC			£23,500.00		£43,000.00			£23,000.00	
GOS	£13,500.00				£44,000.00				£14,500.00
MIS			£11,400.00		£40,000.00				£17,900.00
PER					£37,000.00			£37,500.00	
PRO				£33,000.00	£40,000.00	£16,600.00	£13,000.00		
PUR					£45,000.00				
RAD				£38,000.00	£37,000.00				
SAL		£19,000.00		£37,500.00	£42,000.00				
WAR				£32,000.00	£32,500.00	£19,200.00			£18,000.00

Record: 1 of 9

Figure 39.26. *Cross-tab query with salary totals for each Job category (9 records in all)*

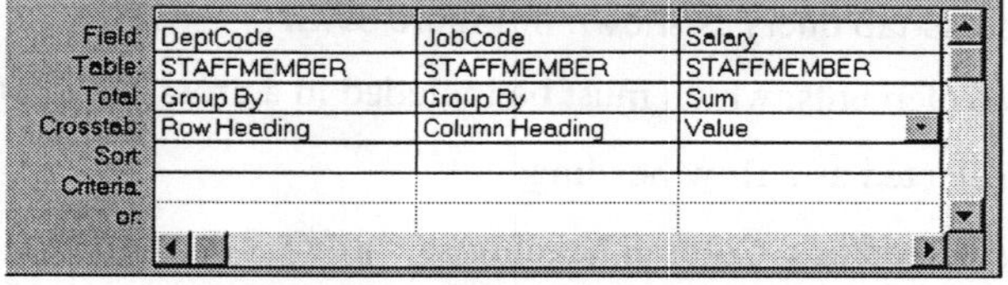

Figure 39.27. *Design of cross-tab query*

Parameter query

A parameter query requests entry of information before it is executed, such as criteria for filtering records or a value to be entered into a field. It is not a separate type of query but rather an extension of the facilities provided by select and cross-tab queries.

Figure39.28 shows an example for a simple select query.

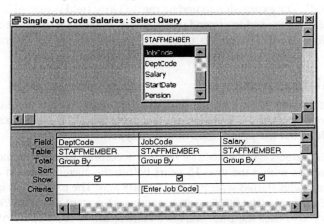

Figure 39.28. *Parameter query design*

The prompt [Enter JobCode] is used in the parameter query dialogue box when the query is executed. The dialogue box and the query results are shown in Figure 39.29.

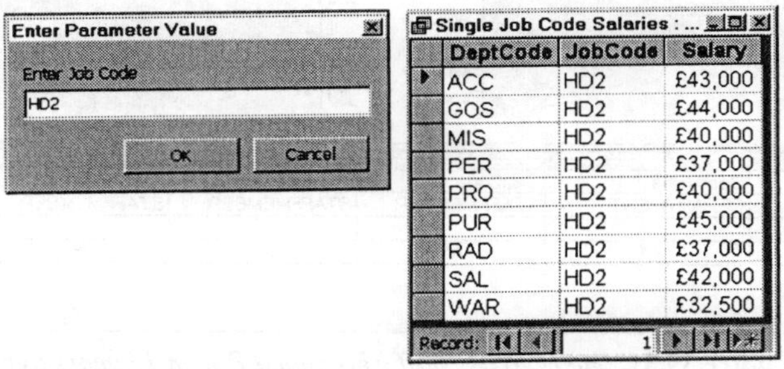

Figure 39.29. *Parameter dialogue box and results of query*

Update query

An update query is an example of an action query and as the name suggests updates all or selected records in a table. The example applies a 3% increase to staff salaries, except for Heads and Assistant Heads of Department. The query design in shown in Figure 39.30.

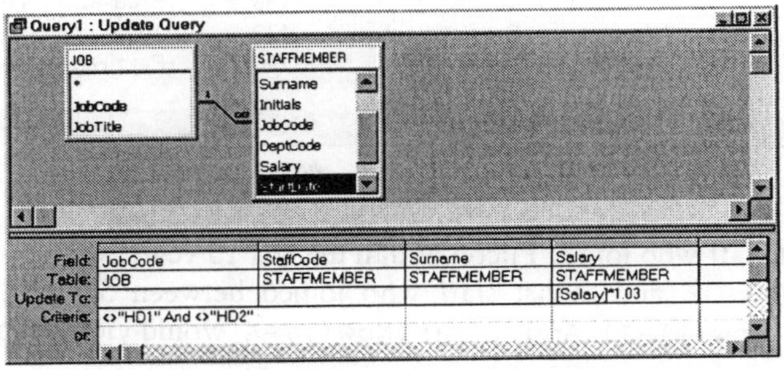

Figure 39.30. *Query to update selected staff salaries by 3%*

The criteria for excluding Heads and Assistant Heads of Departments from the update uses the logical operator 'and'. The expression to update the `Salary` field is placed in the Update row. Other action queries can be used to append new records, or delete existing records in a similar fashion to the update query. The results of action queries can not be reversed by any undo feature.

Query using date criteria

When a database is defined you could choose to use a text field to store dates or times, but you would be unable to carry out any calculation or other processing of those values. For this reason it is always sensible to use the proper date/time data type.

This query example, selects `STAFFMEMBER` records according to whether the StartDate field contains a date which is within the year 15 years before the current year. In other words, the query lists those staff who started with Pilcon 15 years ago. The expression uses the function `Year(Now())-15`. `Now()` takes the current (computer) system date and `Year` extracts the year part. The query also uses the `DEPARTMENT` table to allow the display of the `DeptName` field. The query design is shown in Figure 39.31.

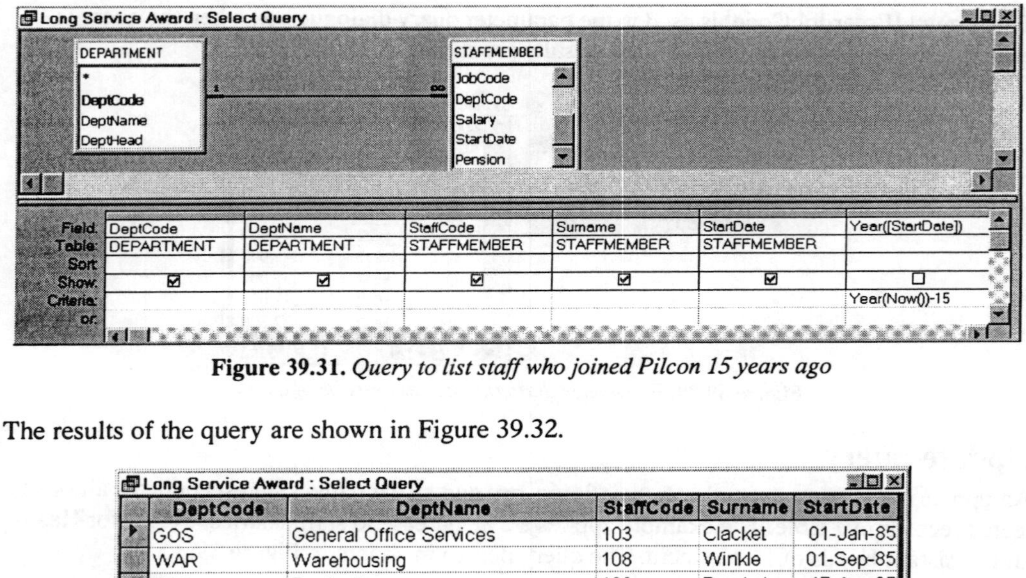

Figure 39.31. *Query to list staff who joined Pilcon 15 years ago*

The results of the query are shown in Figure 39.32.

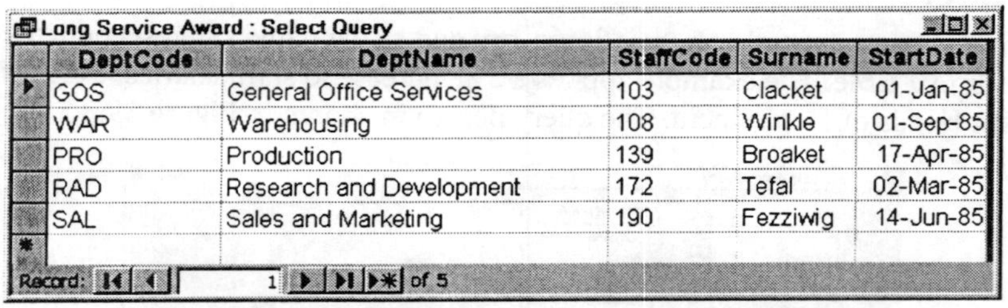
Long Service Award : Select Query

DeptCode	DeptName	StaffCode	Surname	StartDate
GOS	General Office Services	103	Clacket	01-Jan-85
WAR	Warehousing	108	Winkle	01-Sep-85
PRO	Production	139	Broaket	17-Apr-85
RAD	Research and Development	172	Tefal	02-Mar-85
SAL	Sales and Marketing	190	Fezziwig	14-Jun-85

Record: 1 of 5

Figure 39.32. *Staff who started with Pilcon 15 years ago*

If we wished to list staff who joined Pilcon within the last 15 years, we would use the expression `>Year(Now())-16` and to list staff who joined between 5 and 10 years ago, the expression `>Year(Now())-11 And <Year(Now())-4` would yield the required results.

✎ Exercises

1. An extract from a video shop's records is shown below. The data is not normalised for use in a relational database. A member can rent several videos at one time. Members' names and addresses are recorded separately.

VideoCode	Title	CopyNo	Class	Rental	Issued	MemberNo	Date issued
0110	The Dark	1	Horror	£3.00	No		
0110	The Dark	2	Horror	£3.00	Yes	300	3-Oct-00
0110	The Dark	3	Horror	£3.00	No		
0111	The Light	1	Family	£2.00	Yes	501	4-Oct-00
0111	The Light	2	Family	£2.00	Yes	300	4-Oct-00
etc							

   (i) Examine the data in the table and explain what aspects of the data are not normalised.

   (ii) Convert the table into third normal form, showing the first and second stages in the process.

   (iii) Draw an entity-relationship model (ERM) for the video shop database (see Topic 42).

   (iv) Create a data dictionary for the database.

2. Using the above or other suitable examples, define the terms:

   (i) select query;

   (ii) cross tab query;

   (iii) update query;

   (iv) parameter query;

   (v) referential integrity.

Web authoring

The Internet resource referred to as the World Wide Web (WWW) is described in Topic 52. This Topic looks at some of the processes and alternatives for producing the Web pages from which individual Web sites are formed. The standard client (user) software for viewing Web pages is the Web browser.

Web browsers

These are graphical interface client programs to help users to navigate through the Web, to transmit and to receive information from other users or information providers. By using a browser, the user does not have to know the format and location of the information: he or she simply jumps from site to site by clicking on hypertext links. Examples of commercially available browsers are Netscape's *Communicator* and Microsoft's *Internet Explorer* (Figure 40.1). Although there are many different ways to represent a document on the screen, it is often called a *page*. Usually, those responsible for creating a given collection of interrelated documents also create a special document which is intended to be viewed first - one that contains introductory information and/or a master menu of documents within that collection. This type of document is called a *home page* and is generally associated with a particular site, person, or named collection.

Figure 40.1 shows the home page for a web site which provides information and services relating to alternative and complementary medicine.

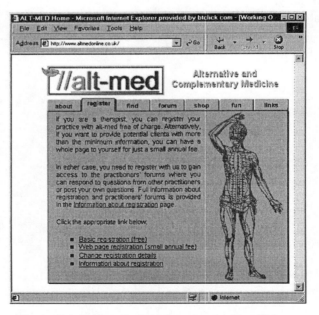

Figure 40.1. *Internet Explorer browser viewing a Web page*

The example document has underlined hypertext phrases. These phrases are hyperlinks (or links) - typically, clicking on one of them with a mouse will cause another document to appear on the screen, which may hold more images and hyperlinks to other places. There is no single way to represent text which is linked to other things - some browsers underline, others use special colours, and many give the user a variety of options. Images which are part of the document and are displayed within the page are called *inline images*. The 'alt-med' logo provides such an example.

The browser provides a toolbar containing buttons which perform frequently used operations. For example, a set of navigation buttons (back and forward) is provided because a user might go to many different pages by selecting links in hypertext and there needs to be some method of retracing one's steps and reviewing the documents that have been explored. A well-designed Web site will include its own hyperlinks to allow the user to easily navigate the site. The example in Figure 40.1 uses the idea of card index tabs to provide immediate information on the site content and to simplify navigation. Sites such as that shown in Figure 40.1 involve complex programming, but most Web pages are based on simple HTML code.

HTML (Hypertext Markup Language)

The standard language the Web uses for creating and recognising hypermedia documents is the Hypertext Mark-up Language (HTML). Figure 40.2 shows a simple Web page and part of its underlying HTML code is shown on the next page.

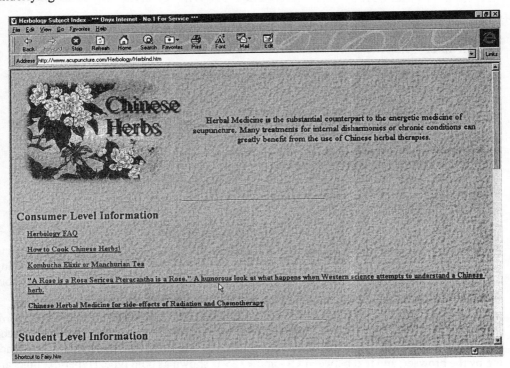

Figure 40.2. *Simple Web page with in-line image and hypertext links*

```
<HTML>
<HEAD>
   <TITLE>Herbology Subject Index</TITLE>
</HEAD>
<BODY BACKGROUND="Back.gif"

<CENTER><TABLE WIDTH="100%">
<TR>
<TD ALIGN=CENTER><IMG SRC="Herb.gif" HEIGHT=233 WIDTH=340
</TD>

<TD><FONT SIZE=+1>Herbal Medicine is the substantial counterpart to
the energetic medicine of acupuncture. Many treatments for internal
disharmonies or chronic conditions can greatly benefit from the use of
Chinese herbal therapies. </FONT></TD>
</TR>
</TABLE></CENTER>

<CENTER><P>
<HR SIZE=2 WIDTH=30%></P></CENTER>

<H2>Consumer Level Information</H2>
<UL>
<H4><A HREF="Herbology.htm">Herbology FAQ</A> </ H4>

<H4>A HREF="Cook.htm">How to Cook Chinese Herbs!</A> </H4>

<H4><A HREF="Man.htm">Kombucha Elixir or Manchurian Tea</A> </ H4>

<H4><A HREF="Fairy.htm">&quot;A Rose is a Rosa Sericea Pteracantha is
a Rose.&quot; A humorous look at what happens when Western science
attempts to understand a Chinese herb.</A></H4>
<H4><A HREF="Chemo.htm"Chinese Herbal Medicine for side-effects of
Radiation and Chemotherapy</A></H4>
</UL>
<CENTER><P>
<HR SIZE=2 WIDTH=30%></P></CENTER>
<H2Student Level Information</H2>
<UL>

.........
```

An important characteristic of HTML is its ease of use. Web documents are typically written in HTML and are usually named with the suffix *.html* or *.htm*. HTML documents are nothing more than standard 7-bit ASCII files with formatting codes which contain information about layout (text styles, document titles, paragraphs, lists) and hyperlinks.

Note the *tags* indicated by keywords enclosed between < and >. Most tags are of the form <tagname>........ </tagname>, with the text being controlled by the tag appearing between the two parts. For example, text enclosed between <H2> and </H2> is shown as a type 2 heading by the browser, and text between <B> and </B> is shown as bold type. Hypertext links are indicated by <A....> and </A>. An example of a hypertext link is

```
<A HREF="Cook.htm"How to Cook Chinese Herbs!</A>
```

This tag causes the browser to show 'How to Cook Chinese Herbs!' as a hypertext link by displaying it in a different colour from ordinary text, and the page to be loaded from the same web site directory as the current document has the file name 'Cook.htm'

Images use the <IMG..> tag. The tag

```
<IMG SRC="Herb.gif" HEIGHT=233 WIDTH=340>
```

indicates, among other things, that the source of the image to be displayed is to be found in the same directory as the parent document under the filename, 'Herb.gif'. The file extension '.gif' is the standard format for Web page inline graphics. A cascading style sheet (.css) is generally used to ensure consistency of styles across all pages in a Web site and to avoid detailed formatting statements within each HTML document. An example of such a style sheet is shown in Topic 33 on Generic Software.

One of the major attractions of using HTML is that every WWW browser can 'understand' it, no matter what machine the browser is being run on. This means that Web page developers do not need to worry about producing different versions for different computer platforms.

Web authoring alternatives

There are three main alternatives:

1. Use an HTML editor (a specialised text editor), although this requires competence in the use of HTML code. Professional Web developers tend to work directly with the code to obtain the greatest control over page design.

2. Use a Web site development package, such as FrontPage or DreamWeaver. A knowledge of HTML is not essential because the software provides templates or 'themes' for Web sites from which the user can choose. A range of tools is also provided for the insertion of all type of Web page content including, for example, images, animations, hyperlinks, backgrounds and text colours. The software also allows users to modify the HTML code directly or import HTML code from other sources without modification. Without editing of the HTML source, it is inevitable that Web pages produced with a proprietary package such as FrontPage will have a particular 'look' because the code has been generated automatically from a limited range of options. On the other hand, a professional Web designer can allow the package to do much of the 'donkey' work and then fine tune the pages by editing the source code.

3. Generate Web pages automatically from, for example, a word processor or desktop publishing package. Unless the user subsequently modifies the HTML code in an editor, this option gives the user no control over the appearance of the Web page, except by modifying the original word processed document. The method is impractical for the effective development of Web sites formed from linked documents but it can be a quick and simple way of distributing a word processed document to many people, simply because browsers are freely available and installed as a standard component on most new computers. Distributing the document without conversion to HTML will prevent some people from reading it if they do not have a compatible word processor.

Forms and scripts

A 'Contact Us' page on a Web site may use a hypertext link to launch the client's e-mail software to allow the sending of an e-mail message, but information can be gathered in a more structured way through a *form*.

A programming script (example languages are CGI and Perl) held on the Web site's host server can take the information entered into the form and convert it to an e-mail message which can be transmitted to the site' mailbox when the 'Submit' button is clicked. Information can also be captured through a form for addition to a Web site's database. An example of such a form is shown in Figure 40.3; clicking the 'Continue' button takes the visitor to a form which gathers information about the practitioner, such as therapy, location and contact information.

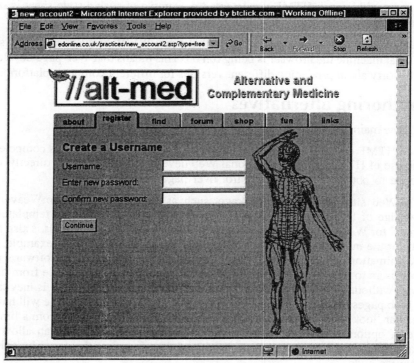

Figure 40.3. *Web page with form*

Uploading pages to a Web server

For a Web site to be viewed by Internet users everywhere all the pages and associated images must be uploaded, using FTP (File Transfer Protocol) to the Internet server which is to host the Web site (the mechanism for associating a physical location with a particular Web site address, such as www.altmedonline.co.uk is beyond the scope of this text). Figure 40.4 shows an FTP package being used to upload pages to a Web site. The left panel shows the directory structure of the local machine and the right panel shows the relevant part of the directory structure on the Web server. The bottom panel shows the pages queued for uploading.

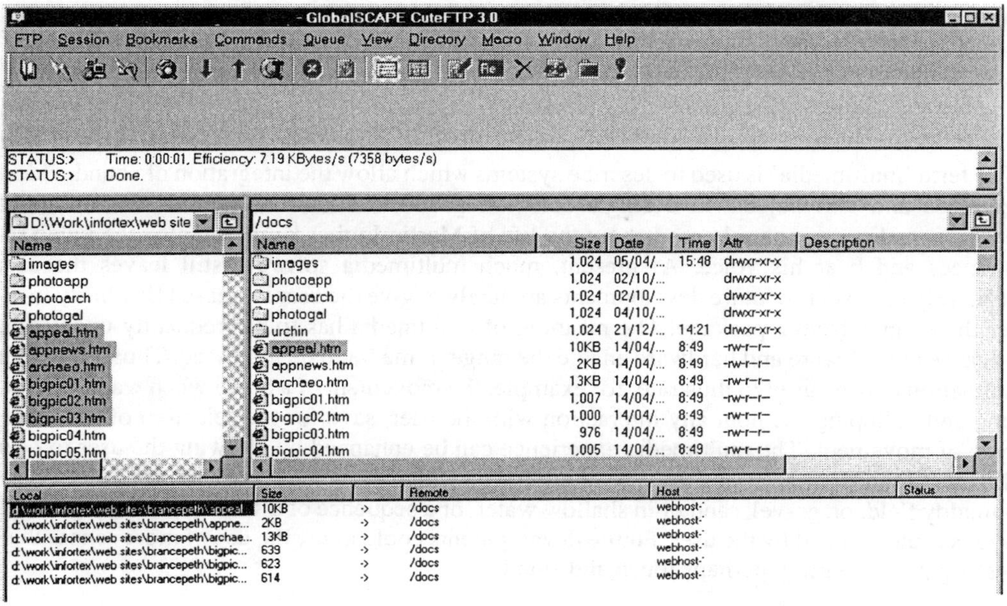

Figure 40.4. *FTP software uploading Web pages to the Web server*

✍️Exercises

1. A company is planning the production of a web site to advertise its products. The site will include a number of web pages, each dealing with a different aspect of the company's business including, for example, the background to the company, a contact form page, special offers and the location of its branches (with photographs and maps, as well as staff contact details).

   Explain how the following relate to the development of the site:

   (i)   HTML editor

   (ii) in-line images;

   (iii) hyperlinks;

   (iv) forms;

   (v)   scripts.

2. Describe alternatives to the HTML editor, pointing out the benefits and limitations of each.

3. Explain the process of uploading web pages to the web server.

Multimedia

The term 'multimedia' is used to describe systems which allow the integration of sound, video, graphics and text objects in a single software product. Thus, the user of a multimedia encyclopaedia, can not only read about the life of Martin Luther King, but also see video sequences and hear his voice. At present, much multimedia software still leaves the user relatively passive, but future developments are likely to give the user increased flexibility to alter the outputs from a package. The meaning of multimedia has to be frequently updated as advances in software and hardware enable the range of media to be increased. Thus, computer animation may be used to illustrate, for example, the movement of a horse when walking, trotting and galloping, without any interaction with the user, save for the selection of the initial type of movement. The multimedia experience can be enhanced by allowing the user to hear different sounds, by selecting the type of ground on which the horse is moving, for example, on a muddy field, on gravel, sand or in shallow water, or a sequence of different surfaces, perhaps over a route planned by the user. Future developments could allow the use of more senses than just sight and hearing, perhaps touch and smell.

Hardware components

At present, microcomputers configured to run multimedia software include a sound card (to process sound files), speakers, a microphone (for voice input) and CD-ROM or DVD (digital versatile disk) drive. Memory and processor requirements are higher than for routine business machines because multimedia software has to handle complex graphics, animation and sound files in real-time.

It should be pointed out that a CD-ROM drive is now a standard component of all microcomputer systems, partly because most software packages are now available on CD-ROM, as well as floppy disk, but also because the storage requirements of packages require the capacity of CD-ROM. The cost of DVD storage is falling and is now available with many multimedia systems.

Multimedia objects

There are four main types of multimedia object:

- ❏ text;
- ❏ graphics;
- ❏ sound;
- ❏ video.

A multimedia production requires the selection of the most appropriate objects, for example, video and sound to demonstrate the techniques of playing a guitar and text to explain them. Having selected the main types of object, a producer needs to decide the precise form of each object and the methods used for capturing and storing the object. For example, graphics objects include the forms of clip art, photographs and *hyperpictures* (Images with 'clickable' links which, in the same way as hypertext, allow connection to other documents). A photograph may be captured with a digital camera, which can then be input directly into the computer, or it may be captured with a conventional camera and then developed and stored on compact disk (CD), from where it can be read from the computer's CD drive. A photographic image can be stored using one of a variety of file types, some of which use image compression to reduce the considerable storage needs of such objects. This section examines each object type, its variations of form and the methods which can be used to capture and store it.

Text

Although picture Images can be very useful in conveying ideas or knowledge to the viewer, text is usually essential for more detailed understanding. Depending on the amount of information to be communicated, text may comprise a simple caption, one or more paragraphs, or pages of text.

The method used to *capture* text depends on its form. Original text, created by the author is likely to be entered through the *keyboard*, although voice input is becoming more widely used. Printed text can be entered in the same way, but a *scanner* and *optical character recognition (OCR)* software can save a considerable amount of time and effort. Text may already be in electronic form and provided that the form is compatible with the multimedia production software, it can be used directly. It has to be said that this is rarely the case and considerable work is needed to adjust layout and format following transfer from the original source. Apart from text and document files held on the producer's computer, other sources of electronic text include CD-ROM titles, such as Encarta and the almost limitless resources of the World Wide Web. Of course great care must be taken to avoid abuse of copyright.

Hypertext

The operation of the World Wide Web (WWW) relies on *hypertext* as its means of interacting with users. Hypertext is basically the same as ordinary text - it can be stored, read, searched, or edited - with an important exception: hypertext contains links to other places within the same document or to other documents. A Web *browser* indicates text links by the use of colour and underlining.

For example, Figure 41.1 shows part of a document called 'Writing Java Programs', which contains three underlying links to other documents, the second one being 'The Anatomy of a Java Application'.

This latter document in turn contains a link to a third document called 'The Hello World Applet'. The first document would be retrieved from the WWW using a browser and the user, by pointing and clicking with a mouse on a link, will cause the browser to retrieve the appropriate document automatically, no matter where it is located. Hypertext is an essential component for any multimedia production which allows the user to navigate their own way through it. The creation of hypertext links can only take place once the text is in an electronic form which is usable by the hypertext creation software.

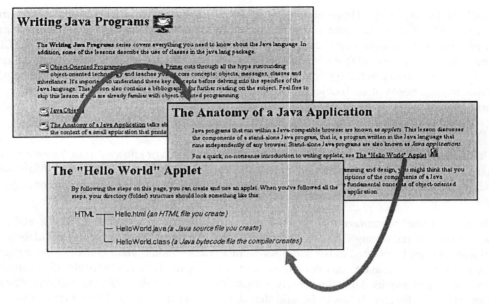

Figure 41.1. *Hyperlinked Web pages*

Text file formats

Electronic text may be stored as one of a number of file formats. It is important to know the facilities and constraints which may attach to each one, so that the correct choice can be made when importing text into a multimedia production. Major word processing packages, such as Word Perfect and Microsoft Word provide *file converters* to allow files produced in one package to be transferred to another. These converters are needed because any given word processing package uses its own, unique coding system for text formatting and layout.

Two 'universal' file formats are recognised by all word processors and most other programs which use text, including multimedia authoring packages.

❑   Text. As plain text, all formatting, such as emboldening, italicising, or underlining is lost and section breaks, page breaks, and new line characters are exchanged for paragraph marks. This file format guarantees recognition by the receiving package, and can be selected if it cannot read other, more suitable, file types.

❑   Rich Text Format (RTF). All formatting is retained in a form frequently recognised by other programs. If the text is already formatted, RTF is preferable to plain text, because it avoids unnecessary re-formatting in the destination package.

HTML format

Web browsers recognise text files, but use *hypertext markup language* to display formatting. A sample of HTML follows.

```
<HTML>
<HEAD>
   <TITLE>Herbology Subject Index</TITLE>
</HEAD>
<BODY BACKGROUND="Back.gif"

<CENTER><TABLE WIDTH="100%">
<TR>
<TD ALIGN=CENTER><IMG SRC="Herb.gif" HEIGHT=233 WIDTH=340
</TD>

<TD><FONT SIZE=+1>Herbal Medicine is the substantial counterpart to
the energetic medicine of acupuncture. Many treatments for internal
disharmonies or chronic conditions can greatly benefit from the use of
Chinese herbal therapies. </FONT></TD>
</TR>
</TABLE></CENTER>
```

The process of inserting the special HTML markers, which tell the browser how text is to be displayed, is a laborious process, so HTML editors have been developed to make the task easier. For the same reason, word processing packages, such as Microsoft Word and desktop publishing packages, such as Corel Ventura, commonly allow files to be 'saved as' HTML documents, whilst retaining much of their original layout and format.

Graphics

As with text files, a knowledge of the various formats of graphics files is necessary, if the most appropriate choices are to be made for any given multimedia production. There are two types of graphics file, *bit map* and *vector*, but there are numerous file formats for each type.

Bit map file formats

There are numerous file formats used to store bit map images. These formats are often named according to the *file extension* (*.ext*) which is attached to the filename when a file is saved in a particular format. Common examples include

❑   *.pcx*. This is the file format for Windows Paintbrush;

❑   *.jpg*. (JPEG - Joint Photographic Experts Group). This type uses a standard for still-image compression, known as the JPEG algorithm and is widely used on the Internet. The format allows the use of 16 million colours which makes it suitable for digitised photographs. JPEG images can be compressed but with loss of quality. A Web page designer has to strike a balance between obtaining a good quality image and a file size which will not take too long to download. It is common practice to use a very small 'thumbnail' image which appears almost immediately and which the Web user can click on to download an enlarged image.

Figure 41.2 shows two copies of a JPEG photograph, one using maximum quality and the other heavily compressed.

File size: 64Kbytes   File size: 4Kbytes

Figure 41.2. *JPEG images of different quality*

❏ *.gif* (Graphic Image File). This type was promoted by CompuServe, a major, Internet service provider, and is still widely used for still images on the Internet. A maximum of 256 colours can be used, which is adequate for images made up of blocks of colour, but photographs and images with graduated shading are not suitable for .gif format.

Images can be made transparent, which allows the background colour to show through a specified colour within the image. Web pages with a background colour other than white will use transparent images to achieve this effect. Otherwise, the image will always appear within a rectangle. Figure 41.3 shows the results of using a transparent and non-transparent GIF on a coloured background.

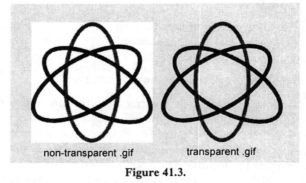

non-transparent .gif   transparent .gif

Figure 41.3.

❏ *animated .gif.* Used extensively in web pages, an animated gif contains one file with multiple frames and each frame contains a different image (or different aspect of the same image. The effect of animation is achieved by cycling rapidly through the frames (the speed can be varied), which is the basis of all traditional cartoon animation.

❑ *.tif* (TIFF -Tagged Image File Format). This is a very widely used standard, commonly used by digital scanners.

❑ *.wmf* (Windows metafile). This format is used by numerous Windows programs, including Lotus Freelance and Harvard Draw.

Vector graphics

A vector image is re-drawn each time that it is displayed on screen. The computer uses mathematical information about the image, which the drawing program uses to generate it. For more information on vector graphics see Topic 37.

Bit map versus vector images

A number of distinctions between the two types of image can be made:

❑ vector images generally need less memory storage than bit map images;

❑ complex vector images can take a long time to re-draw in screen;

❑ bit map images can be displayed very quickly because the calculations are minimal.

❑ vector images can be re-scaled without loss of resolution;

❑ bit map images have a fixed resolution.

Sound

There are a number of audio storage standards for sound files, the most common for PC use being *waveform*. *MIDI* (musical instrument digital interface) is a standard for controlling musical instruments attached to the PC.

Waveform audio

Figure 41.4 represents two physical characteristics of a simple sound object:

❑ amplitude

❑ frequency

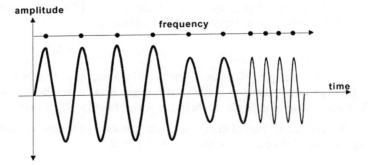

Figure 41.4. *Amplitude and frequency*

Amplitude determines loudness, or volume and frequency determines pitch. *Pitch* is commonly referred to in terms of high and low notes. Increasing frequency raises the pitch of a sound, whereas reducing it lowers the pitch. In the Figure, the amplitude and thereby the volume, begins at one level and is then reduced. Towards the end, the frequency and thereby the pitch, is increased. Frequency is measured according to the number of times a wave form is repeated per second, expressed as Herz (Hz) or cycles per second.

Recording settings

When recording sound on computer, certain settings have to be determined, the *sample rate, sample size* and the number of *channels* (one for mono and two for stereo). A sample of the wave characteristics is taken at regular intervals and the frequency (the number of times per second) with which this is done is known as the *sampling rate*. Waveform editors commonly refer to this measurement in Hz. This should not be confused with the waveform frequency, which determines the pitch.

Figure 41.5 shows the dialogue box for recording settings in Soundblaster's Creative Wave Studio. A higher sampling rate produces higher quality sound, but uses more memory as does a 16-bit sample size compared with an 8-bit sample size. A sampling rate of 11025 Hz is acceptable for voice recording, but 44100 Hz is needed for CD quality.

Figure 41.5. *Sound recording settings*

MIDI

In Soundblaster's AWE32 MIDI Synthesizer; the drop-down instrument list gives access to, for example, a virtual keyboard which uses the PC's own sound card to play a variety of synthesized instruments, plus other noises, such as a gun shot or bird song. Waveform audio requires that the computer generates sounds, whereas MIDI can also place the computer in the role of conductor, determining what musical notes an external instrument will play and how it will play them. This includes effects, such as vibrato. A MIDI interface is two-way, so music played on an external instrument can be stored by the computer as a MIDI file and played back with or without some modification by the computer's MIDI software.

Video

Although animated computer graphics can be used to illustrate, for example, how the internal combustion engine operates, video can show staff trainees how to deal with customers, smile politely and deal with complaints, or it can help show you how to play a guitar.

Video sequences are also a vital part of many computer games. The following sections describe the main components of video capture, editing and playback.

Video sequences

A video recording consists of a number of frames, which when viewed one after another and at a sufficient rate trick the human eye into seeing 'moving' pictures. Cinema film works in the same way, except that each frame is an actual picture, whereas video frames are recorded as magnetic patterns on video tape. Digital video cameras use solid state memory storage, rather than tape, but the principal of playback is the same.

Capturing video sequences

The source of the video can be a tape, or solid state recording, or 'live' video through a video camera. A typical video camera captures and plays back frames at a rate of 25 per second (reasonable quality for computer playback is achievable using a capture rate of around 15 frames per second), so the computer system being used to capture a complete sequence needs to have a fairly powerful specification. The purposes of the components can be described as follows.

❏ Video source. This can be a video camera or VCR. Video cameras are available with different recording standards, including Hi-8, although the most popular is VHS. An enhanced VHS standard is SVHS or S-Video. Some video cameras are digital and do not require tape for recording. Conventional video cameras use small C-type (Compact) cassettes with recording time of a half to one hour. When a tape recording is copied, there is always some degradation in quality, so playback through the original recording device (the camera or VCR) is the best option. Digital equipment does not have this problem as the digitisation process ensures that the recording is always of the same quality.

❏ Connector box. Most video capture products provide an external box to limit the number of connections on the video capture card to a minimum. Typically, the box has *video-out* for monitor connection and *audio-out* (left and right) for connection to speakers. The opposite, video-in and audio-in connections are for connection to the camera or VCR. An S-video connection incorporates sound and vision channels.

❏ A video capture card digitises the video signal and captures the individual frames flowing from the video camera or VCR. Most video capture cards support the different broadcast formats, which for the USA is NTSC and for the UK and most of Western Europe is PAL. During the capture process, the card compresses the signals to reduce the memory and processing requirements, which otherwise would be too much for even a high specification microcomputer. The topic of video compression is dealt with in more detail later.

❏ The compressed data for each frame is handled by the computer's processor and written to RAM. The RAM must be sufficient to hold frames before they can be written to disk.

❏ The video capture software enables the user to view individual frames on screen, in any order, and select those to include in the edited sequence. Other software facilities include transitions (such as 'fade out' or 'dissolve' between frames), titling and adding different sound tracks.

If the sequence is short and the computer has sufficient RAM, all the captured frames can be manipulated through the video editing software, without first saving or 'rendering' them to the hard drive. More usually, the entire sequence is rendered to disk before the editing process begins.

Video compression standards

As indicated earlier, image compression is essential for computer-based video storage, editing and playback. The signals from the VCR or video camera are issued at a rate of around 25 megabytes per second. Clearly, even a short sequence of say, ten seconds requires huge amounts of RAM and disk storage space. The processor must be capable of handling data sufficiently quickly to process all the captured frames, or the smoothness of movement in the original may be lost. Standard hard drives cannot transfer data sufficiently quickly without data compression. Similarly, CD-ROM drives can only play back video smoothly (that is, without 'dropping' frames from the sequence) if the data transfer rate is reduced through compression. As indicated earlier, capturing at a rate of 15 frames per second (fps) will still produce a reasonably smooth sequence, although at 10 fps, the result will be very 'jerky'. Using a capture rate of less than 25 fps will save considerable space and allow reasonable playback on slower machines. Quality can also be maintained by keeping the playback window size small (expressed as a fraction of the full screen). The larger the window, the greater the capture resolution needed to maintain a reasonable, 'non-grainy' quality.

Typical standards use compression ratios of between 3 and 11 to 1. The compression process uses complex mathematical algorithms to sift out duplicated material in the image. *Frame differencing* is a compression technique which uses the fact that much of the image will not change from one frame to the next. This is particularly the case in static shots where the background changes little or not at all during the entire sequence.

Codecs

A codec (compression decompression) is an algorithm used for the compression and decompression of digital video recordings. To play the digital video or 'movie' on a particular machine, the installed *movie file formats* (see next section) must be able to handle the codec used to compress the contents of the movie. Usually, the movie player will handle several different codecs and upon playback detects the right one 'on the fly'. Popular codec formats include JPEG, CinePak, Indeo and MPEG. Except for entirely black and white Images, with much white space, high compression ratios can only by achieved using *lossy* algorithms. If lossy compression is used with continuous tone Images, the decompressed image will not be the same as the original, because some subtlety of tone variation is lost as a result of compression. A certain loss in such subtlety is perfectly acceptable because the differences are not easily detectable and the savings in storage space and decompression processing requirements are considerable. An entirely *lossless* compression of a continuous tone image may only reduce storage requirements by around one-half or one-third. Lossy compression is more acceptable if the original Images are of the highest quality.

Codec formats

MPEG

MPEG stands for Motion Picture Experts Group and refers to a method of image compression. The compression method requires hardware assistance and produces very high quality video. MPEG achieves this quality by only discarding image information which is not easily detectable by the human eye.

CinePak

The CinePak software codec is recognised by QuickTime and Video for Windows. It uses lossy compression and frame differencing. Compression times can be slow but the resulting decompressed playback can be excellent, provided that the original recording is of high quality (otherwise, the lossy compression results may be unacceptable).

Indeo

This codec was developed by Intel to accompany a video capture card, called the Intel Smart Video Recorder and can be set to lossy or lossless compression and is able to use frame differencing to improve compression ratios. Decompression requires more processor power than CinePak, so on lower specification machine, dropped frames can prevent smooth playback. Like CinePak, the Indeo codec is supported by both QuickTime and Video for Windows players.

JPEG

JPEG is a codec which is primarily used for still Images and when used for digital video compression it treats each frame as a still and does not use frame differencing. This means that the data for each frame must be separately decompressed before playback, increasing the likelihood that, on lower specification machines, frames will be dropped. On the other hand, JPEG decompression is often hardware assisted and thus quicker than software only methods. Playback standard is of the highest quality and JPEG is the most widely-used video format. It is not popular on the World-wide Web because many machines do not have JPEG support.

Video player standards

The Movie file formats used by video player packages include QuickTime, Video for Windows (usually known by the extension AVI - Audio/Video Interleave) and MPEG (this is both a codec for digital video and a movie file format).

MPEG

Confusingly MPEG (Motion Picture Experts Group) is a codec (compression decompression) standard and a movie file format. As a movie file format, MPEG has three forms, one for vision only, another solely for audio and a composite for both sound and vision. MPEG produces movies of excellent quality through the use of hardware assisted encoding. Software decoders are available, but require the use of more powerful systems to avoid dropping frames in the sequence. Software-based formats, such as QuickTime, are generally preferable.

QuickTime

Developed originally by Apple for their Macintosh computers, QuickTime is one of the most popular standards for the World-wide Web. As is essential on the Web, QuickTime is usable across most computer platforms (different operating systems). QuickTime movies use the file extension .qt or .mov. PCs can play QuickTime movies through the QuickTime for Windows package and Apple machines use a player called MoviePlayer. QuickTime can handle the main codecs of Indeo, CinePak and MPEG.

AVI

Usually referred to by the file extension it uses (.avi), the Video for Windows (VfW) standard was developed by Microsoft and therefore is the standard for PCs. Multimedia products designed for the PC and there are hundreds, naturally tend to use the .avi standard. Unfortunately, movie players for other platforms are not generally able to read .avi files directly and for Web publishing in particular, QuickTime is a better choice. To achieve the highest quality, a recording can be compressed with a hardware assisted codec, such as JPEG or MPEG and then be exported to a software standard, such as QuickTime, which can then be played directly by, for example, QuickTime for Windows.

✐Exercises

1. Currently, there are four types of multimedia object. What are they?
2. Identify and distinguish between, two text file formats which are most widely accepted by computer systems.
3. Web pages can use two types of graphical image - .jpg and .gif. What sort of images are best stored in each format?
4. What is an animated .gif?
5. Explain the need to consider file sizes when embedding pictures in a web page.
6. Why are .wav files so called?
7. What is MIDI used for?
8. Describe the process of using a computer to edit a video sequence.

Part 2

Further ICT

Sections

- Systems and systems management
- Further networking
- Further database
- Organisations and ICT

Section 9

Systems and systems management

Topics

System life cycle

In business, *systems analysis and design* is the process of investigating a business, existing or new, with a view to determining how best to manage the various procedures and information processing tasks that it involves. Though it frequently means considering the use of a computer system to replace some manual operations, this need not always be the case. The *systems analyst,* whose job it is to perform the investigation, might recommend the use of a computer to improve the efficiency of the information system under consideration, but he/she might equally well decide that a manual system is adequate, or even preferable. Thus, the intention in systems analysis is to determine how well a business copes with its current information processing needs, and whether it is possible to improve the procedures involved in order to make it more efficient, or more profitable, or both. Systems design involves planning the structure of the information system to be implemented. In other words, analysis determines what the system should do, and design determines how it should be done.

The job of the systems analyst starts with studying the current, or proposed, system; this involves collecting facts which will help the analyst to determine whether a computer would improve the information system, and if so, in what areas it would be most beneficial. Once the decision has been made to go ahead with a new or improved system, the analyst must develop a plan for putting the proposed system into practice. This includes specifying all the procedures involved, computerised or otherwise, how data is to be captured, what software will be required to process the data, what equipment will be necessary, what staff will be needed and how they will be trained, and so on. In other words, the analyst must provide a complete plan of every detail of the proposed system. A key feature of this complex task is communicating with staff, whether they are ordinary employees or managers. The people who work in the business are most likely to know what works and what does not, what causes problems and how they can be avoided, and where improvements to the current system are most necessary.

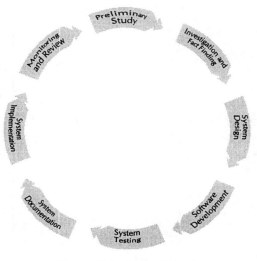

Figure 42.1. *System life cycle*

This Topic describes the *system development life cycle* (Figure 42.1) the sequence of activities involved in analysing, designing and implementing an information system. As well as systems analysts, who play key roles in the process, other personnel such as computer programmers and computer managers are also involved to a large degree.

Though the steps are described separately, in practice they may be performed in a different order, or even be difficult to distinguish one from another; sometimes one part of the system will be in the process of being implemented while another is still being analysed. The cyclic nature of system development is illustrated in Figure 42.1. The system development stages illustrated in the diagram may be repeated a number of times during the life of a system. Each time a significant change or improvement is required, the cycle is repeated.

Preliminary study

Before an organisation embarks on a costly project involving the development of a new information system, it is necessary to determine whether the system is possible to achieve and, if so, whether there will be sufficient benefits in doing so. The main part of this investigation is called a *feasibility study*. However, even before the feasibility study commences, it will be necessary to fully clarify what is being proposed. The systems analyst dealing with the proposal will talk with the people who have suggested the project in order to determine exactly what they have in mind and their reasons.

Once the proposal has been fully clarified, the feasibility study can be undertaken. The feasibility study is usually carried out by a team of people with experience in information systems techniques, with a knowledge of the type of system being proposed and who are skilled in systems analysis and design. The team will be responsible for determining whether the potential benefits of the proposed system can justify the costs involved in developing it. It may be that the consequences of not adopting the new system make the change essential. For example, if a company is unable, through volume of work, to deal with customers effectively, the latter may take their business to more efficient competitors. It then becomes essential to the company's survival to improve its information system.

The feasibility study must also establish whether the new system can operate with available technology, software and personnel. In most instances, for example where a currently manual system is to be replaced or improved by using a computer system, the existing technology will most probably exist, but a new, innovative idea might require hardware or software that don't exist. If this is the case, the feasibility study team will attempt to determine whether the new items can be developed within a reasonable time.

Finally, the team will consider how well the system will be received by the people who will have to use it. This must have been a prime concern, for instance, of the first analysts who considered the use of cash points such as those now commonly provided by banks and building societies: would customers trust them and would they be sufficiently easy to use?

Investigation and analysis

If the feasibility study produces a favourable report, the next stage, that of making a detailed analysis of the current system, will commence. The systems analyst will investigate all aspects of the current system:

- ❏   what services are being offered;
- ❏   what tasks are being performed;
- ❏   how they are being performed;
- ❏   how frequently they are done;
- ❏   how well they are done;

❑   what staff are involved and the nature of their involvement

❑   what is lacking in the system;

❑   any faults with the system;

❑   how the system can be improved.

Finding the answers to these questions requires the analyst to talk to all the people involved in operating the current system, from ordinary employees to managers and directors. This will frequently involve the use of questionnaires as well as personal interviews with employees, the study of manuals and reports, the observation of current working practices, and the collection and study of forms and other documents currently used. As this process is going on, the analyst will be starting to form views on how the new system should work in order to overcome the problems with the current system. At the end of this stage, the systems analyst will thoroughly understand how the current system works and be in a position to begin to design and produce a *Requirements Specification* for the new system.

Requirements specification

The Requirements Specification should clearly present what the system is meant to do and achieve, but design considerations should be left until the Design stage. Of course, some design aspects, such as the need for bar code scanning for an EPOS (electronic point of sale) system, may be obvious and can be taken for granted. Some parts of the design may be constrained by the need for compatibility with existing hardware and software. Otherwise, creating a precise design at this stage is unwise because as the development proceeds new design possibilities or unforeseen 'glitches' are almost certain to arise.

Although the systems analyst is responsible for drawing up the Requirements Specification, he or she needs to ensure that users are closely involved in its development. The systems analyst should listen carefully to users and ensure that their comments and suggestions have been properly interpreted before incorporating the information into the specification. Regular feedback and consultation Fact-finding methods

There are several methods which can be used to gather facts about a system: (i) interviewing; (ii) questionnaires; (iii) examination of records and procedure manuals; (iv) examination of documents; (v) observation. Each method has its own particular advantages and disadvantages and the method or methods chosen will depend on the specific circumstances surrounding the investigation, for example, the size of the business, the number of staff employed and their location and distribution.

Interviewing

This method has much to recommend it, in that the facts can be gathered directly from the person or persons who have experience of the system under investigation. On the other hand, a business with a number of geographically distributed branches makes the process of extensive interviewing expensive and time-consuming. Further, interviewing skills need to be acquired if the process is to be effective. The interviewer needs to know how to gain the confidence of the interviewee and ensure that the information which is given will be of value in the design of the new system. Questions need to be phrased unambiguously in order that the interviewee supplies the information actually required and a checklist of points will help to ensure that all relevant questions are asked. Of course, the interview may need to stray from the points in the checklist, if it becomes apparent that the interviewee is able to provide relevant information not previously considered. For example, clerical procedures may be designed quite satisfactorily but may be made less effective because of personality conflicts between staff. Such tensions may only be revealed through personal interview.

The interviewer also needs to detect any unsatisfactory responses to questions and possibly use alternative methods to glean the required information. Unsatisfactory responses include:

❑ Refusal to answer. Such refusal may indicate, for example, that set procedures are not being followed and that the member of staff does not wish to be 'incriminated'.

❑ Answer with irrelevant information. It may be that the question is ambiguous and has to be re-phrased in order to elicit the required information.

❑ Answer with insufficient information. If a system is to be designed which covers all foreseeable user requirements and operational circumstances, it is important that the analyst has all relevant information.

❑ Inaccurate answer. The interviewer may or may not be aware that an inaccurate answer has been given but it is important that other sources of information are used to cross-check answers.

Questionnaires

Questionnaires are useful when only a small amount of information is required from a large number of people, but to provide accurate responses, questions need to be unambiguous and precise. The questionnaire has a number of advantages over the interview:

❑ each respondent is asked exactly the same questions, so responses can be analysed according to the pre-defined categories of information;

❑ the lack of personal contact allows the respondent to feel completely at ease when providing information, particularly if responses are to be anonymous;

❑ questionnaires are particularly suited to the gathering of factual information, for example, the number of customer orders received in one week;

❑ it is cheap, particularly if users are scattered over a wide geographical area.

A number of disadvantages attach to the use of questionnaires:

❑ questions have to be simple and their meaning completely unambiguous to the respondents;

❑ if the responses indicate that the wrong questions were asked, or that they were phrased badly, it may be difficult to clarify the information, particularly if the respondents were anonymous;

❑ without direct observation it is difficult to obtain a realistic view of a system's operation. The questionnaire often provides only statistical information on, for example, volumes of sales transactions or customer enquiries.

Examination of records and procedure manuals

If existing procedures are already well documented, then the procedure manuals can provide a ready-made source of information on the way procedures should be carried out. It is less likely, however, that procedures will be documented in the smaller organization. In any event, it is important to realise that procedures detailed in manuals may not accord entirely with what actually happens. The examination of current records and the tracing of particular transactions can be a useful method of discovering what procedures are carried out.

Special purpose records which may involve, for example, the ticking of a box when an activity has been completed, can be used to analyse procedures which are causing delays or are not functioning efficiently. The use of special purpose records imposes extra burdens on staff who have to record procedures as they happen and the technique should only be used when strictly necessary.

Examination of documents

It is important that the analyst examines all documents used in a system, to ensure that each:

❑   fulfils some purpose, that is, it records or transmits information which is actually used at some stage. Systems are subject to some inertia, for example, there may have been a 'one-off' requirement to record and analyse the geographical distribution of customers over a single month and yet the summary document is still completed because no-one told the staff it was no longer necessary;

❑   is clear and satisfies its purpose, for example, a form may not indicate clearly the type of data to be entered under each heading. In any case, it may well require re-designing for any new system which is introduced.

The documents, which should include, for example, source documents, report summaries, customer invoices and delivery notes, help to build a picture of the information flows which take place from input to output.

Observation

It is most important to observe a procedure in action, so that irregularities and exceptional procedures are noticed. Observation should always be carried out with tact and staff under observation should be made fully aware of its purpose, to avoid suspicions of 'snooping'.

The following list details some of the features of office procedures and conditions which may usefully be observed during the investigation:

❑   office layout - this may determine whether the positioning of desks, filing cabinets and other office equipment is convenient for staff and conducive to efficient working;

❑   work load - this should indicate whether the volume of documents awaiting processing is fairly constant or if there are peak periods of activity;

❑   delays - these could show that there are some procedures which are constantly behind schedule;

❑   methods of working - a trained observer can, through experience, recognize a slow, reasonable or quick pace of working and decide whether or not the method of working is efficient. It is important that such observations should be followed up by an interview to obtain the co-operation of the person under observation;

❑ office conditions - these should be examined, as poor ventilation, inadequate or excessive temperatures, or poor lighting can adversely affect staff efficiency.

Often the observation will be carried out in an informal way but it may be useful on occasion to, for example, work at a user's desk, so as to observe directly the way that customer orders are dealt with. It is important to realise that a user may 'put on a performance' whilst under observation and that this reduces the value of the information gathered.

Conceptual modelling

By using conceptual models in the Requirements Specification, the systems analyst presents to users and technical designers a clear picture of what the system is to do, without making any assumptions about system design. A complete picture of a system can be obtained with various models, each of which is used to view the system from a different aspect.

Data models

An *entity-relationship model* (ERM) defines a system's data requirements in terms of entities, such as orders, customers or suppliers and the relationships between them (Topic 23). Each entity equates with a table in a relational database. Figure 42.1 shows an ERM with three related entities, Department, Job and StaffMember. The model also shows the degree (one-to-many, in this case) of each relationship. Thus, each department employs one or more members of staff and each job category (Supervisor, Operator etc) is held by one or more staff. Depending on the level of detail required, the ERM may also show (Figure 42.2) the attributes (or fields) associated with each entity or table and indicate those attributes which maintain the relationships. Figure 42.2 shows that the StaffMember entity is linked to Department entity through DeptCode and Job entity through JobCode.

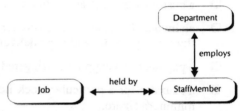

Figure 42.1. *Entity-relationship model*

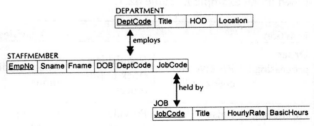

Figure 42.2. *An ERM showing entities and attributes*

Process models

A system will usually involve more than one functional area (Sales, Accounts etc) and process models are used to show the relevant involvement of each area, the activities it undertakes and the events which trigger flows of data or information from one area to another.

A high-level *data flow diagram* (DFD) is used to show the main functional areas and the data flows between them. Figure 42.3 provides an example for a typical trading organisation.

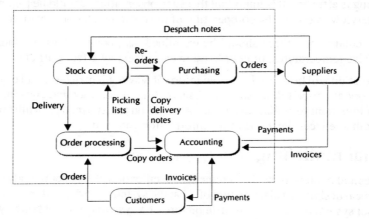

Figure 42.3. *High level data flow diagram*

The data flows in the Figure are 'triggered' by *events*. For example:

❑   a customer order is generated when a customer orders goods;

❑   an invoice for a particular customer is raised when a sale and despatch is confirmed (by the copy order and copy delivery note);

❑   a payment to a supplier is triggered when the invoice payment falls due.

❑   a re-order for a particular stock item is raised when its stock level falls below a minimum figure.

The activities which take place in each functional area may be set out in a Activities table as shown in the example in Table 42.1.

Function	Activities				
Order processing	Receive and check orders	Requisition stock to fill orders	Check credit limits	Produce picking lists from orders	Produce delivery notes and sales details
Purchasing	Raise purchase orders	Provide purchase details	Chase up overdue orders		
Stock control	Receive, inspect and bin stock	Pick, load and despatch goods	Check stock levels for re-ordering	Report current stock levels	Report stock deficiencies
Accounting	Receive suppliers' invoices	Pay suppliers	Issue customer invoices	Receive payments from customers	Set credit limits

Table 42.1. *Activities within functional areas*

A low-level data flow diagram concentrates on the system in question and also provides information on the activities that take place within the system. Figure 42.4 shows a low level data flow diagram for the Sales Order Processing system

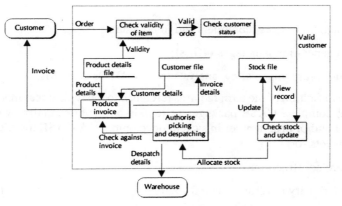

Figure 42.4. *Low level data flow diagram*

System design

This stage produces the details of how the system will meet the requirements identified in the previous analysis stage. A major part of this stage involves identifying the inputs to the system (what they are and how they are to be captured), and the outputs from the system, such as reports, invoices, bills and statements. The designers will also specify in detail what files will be needed, their structures and what devices and media will be used to store them. All this information will be written down in the form of reports, tables and diagrams. Such diagrams as system flow charts and *data flow diagrams* will be used to show how the overall system is integrated. The system designers will also provide detailed specifications on what the software is required to do so that programmers in the next stage will have a clear idea of what they are expected to produce.

Prototyping

A prototype is, in effect, a first try at manufacturing a newly designed product; it is not expected to be perfect, but will form a basis for future development and design improvements. Car manufacturers do this when trying to incorporate revolutionary features and technologies into a new car. A prototype of an information system allows users to test it for achievement of their desired objectives. Prototyping can take place at various stages of the system development cycle, but its use must be planned and anticipated to ensure maximum feedback is obtained from users. In the early stages, a prototype may be developed to test the appropriateness of screen dialogues, without constructing the main files, whilst later it may include a section of database and some applications software. Prototyping is expensive, in terms of time and resources and is unlikely to be used where user requirements are well established or the system is fairly standard.

CASE (computer-aided software engineering) tools

Software engineering is a concept which recognizes the fact that the principles of engineering normally applied to other disciplines, can be highly relevant to the 'engineering' of information systems; the parameters for the effectiveness and quality of an information system have to be set at the design stage, if users' needs are to be properly met.

A CASE tool can loosely refer to any software tool used in the development of information systems, for example:

- ❏   language processors (compilers and interpreters);

- ❏   fourth generation languages (4GLs);

- ❏   graphics programs to allow analysts to draw DFDs or ERMs.

A more precise definition of the term requires reference to the typical features of CASE proprietary software; complete CASE packages or toolkits are commercially available to aid the systems analyst and/or programmer in system development. A CASE toolkit would normally contain components for:

- ❏   diagram construction;

- ❏   data dictionary development and control;

- ❏   interface generation;

- ❏   source code generation;

- ❏   project management.

Diagram construction

This tool is essential for the support of a structured systems methodology. The graphical facilities allow the drawing, storage and modification of diagrams and charts, such as data flow diagrams (DFDs), entity-relationship models (ERMs) and data structure diagrams (for program development).

Data dictionary

Being particularly important in the development of database systems for the control and consistency of data, the function of data dictionaries is described in Topic 54.

Interface generation

Interface generators support the preparation of prototypes of user interfaces, such as screen dialogues, menus and reports.

Source code generation

These tools allow the automated preparation of computer software, in other words, the conversion of a system specification into the source code of a chosen programming language, which can then be compiled into executable object or machine code. CASE tools for code generation are general purpose and are, as a consequence less efficient in the production of source code than specialized applications generators; most code generators will only produce, say, 75% of the code automatically, leaving the rest to be hand-coded by a programmer.

Project management

Such tools support the scheduling of analysis and design activities and the allocation of resources to the various project activities.

Integrated CASE tools

CASE tools can be used as separate, discrete elements or as a complete system. The integrated use of CASE tools can best be managed through windowing software, which allows, for example, the simultaneous viewing of data flow diagrams and data dictionary entries on screen. Integration also has the benefit of allowing data from one component of the toolkit to be transferred to another, for example, data dictionary entries to entity-relationship diagrams.

System Specification

The contents of a typical system specification are as follows:

❑ Objectives. These are brief statements of what the system is expected to achieve and the functional areas it affects.

❑ Output specifications of screen and printed reports, showing layout and data contents.

❑ User interface design (see also Topics 10, 43). The screen dialogue specifications need to show the layout of prompts and data entry points. The involvement of users is important in every area of design, but it is crucial that the user interface designs properly meet their requirements and are consistent with data requirements. For example, a general-purpose application with many different functions needs to allow intuitive use and provide on-line help if users are to become quickly competent in its use. Conversely, an order entry system can make use of brief prompts and provided they are consistent with the sequence of data items on the order form, users can become quickly competent

❑ File specifications, detailing the data contents of records and the file organisation and access methods to be used.

❑ Software specification, including details of inputs, outputs and processing requirements, validation controls, test data and a testing plan.

❑ Implementation plan and timetable. This identifies all the stages, deadlines and the order in which they are to be completed. Because some stages must be completed before others, the plan will be defined using *critical path analysis*. The plan will also specify the method to be used for the transition from the old to the new system.

❑ Test plan to determine whether the system is performing as required, reliably and consistently.

❑ Hardware requirements.

❑ Supporting clerical and administrative procedures which are needed to provide system inputs, (such as the collection and batching of order forms), distribute system outputs and deal with accuracy controls, such as the preparation of batch control totals.

Software development

Depending on the system requirements, existing software may be purchased or it may be necessary to have software written specially. Software that is already available will usually be much cheaper than software that has to be custom-designed, but in many instances suitable software will not be available. Large organisations frequently employ their own systems analysts and programmers, but smaller firms may have to resort to using a software house for the necessary programs.

System testing

Before the system is put fully into operation, all aspects of it must be tested, not just the software that has been developed, but also the manual procedures involved. Personnel who have not been directly involved in developing the system will often be used to test the system after they have been given some appropriate training; such people may do things that were not anticipated by the system designers. In fact, the people testing the system will often deliberately attempt to make it fail in some way. It is vitally important to discover any serious shortcomings in the new information system before it is fully operational.

System documentation

System documentation serves much the same purposes as program documentation described briefly in the earlier section on software development. All aspects of the system's operation will need to be described in detail. The documentation will include:

- ❑ user manuals describing the operation of the system;
- ❑ technical manuals for the computer hardware;
- ❑ program documentation.

This documentation serves a number of purposes:

- ❑ To provide reference material for training purposes. This will be of value to all employees using the new system. Each task and procedure will be clearly detailed and explained to the relevant staff involved.

- ❑ To explain in detail how the system is intended to work so that the people using the system can cope with problems and unfamiliar situations. This will be of particular value to managers and supervisors responsible for organising the work.

- ❑ To specify how to test the system to ensure that it is working correctly.

- ❑ To make it easier to modify or improve the system in future.

Implementing the system

In this stage the system designers will actually install the new system, putting new equipment into operation, installing and setting up software, creating data files and training people to use the system. There are three generally recognized approaches to implementation:

- ❑ **Parallel running**. With this approach, the old and new systems are run concurrently and the results of each are compared with the other for accuracy and consistency. The old system is not abandoned until the user has complete confidence in the reliability and accuracy of the new one. Obviously, parallel running places a great administrative strain on the business, in that staff are effectively doing many of the jobs twice. Any inconsistencies in results have to be cross-checked and the source of errors located (they may result from the old or the new system). The major advantage of parallel running is that the old system can be used whenever the computer system crashes or fails to function as it should.

❑ **Pilot running.** This strategy requires that only a portion of live transactions go through the new computerized system, the rest being processed by the old method. Thus, for example, the transactions for one section of the business, or a sample of transactions from the whole business, could be used to test the system. This is a reasonably safe strategy but again, the transactions which cause errors may be amongst those which do not pass through the computer system.

❑ **Direct changeover.** This is the riskiest option in that the new system completely replaces the old, without any interim parallel or pilot running. Its major benefit is the lack of administrative costs experienced with the other two methods. The potential costs can be severe, in that system failure could mean complete loss of data access and business failure. To minimize these risks, changeover should be preceded by careful system testing and thorough staff training. It is also helpful if the changeover is carried out during a slack period so that staff are not under pressure. The considerable cost of parallel and pilot running mean that this, the riskiest strategy, is often used in small businesses.

System maintenance

When the system has become fully operational, there will still be the possibility of unforeseen events causing problems. Feedback from users on general usability, shortcomings and error conditions, the latter being recorded in a fault log detailing date, time and nature of error. The system developers will therefore need to be available to deal with any problems that do arise, as well as making modifications as circumstances change. If an outside firm has developed the system, this *system maintenance,* normally will be subject to a separate financial arrangement such as an annual charge.

During maintenance some parts of the system may be temporarily unavailable and the organisation must have contingency plans if it is to continue to function effectively. For hardware maintenance the organisation should either maintain a backup system or if this is too costly have leasing arrangements for temporary hardware replacement. With the latter option, the hardware will have to be configured and software installed before maintenance on the main system begins. Software maintenance should be carried out on a duplicate system to prevent interference with the live applications. If possible, installation of the newly modified software should take place outside of working hours, and if changes are significant, a suitable changeover method needs to be adopted. A period of diagnostic testing and monitoring can then follow to ensure that the maintenance changes are working properly.

Monitoring and review

The final phase of the system development process is the assessment of the completed system. In this *review*, or *evaluation*, a number of factors are examined, including:

❑ How well the system is performing with reference to the needs that were initially identified.

❑   The final cost of the system compared to its original budget.

❑   The time taken to complete the work.

Even after the system is fully operational its performance is continually *monitored* throughout its life. At some stage, monitoring will identify needs that are no longer satisfied by the current system, and the system development process will begin once more with a preliminary study.

🖋Exercises

1. (i)   List and describe the main stages in the development of a *system specification* for a new ICT system.
   (ii)   List the typical contents of a *system specification*.
   (iii)   Identify, and describe, two different approaches to the *implementation* of a new ICT system, pointing our the benefits and drawbacks of each approach.
   (iv)   What is meant by system *maintenance* and why is it necessary?
   (v)   Explain the factors which need to be considered when undertaking a system *review* or evaluation.

2. (i)   Distinguish between *data* and *process models*.
   (ii)   Which type of model, data or process, would be used to design a database definition?

3. Identify the *data flows* (and the 'trigger' *activities*) which would typically occur between the following functional areas:
   (i)   accounting and sales;
   (ii)   accounting and purchasing;
   (iii)   order processing and stock control.

4. Draw an *entity-relationship model* to define the relationships between MultiplexCinema (one only), Film (8 screens) and Showing (each Film shown several times each day).

5. What is *prototyping* and under what circumstances may it be useful?

6. Describe the typical facilities provided by CASE tools.

Topic 10 describes a number of user interface design alternatives. Here we describe some of the theoretical principles and a particular model (the Model Human Processor developed by Card, Moran and Newell) which can be related to the development of user-friendly and efficient interfaces. We also examine the way various input and output devices have been developed as part of the user interface.

The technology of the user interface

The typical user interface is supported by hardware devices such as the bit-mapped display, pointing device, microphone, speakers and scanner and software to present various metaphor (for example, desktop metaphor - Topic 10), menu or command-driven alternatives. These components comprise the technology of the user interface.

Computers are designed to assist humans in the performance of tasks, some of which are simple and some of which are intellectually complex. If we ignore the constraints of processing power and memory capacity, it is the user interface that limits the complexity or sophistication of the problems which can be tackled. For example, with suitable sensor devices, we could ask the computer to use its sense of smell to distinguish between different coffee beans and roasts, or with suitable input and output devices, we could transmit the sense of touch remotely. Video conferencing systems allow meeting participants to hear and see one another, but subtleties of body language and the 'atmosphere' that can be felt in a physical meeting cannot be communicated with current interface technology. A graphical user interface (GUI) undoubtedly makes computers easier to use but it also extends the range and complexity of tasks which can be undertaken by most users. It is doubtful that applications such as desktop publishing and graphic design would be so widely used if the interface was largely command driven and pointing devices did not include the mouse. Similarly, the World Wide Web would not have found such popularity without its multimedia content and hyperlink-driven form of navigation.

Cognitive theory in interface design

There has been considerable research into cognition, that is the mental processes by which the mind becomes aware of things, as an aid to the interface designer. Card, Moran and Newell published their research findings in 1983 in a book entitled "The Psychology of Human-Computer Interaction". They divided their examination of the interface into four areas:

❑ the physical interface. This area concerned the input and output devices with which the user communicated with the computer system, for example, the mouse, keyboard and display screen.

❑ the cognitive interface. To allow understanding of this area, the researchers developed the Human Processor Model (see next page). The model identifies various human characteristics, such as limited short-term memory, which we use to process information. It also shows how these characteristics and the tasks we undertake, affect they way we work with a computer.

❏   the conceptual interface. This area concerns the presentation of the computer system, which is highly complex, as a model which the user can assimilate and use. The graphical user interface seeks to simplify, for example, many file processing operations with the use of familiar symbols, such as folders and waste bins, and 'drag and drop' operations which avoid the typing of complex and formalised commands. Without an appropriate mental model, a user will find it difficult to make effective use of a computer system.

❏   the task interface.

The Model Human Processor

The Model Human Processor pictures the user as a computer with memory areas and processors. Figure 43.1 is a simplified version of the model (for the original diagram see "The Psychology of Human-Computer Interaction", by Card, Moran and Newell published in 1983). The model features are explained below.

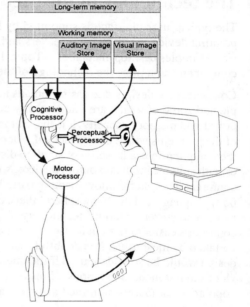

Information received through the eyes and ears (input) is passed to Working Memory (there are two separate storage areas for visual and auditory images) by the Perceptual Processor. Working Memory comprises those sections of Long Term Memory currently of interest to the user and which are needed for task completion. This can be equated with the process of loading data from disk into RAM.

The model's equivalent of the computer's fetch-execute cycle is the Recognise-Act Cycle of the Cognitive Processor. On each cycle the current contents of Working Memory are used to trigger actions by the Motor Processor. The

Figure 43.1. *The Model Human Processor*

Model Human Processor draws on the relevant Long Term Memory information on how to complete the action. For example, the Working Memory may hold the information "Click the right mouse button", but the associated information needed to complete the process is held in Long Term Memory.

For simplicity, some details of the Model are not shown. In particular, the complete Model identifies timings for the completion of certain processes, such as eye movement, information retrieval from Working and Long Term Memory and completion of an action initiated by the Motor Processor.

Working Memory highlights the importance of the user's short-term memory for the completion of tasks. If the memory becomes overloaded with information before a task can be completed, the user will have to pause or perhaps re-read supporting information and will probably start to make mistakes. To avoid mistakes, a user will break down a task into manageable chunks and the software interface must enable this to happen. Help systems, for example, should allow the user to be highly selective in what information appears and menus may be sub-divided hierarchically for the same reason.

Uses of the Human Processor Model

The timings, obtained through user observation, allow the model to be used to predict how quickly users should be able to complete various tasks, such as reading screen text, recognising symbols and abbreviations or moving the mouse pointer to the correct target. This latter information was used to determine the maximum velocity of the mouse pointer on the Xerox Star workstation. The model also provides useful data for the production of effective and realistic animations. For example, to simulate the smooth trajectory of a ball thrown through the air requires that the image appears and then disappears at various points on the trajectory path. Too few images and the movement will appear jerky and too many will require more processing power to achieve the required smoothness and speed. Figure 43.2 shows the process of 'in-betweening' used to create the movement effect. The left image shows the key start and end positions, and the second image shows the intermediate drawings of the ball that are created by the computer.

Figure 43.2. *In-betweening bouncing balls*

Problem solving and cognitive skill

The term "cognitive skill" is used by Card, Moran and Newell to identify a form of cognitive behaviour which was made apparent when using the Human Processor Model. The researchers were studying the behaviour of expert users undertaking the task of text editing by referenced to proof marked documents. The task was viewed initially as one of problem-solving, but the research showed that the users did not use the 'identify problem and search for solution' model for text editing. It became apparent that the users' training and experience allowed them to draw on a bank of skills, more or less automatically, as required. This cognitive skill can be seen in many other areas of human activity, For example, an experienced car driver does not need to 'think' about changing gear or braking, but applies the skills automatically as necessary.

The researchers then began to develop models, known as GOMS, to deal with these cognitive skills. A GOMS model has 4 components:

- ❑ a set of familiar Goals which the user recognises within a range of tasks. For instance, in text editing, Goals may include 'turn the page', 'look at the document', 'type a string of characters', or 'look at the screen'.

- ❑ a set of primitive Operators or actions which formed the user's skill set and from which the user could select.

- ❑ a set of Methods, each of which consisted of a number of sub-goals and relevant Operators. This can be seen as the human equivalent of the macro or a sub-routine in a computer program.

- ❑ a set of Selection rules which the user can apply when choosing which Method to use to achieve a particular Goal.

Models to predict human behaviour when problem solving or using cognitive skills can be used by interface designers to cater for different applications and different types of users. For example, modern interfaces can be tailored to suit the requirements of novice and more advanced users.

A mental system model

It is a truism to say that users who understand the general principles of a computer's operation will perform tasks more quickly and effectively than those who do not. Novice users will read a sequence of instructions and follow them blindly, without any idea of how the computer performs the tasks and as a result, may not be able to deal with machine responses which are not identified in the instructions. For example, when a novice user saves a document and has no knowledge of the computer's filing system, it is quite possible that the user will be unable to find it at a later date. Computer use is more effective if the user has a mental model of the system and therefore knows 'how it works'.

A user's mental system model could include knowledge of, for example, RAM, disk storage features, file management software, communication links to remote servers. Apart from this general information, the mental model may include knowledge more specific to the applications. For example, when using a word processor, concepts of 'wrap around', spaces, paragraph alignment and carriage returns are of fundamental importance if the user is to produce the simplest of documents effectively.

Computers would have remained the preserve of specialists if 'user-friendly' interfaces had not been developed. Part of their success stems from their ability to provide the user with appropriate conceptual models of the system. For example, the use of folders for file management, a clipboard for copying and pasting, buttons for opening and saving all help the novice user to understand what the computer is doing. With experience, the mental model and the effectiveness of computer use are improved.

A designer needs to provide the user with a system model which can be easily learned and is appropriate to the type of user and the application.

Other interface design influences

There have been a number of important influences on interface design:

❏ ergonomics.

❏ artificial intelligence.

Ergonomics

This subject is dealt with in more detail in Topic 32. Ergonomics is the "study of efficiency of workers and working arrangements" (Oxford English Dictionary). Although a separate science in its own right, ergonomic principles are applied increasingly to the design of:

❏ computer equipment for person/machine interfacing, for example, screen displays and keyboards - the Hardware User Interface (HUI);

❏ software - primarily the Graphical User Interface (GUI).

HUI (Hardware User Interface)

It is important that the hardware does not inhibit communication with the computer system. For example, a user may be prevented from making optimum use of a system because the screen causes eyestrain or the mouse operation is difficult to control. Another user may have a physical disability which prevents use of a keyboard or mouse, so alternative devices such as the foot mouse or head tracking device (Topic 4) are needed.

Ergonomics has made very limited impact on keyboard design, which for the majority of users still has the standard QWERTY layout inherited from the mechanical typewriter. Microsoft's Natural keyboard attempts to make some ergonomic improvements by splitting the keys into two main areas and angling the keys slightly, to allow the user to keep a straighter, more comfortable, wrist posture.

Mouse design has continued to develop as ergonomic research highlights the need for change. A mouse generally has two buttons, one for selection and execution and the other for accessing additional functions, generally through pop-up menus. The avoidance of carpal tunnel syndrome (Topic 32) has been a major aim of the more recent development of an integral wheel to make screen scrolling a simpler task. Other ergonomic innovations include cordless mice and alternatives to the mouse, such as the touch pad commonly used in notebook computers. For other devices, see Topic 4.

Software interface

The vast majority of microcomputer users are interested merely in using a computer as a tool, without any real interest in the technical details of its operation. A typical user will probably want to run one or more common general-purpose applications, organise files into directories, delete files and format disks. Though the operating system will provide these services, the user needs to have a certain amount of technical knowledge to perform these tasks. Graphical user interfaces (or GUIs, pronounced *Gooeys*) provide a more intuitive means of performing common tasks. They usually make use of a pointing device, typically a *mouse,* by means of which a *pointer* is moved around the monitor screen on which small pictures (or *icons*) are displayed. These icons represent, among other things, programs which can be run by moving the mouse pointer over the icon and then clicking one of the buttons on the mouse. Applications run in their own self-contained areas called *windows*. In addition, it is usually possible to activate *pull-down menus* which provide access to standard functions. When a GUI uses **W**indows, **I**cons, **M**ouse, **P**ointers and **P**ull-down menus, it is referred to as a WIMP environment.

Voice recognition software has been developed to allow quite complex command and text input and constitutes an important advance for some disabled users in particular.

Contextual Help and Help Agents such as the animated characters in Microsoft products and 'cue cards' which take the user through processes step-by-step and the ability to set user preferences are all examples of interface design improvements which aim to simplify computer use.

Artificial intelligence (AI)

Artificial or machine intelligence has been applied to the development of a variety of computer applications, such as games playing (particularly chess), expert systems (Topic 2), neural networks (simulation of intelligence using connections similar to those in the brain), robotics to allow interaction with external environments and natural language (software to enable a computer to 'understand' human language). Neural network research is also helping in voice recognition and natural language development.

The use of truly natural language is still a long way off, although systems for command input and text dictation are now commonly available for PC systems. Voice input and voice synthesis are already providing important additions to the user interface.

Natural language is commonly used for database interrogation. Instead of typing commands to a strict format, the user can enter an expression, such as "FIND ALL RECORDS WHERE SUPPLIER IS "Acme". Fourth generation languages, or 4GLs, allow this form of expression and are still quite strict in terms of the format and vocabulary.

Exercises

1. (i) Describe the main components of the *Model Human Processor*, developed by Card, Moran and Newell.
   (ii) Describe, with examples, the uses of the Model Human Processor.
   (iii) What is the user's *mental system model* and why is it thought to be important for interface design?
   (iv) Using suitable examples of user tasks, distinguish between *problem solving* and *cognitive skill*, as defined by Card, Moran and Newell.

2. (i) What is a *WIMP* environment and how is it evident in the design of modern interfaces?
   (ii) Describe ways in which the *graphical user interface* (GUI) benefits users.
   (iii) Give examples of the influence of *ergonomic* research into the design of the Hardware User Interface (HUI).
   (iv) Give examples of ICT applications which make use of *artificial intelligence* (AI) principles.

Alternative sources of software

An analysis of the uses to which companies and individuals put computers would reveal that the same types of tasks appear time and time again. Many organisations use computers for pay-roll calculations, others to perform stock control functions, accounting procedures, management information tasks and numerous other common functions. An organisation wishing to implement one of these tasks (or any other vital to its efficient operation) on a computer has several alternatives:

❑ Ask a software house, that is, a company specialising in the production of software, to take on the task of writing a specific program for the organisation's needs.

❑ Use its own programming staff to produce the software in house.

❑ Buy a commercially available program off the shelf and hope that it already fulfils, or can be modified to fulfil, the organisation's requirements.

❑ Buy a general purpose program, such as a database or spreadsheet package, that has the potential to perform the required functions.

The final choice will depend on such factors as the urgency of the requirements, financial constraints, size of the company and the equipment available.

Using a software house

This alternative may be appropriate when there is no suitable packaged software and the expertise for software development is not available in house. However, there may be potential difficulties with this approach.

❑ The systems analyst or analyst/programmer may be unfamiliar with the application and in any case, will have to spend considerable time gathering information about the organisation and the part that the new application is to play in its global information system. This process can be extremely expensive.

❑ The maintenance agreement may not allow for alterations to the software function without significant additional charges.

❑ The software house may cease trading and leave the organisation with software which cannot be modified as information needs change. The organisation does not have the in-house expertise and other software houses are unlikely to agree to the maintenance of 'foreign' products.

❑ The claimed expertise to develop the application may not exist, leaving the organisation with a non-functioning or incomplete solution.

The most significant potential drawback relates to lack of or failure of suitable software maintenance. For this reason, the option is most likely to be used by an organisation which has the in-house expertise to maintain the software, but does not have the capacity to produce it from scratch. To allow for in-house maintenance, the client organisation will need to ensure that comprehensive programming documentation is provided as part of the contract.

In-house development

This is only practical if an organisation employs the necessary specialist staff, including systems analysts to determine user requirements and produce the system specification (Topic 42) and programmers to write the software. These specialist staff must be able to work as a project team (Topic 45) and be able to communicate effectively with management and users. Programming expertise also needs to be appropriate; certain applications are best developed with a particular type of programming language or application generator (Topic 64).

There are potential drawbacks to in-house software development.

❑ The project may be well under way before inadequacies in expertise are identified.

❑ Project team staff may leave before the project is complete and be difficult to replace at short notice.

Off-the-shelf solutions

Some off-the-shelf software is application-specific. Those for common applications such as accounting, stock control and payroll can often be perfectly satisfactory for many organisations, but where important functions are not available, a tailor-made solution may be needed. *General-purpose packages* are playing an increasingly important role both for simple application requirements and more complex applications where some tailoring and programming is needed.

General-purpose packages

Discussion of this class of software will be restricted here to the following headings, though they are not intended to represent an exhaustive list of all the categories of general purpose packages which are available:

❑ word processors;

❑ spreadsheets;

❑ databases;

❑ graphics packages, including desktop publishing (DTP), business graphics, graphic design and computer aided drawing (CAD).

What characterises these software types as belonging to the category of general-purpose packages is that they have been designed to be very flexible and applicable to a wide range of different tasks. For instance, a spreadsheet can be used as easily for simple accountancy procedures as for stock control; a database can be used with equal facility to store information on technical papers from journals, stock item details and personnel details for payroll purposes. In fact, particularly in respect of modern personal computer software, the trend is for general-purpose packages to do more and more. For example, recent word processors, such as Microsoft's Word for Windows and WordPerfect, include facilities, once only found in desktop publishing packages, for drawing diagrams and for producing graphs, in addition to the normal functions associated with a word processor; the graphic design package CorelDraw, includes some word processing functions and graph drawing functions; the spreadsheet Excel has a number of facilities normally associated with database packages. Fierce market competition has resulted in the major software houses continually improving on their last version of a piece of software, attempting to outdo their competitors. The suitability of a particular general-purpose package for a specific application will be largely dependent on the particular characteristics of the package. Though the general facilities afforded, for instance, by different database packages may be roughly equivalent, each manufacturer will adopt its own style of presentation and will provide certain services not offered by its competitors. A prospective buyer should have a clear idea of the main uses for which the package is to be purchased right at the outset, because some packages may be much more suitable than others. Some advantages of general-purpose software compared to other forms of applications software are as follow:

❑   Because large numbers of the package are sold, prices are relatively low;

❑   They are appropriate to a wide variety of applications;

❑   As they already have been thoroughly tested, they provide a great reduction in the time and costs necessary for development and testing;

❑   They are suitable for people with little or no computing experience;

❑   They are very easy to use;

❑   Most packages of this type are provided with extensive documentation.

Some of the disadvantages are:

❑   Sometimes the package will allow only a clumsy solution to the task in question;

❑   In the case of a spreadsheet or database, for example, the user must still develop the application. This requires a thorough knowledge of the capabilities of the package, which are frequently extensive, and how to make the best use of them;

❑   The user will need to provide his own documentation for the particular application for which the package has been tailored;

❑   Unless the software is used regularly, it is easy to forget the correct command sequences to operate the package, particularly for people inexperienced in the use of computer software of this type;

The user must take responsibility for security measures to ensure that vital data is not lost, or to prevent unauthorised personnel gaining access to the data.

Upgrading software

A decision to upgrade existing software may result from changes in the organisation's information system requirements or, more usually, because it wishes to take advantage of additional functions, or even to rid itself of problems caused by an existing 'buggy' version. Whatever the reason, a number of factors need to be considered before a decision is made.

Costs

Several areas of potential cost can be identified:

❑   Development costs. For software produced by a software house revision costs may be included as part of the maintenance contract, but there is likely to be a limit on the number and level of revisions which can be made without additional charges. In respect of software developed in-house costs must still be borne for the time taken to re-analyse requirements, alter specifications, rewrite, compile and test software.

❑   Off-the-shelf package upgrade. Normally, upgrading from one package version is cheaper than a first time purchase. For general-purpose software which has been tailored for a particular application, perhaps using the built-in programming language, upgrading may require alteration of the code, recompilation and testing.

❑   Hardware upgrade costs. New versions of software will inevitably add new features to keep up with the competition and as a result tend to use more memory and require faster processors if they are to operate as quickly as the older versions. The new version may allow and encourage the user to use additional hardware, such as scanners and cameras to obtain improved results. Typically, progressive software upgrading requires hardware replacement or upgrading every two, or at the outside, three years.

❑   Staff training. The amount of user training which is necessary will depend how different a new version is from the old version. Changes may also need to be made to administrative and operational procedures which affect or are affected by the software upgrade, thereby extending training requirements to other staff.

❑   Changeover costs. If an application is of great importance to an organisation and perhaps affects other applications, then a period of parallel running (Topic 42) may be necessary. The duplication of work involved in running both the old and new systems can result in significantly higher costs.

Benefits

New software versions can provide significant benefits for an organisation:

❑   improved presentation, perhaps through the use of new layout features in a word processor, report generation facilities in a database package, or drawing tools in a graphics package which simplify the production of sophisticated graphics and animations for multimedia presentations.

❑   improved information provision. For example, new versions of spreadsheet and database packages may provide additional facilities for the analysis and extraction of operational and management information.

❑   improved communication. Apart from improvements in the presentation of information, further benefits are obtained from video conferencing, e-mail and other Internet communications.

❑   improved efficiency. Although new software often makes greater demands on hardware, there are often performance improvements. For example, the Windows 98 operating system loads applications much more quickly than its '95 predecessor. 'Wizards' allow users to complete complex tasks, such as the setting up a new Internet connection or the creation of standard document, in a few simple steps.

Software evaluation

Some aspects of software can only be effectively evaluated in the context of a particular use and target user group. To give an extreme example, a drawing package designed for use in a primary school could not meet the needs of a professional graphic designer, no matter how clear the documentation and user friendly the interface. However, there are general criteria which can be applied to the evaluation of any software and a possible checklist is given below.

General information

This would include an examination of:

❑   Product name, producer and licence costs (single user, network etc).

❑   Purpose of the software and application(s) for which it is suitable;

❑   The stated target audience and the level of computer and other skills (for example, knowledge of engineering principles) which are needed for effective use of the software.

❑   The documentation and its usefulness. This would include technical documentation on hardware requirements, installation instructions, troubleshooting guide, statement of limitations (for example, database with maximum of 1000 records) and user guide.

General software features

These may include assessment of the following.

❑   Error-free operation. The **alpha** stage of testing is carried out by the software producer and a beta stage is supposed to be testing in the outside world, but not by actual buyers. **Beta** testing should involve outside organisations and individuals who are invited to "test the software to destruction", in other words, to try and make it fail. However, the complexity of modern software and the competition to produce new, enhanced versions every year or so means that the beta testing stage is often carried out by end-users when they buy a product. It is fair to say that there are few modern software products which perform absolutely reliably and effectively under all circumstances - at some point a program will either crash or demonstrate some instability, such as the loss of a picture from a document or the corruption of a file which prevents the package from subsequently opening it.

❑   Ease of access to software facilities and functions. A user-friendly interface could be evidenced by, for example, a clear, consistent and logical menu structure, the availability of uncluttered toolbars which give access to commonly used facilities, intuitive operation, wizards to guide the user through common problems, examples and on-line procedural, conceptual and contextual help facilities (Topic 33).

❑   Ability to provide for differing levels of expertise. 'Hot' keys, for example, tend to be sought by expert users in preference to working through menus.

Technical features

These may include assessment of:

❑   Hardware and software requirements.

❑   Ease of installation and flexibility in tailoring the installation to suit different user requirements. Most generic software packages, such as word processors and spreadsheets provide options for standard, compact and custom installation.

Technical support for error conditions which may occur and for help with features which are not well documented. The support may be provided by telephone, e-mail or by FAQs (frequently asked questions) or other Web site facilities.

✍️Exercises

1. A book shop wants to store details of its stock and suppliers in a database and is wondering whether to buy an *off-shelf package* specially designed for this kind of application, use the services of a *software house* to develop the application, or to make use of a *general-purpose*, relational database package to develop the database system in-house.

    Describe two benefits and one drawback for each option.

2. A business is considering *upgrading* an existing word processing package which is used throughout the organisation, via the network and various stand-alone and portable PCs.

    Describe three potential benefits and three potential drawbacks for the business of upgrading this software.

3. (i)   Distinguish between *alpha* testing and *beta* testing of software.

    (ii) Apart from error-free operation, describe three other criteria which may be used to *evaluate* software.

A project is a relatively short-term activity (weeks, or months usually), designed to achieve specific objectives. Working on a project team, therefore, is not usually a person's main job. So, programmers, systems analysts and other ICT and user specialists are assigned to a project team as and when the need arises. Examples of ICT projects are:

❑ implementation of a new computerised payroll system;

❑ extension of a local area network to a new laboratory;

❑ introduction of a products database, through which customers can browse.

The stages which lead to the completion of an ICT project are formally described in Topic 42 and include, for example, a preliminary study, systems analysis and design, implementation, maintenance and review.

Project teams

A project team should comprise people with the necessary mix of personal qualities, skills and knowledge to achieve the objectives of the project. Departmental barriers should not restrict the choice of team members and where appropriate they should be selected from across the organisation and, if necessary, from outside it, as consultants. Apart from the project manager, an ICT project team is likely to include systems analysts and designers, programmers and depending on the type of system, database administrators and network engineers. The team may also include specialists from the particular function for which the system is being developed, such as the Head of Department. If departmental representatives are not included in the team they will have a considerable consultancy role to play.

Project activities

Identifying a project

Very often the need for a major new system, product or facility is identified by corporate management. This is because management has the benefit (or should have) of a 'bird's eye' view of the organisation, are responsible for decisions to move it in one direction or another, and control its resources, including finance, staffing, equipment and so on. Thus, a decision to computerise a personnel management system and the initiation of a project to achieve that objective is likely to be 'top-down'. Occasionally, needs are identified by staff working at an operational level, precisely because they have a more intimate understanding of the day-to-day problems they experience.

Identifying project objectives and scope

The objectives of a project need to be clear, because they describe its main functions and what it seeks to achieve. Without objectives, the tasks of team members will be unclear. The scope of a project identifies its boundaries, so the limits of the project are set. Formally, the objectives of an ICT project are detailed in a document titled the Statement of Requirements (Topic 42).

Planning the project

Before starting any project, a number of questions need to be asked: What results are wanted? When does it have to be completed? What resources, including accommodation, equipment, finance, components and people are needed to carry out the project? What are the main tasks? Can some tasks be progressed at the same time or be overlapped? Which tasks have to be completed before which others? In what order do the tasks have to be completed? When does each task have to be started and completed? How do the tasks relate to one another and contribute towards the successful completion of the project? Who needs to be on the team? Who is responsible for dealing with each task? Is best use being made of each member's personal qualities, knowledge and skills?

All these questions point to the need for *planning* a project before it is started. Perhaps the most important questions are:

- ❑ What has to be done?
- ❑ What is the sequence of tasks and events?
- ❑ What time is needed to complete the tasks?

Why plan?

Asked the question, "Why plan?", you would probably say something like, "It's obvious. If you plan something, you're more organised and more likely to achieve what you want." Figure 45.1 illustrates the main purposes of planning.

The Figure shows that *resources* include: people (members of the team and users and managers involved in the project); finance; materials (such as paper and other consumables); equipment (IT and any other special equipment); software (for example, word processor, charting and critical path analysis packages); accommodation (for planning work and team meetings). *Control* is needed, not only to ensure that necessary resources are made available, but also to promote efficiency in their use and keep the project within the planned budget.

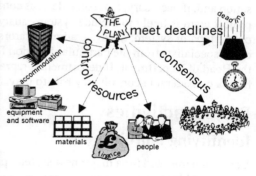

Figure 45.1. *Purposes of project planning*

Consensus shows a two-way arrow between the plan and the people involved in the project. To achieve consensus, requires that when feedback on progress is provided by participants, their comments are properly considered and, if necessary, used to modify the plan.

A plan also sets *deadlines*, dates or times when particular tasks should be completed. It is important that team members keep to deadlines. Each team member is given a role and some responsibilities and lateness is likely to prevent progress of dependent tasks, for which other team members are responsible. This delays the project and probably causes discord and resentment within the team. However, difficulties, unanticipated problems and modifications to the plan, are bound to result in changes to deadlines, hence the two-way arrow in Figure 45.1.

Analysing the project

This requires a detailed analysis of the project objectives, to determine the solutions to achieve them. The detail of this work is covered in Topic 42. To summarise, team members need to break the problem down into smaller component parts, suggest possible solutions, evaluate them and either accept or reject them. This will be an *iterative* process, as decisions on one aspect of the project may require a re-examination of other aspects. The formal method of analysing a problem into progressively smaller components is known as *top-down design*. Analysis also requires that a sequence of activities is identified for the achievement of each project component, as well as the resources which are needed at various points in the sequence. This is known as *scheduling*.

Co-ordinating and integrating the project

The aim of a schedule is to plan the timing of events, activities and resource usage, such that a particular aspect of a project is completed at a particular time. A project is likely to consist of several separate 'strands', each occupying different members of the team. The work of team members needs to be co-ordinated, or properly related. If we say that someone is uncoordinated, we mean that their various physical movements do not properly relate to one another. Lack of physical co-ordination manifests itself in clumsiness, and for example, an inability to dance or do gymnastics. Co-ordination of a project, therefore, means ensuring that the activities of team members and the tasks on which they are working, are related and complement one another. Loss of co-ordination may manifest itself in a team member working hard on a task, which bears little relation to and does not properly contribute to, the progress of the project. Co-ordination is necessary between team members, but also between the team and others who may contribute to the project (in other departments or from other organisations). For this reason, there should be *team* and *steering group meetings* (with user and management representatives and perhaps consultants from outside the organisation). Integration is the fitting together of separate components.

Budget monitoring and control

Every project has a budget, that is, a limited amount of money allocated for its development. The amount depends on the importance of the project to the organisation and the type of project. Not all projects proceed, perhaps because it is not seen to give value for money, or another project, viewed as more important, gains priority. For example, in a college, it may be highly desirable for maths and science students to have a new computer laboratory, but the travel and tourism courses attract far more students and their project for a travel agency office gains priority. The computer laboratory project may be cancelled or scaled down to half the number of computer workstations.

Cost control

Given a financial budget, it is necessary to control money costs to stay within it. Careful thought needs to be given to what constitutes a cost. If you were asked to estimate the costs of installing a computer network, you may check catalogues for the prices of computer file servers, workstations, desks, printers, cabling, connectors and so on and come up with a total cost. You may also consider the costs of software and installation charges. Obviously, these are major items, but they do not reflect the complete cost of the project. You also need to consider staffing costs, not only those of the team, but also the salary of a technician or network administrator who is to manage the network. If users are unfamiliar with the software, training charges will be incurred.

If the members of the project team are salaried employees of the organisation, the difficulty arises of separating their responsibilities to the project, from their other work. Members of a project team are rarely fully occupied by the project, and have other responsibilities. For example, a sales supervisor may be seconded to a sales marketing project team and spend approximately two days per week working on the project. It is more likely that the time given to the project will be highly variable, from week to week, depending on the stage reached. Despite this difficulty, efforts have to be made to calculate the cost of the sales supervisor's (and any other team members) secondment to the project. Otherwise, the actual cost may, in reality, veer drastically from the budgeted cost (although this may not be apparent at the time).

A large project will probably need a complex accounting and cost control system, but a smaller project can be measured by the number of people and the hours they spend working on it. To summarise, in seeking to control costs, you need to recognise what they are and the items in Figure 45.1 provide a useful checklist. Using the example of a computer network, we can identify the following likely costs:

❏ project team members' time, costed according to their hourly rate of pay;

❏ consultancy charges, both from outside the organisation and from other departments (if charged by them); this will be a corporate decision. If a department has a budget, it will need to charge other departments for work they do for them;

❏ computer and network hardware;

❏ software licences;

❏ carpets, air conditioning, blinds; tables, chairs, cable conduit.

❏ installation charges (unless carried out by the project team);

❏ training costs for users on use of new software;

❏ training/employment of network manager;

❏ accommodation, both for the project team and for location of the new network.

The team member with budget monitoring responsibility must record and monitor these costs as the project progresses. Costs give a guide to progress, in the sense that it is a measure of the value of work done. This is particularly so with tangible items, such as computer equipment. The accountant must also monitor the costs against the allocated budget and report to the project manager, or member of senior management, if the project is going over budget.

Project implementation

This includes systems analysis, design, implementation and review, all of which are covered in Topic 42 on the Systems Life Cycle.

Evaluating the project

This activity is associated with the monitoring and review of the project, during and after its completion. Evaluation should include the following.

❑ Measuring progress against schedules and budgets. Has the planned stage been achieved at the budgeted cost?

❑ Are resources being used economically and effectively? If not, this may be because the strengths of team members are not being used in the most effective way. One person may be particularly skilled in one area, but is assigned a role, in which they are under-used or inadequate to the task.

❑ If the project is behind schedule, what are the causes? The problem may be inadequate definition of project, unclear solutions, lack of suitable resources, weakness of team member(s), either in commitment, knowledge or skills. Evaluation will tackle these problems and examine remedies which allow the project to progress (or if it is supposedly completed, correct the deficiency).

❑ The identification of potential problems and ways of avoiding them. In this way, the team should avoid 'management by crisis', by ignoring potential problems, hoping they will simply go away and only re-acting when forced.

❑ Analysis of alternative courses of action, referred to in spreadsheet jargon as 'what if' analysis (Topics 35, 61). In this way, likely effects of different approaches to the project can be anticipated. For example, during a project to install a computer network, consideration may be given to alternative shared printer solutions. The costs of these alternatives can be projected and a judgement made as to the project budget's sufficiency. If a more expensive printing solution is chosen, it may be that savings can be made in other areas of the project. Alternatively, an approach may be made to the project sponsor for an increase in the budget. However, this would require a submission of arguments as to the cost effectiveness of the change.

❑ Quality assessment. Measuring the quality of a product, such as a car, is fairly straightforward. The number sold in comparison with other cars in the same category and continuance of good sales over a long period indicates a high quality product. Measuring the quality of a service is much more difficult. ICT systems provide services to fulfil the needs of various organisational functions and assessment of quality is sometimes highly subjective. The most important quality assessment is that of the project's customers; has the project achieved its objectives?

People, roles and responsibilities

Another word for 'role' is 'function'. Put another way, if your function is to take the minutes of team meetings, your role is 'minutes secretary'; in that role, it is your *responsibility* to take the minutes. The range of roles needed for a project will depend on its size, complexity and scope. Some roles can be regarded as *internal* and relate to the project team, whilst others are external; the latter may relate to people who are not directly involved in the project, but are affected by it, have an interest in its outcome and may be of occasional assistance to the project team. For example, a similar project may have been completed elsewhere (within the organisation, or outside it) and it makes sense to consult the people involved. If the project is being financed by a bank or other external agency, clearly the role of bank manager is going to impinge on the work of the team. Other team responsibilities include: resource allocation, monitoring of resource usage (records need to be kept) and monitoring of progress against schedules.

Team building

Building a team involves the development of: ways of working to improve efficiency and productivity; relationships among members; mutual respect of each others' strengths; the team's adaptability to changes in circumstances, such as a cut in budget, or a reduction in the time allocation.

If a team works successfully over a longer time (perhaps months, or years), or on different successful projects, the initial stages of team building should be unnecessary.

Achieving consensus

Making decisions by consensus is desirable, but not always achievable, at least in the sense of absolute and unreserved agreement. Consensus can only be obtained when each member has clearly expressed his or her views and disagreements, listened to and understood those of the others, and presented any alternatives they wish to be discussed. When, through discussion and negotiation a decision, which everyone understands, is reached then we can say a consensus decision has been made.

Measuring team performance

Leadership

A team does not always have the same leader. Any team member must be willing to take that role. This is because, as a project progresses, different specialisms are needed. Thus, for example, during the analysis stage, when questionnaires are being drawn up and user interviews conducted, the team has a particular leader. When the project moves onto the production stage, entirely different talents are called for, such as technical knowledge of project equipment and computer software, and another member takes the team leader role. Teams should be democratic, so leaders should lead, not dictate.

Team leader role

A team leader should:

❏ gain consensus on the project objectives and clarify members' expectations of the project. If all the team are clear about the objectives, in the short and longer term, they are more likely to be able to co-ordinate and integrate their activities;

❏ make the best use of the available skills and talents. This means that task assignment must be carefully considered, so members work to their strengths and not their weaknesses;

❏ hold regular meetings to discuss progress and problems as they arise;

❏ monitor and give feedback on team and individual performance;

❏ ensure co-ordination and integration of separate tasks;

❏ ensure that the project is completed (as explained earlier, this is likely to be a stage or one aspect, as the team leader role may be occupied by different members, as appropriate).

Leadership styles

Various leadership styles can be adopted, depending on the experience, competence and confidence of the team's members (and the team leader):

❑ lead by good example (but don't do it all);

❑ delegation and trust (assign tasks and leave them to get on with it, until the next review meeting);

❑ participate and support; this style may be appropriate where none of the members have strong experience of leading a team and need extensive support from one another. The team leader must still lead, otherwise direction and momentum are lost.

Co-operation, enthusiasm and adaptability

Co-operation means working together to achieve common objectives. It does not mean obeying orders from dictators! Enthusiasm comes from genuine interest in the work, so although people cannot always do what they most enjoy, they tend to be more enthusiastic when using their talents, rather than struggling with weaknesses. Enthusiasm also tends to come from previous success and recognition by others of achievement. Adaptability is important, because a project will not go absolutely as planned. Members may have to learn new skills or extend existing ones (for example, a new version of a software package may be provided), work with different team members at various times and possibly, take the role of team leader.

Technical knowledge and competence

It is not necessary for every member of a team to be expert in the same technical areas. Each person is assigned to a team because they have a particular contribution to make; this contribution is likely to be a mix of the personal qualities already mentioned and competence in a particular area. For example, a team member with good communication skills may chair meetings, take minutes, or take the role of team leader. Of course, a team leader has to have the technical knowledge to understand the task or tasks for which they have responsibility. Some members of the team are likely to be, for example, better programmers and some may have highly developed design skills. The assignment of people to particular roles should take account of a range of factors, but technical knowledge and competence are fundamental to the production of a good product. It is useless to compose a team of good communicators, if their knowledge of the project subject is sketchy.

Effort and efficiency

Non-productive effort is wasted. However, this does not mean that every effort should achieve instant success. By working on a task, finding that the results are unsatisfactory and repeating or modifying the work, we can learn and ultimately improve the end product. Of course, with proper preparation and planning, the chances of success are increased. For example, a programmer should not tackle a problem by immediately coding the program, but should follow a disciplined program design method. Without this preparation, the program is likely to be difficult to debug and modify. Efficiency comes from properly channelled effort. To carry out a task efficiently requires that all the components (materials, tools, technical knowledge, accommodation and so on) are available as and when they are needed.

✍️Exercises

1. A large organisation is planning the development of a new ICT system.
    (i)   Identify the main categories of staff who ought to be members of the *project management team*.
    (ii) Why is it important to define the *scope* of a project?
    (iii) List the main *resource categories* which may be required for the development of the project.
    (iv) Why is it important to set various *deadlines* during the project?
    (v)   Many processes within a project will tend to be *iterative*. Why is this?
    (vi) Describe the main *categories of cost* which may be incurred during the project and following its implementation.
    (vii) Describe three criteria for the *evaluation* of a project.
    (viii) Using a suitable example, explain why *consensus* is important but not always achievable.
2. (i)   Identify two qualities which are desirable in a *project leader*.
    (ii) "All members of a project team should have sufficient technical knowledge to understand and sufficient competence to play an active role in, all aspects of the project."

    To what extent do you regard this statement to be true or false? Explain your answer.
    (iii) Why is important that project team members are able to distinguish between *effort* and *efficiency*?

Critical path analysis

Techniques such as PERT (*Project Evaluation and Review Techniques*) and CPA (*Critical Path Analysis*) use a branch of mathematics called *network analysis* to systemise and aid project management. Networks allow projects to be represented graphically as a series of activities connected by nodes representing their start and end points. Network analysis allows the crucial activities which determine the total duration of the project to be identified. Project management software is available for all these techniques. The following case study uses a network to perform a critical path analysis of a project involving the installation of a LAN in a college.

Case study: installing a local area network

A college has decided to install a local area network of PCs in a classroom. As well as obtaining and installing the network, the project involves refurbishing the classroom to be used - replacing the ceiling, redecorating, providing blinds on the windows, new carpets, air conditioning, benches for the workstations and chairs - and also appointing a technician who will help with the installation and testing of the network. It has been decided that tenders will be invited for suppliers of the network system and for the classroom conversion work. The suppliers of the office furniture and application software required - word processors, spreadsheets etc - will be selected and ordered by the college's computer manager directly. One of the first duties of the newly appointed technician will be to test the computer equipment before it is installed in the network room. Once the classroom has been converted the office furniture and computer hardware will be installed and then the system will have to be tested and any faults corrected. Documentation will need to be provided for users of the network - one type for students and another for teaching staff - and finally, before staff start to use the network, they will need some training.

Identifying activities

The first stage in managing a project such as this is to identify the activities involved and to assign a letter to each one. The list of activities for this project is as follows:

	Activity		Activity
A	Carry out initial study of needs	I	Test computer hardware
B	Invite tenders from suppliers	J	Procure office furniture
C	Appoint suppliers	K	Install furniture and network system
D	Obtain computer equipment	L	Procure network application software
E	Convert classroom	M	Prepare documentation for network users
F	Advertise for technician	N	Test network
G	Shortlist candidates & invite for interview	O	Correct system faults
H	Interview candidates	P	Train staff

At this stage it is not possible to assign a precise order to the activities since some of them can occur in parallel with others. The next stage is to estimate the length of time required to complete each activity. These estimates may be based on experience, discussions with prospective suppliers and building contractors, information obtained from equipment suppliers regarding probable delivery times, or from other sources. It should also be possible at this stage to identify, for each activity listed, which activity or activities must be completed before it can commence. For example, before tenders can be invited from network suppliers, the college must have conducted a study of its requirements so that the type and size of the network could be specified precisely. Similarly, before the network can be installed, the room must be ready and the equipment must have been delivered.

Activity dependence tables

An *activity dependence table* lists each activity together with activities that must be completed before this particular one can begin. The activity dependence table for our case study is shown below. Included in the table is a column which shows the estimated amount of time required for each activity.

	Activity	Duration (Days)	Preceding activity
A	Carry out initial study of needs	15	None
B	Invite tenders from suppliers	19	A
C	Appoint suppliers	5	B
D	Obtain computer equipment	10	C
E	Convert classroom	40	C
F	Advertise for technician	21	A
G	Shortlist candidates and invite for interview	10	F
H	Interview candidates	2	G
I	Test computer hardware	10	H
J	Procure office furniture	20	A
K	Install office furniture and network system	15	D, E, I, J
L	Procure network application software	28	A
M	Prepare documentation for network users	15	K, L
N	Test network	10	K, L
O	Correct system faults	6	N
P	Train staff	10	M, O

Network analysis

A common method of representing activities and how they relate to each other is by means of a *network* in which each activity is represented by an arrowed line and the starting point and finishing point are each represented by a circle called a *node*. The nodes are numbered such that the node at the start of an activity is always lower than the node at the end of the activity. The following diagrams illustrate how nodes and activities are drawn.

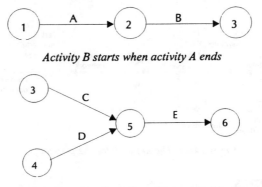

Activity B starts when activity A ends

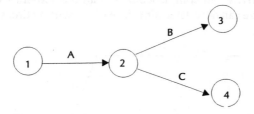

E begins when both C and D have finished

B and C can start when A is complete

Drawing the Network

A network diagram illustrates how all of the activities identified depend on each other. Note, however, that there are a number of rules to be observed when drawing the network:

1. There must be only one start node and one finish node.

2. No activities are allowed to have the same start and finish node.

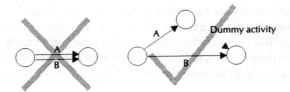

To avoid this, dummy activities, which have a duration of zero, are introduced as shown above.

3. Arrows should go from left to right.

Using these ideas, we can produce the network shown in Figure 46.1 for our case study project. The diagram clearly shows the order of the activities, which ones can be undertaken at the same time and dependencies between activities. What we now need to determine is how long the project will take overall.

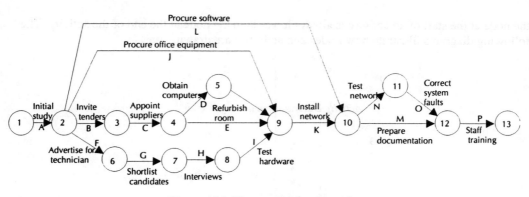

Figure 46.1. *The network for the project*

Earliest starting times

Remembering that no activity can commence before all the activities which converge on its start node have finished, we can now determine the earliest starting times for each activity. This is shown in Figure 46.2.

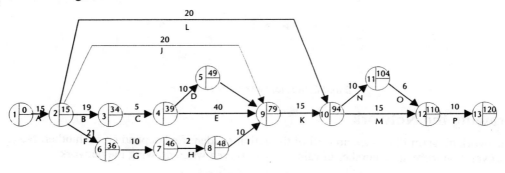

Figure 46.2. *Earliest starting times for the project*

The time taken for each activity is shown above the activity letter. The extra figure inside the node now shows the earliest day on which the project can start. Thus B starts 15 days after A has commenced, and since B requires a further 19 days for completion, C starts on the 34th day. Where two or more activities finish on the same node, for example on node 9, the highest accumulated figure is always shown. Thus, although activity I finishes after 48 days, D finishes after 49 days, and J after 35 days, it is the finish time of activity E, that is 79 days, which is recorded in node 9.

The diagram shows that the *total project time* is the longest path through the network, and it amounts to the figure shown in the last node, namely 120 days.

Latest starting times

We are almost at a position now to determine the *slack time*, or *total float*, for each activity (see Figure 46.3). This will tell us by how many days each activity could be extended, or delayed, without delaying the whole project. In order to do this we must first calculate the latest starting time for each activity.

Starting with the figure in the last node (120 days in this case), we work backwards through the network calculating the latest possible time each activity could commence without overrunning the time shown in its finish node. In practice this involves subtracting the duration of the activity from the latest starting time shown in its finish node and writing this in its start node. If a choice of two values occurs, the smallest figure is always chosen.

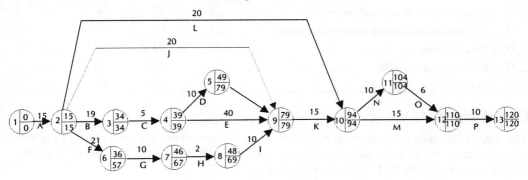

Figure 46.3. *Latest starting times for the project*

For example, the latest start time of activity P is found by taking its duration of 10 days from the value 120 in its finish node. This gives a latest starting time of 110. For activity O, we subtract 6 from 110 to give 104; for N 10 from 104 gives 94. When we get to M, subtracting 15 from 110 gives 95, but activity N gave a value of 94, which is smaller, so we use 94 as node 10's latest starting time.

Slack time

Slack time is the extra time that the activity could take without delaying the whole project. The diagram below illustrates how it is calculated.

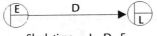

Slack time = L - D - E

Thus the slack time for activity I is 79 - 10 - 48 = 21 days. This means that testing the hardware could be allowed to take up to 21 days more to complete than was originally estimated without affecting the total project time. The following table shows the slack times for all the activities.

	Activity	Duration (Days)	Latest start time	Earliest start time	Slack time
A	Carry out initial study of needs	15	0	15	0
B	Invite tenders from suppliers	19	15	34	0
C	Appoint suppliers	5	34	39	0
D	Obtain computer equipment	10	39	79	30
E	Convert classroom	40	39	79	0
F	Advertise for technician	21	15	57	21
G	Shortlist candidates and invite for interview	10	36	67	11

H	Interview candidates	2	46	69	21
I	Test computer hardware	10	48	79	44
J	Procure office furniture	20	15	79	44
K	Install office furniture and network system	15	79	94	0
L	Procure network application software	28	15	94	51
M	Prepare documentation for network users	15	94	110	1
N	Test network	10	94	104	0
O	Correct system faults	6	104	110	0
P	Train staff	10	110	120	0

Critical activities

The critical activities are those with zero slack time. In other words, the total project time will be increased if any of these activities takes longer than was anticipated. For our network the critical activities are A, B, C, E, K, N, O and P.

Critical path

This is the path, or paths, through the network consisting of only critical activities. In our example there is only a single critical path, but it is possible for other projects to have more than one critical path. The critical path is shown by the heavy line in Figure 46.4.

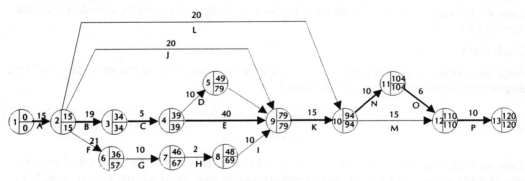

Figure 46.4. *The critical path*

The critical path is always the longest path through the network, and it tells us what the total time will be for the project. During the course of a project, the critical activities will need to be monitored very carefully to ensure that they do not overrun and thereby increase the total project time. If this is in danger of occurring, it may be possible to divert manpower from non-critical activities in order to ensure that critical activities are completed on time.

Gantt charts

A Gantt chart is a diagram which clearly illustrates when activities can start and finish. Each activity is represented by a solid line and any associated slack time by a dotted line as shown in Figure 46.5. The start, end and duration of every activity can be read from the horizontal axis which shows the time scale in days.

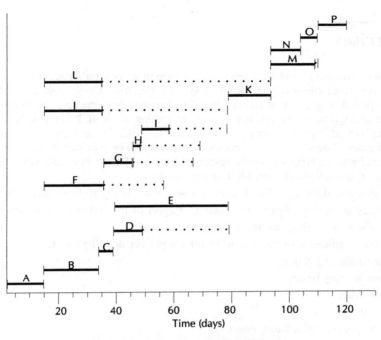

Figure 46.5. *The Gantt chart for the project*

Resource scheduling

Resource scheduling is concerned with minimising the numbers of people required at any one time for the project. The Gantt chart shows us where overlapping activities can be moved to reduce the amount of overlap. For example, each of the activities D, E, G, H and I overlaps with one or more of the others, but D, G, H and I each have a considerable amount of slack time allowing them to be delayed. So, if, say D and G could each be carried out by one person, but not at the same time, then D could be delayed so that it starts when G finishes, thus allowing the person to do both jobs but one after the other.

In projects involving large numbers of human resources, this type of adjustment can result in a significant reduction in the number of people who need to be employed, and consequently result in a large reduction in cost.

Cost scheduling

Cost scheduling uses the network to find the cheapest means of reducing the total project time. Activities can be shortened by, for example, using extra personnel, or by paying them overtime to work longer hours. This invariably incurs a cost penalty, but shortening some activities may be cheaper than others. The average cost of shortening each activity on the critical path by one time unit (a day for instance) can be calculated - this is called the *cost slope* of an activity - assuming accurate costing information is available. By repeatedly finding the critical activity with the least cost slope and reducing its duration, the overall project time can be shortened for the least cost.

Exercises

1. A college is setting up a technical and software support service for its academic staff. Some staff are not making best use of their ICT systems because of their inability to deal with hardware problems and lack of training in the various packages they are called upon to use. A project management team has been set up, consisting of the ICT Services Manager and representatives of technical support and academic staff. Some technical support staff appointments will need to be made. Hardware support will be provided by technical support staff and software training will be the responsibility of ICT academic staff and in respect of some specialist applications, outside training agencies.

    (i)   Suggest and draw up a list of *activities* which are likely to form part of this project.

    (ii) Produce an *activity dependence table* in respect of the activities identified in (i).

    (iii) Draw a *network diagram* for the project.

2. Explain the significance of the following for the project described in 1.

    (i)   Earliest starting times.

    (ii) Latest starting times.

    (iii) Slack time.

    (iv) Critical path.

3. Explain the purpose of a *Gantt chart*.

4. Explain the significance of *resource scheduling* and *cost scheduling*.

An information system is made up of hardware, software, people, systems and procedures and it is inevitable that one or more of these will, at some time, cause damage or loss to the system. Many failures in a system will not be disastrous and may be barely noticed, because the organisation has taken the necessary steps to recover from them. Occasionally, failure or damage to the system may be so catastrophic that the organisation cannot function. For example, a trading company which loses all of its 30,000 customer account records will almost certainly go out of business.

Of course, the risk of disaster will depend on the size and complexity of the organisation and its degree of dependency on a particular information system. The example of losing 30000 customer account records is clearly one which illustrates a disaster, but a small car repair business which loses its computerised parts catalogue is unlikely to be subjected to more than inconvenience and can probably obtain a fresh copy from the manufacturer. To ensure that the measures which are taken to protect against and recover from disaster are sufficient for but not disproportionate (and needlessly costly) to the risk, its analysis can be useful.

Risk analysis

Risk analysis identifies the potential threats, such as fire, malicious damage and equipment failure and determines the level and nature of the safeguard which is needed to recover from each one. Most risk analysis is concerned with security threats from people who may, for example, carelessly or maliciously damage equipment, fraudulently alter data files, obtain unauthorised access to confidential information and sell commercially sensitive information. Risk analysis can be carried out by staff within the organisation, but judgements will tend to be highly subjective and be unlikely to identify the true nature of risks. To ensure objective risk analysis, the organisation should use the services of risk management experts.

Perpetrator analysis

Perpetrator analysis uses various assailant profiles which detail personal characteristics, tendencies and opportunities to carry out the various forms of attack on computer systems. The analysis also identifies whether or not a perpetrator class has the necessary knowledge or skill and level of system access to undertake an attack. Formal risk analysis draws on the case histories of actual perpetrators and various theories of human behaviour which cannot be detailed here. However, it is likely that a disgruntled programmer or systems analyst would pose more of a threat than a sales enquiry clerk with limited access and no knowledge of computer technology beyond use of the sales enquiry terminal. Motives for fraud include, frustration at lack of career advancement, jealousy of others' success, greed, dishonesty and malice.

The analysis should also identify those parts of the system which may be subject to attack by each class of perpetrator and assess the impact that each successful attack would have on the organisation and its ability to recover.

Testing the risk

Having identified, for example, that accounts staff have the opportunity to create fictitious supplier accounts and thereby obtain fraudulent payments from their employer, the system needs to be tested for that risk. A particularly successful method is to challenge individuals to create a fictitious supplier account and obtain fraudulent payments, a process known as *penetration* testing. Proper auditing (Topic 31) procedures and audit trails should readily highlight such a fraudulent activity.

Quantifying the risk

It is essential to estimate the tangible and intangible costs that the organisation would incur as a result of a successful attack and measure these against the costs of protecting against the attack. Some examples of costs are:

- ❏ loss of hardware and premises;
- ❏ loss of goodwill and software;
- ❏ loss of information files and the costs of their recovery;
- ❏ legal costs in the event of inability to complete a contract;
- ❏ injuries to personnel;
- ❏ overtime working;
- ❏ loss of business;
- ❏ uncollected debts when debtor accounts are lost.

To determine whether a particular protection measure is cost-effective requires that each risk, whether it is tangible or intangible is quantified in financial terms.

Securing the risk

Unauthorised access to a system may: provide vital information to competitors; result in the deliberate or accidental corruption of data; allow fraudulent changes to be made to data; result in loss of privacy for individuals or organisations.

To avoid such hazards an information system should be protected *physically*, by *administrative procedures* and *software*. To detect any unauthorised access or changes to the information system:

- ❏ users should require *authorisation* (with different levels of authority depending on the purpose of access);
- ❏ the computer should *log* all successful and attempted accesses;
- ❏ users should be *identifiable* and their identity *authenticated;*
- ❏ the files should be capable of being *audited*;
- ❏ the actions of *programmers* should be carefully controlled to prevent fraud through changes to software.

Physical protection

These include the use of security staff, mechanical devices, such as locks and keys and electronic alarm/identification systems.

Computer systems with terminals at remote sites present a weak link in any system and they must be properly protected and here software plays an important protection role. Disk and tape libraries also need to be protected, otherwise it would be possible for a thief to take file media to another centre with compatible hardware and software. A variety of methods may be used to *identify* and possibly *authenticate* a system user. They include:

❏ Identity cards. Provided that they cannot be copied and have a photograph, they can be effective and cheap. The addition of a magnetic strip which contains encoded personal details including a *personal identification number* (PIN), which the holder has to key in, allows the user to be checked by machine. This method is used to allow access to service tills outside banks. Of course, the user of the card may not be the authorised holder, possession of the PIN being the only additional requirement; the following methods allow authentication as well as identification.

❏ Personal physical characteristics. Voice recognition or fingerprint comparison provide effective, if expensive, methods of identification and authentication.

Such methods are only effective if the supporting administrative procedures are properly followed.

Software protection

Ideally, before a user is given access to a system, the log-in procedures should check for: *authorisation*; *identification*; *authentication*.

Authorisation is usually provided by an account code, which must be keyed in response to a computer prompt; similar prompts may appear for a user-id *(identification)* and a password *(authentication)*.

Further control can be exerted with *fixed terminal identifiers*, whereby each terminal and its location is physically identifiable by the controlling computer, thus preventing access from additional unauthorised locations. Such controls can also be used to restrict particular terminals to particular forms and levels of access.

Password controls

Access to files can be controlled at different levels by a series of passwords, which have to be keyed into the terminal in response to a series of questions displayed on the screen. For example, a clerk in a Personnel Department may be given authority to display information regarding an employee's career record but only the Personnel Manager is authorised to change the information held on file.

Passwords should be carefully chosen, kept secure (memorised and not divulged) and changed frequently. Using people's names, for example, may allow entry by trial and error. Characters should not be echoed on screen as the password is entered.

Handshaking is a technique which requires more than a simple password and may be used between two computers or a computer and a user, as a means of access control. In the latter case, the user would be given a pseudo-random number by the computer and the expected response would be a transform, of that random number. The transform may be to multiply the first and last digits of the number and add the product to a value equal to the day of the month plus 1. Provided the transform is kept secret, handshaking provides more security than simple passwords.

One-time passwords. The computer will only accept a password for *one access occasion*; subsequently, it will expect the user to provide a different password for each additional access, in a pre-defined sequence. Provided the password list and their expected sequence list are kept separate, then possession of one list only will not be of any assistance. The number of attempts at logging-on should be controlled, so, for example, after three unsuccessful attempts, the user should be locked out and a record kept of the time and nature of the attempt.

Authorisation tables

These are held with the relevant files and detail the kinds of access permitted by particular users or groups of users - read only, read and write or delete. Control may also be exerted at a record or field level.

Data encryption

If data signals being transmitted along the telecommunication links are not properly protected, *hackers* can pick up the signals and display them on their own machines. To prevent such intrusion, data encryption methods are used to protect important financial, legal and other confidential information during transmission from one centre to another. Encryption scrambles the data to make it unintelligible during transmission. As the power and speed of computers has increased, so the breaking of codes has been made easier.

Code designers have produced methods of encryption which are currently unbreakable in any reasonable time period, even by the largest and most powerful computers available. An example of such an elaborate coding system is illustrated by the operation of the Electronic Funds Transfer (EFT) system. This is used by banks and other financial institutions to transfer vast sums of money so these transmissions are protected by the latest data encryption techniques. The Data Encryption Standard (DES) was approved by the American National Bureau of Standards in 1977, but as costs of powerful computers have fallen and come within the reach of criminal organisation, EFT makes use of the DES standard, plus additional encryption techniques.

Recovery measures

Possible measures include:

❑ Regular backing up of master files and transaction logging (Topic 21).

❑ Manual systems to fall back on in the event of computerised system failure. This is often not practical because of the volume of transactions which only the computerised system can handle. At the simplest level, a fall-back system may provide hard copies of, for example, catalogues and customer orders.

❑ Replication of the entire system, hardware and software, to allow uninterrupted operation if the main system fails.

❑ Ready source of replacement hardware and software.

❑ Overtime working or the employment of other agencies, such as software houses.

There are some disasters, such as major fraud, from which none of the above measures would allow the organisation to recover.

✍️Exercises

1. What is *risk analysis* and why is it important in the design of information systems?
2. (i) Identify three *costs* which may be incurred by a mail order business if a disgruntled employee causes a system fault which prevents access to its customer records for a week.
   (ii) Briefly outline two measures which can be taken to allow *recovery* from system failure or loss.
3. (i) Research and describe products which provide *physical protection* against unauthorised access to information systems.
   (ii) By what software mechanisms may a user be *identified* and *authenticated*?
   (iii) What is *data encryption* and why is it important in some electronic communications?

Section 10

Further networking

Topics

The data communications industry has always had to deal with problems of *incompatible* standards. Standards have to do with all aspects of a communications system, including, for example, the *hardware devices*, the *encoding* of data and the forms of *signals* used. At first, the only computer systems available for use in data communications systems were mainframes and later, minicomputers. These computer systems were produced by a small number of very large manufacturers, the most important being IBM; they also produced the communications devices that worked with their computers. In competition with one another, each manufacturer set the standards for use with its equipment. These *closed* systems prevented a customer from using equipment, produced by different manufacturers, in the same data communications system.

The huge expansion in the uses of data communications, both nationally and internationally has been made possible through the adoption of some common standards. Common standards lead to *open* systems, which allow users to use components from more than one manufacturer. A number of bodies are concerned with the establishment of international standards and these are listed below. Frequently, a standard arises initially from the work of a particular manufacturer, and then, often because of the importance of the manufacturer, it is included in the recommendations of the standards authorities.

❑ CCITT (International Consultative Committee on Telegraphy and Telephony). This is an organisation that has its headquarters in Geneva, Switzerland. It is part of the United Nations International Telecommunications Union (ITU). The CCITT makes recommendations on most aspects of data communications, for example, modems, networks and facsimile transmission or FAX and publishes them every four years. These recommendations usually obtain world-wide acceptance. CCITT's 'V' series of standards cover equipment used on telephone lines and its X series relate to digital packet transmission standards. Some examples of these standards are mentioned later in this Topic.

❑ IEEE is the acronym for the Institute of Electrical and Electronic Engineers. The organisation has set numerous standards for various aspects of telecommunications and computing. Notably, the IEEE has defined standards for local area network (LAN) access protocols (see Topic 26).

❑ The ISO (International Standards Organisation), has its headquarters in Geneva, Switzerland and is responsible for the definition of the Open Systems Interconnection (OSI) model. This model aims to ensure that any computer terminal is able to connect to any network and communicate with any other terminal, whether it is connected to the same or any other linked network.

Communication protocols

A protocol is a set of rules for the transmission of data between two devices. A protocol may include rules to deal with:

❑ the establishment of which device currently has *control of the communications link*;

❏ *error detection and correction*;

❏ *data flow control*; this is to ensure that data transmission flows smoothly, that the communications channel is not overloaded and that the transmitting device does not send data more quickly than the receiver can handle.

Protocols are often developed by manufacturers and then become recommended by Standards Authorities (such as the CITT) but sometimes, they are developed by the latter. Not all protocols cover all three items listed above. For example, the V24 (CCITT standard) and RS232 protocols, which are computer-modem interfaces (see Connectors or Interfaces), do not provide error detection facilities; they are *low level* protocols. Similarly, the X25 interface is a protocol and interface standard for connection to a packet switching network; there are a whole series of X protocols established by the CCITT relating to packet switching networks. A higher level protocol, such as V42 (see Topic 26) includes error detection and correction facilities. The rest of this section aims to give a brief introduction to this very complex area of data communications.

The OSI (open systems interconnection) model

Many computer devices are now designed for use in networked systems. Manufacturers are now tending to conform to standard protocols that make their equipment compatible with a variety of user networks. *Closed* networks, that are restricted to one manufacturer's equipment and standards, are not attractive to the user, because it restricts the choice of equipment which can be used. The aim of standardisation is to achieve more open systems which allow users to select from a wider range of manufacturers' products. A Reference Model for Open Systems Interconnection (OSI) has been under development by the International Standards Organisation (ISO) since 1977. Other standards, including SNA (IBM's System Network Architecture) and Ethernet, are largely incompatible with one another. Certain standards in the OSI model have been set by manufacturers as their commercial products have gained in popularity.

The OSI reference model for communications protocol identifies a hierarchy of seven layers. The layers and their functions are briefly described below.

Application layer

This is the highest layer in that it is closest to the user. It supports the transfer of information between end-users, applications programs and devices. Several types of protocol exist in this layer, including those for specific applications and those for more generalised applications, such as accounting, directory services, network management, entry control and user identification. The applications layer hides the physical network from the user, presenting a user-orientated view instead. For example, the user need not know that several physical computers are involved when accessing a database.

Presentation layer

This layer covers standards on how data is presented to the end-user devices. The aim is to ensure that different devices, which may be using data in different formats, can communicate with one another. The presentation layer can, for example, handle conversions between ASCII and EBCDIC character codes. It may also carry out encryption to ensure data security during transmission over vulnerable telecommunication links. The presentation layer also attempts to deal with conversions between terminals which use different line and screen lengths and different character sets.

Session layer

The session layer is concerned with the exchange of information between different applications and users; it is the users' interface into the network. When a user requests a particular service from the network, the session layer handles the dialogue.

Transport layer

The data transmission system on any network will have its own peculiarities and the function of the transport layer is to mask out any undesirable features which may prevent a high quality transmission for the network. For example, a message may have to be divided into packets or frames of a particular size before it is passed over to the network layer for routing though the network. The transport layer also ensures message delivery and provides acknowledgements.

Network layer

The function of the network layer is to perform the routing of information around the network and also to connect one network to another. The software can also carry out accounting functions to enable the network owner to charge users.

Data link layer

The physical data transmission media used in a network are subject to interference which can corrupt data and other signals. The data link layer handles data transmission errors and thus improves the quality of the network. The techniques used, for example, for the receipt and acknowledgement of data by a receiver device, are determined by the data link layer. The CCITT V42bis protocol, with its error detection and correction facilities falls into this level.

Physical layer

The physical layer provides the means to connect the physical medium and is concerned with the transmission of binary data within the communication channel, such as determining what signal state represents a binary 1. Standards are set regarding the mechanical, electrical and procedural aspects of interface devices. For example, standards are set for the number of pins a network connector should have and the function and position of each pin. The RS232 and V24 protocols are within this level.

The purpose of layering

Layering allows the separation of system components into the physical and a range of logical levels and makes them independent of one another. This separation facilitates the development and production of platform (different hardware and operating systems) components which can communicate with one another. For example, by using a common language to write network card drivers, the same network card can then handle different network protocols, say IPX (Novell) and TCP/IP (Internet Protocol).

Handshaking

Synchronisation of data transmission between communicating devices is essential, primarily because they often operate at different speeds, and sometimes, a device may have to wait because the other device is not ready. For example, if a file is being transferred from a remote terminal to a receiving computer, and the file is too large to fit into the computer's memory, then it will have to save sections of the file at intervals. If the computer has no multi-tasking capability, then data may be lost if it is transmitted during a save operation. To prevent such data loss, the flow of data has to be controlled and the activities of the communicating devices need to be properly synchronised.

Handshaking is necessary for both parallel and serial transmissions and involves acknowledgement signals between devices that they are ready to communicate with one another. The process of handshaking can be software or hardware controlled. A hardware handshake, for example, between a computer and a printer, involves the exchange of signals, through dedicated lines or conductors; the signals indicate the readiness of each device to send or receive data. A software handshake, usually employed for serial transmissions through modems, enables each device to establish the particular protocols which will be used for transmissions. Error control and data compression (to improve the transmission rate) can be built into the modems specification and thus be hardware controlled, or they can be provided by a communications package.

Flow control

Flow control enables communicating modems to pause and restart data transmission, as necessary. The need for pauses and restarts stems from the fact that a receiving modem has to use buffer memory (of limited capacity) and may not be able to empty it (pass it on) as quickly as it is being filled. This could be because the computer to which it is connected is busy with another task, such as printing. If transmission is not paused once the buffer is full, data will be lost. To exert flow control, the receiving modem must signal the sending modem that transmission has to be temporarily interrupted. This can be done, either by the modem or the terminal software.

Error detection

Block check characters (BCC)

The idea of even and odd parity bits for each character is introduced in Topic 26 and is shown to be inadequate for the detection of even numbers of bit errors. Block check characters (BCCs) aim to conquer this problem by checking the parity of blocks of characters within a data transmission stream. BCCs may carry out *longitudinal* or *cyclic* redundancy checks.

Longitudinal redundancy checking (LRC)

By reference to Table 48.1, the principles of LRC can be explained as follows.

Each BCC consists of a group of parity bits which carry out LRC. However, each LRC bit is a parity check on the corresponding bits in all the characters in a block. Thus, the first parity bit in the BCC relates to the bits which occupy the first position in each character in the block, the second parity bit in the BCC relates to the second position bits in each character in the block and so on. LRC ensures that multiple errors, whether even or odd, are likely to be discovered, so at the receiver end of the transmission, the parity of individual characters and blocks of characters is checked.

	7	6	5	4	3	2	1	0
	0	1	0	0	1	0	1	1
	0	1	0	0	1	1	1	0
	1	1	0	0	1	1	1	1
	1	1	0	1	0	1	0	0
	1	1	0	1	0	1	0	0
VRC (bit-7) on	1	1	0	1	0	1	1	1
each character	0	1	0	0	0	0	0	1
	1	1	0	0	1	0	0	1
	1	1	0	1	0	1	0	0
	1	1	0	0	0	1	0	1
	0	1	0	1	0	0	1	1
	1	1	0	1	0	1	1	1
	BCC to check LRC parity (per block)							

Table 48.1. *Vertical (VRC) and longitudinal redundancy checks (LRC)*

Cyclic redundancy checking (CRC)

The BCCs described previously treat a data block as a set of characters, whereas cyclic redundancy checking (CRC) uses a BCC which views each data block as a continuous *stream* of bits.

Firstly, the data block is regarded as one large binary number. That number is divided by another agreed binary number, the quotient is discarded and the remainder (sometimes referred to as a *checksum*) is attached to the data block as a BCC. Upon receipt of the data block, the receiver repeats the calculation used to generate the BCC and compares the result with the BCC attached by the transmitter; any difference between them indicates some corruption of the block.

Hamming code

Certain codes can be used, not only to detect the occurrence of an error, but also to identify its precise location. In addition, some errors can be rectified. The Hamming code described here utilises three *code* bits and four *data* bits, making seven in all, although there are circumstances when more bits may be used.

Table 48.2 illustrates the format which positions each code bit, C_2, C_1 and C_0 in a column position which equates with its binary weight, 4, 2 and 1, respectively. The data bits (D_3, D_2, D_1 and D_0) occupy the other positions. Thus, C_0 ($2^0 = 1$) is in column 1, C_1 ($2^1 = 2$) in column 2 and C_2 ($2^2 = 4$) in column 4.

7	6	5	4	3	2	1
D_3	D_2	D_1	C_2	D_0	C_1	C_0

Table 48.2. *Hamming code format*

Parity is maintained in sub-groups, such that the C_0 relates to D_3, D_1 and D_0, C_1 to D_3, D_2 and

D_0, and C_2 to D_3, D_2 and D_1. Thus, each sub-group of data bits has a single code bit. This is illustrated further in Table 48.3.

group	7	6	5	4	3	2	1
C_0	D_3		D_1		D_0		C_0
C_1	D_3	D_2			D_0	C_1	
C_2	D_3	D_2	D_1	C_2			

Table 48.3

Echoplex is used in asynchronous communications, for low speed, *dumb* (see Devices) terminals connected to a remote host computer. When a character is transmitted (in other words, when a key is pressed) the host device immediately sends it back to be displayed on the dumb terminal's screen. If the displayed character does not match the character selected from the keyboard, the operator should detect this; the host device can be advised, by the terminal operator, to ignore the incorrect character, by the sending of an agreed *control* character. Clearly, the method is slow and crude. A character could have been received correctly by the host device and an error could corrupt it on its way back. The operator has no way of knowing how and at what point an error occurred. Another disadvantage is that error correction is manual; in an interactive system, the user needs to rely on automatic error control and correction.

Error correction

Automatic repeat request (ARQ)

When a receiver detects an error it must tell the sending device to re-transmit the erroneous data; this is known as *automatic repeat request* (ARQ). The technique is most appropriate to the handling of data streams, that is, synchronous communications, in conjunction with cyclic redundancy checking (CRC - see earlier). ARQ can take one of three forms:

❑ *Stop and wait ARQ or ACK and NAK*. With this form the receiver acknowledges every block of data, with ACK if it detects no error and NAK if an error is detected. The sending device cannot send the next block until an acknowledgement is received. Any NAK block is re-transmitted repeatedly, if necessary, until an ACK is received.

❑ *Go-back N ARQ*. With this form, a block is only acknowledged if an error is detected. The sending device can continue transmitting without waiting for an acknowledgement. When a NAK is received, the block in which the error occurred is identified and that block, plus any transmitted since (N blocks), must be re-transmitted.

❑ *Selective-repeat ARQ*. This is the most sophisticated form of ARQ, in that blocks transmitted since the erroneous block (correct ones are not acknowledged), do not have to be sent again. Thus the sender only re-transmits the identified block and then continues from where it left off, when the NAK was received.

✍️Exercises

1. The OSI reference model identifies seven *layers* for the design of communication system protocols.

   What is the purpose of *layering* and why is it important?

2. Define the terms *handshaking* and *flow control* and explain their importance in electronic communication.

3. (i) What is a *parity bit* and how can it be used to detect errors in data transmission?

   (ii) Why is a single parity bit for each character inadequate for the detection of some transmission errors?

   (iii) Describe the operation of a *longitudinal parity check*.

   (iv) Describe the operation of a *cyclic redundancy check*.

4. What particular error control facility distinguishes the Hamming code check from the checks mentioned in 3?

5. Describe the options for error correction using *automatic repeat request (ARQ)*.

Inter-networking components

The term inter-networking is used to describe the formation of integrated network systems, through the connection of separate networks, locally and remotely. This enables organisations to construct organisation-wide information and communications systems, even if sections of it are a few or thousands of miles apart. This section looks at the devices used to make connections between LANs and between LANs and wide area networks. In general, these devices deal with the:

❑ connection of networks operating on different protocols;

❑ connection of LANs to LANs

❑ connection of LANs to WANs;

❑ connection of networks of different architecture, cabling and protocol;

❑ routing of packets (see packet switching in Topic 51) along the most efficient path;

❑ conversion between different packet formats, protocols and transmission speeds.

Computer networking is a relatively new industry and terminology is not entirely standardised. For this reason, definitions of terms, such as bridge, router and gateway can vary from one manufacturer's specification to another. Some devices, for example, combine the features of bridges and routers and are referred to as bridge/routers. Bearing this in mind, the following definitions are generally accepted.

Repeaters

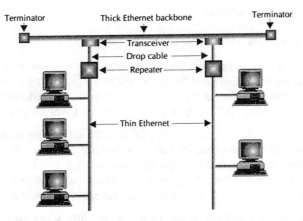

Figure 49.1. *Repeaters connecting segments of an Ethernet network*

Repeaters allow the effective length of a LAN cable to be increased. For example, the maximum length of an Ethernet segment is restricted because of signal loss and distortion which occurs as a data packet travels along the cable.

A repeater re-strengthens, that is, *re-amplifies* the signal and resets its timing, so that the effective length of the segment can be increased. It is also used to enable a signal to travel to another segment of a network. A repeater can normally connect any kind of cable medium: thick or thin Ethernet, twisted pair or optical fibre. In relation to the Open Systems Inter-connection (OSI) model, referred to in Topic 48, a repeater works at the Physical level and only needs to know how to interact with the physical transmission medium.

Bridge

A bridge is used to connect two LANs of the same type, that is, two IBM token ring or two Ethernet LANs. This is known as *local inter-networking*. Packets crossing such a link are *forwarded* by the bridge device. Some bridges are *protocol transparent* and the otherwise similar networks can be using different protocols, for example, IPX (Novell) or IP (Internet Protocol). They can also be used to divide large networks into smaller segments. Segmenting large networks can improve administrative control and the performance of the separate segments. In the latter case, the bridge can be configured such that only data which needs to cross the bridge actually does. For example, if there are two segments, one for the Sales department and the other for Accounts, the data traffic for each function will be isolated within the respective segments, except when data needs to travel between the two. This improves the performance of each segment and thus the effectiveness of the whole network. A bridge operates at the Data Link Layer in the OSI model (Topic 48).

Hubs and switches

A hub has multiple ports to allow devices (or other network segments) to share a common connection point to the LAN cable. Some hubs are passive and simply pass packets between the devices and the network cable, but others provide device status information which allows, for example, a technician to identify a faulty device and disconnect it without affecting the operation of the remainder of the network. A hub contains devices called *switches* which forward packets from one segment to another.

Gateway or router

A gateway, or router, is used to connect two LANs of different (they do not have to be) type ; thus, for example, an Ethernet LAN can be connected to a Token Ring LAN, or the connection may be Ethernet to Ethernet. The LANs may be remotely connected through, for example, a packet switching WAN (Topic 24) , with a gateway at each LAN's entry point to the WAN.

The term *router* is used to signify that the device is more intelligent than a bridge, in that it makes decisions about the route a data packet (by reference to its destination address) should follow to reach its destination; in this way, packets can be made to take the most efficient path. It may determine an alternative route for a packet, in the event of, for example, congestion or breakdown on a particular link. Networks may have different architectures and protocols.

A LAN using IPX (Novell) protocol can use a gateway to allow users access to, for example, a remote IBM network, which uses SNA protocol, through the Kilostream packet (X.25 protocol) switching network. In the OSI model, a router operates at the Network Layer level.

Multiplexer

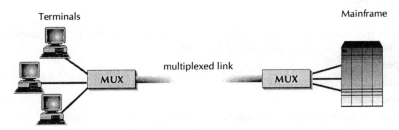

Figure 49.2. *Multiplexers to allow several terminals to use a single link*

A multiplexer allows a number of low-speed devices to share a high-speed line. The messages from several low-speed lines are combined into one high-speed channel and then separated out at the other end by a demultiplexer.

In two-way transmissions, both these functions are carried out in one unit at each end of the higher speed channel. Multiplexers send data from multiple sources along a single, high speed, communications link by dividing it into different channels, allocated as time slots. A brief time slot it given to each of a succession of terminals in which to send a block of data. The transmission rate of each terminal is relatively slow and limited by the speed of its human operator, so the high speed link can easily accommodate the transmissions of many terminals. The multiplexed link's capacity is known as its *bandwidth* (the rate at which data can be sent, measured in bits per second). The process of dividing this bandwidth into many channels is known as *time division multiplexing* (TDM).

Concentrator

A concentrator is a type of multiplexer which greatly increases data throughput by increasing the number of low-speed channels and instead of transmitting a null character, empties the contents of the next full register. The data from each low-speed device is identified by extra identification bits and this constitutes an overhead.

Front-end-processors (FEP)

A front-end-processor is the most sophisticated type of device for communications control and is usually a minicomputer held at the site of a mainframe host computer. Its main task is to handle all the communications traffic, leaving the mainframe free to concentrate on other processing tasks. Its main tasks include: parity checking; stripping of overhead characters from serial transmission, such as start-stop bits and synchronisation characters (refers to synchronous transmission - see Topic 26); conversion from serial to parallel transmission and vice versa; network control; network accounting; character conversion.

✎Exercises

1. Explain the purpose of each of the following network hardware components, identifying the kind of network(s) in which each could be used.
   (i)   repeater;
   (ii) bridge;
   (iii) router.
2. Explain the purpose of *hubs* and *switches* and distinguish between the two.
3. Describe the principle of *time division multiplexing* (TDM).
4. What is the purpose of a *front-end processor*?

Television and radio broadcasting

When a television studio broadcasts a programme, the signals are carried to television receivers through a network of transmitters; radio programmes are broadcast from a studio in a similar fashion. An out-of-date term for a radio is a wireless; thus the transmissions in these broadcast networks are all carried out without the use of wires, that is, as *radio waves*. Radio waves vary in *frequency* and different frequency bands are used for different kinds of broadcasting. It is beyond the scope of this text to go into detail concerning these frequency bands, but the abbreviations VHF (very high frequency) and UHF (ultra-high frequency) should be familiar. The term *broadcast* is used because the radio wave signals can be received by any number of receivers within the broadcast area. The geographical area which can be reached by a broadcasting station depends on which method is used, namely:

❑ *cable* connections; this is an exception here as it clearly involves the use of wire or cable;

❑ *terrestrial* transmitters;

❑ *communications satellites*

Cable television

A broadcasting company may use a combination of cable, terrestrial and satellite transmitters to distribute its programmes. For example, the American company WTBS, in Atlanta, Georgia uses satellite to transmit low-cost sports and entertainment programmes to cable systems across the USA. Cable broadcasting, as the term indicates, uses physical cabling and is only economic over a limited area, such as a large city. Figure 50.1 shows the structure for a typical, city-wide cable television network.

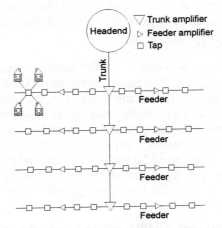

Figure 50.1. *Cable television network as tree and branch structure*

The *headend* is the control centre for the network and distributes services through the main trunk and branches to consumers. City networks can be linked through the headends by fibre optic cabling.

In combination with satellite broadcasting, cable television plays an important communications role. A single cable connection into a house can provide telephone, fax, television and computer data services. Cable companies also provide comprehensive business services, such as closed circuit television, voicemail, private digital circuits, ISDN, LAN to LAN and LAN to WAN connections.

Although terrestrial transmitters allow a much larger broadcast area than cable, satellites are essential to modern television broadcasting. Within the UK, pictures and monophonic sound are transmitted as analogue signals. The BBC has developed and transmits NICAM stereo sound, using digital encoding techniques. Digital channels are now receivable via satellite receiver dishes or through aerials. Television broadcasting allows the transmission of *moving pictures*, *sound* and *data* to television receivers within the area served by a broadcasting station. Database services provided by television are *one-way* only, to television receivers and are collectively known as *Teletext*. The BBC teletext service is known as Ceefax. To access these services a television receiver must have a Teletext *decoder*.

Cable modems

A cable modem connects to the television cable and provides Internet access at speeds up to ten times quicker than a conventional modem.

Microwave transmissions and communications satellites

Microwaves are super-high frequency (SHF) radio waves and can be used where transmitter and receiver are not in sight of one another. The communication path must be relatively obstruction-free. Microwaves can also be transmitted, through earth transmitters, to communications satellites; microwaves can penetrate cloud. Earth stations must be no more than 25-30 miles apart, because humidity in the atmosphere interferes with microwave signals. Each station in a communication path acts as a *repeater* station. Obviously, it is impractical to build sufficient repeater stations to deal with all transmissions, so communications satellites are essential. Once a satellite has received a signal, it amplifies it and sends it back to earth.

There are three basic types of satellite:

❏   GEO (geosynchronous earth orbit). A GEO satellite remains fixed above a given point on the earth's surface. This means that terrestrial stations, once set to point at the satellite, do not require further adjustment. It is the most expensive to build and launch, but its powerful transmitters mean that few are needed to maintain global coverage. It also has an orbital life in excess of 12 years. A weakness of GEO satellite communication is *latency*, or propogation delay. A transmission passed via a GEO satellite from one terrestrial station to another takes more than two tenths of a second, which may make it unsuitable for use in high speed networks, but perfectly suitable for television broadcasting, mobile communications and global positioning services (GPS).

❏   MEO (medium earth orbit). A MEO satellite moves relative to a point on the earth's surface. This means that ground-based stations must have tracking equipment to maintain contact with a MEO. Global coverage requires the use of more MEOs than is the case for GEOs, but they are cheaper to build and launch and the transmission delay is insignificant. Its orbital life is between 6 and 12 years.

❏ LEO (low earth orbit). A LEO satellite moves quickly relative to a point on the earth's surface and many are needed to provide global coverage. LEOs are the cheapest to build and launch, provide the greatest bandwidth and suffer from virtually no transmission delay. However, a LEO satellite may have a lifespan of only 5 years.

Applications of satellite communication

Telecommunication networks

Undersea cabling used to be the only way of connecting telephone networks on different continents but satellite communication provides a much cheaper alternative. Satellites also make it feasible and cost effective to extend networks to geographically remote and poorer countries which do not have established telecommunications systems.

Television broadcasting

Satellite communications have been used in television broadcasting for over thirty years by traditional aerial delivery networks and cable networks. The bandwidth available through satellite communications allows the transmission of hundreds of television channels. Today, Direct Broadcast Satellite (DBS) allows television networks to transmit direct to individual users. A DBS satellite is geosynchronous and can transmit up to 150 channels, using digital signals to provide high quality reception to consumers.

Mobile satellite services

Satellite communications allow ship to shore communications, linking a ship to a land-based receiver/transmitter anywhere in the world; aircraft use a similar service. A satellite phone can be used, even in the most remote parts of the world for voice and data communications; Inmarsat, for example, provides for 64 K ISDN communication (Topic 51). Global positioning services (GPS) can be used by ships, aircraft and land vehicles to determine their precise geographical position. Multiple geosynchronous satellites triangulate their signals to produce geographical co-ordinates.

Weather forecasting

Weather forecasting involves reporting, predicting, and studying the weather, including temperature, moisture, barometric pressure, and wind speed and direction. Satellites are vital for the rapid collection and transmission of meteorological data from the many terrestrial and atmospheric sources which contribute to more accurate weather forecasting.

Cellular telephone networks

These networks use *cellular radio* communications, which operate in the UHF (ultra-high frequency) band. Local *base stations* allow cellphone (hand-held or vehicle-based) users to access the pstn. Each base station covers a *cell site*, an area within which it can pick up cellphone signals. Within the UHF band, signals can penetrate buildings and other barriers, but a user must be within a few miles of a transmitter, particularly in urban areas, where the largest numbers of users tend to be found. Thus, a base station in a rural area, serving fewer users, can cover a larger cell site than is possible in an urban area. Computers are used to allow links to be maintained even while the caller is moving from one transmission area to another. Thus, when a base station receives a signal from a cellphone, it monitors the strength of the signal continuously to determine if it is still the most suitable base station to handle the transmission. Obviously, if the user is driving while making a call, a different base station may be handling the call at different points on the journey. The only effect of these changes is a brief (about one-fifth of a second) interruption to the call as the switch is made to a different base station. Two major cellular radio operators in the UK are Cellnet and Vodaphone.

New generation mobile phones

Apart from voice transmission, mobile phones can be used to transmit text messages and those that support Internet Protocol (IP) or the newer WAP (Wireless Application Protocol - see later) can be used to access Internet services, albeit very slowly. The delivery of Internet services through mobile networks is hampered by the mobile phone itself, with its slow processor, poor battery life, mono display and awkward keypad, as well as by limited bandwidth.

The development of broadband mobile networks and more sophisticated phones is vital if the full potential of the Internet's multimedia content is to be made as accessible through a mobile phone as it is through a PC. In the meantime, services are largely text-based and perfectly adequate for the viewing of such information as travel, weather, sport results, share prices and the delivery of bank, ticket and message services.

New generation mobile phones are making use of larger flip-up screens with touch-sensitive input and handwriting recognition as additions to the usual keypad.

WAP and WML (Wireless Markup Language)

Although mobile phones have been able to access Web pages coded in HTML (Topics 40, 52) for some time, a WAP-enabled mobile can use its WAP browser to access pages coded in WML, a language specially designed to take account of the limitations of mobile networks and phones. Access to the Internet must be provided through a *gateway* which supports the WAP protocol. All the major cellular networks provide WAP gateways to allow their users to access Internet data services and as the market expands it is likely that conventional Internet Service Providers (ISPs) will provide a similar service.

Once cellular networks are able to provide the bandwidth presently available to PC users, full Java-enabled HTML content will be easily accessible to mobile phone users and the need for WAP and WML is likely to be reduced.

Use of satellites in cellular networks

In common with other communication networks, digital signalling (the European standard for digital mobile communications is GSM - Global System for Mobile communications) has largely replaced analogue signalling. Each cell in a network provides a number of communication channels. In the case of analogue signalling each channel occupies a separate frequency band (frequency division multiplexing or FDM). Digital networks divide the cells into channels by time slot (time division multiplexing). When a network is busy, all the channels in a particular cell may be occupied, preventing other callers from using that cell. Satellites which are operating within a different bandwidth to the cell are able, when they have free bandwidth, to provide extra channel space for overloaded terrestrial cells. Digital cellular networks provide better performance (analogue networks can be subject to cross call interference) and more channels.

✍Exercises

1. With the aid of a diagram, describe a *tree-structured* cable TV network.
2. Describe the costs and benefits of the three types of satellite used in communications networks, namely *GEO* (geosynchronous earth orbit), *MEO* (medium earth orbit) and *LEO* (low earth orbit).
3. Briefly describe three applications of *satellite* communications.
4. Identify the main components of a *mobile* (cellular) network and briefly describe the way in which it allows mobile phone communication.
5. Research and describe the most recent *communication services* provided by mobile networks, in particular those related to the Internet.

Public switched telephone network (pstn)

The *pstn* is the main telecommunications network for the United Kingdom. It was originally designed for voice transmission, using analogue electrical signals; these electrical signals represent what is spoken and heard at each end of a link. A telephone mouthpiece contains a diaphragm, which vibrates when struck by sound waves. The vibrations are converted into electrical impulses and are sent over the network to the earpiece on the receiving telephone; a diaphragm in the earpiece converts the impulses back into sound.

Much of the pstn is now digital, in particular the national trunk network and call switching exchanges; the analogue connections are mainly confined to the pstn's local links to homes and businesses. Digital voice transmission uses coded patterns of digital impulses, which are similar to those used to represent computer data. To transmit computer data over analogue sections of the pstn, requires use of a *modem* (see Data Circuit Termination Equipment or DCE). This device converts the computer's digital signal into an appropriate analogue form before transmission; a modem at the receiving end converts the analogue signal back to the digital form required by the computer.

Digital network systems

Public switched data network (psdn)

The psdn is a *packet switching* network. Modems are not required and transmission performance is better than that achievable over the partially analogue pstn.

Circuit switching

In any network, setting up a connection between two devices may involve circuit switching. For example, if a network is busy a connection may be established through a series of switches, from one circuit to another, over an alternative route. Thus the actual distance the signals travel may be greatly in excess of the geographical distance between the two points. Charges, whether the connection is for voice or data, will be made according to the geographical distance between the devices (local, medium, long distance), rather than the distance the signals actually have to travel through the various switches.

Circuit switching establishes connections between pairs of devices and dedicates the connection to their use until they no longer require it. This is wasteful of line capacity in that the line is not available for other devices, even when the line is idle.

Packet switching

The main components of a packet switching network are: high speed data lines; packet switching exchanges (PSEs); packet assembler/disassembler (PAD); packet terminal.

With the use of a specialised computer, called a *packet terminal*, a customer can create the packets and connect directly to the network through a dedicated dataline. If the customer is not using a packet terminal, a dial-up connection is used and the data has to go through a *packet assembler/disassembler* (PAD). This device converts data to and from the networks protocol as it enters and leaves the network. Figure 51.1 illustrates these features.

The principles of packet switching are as follows. Messages are divided into data packets, which are then directed through the network to their destination under computer control. Besides a *message* portion, each packet contains data concerning:

❑   the destination address;

❑   the source identification;

❑   the sequence of the packet in the complete message;

❑   the detection and control of transmission errors.

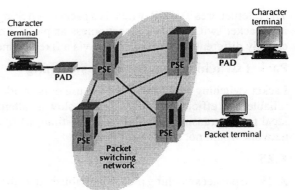

Figure 51.1. *Packet switching network*

The progress of a packet is monitored and controlled by *packet switching exchanges* (PSE) located at each *node* in the network. A node is a junction of network lines, which could be a computer or a computer terminal or other device.

As a packet arrives at a node, the exchange checks the addressing instructions and unless it corresponds to its present location, forwards it on the most appropriate route. Each node has an *input queue*, into which all arriving packets are entered (even those which are addressed to the node itself) and a number of *output queues* (to allow for the possibility of network congestion). Network traffic information is continually transmitted between the various nodes, so that each switching computer has information to allow, for example, the avoidance of congested routes.

Figure 51.2 shows how a network structure provides alternative routes by which a packet may reach its destination.

For example, a packet sent from terminal T(2) to terminal T(6), would go into the input queue of packet switching exchange PSE (a). Depending on the routing strategy and network traffic conditions, the packet could be directed to an output queue leading to any of the other PSEs. If PSE (e) was inoperative, the alternative routes would be cut drastically; in fact the packet would either have to go through PSEs (b), (c) and (d), in that sequence, or direct from PSE (a) to PSE (d). Packet switching allows packets relating

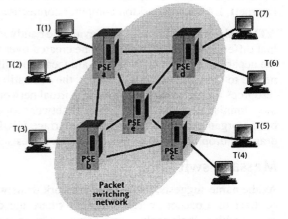

Figure 51.2. *Routing in a packet switching network*

to a single message, to be transmitted on different routes. This may be necessary, either because of the breakdown of some routes, or because of variations in traffic conditions over different routes.

The Internet uses TCP/IP, which is a packet switching protocol. In contrast with circuit switching, packet switching is connectionless as packets of data from the same source may travel entirely different routes, rather than via a fixed connection.

Packet switching versus circuit switching

Packet switching networks maximise use of network connections and provide a cheaper, more reliable and efficient, though slightly slower, alternative. Circuit switched connections are ideal for the transmission of data in real-time, when the delays inherent in a packet switching network would not be acceptable.

X.25

X.25 is a packet switching protocol established by the CCITT (see Topic 48). The protocol provides users with the following facilities.

❑   Division of a message into packets.

❑   Error checking and re-transmission of any packet effected by an error.

❑   An addressing format that allows international transmission.

The standard is supported throughout the world, allowing connection to over 200 networks in over 130 countries. Its support for the TCP/IP protocol means that most LANs can connect to an X.25 network.

ATM (Asynchronous Transfer Mode) and virtual networking

ATM evolved partially from the X.25 protocol and offers high bandwidth, packet switching and multiplexing support. ATM's bandwidth can handle data, video and voice transmissions through a single communication link. Its support for TCP/IP and other protocols allows ATM to handle a variety of traffic and services across network backbones, WANs (including the Internet), LANS and desktop computer connections.

ATM makes maximum use of the available bandwidth by using virtual networking. This means that different logical networks can be created over the same physical network. For example, if the departments of an organisation are located in different parts of the country and are not connected to the same network segment, they can still be given access to the same set of network resources through a virtual network. Virtual network management software is needed to allow the administrator to view the physical network topology and create the logical views required by the organisation. Graphical user interface (GUI) software allows the administrator to use drag and drop functions to move network nodes and create the desired logical structure.

Message switching

As the name suggests, this type of network deals with identifiable and complete messages, in contrast to a packet switched system where the destination user nodes are responsible for re-assembling their packets into complete messages upon receipt. A number of points can be made when comparing and contrasting packet switching and message switching networks:

❑   both use a store and forward principle; each node in the network has storage facilities for the accumulation of data prior to its onward transmission and the intelligence to examine the destination data before forwarding it;

❑   packet switching networks treat data transparently. Individual packets generally do not contain complete messages and the network does not recognise connections between packets, except from identification of their destination. The destination user nodes are left with the responsibility of re-assembling individual packets into complete messages;

❑   the store and forward facilities in message switching networks need to be much larger than those for packet switching systems, because complete messages must be accumulated at each point of transfer in the network;

❑   message switching requires increased processing time at intervening nodes while messages are accumulated before onward transmission;

❑   message switching provides users with greater confidence that messages will be transmitted and received in complete form.

Integrated Services Digital Network (ISDN)

Many forms of data, including text, voice and video images, can be digitised and an Integrated Services Digital Network (ISDN) is designed to allow the *integrated* transmission of these various data forms over the same network.

An Integrated Services Digital Network exists in various forms in different countries, although the ultimate aim is to achieve an international system. It is defined as a wholly *digital* system, with end-to-end digital connections and digital exchanges throughout. ISDN has become achievable because the telephone network has become largely digital. The public telephone network is, by far, the largest communications network, so once it is fully digitized, every business and home user will have access to ISDN services. British Telecom's ISDN began with a pilot scheme in 1985, which was extended in 1986 and has continued to develop since. BT's Highway service provides an ISDN connection and two analogue lines through a single telephone socket. The ISDN network provides three types of access:

❑   *single-line* IDA (integrated digital access). The user gains access with *Network Terminating Equipment* (NTE);

❑   *line adapter module* (LAMs). A LAM allows two terminals to simultaneously share the same, two-wire, connection; this could provide a cheap method of communicating with a remote computer system;

❑   *multi-line* IDA, which provides 30 independent channels, each being capable of transmitting voice or data.

Use of ISDN has expanded considerably since the introduction of BT's Highway services for home and small business users. The Highway package provides two analogue lines in addition to the digital connection for a computer.

ADSL (Asynchronous Digital Subscriber Line)

ADSL is a relatively new service, similar to ISDN, which operates over standard telephone lines and provides Internet access at around 10 times the speed of a conventional modem. As with ISDN, simultaneous voice communication is also provided. Transmissions are separated at the telephone exchange to channel the voice calls through the standard public switched telephone network and the computer transmissions through fibre optic connection to the user's Internet Service Provider.

Multiplexed network services

Kilostream

An alternative to packet switching is to use *multiplexing*. The Kilostream service uses this technique for data transmission. The service provides a high speed direct link between two points. Data can pass in both directions at the same time; this is known as *full duplex* mode. The main link can transmit data at a rate of 2048 megabits per second (Mbits/s); this allows a number of low speed terminals to be connected to the high speed link through separate low speed links, each transmitting at either 128 kilobits per second (Kb/s) or 64 Kb/s. The signals from each terminal can then be merged for transmission along the high speed link, using a technique known as *time division multiplexing* (TDM). The process of multiplexing is carried out by a *terminal multiplexer*. At the receiving end of the link, the signals are separated out for transmission along low speed lines connected to their respective terminals. The terminal multiplexer at each end of the link can carry out the functions of multiplexing (combining signals) and demultiplexing (separating the signals). The is obviously necessary for full duplex operation.

Multiplexers fall into two broad categories according to the methods used to combine signals and separate them:

❑ *Frequency Division Multiplexing (FDM)* differentiates between the data signals sent from different devices by using a different *frequency range* for each and is used in analogue networks. This can be likened to tuning a radio or television to receive particular programmes. So that any given radio programme does not interfere with the transmissions of another (although, they sometimes do), it is assigned a frequency that is not too close to the other assigned frequencies. In the same way, when a data transmission channel is multiplexed to accommodate signals from separate devices, some space must be left between the frequency ranges to avoid confusion of signals. Spaces between the different frequency ranges are know as *guard bands*.

❑ *Time Division Multiplexing (TDM)*, as the term suggests, provides a *time slice* on the higher-speed line for each terminal. It is used in digital communications. The multiplexer has a number of registers, one per low-speed channel. Each register can store one character. The multiplexer scans each register in sequence, emptying the contents into a continuous stream of data to be transmitted.

Figure 51.3 illustrates the multiplexing of signals from three terminals to a remote mainframe computer.

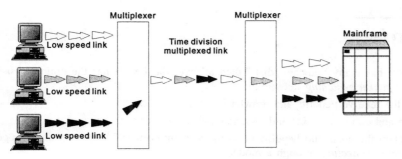

Figure 51.3. *Time division multiplexing*

Megastream

This service is similar to Kilostream, except that no terminal multiplexing equipment is provided. Data can be transmitted at 2.048, 8, 34 or 140 Mbits/s. A user can choose to use the high speed circuit directly or multiplex the circuit, such that a number of low speed channels are made available across the link. Each separate lower speed channel can then be used to carry data or some may be left for the transmission of digitized speech.

Optical communications and WDM

Optical fibre cable consists of thousands of clear glass fibre strands which transmit light or infra-red rays instead of electrical signals and is not subject to magnetic interference. The data is transmitted by a light-emitting diode (two-state signals) or injection-laser diode. Bandwidth is measured in gigabits per second and repeaters are only required after around 60 miles (copper cable requires repeaters every 3 or 4 miles). The other end of the cable has a detector which converts the light pulses into electrical pulses suitable for the attached device. Optical fibre cable is slightly more expensive than electrical cable, is used widely in WANs, but is also finding increasing use in LANs, particular for network backbones.

The high bandwidth of optical fibre makes it suitable for multiplexing. WDM (Wavelength Division Multiplexing) modulates signals to create several channels within the light spectrum and is the digital equivalent of FDM (frequency division multiplexing) used with analogue transmissions on coaxial cable. Even greater bandwidth can be obtained with D(Dense)WDM. It is protocol independent and can carry, for example, IP (Internet Protocol), ATM (Asynchronous Transfer Mode) and Ethernet traffic at rates between 100 megabits/sec and 2.5 gigabits/sec.

✍️Exercises

1. A business has many branches, distributed all over the UK. It has the option of using a *circuit* or *packet switching* network.

   Explain the relative benefits and drawbacks of each option.

2. Compare and contrast *packet* and *message* switching services.

3. (i) Explain the costs and benefits of using an permanent *ISDN* connection as opposed to a *dial-up connection* through a modem.

   N.B. You should be able to find examples of commercial services for these options by visiting an ISP's (information service provider) web site.

   (ii) What is *ADSL* and what improvements does it offer over the ISDN service?

   (iii) Research the costs of BT's *Kilostream* and *Megastream* services, for different levels of service.

4. What particular benefits are provided by *optical* communications?

Networks can be defined in terms of the services they provide and whether they are open or private. A distinction also needs to be made between private networks which use their own infrastructure and are not accessible from outside and those which operate on a public infrastructure but use various protection measures to limit access to authorised users. Owning a private network infrastructure is an expensive option and most organisations opt to use public networks and protect their privacy with the use of physical and software security measures. Some network services have a specific purpose, whilst others can be used for a range of applications. For example, the Euronet-Diane network has a bibliographic database (publications and research documents on scientific, medical and engineering etc) accessible through networks such as the Internet, but network owners such as BT provide general network access services, such as ISDN, packet switching and multiplexing. Both are examples of VANs (value added networks). Network services are described in Topic 27.

The Internet

The Internet is a world-wide network composed of thousands of smaller regional networks funded by commercial, government and educational organisations and scattered throughout the globe. All types of computers make up the hardware connected on the Internet. They vary from PCs, Macintoshes and UNIX workstations to minicomputers, mainframes and supercomputers. A common set of communication protocols enables every computer connected to the Internet to interchange information with every other computer so connected. It has developed to handle larger volumes of data, software has become more powerful and user-friendly, and the types of services available have grown. Anyone who wants to have access to the enormous amount of information available regionally or around the world can use the Internet. They can access electronic libraries, receive periodicals, exchange ideas, read the news, post questions with newsgroups, examine the weather (from reports or satellite photos), obtain the latest stock market prices and currency exchange rates, and access public government information on trade, laws, research and other subjects.

Uses of the Internet

The Internet is essentially a tool for transferring information between computers. This can be achieved in numerous ways and for various purposes. For example, *E-mail* is a convenient, quick and cheap alternative to the postal system for business and personal correspondence; *File Transfer Protocol (FTP)* allows large amounts of information to be transferred between two computers very conveniently; *Usenet,* the world-wide collection of interest groups, or *Newsgroups*, allows groups of people with similar interests to exchange views and information. Another important use of the Internet is the remote control of computer systems via *Telnet*. The *World-Wide Web* provides a uniform means of accessing and transferring information in the form of hypermedia documents. Accessing these documents does not require any particular machine or operating system. These and other Internet services are discussed in the following sections.

Note that programs used on the Internet can be classified as being either *server* or *client*. Server programs operate at Internet sites where the particular Internet service being used is provided; the program which is used to access a site, on a home PC for example, is the client program. For instance, a Web server at a Web site processes requests made by client programs called Web *browsers*, for example, Microsoft's Explorer and Netscape's Communicator.

The World Wide Web (WWW)

Abbreviated to the Web and WWW, this is the fastest growing Internet service. Though the World-Wide Web is mostly used on the Internet, the two terms do not mean the same thing. The Web refers to a world-wide collection of knowledge, while the Internet refers to the physical side of the global network, an enormous collection of cables and computers. The World-Wide Web uses the Internet for the transmission of hypermedia documents between computer users connected to the Internet. As with the Internet, nobody actually owns the World-Wide Web. People are responsible for the documents they author and make available publicly on the Web. Via the Internet, hundreds of thousands of people around the world are making information available from their homes, schools, colleges and workplaces. The aim of WWW is to make all on-line knowledge part of one interconnected web of documents and services.

The World-Wide Web is officially described as a wide-area hypermedia information retrieval initiative aiming to give universal access to a large universe of documents. What the World-Wide Web (WWW, W3) project has done is provide users on computer networks with a consistent means to access a variety of media in a simplified fashion. The WWW has changed the way people view and create information. The first true global hypermedia network, it is revolutionising many elements of society, including commerce, politics, and literature.

The operation of the Web relies mainly on *hypertext* as its means of interacting with users. Hypertext is basically the same as ordinary text - it can be stored, read, searched, or edited -with an important exception: hypertext contains links to other places within the same document or to other documents. *Hypermedia* is hypertext with a difference - hypermedia documents contain links not only to other pieces of text, but also to other forms of media, namely sounds, images, and movies. Images themselves can be selected to link to sounds or documents. Hypermedia simply combines hypertext and multimedia.

The appearance of a hypermedia document when it is displayed by a browser is determined partly by the browser which provides a certain amount of control over such things as text fonts and colours, but mainly by the language used to encode the document. This language is *Hyper-Text Mark-up Language* (HTML).

How the Web works

Web software is designed around a distributed client-server architecture. A Web client (called a Web browser if it is intended for interactive use) is a program which can send requests for documents to any Web server. A Web server is a program which, upon receipt of a request, sends the document requested (or an error message if appropriate) back to the requesting client. Using a distributed architecture means that a client program may be running on a completely separate machine from that of the server, possibly in another room or even in another country. Because the task of document storage is left to the server and the task of document presentation is left to the client, each program can concentrate on those duties and progress independently of each other. Since servers usually operate only when documents are requested, they put a minimal amount of workload on the computers on which they run.

Here is an example of how the process works:

1. Running a Web browser, the user selects a hyperlink in a piece of hypertext connecting to another document - Java Programming for example.

2. The Web client uses the address associated with that hyperlink to connect to the Web server at a specified network address and asks for the document associated with Java Programming.

3. The server responds by sending the text and any other media within that text (pictures, sounds, or video clips) to the client, which the client then renders for presentation on the user's screen.

The World-Wide Web is composed of thousands of these virtual transactions taking place per hour throughout the world, creating a web of information flow. Web servers are now beginning to include encryption and client authentication abilities, allowing them to send and receive secure data and be more selective as to which clients receive information. This allows freer communications among Web users and ensures that sensitive data is kept private. In the near future, it will be harder to compromise the security of commercial servers and educational servers which want to keep information local.

HyperText Transfer Protocol (HTTP)

The language which Web clients and servers use to communicate with each other is called the *HyperText Transfer Protocol* (HTTP). All Web clients and servers must be able to 'speak' HTTP in order to send and receive hypermedia documents. For this reason, Web servers are often called HTTP servers.

Uniform Resource Locators

The World-Wide Web uses what are called Uniform Resource Locators (URLs) to represent hypermedia links and links to network services within HTML documents. It is possible to represent nearly any file or service on the Internet with a URL. The first part of the URL (before the two slashes) specifies the method of access. The second is typically the address of the computer which the data or service is located on. Further parts may specify the names of files, the port to connect to, or the text to search for in a database. A URL is always a single unbroken line with no spaces.

Sites which run World-Wide Web servers are typically named with a "www" at the beginning of the network address.

Here are some examples of URLs:

```
http://www.nc.edu/nw/book.html
```

Connects to an HTTP server and retrieves an HTML document called 'book.html' in a directory called 'nw'

```
file://www.nc.edu/sound.au
```

Retrieves a sound file called 'sound.au' and plays it.

```
file://www.abc.com/picture.gif
```

Retrieves a picture and displays it, either in a separate program or within a hypermedia document.

```
file://www.bcd.org/dd/
```

Displays the contents of directory 'dd'.

```
ftp://www.wer.uk.co/pub/file.txt
```

Opens an FTP (see later) connection to www.uk.co and retrieves a text file.

Most Web browsers allow the user to specify a URL and connect to that document or service. When selecting hypertext in an HTML document, the user is actually sending a request to open a URL. In this way, hyperlinks can be made not only to other texts and media, but also to other network services. Web browsers are not simply Web clients, but are also full-featured FTP, Gopher, and telnet clients (see later for a discussion of these Internet services).

WWW search engines

The WWW is a vast, distributed repository of information, and more is being added to the Web each day. However, the only consistent characteristics of the information available are the manner in which it is coded, that is, in HTML, and the way in which it can be located, that is, by using URLs. To access this huge bank of information, dispersed over the entire world, and locate specific information on a certain subject, there are numerous information retrieval utilities which provide access to databases of Web page details. These *search engines* allow Web users to enter search criteria in the form of keywords or phrases and they retrieve summaries of all database entries satisfying the search criteria. Of the many information retrieval services available, some of the most well known include *Excite*, *Lycos* and *Yahoo*

Gopher

Gopher is an Internet-wide tool used to search for and retrieve text-based information stored at Gopher sites throughout the world. One way to picture Gopherspace is to think of each Gopher site as a page in an extremely large index of information. Gopher resources include research results (both governmental and commercial), special-interest groups and databases of almost any kind of documented information.

A Gopher *client* is a software package which allows you to search this master index for information which meets your criteria. There are Gopher clients available for most computers. With its user-friendly menu-based interface, Gopher spares the user the need to learn many computer commands. In effect, Gopher presents the Internet as if it were all part of a single directory system.

WAIS (Wide Area Information Servers)

WAIS is a networked information retrieval system. Client applications are able to retrieve text or multimedia documents stored on the servers. and request documents using keywords. Servers search a full text index for the documents and return a list of documents containing the keyword. The client may then request the server to send a copy of any of the documents found. Although the name Wide Area implies the use of the large networks such as the Internet to connect clients to servers distributed around the network, WAIS can be used between a client and server on the same machine or a client and server on the same LAN. Currently, there are a large number of servers running and topics range from recipes and movies to bibliographies, technical documents, and newsgroup archives.

The information which is provided by WAIS is not limited to ASCII text only. With WAIS you can also get multimedia information like pictures, graphics, sounds and even video. WAIS uses natural language queries to find relevant documents. The result of the query is a set of documents which contain the words of the query. The documents which provided the most hits with the given query are placed at the top of the list of documents. WAIS databases can be accessed using specific WAIS client programs, or alternatively Gopher, Telnet and Web browser client programs.

E-mail

The most used application of the Internet is electronic mail, or *e-mail* as it is widely known. E-mail is primarily used to send and receive text-based messages such as personal or business letters, orders, reports and statements.

To use Internet e-mail, access to a computer which is connected to the Internet and has e-mail software is required. Most commercial Internet service providers include e-mail facilities in their subscriber services. Subscribers are given an identifying code called an e-mail *address*. The service provider collects and forwards mail sent from that address and holds mail to be received by that address until able to deliver it. The service provider thus acts like a post office, and in fact there is a close analogy between the way which e-mail is implemented and the traditional manual postal system (which is disparagingly termed 'snail mail' by e-mail devotees). The same principles apply to e-mail users who do not rely on commercial service providers - messages are automatically forwarded from users to their destinations and incoming mail is stored on their service provider's computer until the user is able to accept it.

FTP

File Transfer Protocol (FTP) provides the facility to transfer files between two computers on the Internet. There are thousands of FTP sites all over the Internet with data files, software, and information for almost any interest. Though there are other methods of transferring files between computers on the Internet, FTP allows such tasks to be performed quickly and easily. It is worth noting, however, that in order to access a remote host computer in this way, you need to have:

❑ The host name, that is, the Internet name of the computer system to which you hope to connect. This will be used by your FTP software to establish a link to the host. A typical host name might be of the form `ftp.layton.com`.

❑ A valid login name and a password which will allow you to access the host. These are obviously for security purposes - many computer systems on the Internet contain confidential information which only authorised personnel should be able to access. However, unrestricted files which are available on host computers can often be accessed by using the special visitor password *anonymous*.

Telnet

Telnet allows you to use a remote computer system from your local system. For example, an employee of an organisation which is on the Internet and supports Telnet working, could use the firm's computer system from home. The employee would simply Telnet the employer's computer system using his/her home PC and, once connected, could run programs available on the remote system. The Telnet software provides an interface window through which commands can be issued and results displayed.

This *virtual terminal* allows the remote computer to be controlled as if it were the local computer. Any task which can be performed on a workstation connected directly to the remote computer can also be done using a Telnet connection.

Usenet

Usenet is a large collection of newsgroups, of which there are many thousands. Newsgroups allow people with common interests to exchange views, ask questions and provide information using the Internet. Almost anything you care to find can be found as a newsgroup, which acts like a community bulletin board spread across millions of computer systems world wide. Anyone can participate in these groups, and moderation ranges from strict to none. Everything imaginable is discussed, from selling and trading goods and services, to discussing the latest episode of a popular TV show. Subscribers can read news articles, and reply to them - either by posting their own news articles, or by sending E-mail to the authors.

Since Usenet news is not limited to any political or geographic boundaries, it provides the possibility of being able to interact with an enormous number of individuals.

A program called a *newsreader* allows access to a newsgroup and the articles available for reading, retrieval of articles of interest and the posting of articles for others to read. Each article has a header which summarises the contents of the article, and the newsreader can be configured either to read all available article headers or those which meet certain criteria.

IRC

IRC, or *Internet Relay Chat*, is a multi-user talk program. IRC allows several people to simultaneously participate in a discussion over a particular channel, or even multiple channels. There is no restriction to the number of people who can participate in a given discussion, or the number of channels which can be formed over IRC.

All conversations take place in real time and IRC has been used extensively for live coverage of such things as world events, news and sports commentary. It is also an extremely inexpensive substitute for long distance calling.

Intranets and Extranets

An intranet is a private Internet which uses Internet software and the TCP/IP protocols. Its appearance is that of the Web and the familiar browser is its user interface. 'Out of the box' Web servers provide a convenient and relatively cheap method of developing internal network requirements and many organisations have built intranets as part of their overall Internet strategy. Employees are usually familiar with the Web and require little training to access the resources they need on the company intranet.

Web tools, such as HTML editors, are relatively cheap and application development only becomes expensive when large and complex databases are needed, as in the case of an on-line store's product database.

An intranet may be developed on private corporate LANs or WANs but organisations frequently wish to provide appropriate and limited access to clients and suppliers and develop an outward facing extension for those purposes. As an intra/Extranet, outside access only requires the use of a Web browser, which is generally available.

Extranets can be a valuable way of providing customer support and services. For example, the progress of a project can be monitored by the client, products can be developed by sharing information with partner organisations, customers can check on product availability, or the status of a delivery.

Access to an Extranet needs to be carefully controlled and entry will normally require a user-id and password.

✍️Exercises

1. Distinguish between the *Internet* and the *World Wide Web*.
2. (i)   What is the purpose of a *browser*?
   (ii) Give two examples of the use of *hyperlinks*.
   (iii) Distinguish between *hypertext* and *hypermedia*.
   (iv) What does *HTML* stand for and what is its purpose?
3. Give a well-known example of a *URL* (Uniform Resource Locator).
4. What is the purpose of a *search engine*? Name three.
5. Define the terms *Intranet* and *Extranet* and suggest applications of each for an organisation.

Internet security

An organisation's network needs to be secure against unauthorised access to maintain the integrity and confidentiality of its resources and protect the privacy of any clients whose details they hold. There are general security issues which apply to all networks, closed and open, but this Topic deals with the particular problems thrown up by the Internet and the new security measures developed to cope with those problems.

Security threats

Viruses and hostile applets

A computer virus is program code designed to create nuisance for users, or more seriously, to effect varying degrees of damage to files stored on magnetic media. Files downloaded from *bulletin boards* on the Internet (Topic 52) may be infected and uncontrolled use of these services is likely to result in the receipt of viruses.

A feature of all viruses is that they replicate themselves. Once into the computer's memory, it transfers from memory on to any integral storage device, such as a hard disk and commonly conceals itself in the boot sector (and sometimes in the partition sector where it is less likely to be traced), from where it can readily infect any other media placed on line in that computer system, whether it be stand-alone or networked. Naturally, any write-protected media cannot be infected.

Some virus codes are merely a nuisance, whilst others are developed specifically to destroy, or make inaccessible, whole filing systems.

Boot sector virus

This type of virus stores itself in the boot sector of the hard drive and so is activated when the system is started up. From there the virus can carry out various types of damage to files on the hard drive and copy itself to any disks accessed from floppy drives. Some are able to change their form to avoid detection by virus detection software. One such virus, Hare, only affects Windows 95 systems and is picked up from Usenet News on the Internet. It activates when an infected machine is booted on the 22nd August or the 22nd September and overwrites the contents of the hard disk.

Macro virus

This is probably the most common type of virus, new ones being reported almost daily. It embeds itself in documents created with general-purpose packages, such as Microsoft Word and Excel, each of which provides its own *macro language* (a type of programming language). The language can be used to automate certain procedures, such as formatting a document in a particular way, or customising the package for a specific application. Macro viruses have the following features.

❑ Once a macro virus has infected a machine, it embeds itself in all documents subsequently created with that machine.

❏ Macro viruses may change or delete file contents, or prevent subsequent saving or opening of a file.

❏ It spreads quickly because so many people use these packages and exchange files on portable media, such as floppy disks and increasingly via e-mail as attachments..

❏ Some macro viruses are of the 'Trojan' variety. They do not reproduce themselves, but destroy or corrupt the data in the infected document as soon as it is opened.

Largely because of the widespread use of Internet e-mail, the macro virus now presents the greatest threat of system infection.

Trojan horse virus

Named after the wooden horse at the siege of Troy, this type of virus does not reproduce itself, but pretends to be a real application program. Ironically, one such program claims to remove viruses, but in fact introduces viruses into a computer system.

Hostile Applets

An applet is a small, self-contained application written in the Java programming language and executable by all modern browsers.

Virus and hostile Applet protection

Ant-virus software can be installed on individual machines on a network, but additional protection needs to be provided at network server level. A variety of package solutions exist to check incoming e-mails for infected attachments. If an infected attachment is found the user is sent the e-mail, minus the attachment and with a warning that the e-mail was infected. To keep track of new viruses and quickly develop 'cures', IBM has developed a technology called the Immune System for Cyberspace. Company networks which are connected to the system automatically send any viruses they receive to IBM's automated lab which develops 'cures' and distributes them to the company networks.

Many products developed for Internet-delivered viruses also include protection against hostile Applets.

Service attacks on Internet servers

There are numerous ways in which the service provided by an Internet server can be damaged.

❏ Ping of death. 'Ping' stands for Packet Internet Groper which is an Internet utility used to check whether an IP (Internet Protocol) address is on-line. This is confirmed if the packet sender receives a response. By using a very large 'ping' packet, the volume of data can overwhelm an Internet server and cause it to crash.

❏ E-mail 'bombs' can be created by duplicating and sending a message duplicated hundreds of times or by attaching large files which fill up the Internet server's space and clog the system.

❏ SYN flooding. A 'SYN' is the first part of the TCP (Transmission Control Protocol) packet for an Internet connection request. Such requests are received and handled by Internet servers. When flooded with requests for connections to invalid IP addresses, the server SYN queue becomes full and cannot handle further requests.

Nuisance attacks

'Spam' e-mail (Internet junk mail) is the most common type of nuisance attack and although no damage is done, it can be extremely annoying for users when their mailboxes are filled with un-wanted communications. Legislation has been introduced in the USA to combat the problem, but there are numerous software products to protect Internet Service Providers and their users from 'spam' e-mail. The main method of protection filters out e-mails from the IP (Internet Protocol) addresses of well-known sources of 'spam'.

Security measures

Firewall protection

Firewalls are considered essential for the protection of corporate networks, such as intranets, from external networks such as the Internet. A firewall protection system may use both hard-ware and software components. Its purpose is to checks all packets before they enter or leave the intranet, stopping any that do not pass the relevant security standards. Most firewalls are concerned with checking incoming messages from the Internet, but they can also be used to screen out Internet sites which the organisation does not want to be accessible by staff. This may be because they contain objectionable material or because they will cause staff to waste time.

E-mail encryption

An e-mail transmission over the Internet is transferred from server to server on the way to its destination and the only way to maintain the confidentiality is to use encryption. The S/MIME (Secure/Multipurpose Internet Mail Extension) encrypts the standard MIME message and adds a digital signature (see later). To use this security system requires that sender and recipient must both have e-mail software which can handle S/MIME.

Payments through secure servers

Unlike e-mail transmissions, credit card payments can be made direct to a particular Internet server which can be secured with both hardware and software. The growth of electronic retail-ing is dependent on customer confidence in the security of Web-based transactions. In fact, credit card payments over the Internet can be more secure than using the telephone or post. Se-curity is achieved with the use of Secure Servers by the vendors or third party businesses that receive and process transactions on their behalf. The banks and credit card companies specify the physical and software security measures for a Secure Server. In the UK, card authorisation and processing is handled by Streamline.

The secure server is in effect the Web-based equivalent of the Streamline terminal used in con-ventional retail outlets. A modern Web browser will indicate when a 'secure environment' is entered, normally at the point when credit card details need to be provided. In addition to this *automatic* reassurance to the customer that the transaction is safe, your Web pages can be de-signed to reinforce customer confidence by explaining what a 'secure environment' actually is.

The Web-based retailer takes payment before the product or service is delivered to the cus-tomer, so is in the same position as a conventional retailer who takes credit details over the telephone or by post.

Finally, e-commerce transactions are subject to the same framework of domestic and international rules as traditional means of shopping including, for example, existing rules on "distance selling", advertising and customer credit.

S-HTTP (Secure HyperText Transport Protocol)

This extension of the standard HTTP (Topic 52 The Internet) supports the encryption of both client (browser) and server transmissions and is essential for the security and confidentiality of commercial transactions over the Internet. When making a payment to an Internet store, the normal IP address of, for example, http://www.ourshop.com, becomes s-http://www.ourshop, indicating that the user is now connected to a secure server.

Encryption and authentication

Authentication of both client and server sides of a connection is important for network security and the confidentiality and integrity of data passing between them. Apart from password solutions, authentication can be effected with the SSL and SET protocols (widely used to protect the confidentiality of credit card payments made over the Internet) and digital signatures.

Secure Sockets Layer (SSL)

SSL (Secure Sockets Layer) is the de facto standard for encryption between client browsers and Internet servers. The identity of the server is always authenticated, but authentication of the client is optional. An electronic 'handshake' between server and browser authenticates the server and enables the client to be confident that a secure and private link has been established. Optionally, the identity of the client can be authenticated if he or she has a digital certificate issued by a Certificate Authority. To allow the client and server to be confident that a message has not been altered during transmission, a digital fingerprint is transmitted with the message. The digital fingerprint is a 'hash' value generated from a computation carried out on the data (a 'hash function'). The same hash function is applied to the message upon receipt and if it generates the same digital fingerprint, the message cannot have been altered.

Before a transmission from the client browser, it sends a request to the Internet server, and in return receives the server's public encryption key and other cryptographic details. The browser generates its own random key and encrypts it with the server's public key. Now the browser's random key can only be decrypted with the server's private key. The encrypted random key is sent to the server, which uses its private key to decrypt it. The server returns a message, encrypted with the browser's original random key. If the browser is able to decrypt the message with its original random key, the server is authenticated.

Secure Electronic Transactions (SET)

Like Secure Sockets Layer (SSL), the Secure Electronic Transaction (SET) protocol was developed (jointly by Visa and MasterCard) as a method to secure bankcard transactions over open networks, including the Internet. Compared with SSL, SET places greater importance on the validation of *both* parties to the transaction.

Although SSL allows the customer's browser to authenticate the Merchant's Web server, it does not assure the Merchant that the user of a credit card is in fact the owner of the card. Of course, this weakness also applies to transactions conducted by telephone or post. SET uses digital signatures to enable merchants to verify the identity of buyers. SET also protects customers by providing a mechanism for the credit card number to go directly to the card issuing bank for verification and billing without the merchant seeing it. Another limitation of SSL is that, outside the US, it is only available with a maximum 40-bit encryption key, which allows relatively weak encryption.

The SET protocol authenticates all aspects of a transaction by controlling the interactions that take place between all parties including, for example, credit card holders, Merchants and card issuing banks. SET provides greater confidentiality, greater transaction integrity and less opportunity for fraud than SSL or any other secure payment system.

When a SET virtual store customer has finished shopping, that is, accumulated all required items into the virtual shopping basket, the Merchant's Web server displays the completed order for the customer's review and approval. After approval, the customer chooses to use a bankcard for payment. Before transmission from the customer's computer, the payment details are encrypted using a randomly generated encryption key. Then, using the Merchant's public key received from the Web server, the key is itself encrypted, effectively placing it inside a "digital envelope". The digital envelope can only be 'opened' with the Merchant's private key, known only to the Merchant. Upon receipt, the Merchant's server opens the digital envelope and uses the enclosed key to decrypt the message.

SET also authenticates both parties to the transaction with a distinct public/private key pair to create a "digital signature". This digital signature Authentication is further strengthened by the use of certificates issued by a trusted third party Certificate Authority (CA).

Before they can shop at SET sites, cardholders must register with a CA to obtain the necessary digital certificate. The certificate provides the digital signature needed to prove a cardholder's identity in e-commerce transactions. The certificate can be held, along with other payment information, on the customer's PC, using encryption software called an electronic wallet – see below.

Virtually all the major players in electronic commerce, including Microsoft, Netscape, Visa, and MasterCard have endorsed SET. Acceptance in the US has been slow, but SET is the most widely used protocol for electronic transactions within Europe.

Digital signatures

Before transmission from the client computer, the message is encrypted using a randomly generated encryption key. Then, using the public key received from the Web server, the key is itself encrypted, effectively placing it inside a "digital envelope". The digital envelope can only be 'opened' with the server's private key, known only to the server. Upon receipt, the server opens the digital envelope and uses the enclosed key to decrypt the message.

This authenticates both parties with a distinct public/private key pair to create a "digital signature". This digital signature Authentication is further strengthened by the use of certificates issued by a trusted third party Certificate Authority (CA).

✍️Exercises

1. A business is making extensive use of e-mail and the Internet in general and has experienced some minor problems from nuisance viruses. It is concerned that it may be suffer real damage from viruses in the future.

   (i) What is a computer *virus*?

   (ii) Describe the main types of computer virus.

   (iii) Explain the measures which can be taken to minimise the risk of virus damage.

   (iv) What is a hostile *applet*?

2. An Information Service Provider (ISP) has been receiving numerous complaints from its users concerning a slowing down of Internet access. Its servers are also tending to crash more frequently. The ISP suspects that it may be being subjected to '*ping of death*', '*SYN flooding*' or '*e-mail bomb*' attacks.

   Explain each of the italicised terms.

3. The business is also planning to set up an Extranet to provide restricted Internet access to its Intranet, primarily for staff working away from the main office. The Intranet is to be protected with the use of *firewalls* and *encryption*.

   Define the italicised terms.

4. The business is planning the development of an e-commerce site to sell its products over the Internet. It does not have the *secure server* facilities demanded by the merchant banks, for the acceptance of on-line credit card payments and plans to use the services of a *Payment Service Provider* (PSP).

   (i) What is a *secure server* and why is it an essential part of an e-commerce site?

   (ii) What does *S-HTTP* stand for and what is its significance for an e-commerce consumer?

   (iii) What advantage has the SET protocol over the SSL protocol for the business?

   (iv) Explain the function of a Payment Service Provider.

5. Explain the term *digital signature* and consider its significance for the conduct of business electronically.

Section 11

Further database

Topics

Database administrator

A database administrator (DBA) appointed with a corporate function has special responsibility for:

- ❏ database design and development;
- ❏ selection of database software;
- ❏ database maintenance;
- ❏ database accuracy and security.

A DBA should have a working knowledge of both the DBMS and the organisation. A DBA will supervise the addition of new data items to the database (changes to the schema). Supervision of the data dictionary is also the DBA's responsibility (see next paragraph). The DBA has to ensure the consistent use of data across the whole database. For example, a functional area may request new data to be added to a database, when it already exists. This can happen when different departments in an organisation refer to a field by different names. For example, a Sales department may refer to the name Product Code, whilst the Warehouse staff may use the term Stock Code, when referring to the same field. During database development, it is easy to forget the precise definitions given to a field and when adding the field to another table, introduce inconsistencies.

Data dictionary

An essential part of the database design process is to maintain a data dictionary. Its main function is to store details of all the data items in a database. Such details can be wide ranging, but should include, as a minimum:

(i)   field names and the table(s) in which they occur;

(ii)   field definitions, including field types and lengths;

(iii)   additional properties, concerning, for example, data formats and validation controls;

(iv)   synonyms. Sometimes, the same field occurs in more than one table, but using different names. Generally it is better not to use synonyms.

The dictionary's main role is to ensure consistent data usage; if synonyms are used (different data names may be used by different functional areas of an organisation to refer to the same field), the dictionary must record their use accordingly to prevent duplication. An example of a data dictionary is provided in Topic 39.

Database recovery

Recovery techniques can be used in certain circumstances to recover lost data when a database is corrupted. Most recovery techniques depend on making a *dump* (copy) of the whole (or a selected part) of the data in the database. Recovery of a database requires:

❑ that the cause of the failure be diagnosed and remedied;

❑ replacement of the corrupted database with the most recent dump of the database;

❑ updating of the database with all the transactions and amendments which occurred since the last dump until the time of the database's failure.

Difficulties are apparent in this procedure; re-processing may take a long time and all updating transactions which have taken place since the last dump must be recorded, together with their sequence of entry, since the order of processing can determine the eventual state of the database. To allow for this, a DBMS will record each entry in a sequential file or transaction log; re-processing can then take place in the correct sequence, without any re-keying of data.

Data sharing and data integrity

Sharing of data by different users is fundamental to the database concept and the DBMS has to allow for it, whilst at the same time protecting the *integrity* of the database. Such access may be through different applications programs or through the same one. Database integrity is not affected by accesses which only read data; no matter how many users are reading the same data, its integrity will not be affected. *Concurrent* updates present the possibility of updates being lost.

Consider, for example a database schema which held the following stock record type.

```
STOCK(Item#, Item-Description, Quantity-held)
```

Two applications programs PR1 and PR2 are updating the Quantity-held for Item# 3254; following the delivery of units of that item, PR1 is to increase the balance by 200, whilst PR2 is to reduce it by 150 in respect of stock issues. If the initial value of Quantity-held is 200, then the following sequence of events could occur:

(i)   PR1 reads Stock record, Item# 3254;

(ii)   PR2 reads Stock record, Item# 3254;

(iii) PR1 increases Quantity-held by 200 and re-writes the record to the database;

(iv)   PR2 decreases Quantity-held by 150 and re-writes the record to the database.

At this stage, Stock record, Item# 3254, would show a Quantity-held value of 50, when it should be 250. This error has occurred because PR2 read the record before PR1 had re-written its updated version to the database.

With the use of *integrity locks*, a DBMS can ensure that any program which reads a record for the purpose of updating, must result in the *locking* of that record against access by any other updating program, until the updated version has been re-written to the database. Programs accessing the record for *reading purposes only*, are not prevented access by an integrity lock.

Integrity locks can be implemented through the use of an additional data item within a record, the value of which can be set to *on*, as and when required. Integrity locks can present their own problems, but they are not of concern in this text.

Database security

Security is concerned with controlling access to data, both to prevent its accidental or deliberate corruption and, in the case of confidential data concerning individuals or organisations, to maintain appropriate privacy.

Access control mechanisms

Identification, authentication and authorisation

Before being granted access to a database, users must identify themselves, normally with an assigned account number or identification code. Authentication of a user's identity normally requires provision of a password, known only to the system and its legitimate users. The system holds information, supplied initially by the database administrator (DBA), on each user or category of user. This information is held to allow the system to carry out its identification and authentication procedures and to determine the level of authorisation - the kinds of access any particular user is permitted.

Control locks and keys

Another mechanism for controlling access uses access control locks and access control keys. Consider the following example of how a very simple access lock could work; the extracts of a schema (logical definition) description and application program are coded in the Codasyl Data Description Language and Data Manipulation Language.

Schema extract

```
RECORD NAME IS CLIENT
CLIENT-NUM PICTURE 9 (8)
DATE-OF-BIRTH PICTURE 9 (6)
BALANCE PICTURE 9 (6) V99
ACCESS CONTROL LOCK FOR GET IS 'ZEBRA'
```

Program extract

```
MOVE 'ZEBRA' TO KEY-CHECK
USE FOR ACCESS CONTROL ON GET FOR CLIENT
```

The character string 'ZEBRA' is declared as being the access control lock on the command GET for the data item BALANCE, only. Thus, the Balance data cannot be used by an application program unless the access control key 'ZEBRA' is provided and transferred to the location called KEY-CHECK, where it is compared by the DBMS with the access control lock. If the values do not agree then access is prevented to the Balance data. This is a fairly trivial example and not particularly secure, as a glance at the schema listing would reveal the access control lock's value; more sophisticated ways of assigning the access control lock are generally used.

Levels of authorisation

A fundamental principle of security is that access is limited to those persons who require it and that the degree of access is limited to that which is necessary to their jobs. For example, authorisation to alter schema or sub-schema descriptions may be limited to the DBA; user A may be given access to particular data for enquiry, but not for alteration purposes, whilst User B may be the only person authorised to change prices in the Stock File.

Exercises

1. Describe the role of the following in database administration.

   (i)   Database administrator.

   (ii) Data dictionary.

2. Describe the mechanisms needed for database *recovery*.

3. Explain the problems presented by *concurrent* updates in a database and describe the mechanisms used to maintain the *integrity* of its contents.

4. Describe the following database *access control mechanisms* and explain how they can help to protect it against unauthorised access.

   (i)   Identification, authentication and levels of authorisation.

   (ii) Control locks and keys.

Distributed databases

Put simplistically, a database is a central store of information accessible by multiple applications. A <u>distributed</u> system subdivides the database over multiple computer systems, but it still appears as a single database to applications and users. When a complete database is replicated at different sites, it is still referred to as a distributed database because the technical problems of database management are similar to those of a truly distributed database. We will look at the principles of and options for database replication and then examine true distributed database systems.

Database replication

Copies of a database or partial database may be held on multiple servers to improve performance and ensure access to data is maintained.

Single master replication

Figure 55.1 illustrates a replication model which allows read-only access to distributed copies, only allowing updates to be effected on the master database.

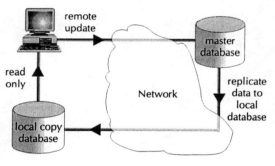

For example, an application can access a local version of the database for enquiry purposes if the communications link to the master database is temporarily unavailable. Depending on the method used to maintain consistency between the various copies and the master database, such local access may mean that data is not entirely up-to-date. For reasons which will be explained later, updates must be effected through the master database only.

Application

Following an update to the master database, the changes are copied to the local database(s). The replication may not be immediate, either because the process is only carried out periodically, or because the network connection to a local database is temporarily unavailable. Provided that the organisation plans for such differences in data values and absolute currency is not essential to applications, the model may work well. For example, a supermarket chain may only make price changes every two days, which it applies to the master database at its headquarters and then replicates to the copies at supermarket branches. This is, in effect, batch processing.

If updates are carried out in realtime and replication required more or less immediately, network links or a high volume of update transactions may prevent local copies from being properly updated. This could have serious consequences for some applications. For example, suppose that enquiries are made locally on stock levels and orders to customers are agreed on the basis of those enquiries. If there have been numerous stock issue updates without frequent replication orders may not be met, resulting in the loss of valuable custom.

The model is useful for systems where the high volume of updates to the master makes it difficult to handle queries efficiently. If enquiry-only applications use the local copies this removes the burden from the master database. The more copies there are, the more the load is shared.

Peer-to-peer replication

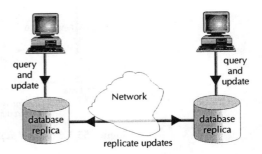

Figure 55.2. *Peer-to-peer database replication*

In this model, there is no master and all replicas (copies infer use of a master database) are treated as equal for the purposes of enquiry and updates, hence the term peer-to-peer. The database management system (DBMS) software must ensure that an update of one replica is then copied to the other replicas. Updates at each site may be queued and replicated at set intervals (a kind of batch processing known as *store and forward*) or, if the application requires it, they may be applied immediately to all replicas in *real-time*. Replication is essential to maintain consistency of database values across all database replicas. Figure 55.2 illustrates a peer-to-peer replication model.

Application

Peer-to-peer replication can be used to

❑   distribute the load in a high volume, transaction processing, system.

❑   ensure continued database access, a vital feature for many applications including, for example, those of the emergency services. In the event of failure of a replica, its users can be automatically switched to another.

❑   updating a centralised database from a number of locally held databases. This is a common requirement for organisations with sales or servicing staff whose jobs depend on the use of, for example, notebook computer systems. For example, following completion of a servicing job, a gas engineer will update the customer record on a notebook computer. At the end of the day, the database changes can be uploaded to the centralised database.

Replication update conflicts

The consistency of database replicas can be lost when updates can be applied to different replicas of the same database. The problem does not apply to single master replication because updates are only applied to the master database - copies cannot be updated, except by replication from the master database. Real-time replication is not subject to conflicts because all replicas are immediately updated and at the time that a record is being updated at one site, it is *locked* to other sites. As soon as the update has been completed and replicated to all sites, the record is unlocked. Real-time replication relies entirely on the continued availability of the high-speed network connections which are need to connect the sites to one another. However, the following types of conflict can occur when replication is not immediate, that is for peer-to-peer, store and forward replication:

❑ primary key duplication, as illustrated in Figure 55.3;

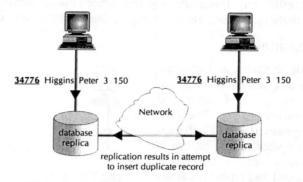

Figure 55.3. *Potential duplicate primary key conflict*

❑ simultaneous updating of the same record at different database sites (Figure 55.4);

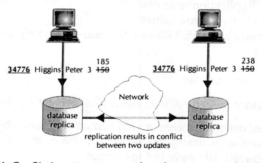

Figure 55.4. *Conflicting attempts to update the same record at the same time*

❑ attempt to delete or update a record already deleted at another site (Figure 55.5).

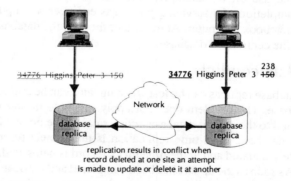

Figure 55.5. *Conflicting attempt to update a record already deleted at another site*

Detecting and resolving conflicts

The database management system (DBMS) must be able to detect and resolve any of the conflicts outlined above. For example, in the case of the attempt to update or delete a record which has already been deleted at another site, this can be resolved by only setting record deletion markers, rather than physically removing records from the database. Periodically, such marked records can be permanently removed or *purged*.

Distributed databases

A true distributed database partitions an organisation's 'global' database into a number of individual databases, perhaps one or two for each branch or division. Figure 55.6 provides an example.

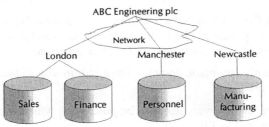

Figure 55.6. *Example hierarchy of a distributed database*

Each database contains network links to connect it with other databases (not necessarily all) to form the global database. Each link needs to indicate the location of the database and the relevant table. For example, the Sales database in London may include a link to the JobHistory table in the Personnel database in Manchester, as follows.

```
jobhistory.personnel@manchester.abcengineering.co.uk
```

The Figure illustrates an example structure of a distributed database but does not attempt to show the network connections which would be needed to connect the various databases.

Database transparency

Although there is not replication in this model, individual transactions will sometimes affect more than one table. A transaction may affect local or remote tables, but to retain database consistency the updates must be applied to all affected tables simultaneously. Usually, the physical location of individual databases will be hidden from both applications and users. A programmer can develop an application according to the restricted logical view or sub-schema (Topic 22) provided by the database administrator (DBA). This *transparency* allows a distributed database to appear as a single, global database. Distributed databases reduce central processing requirements, but can be vulnerable when network links are unavailable. For databases which are updated in real-time, uninterrupted network communications are essential.

The security issues relating to distributed databases are similar to those for the control of access to computer networks. Levels of access are controlled through the use of user accounts. A database administrator (DBA) is given *global* or *supervisor* user status and has unrestricted access to a local, and possibly, the global database. The DBA must be able to modify database definitions as the application and user requirements change. For a fuller description of the DBA's role, see Topic 54. Programmers and users are restricted to the database areas they need and are given access rights appropriate to their tasks. For example, staff who respond to customer enquiries should have read-only access, whereas, supervisory staff may be able to modify data.

Centralised versus distributed systems

The main benefits for an organisation of a distributed system may be as follows.

❑ The delegation of control of some information processing to branch level management, hopefully resulting in systems which respond to local requirements.

❑ More rapid, up-to-date information at the local level, because it is processed locally.

❑ The rapid distribution of centrally produced information through network systems.

❑ Provided that the local systems are linked to a central facility, then information which is locally produced can be transmitted and stored so as to be available at a corporate level. Overall control is not lost, but enhanced.

The above benefits are not automatic and may have certain implications for an organisation. The main implications are:

❑ New hardware and software needs to be purchased, which is compatible with any existing centralised facility.

❑ Local management and workers need to be trained in the operation of any new system introduced, if the maximum benefit is to be obtained.

❑ A complete re-appraisal of specialist staffing may be needed as a result of distribution. For example, systems analysts already familiar with the design and implementation of distributed systems may need to be recruited.

❑ Specialist personnel, including programmers and operators, may be needed at the local level.

❑ Distributed systems present new problems in terms of controlling the security of information. The added risks must be considered and covered.

✍️Exercises

1. (i) Distinguish between database *replication* and *distribution*.
   (ii) A wholesaler has a single central orders database which it *replicates* to each of its distribution warehouses at the end of each day.

   Comment on the quality of information which will be held by the branches.
   (iii) Explain the problem of *update conflicts* when *peer-to-peer* replication is used.
2. (i) Examine Figure 55.6 in this Topic and comment on the benefits and drawbacks of the *distributed* system it represents in comparison with a wholly *centralised* system.
   (ii) Use the example in Figure 55.6 to explain the term *database transparency*.
3. Outline two advantages of a distributed database over a centralised database.

Section 12

Organisations and ICT

Topics

Need for organisations

The society in which we live is complex and sophisticated. As consumers we demand a variety of goods and services to enable us to maintain the quality of life we enjoy. In order to satisfy these demands, suppliers must produce the goods and services which the consumer wants by combining factors of production such as land, labour and capital in the most efficient manner. By this we mean producers must hire workers, rent or buy premises, perhaps invest in plant and machinery and purchase raw materials, and then organise the manufacture of the final product in such a way that they will make a profit. Society may also gain, as its scarce resources are being used in the way consumers wish rather than being wasted in producing things people do not need. Suppliers under such a system are known as commercial organisations. Many public sector organisations also provide goods and services to society and, in the same way as commercial organisations, these public sector bodies must employ staff, occupy premises and raise capital. The fundamental difference between these two types of organisation lies in the objectives they seek to fulfil. The private sector tends to be motivated by profit, while public sector organisations will often have a much less mercenary motive, such as providing for the public good and improving the state of society. If we wish to see society ordered and governed in such a way that individuals are free to express their demands and producers are able to meet such wants, it becomes necessary to form organisations to control and regulate society through a variety of administrative structures. These are the bodies which make up the organisations of the state. In the UK, these are Parliament, the Government and its Executive, the Civil Service, the Local Authorities and the Courts and justice system. These bodies are required to carry out legislative, administrative and judicial functions.

If you examine the nature and range of individual demands in an industrialised society you soon realise that most of them cannot be met other than by organisations. Individually we lack the knowledge, skills and physical resources to manufacture products that fulfil our needs, whether these are simple or sophisticated. It would be as difficult for us to make a biro or a floppy disk as it would a television or a computer. Admittedly, some goods and services can be supplied by an individual working alone. A farmer may be able to grow sufficient food to satisfy himself and his family without any help from others. But what if he requires other goods and services? It is unlikely that the farmer will also have the ability or resources to produce his own combine-harvester or tractor. If he did not have such products which are manufactured by others, his life would be much simpler, but no doubt much harder.

A similar situation exists in the supply of services. A strong and resourceful individual may try to protect himself and his property from the dangers imposed by thieves or vandals. If he cannot, however, then he may turn to the state to demand protection. Recognising that a failure to respond to such demands from its citizens would lead to an anarchic system, the government must accept the responsibility and establish a legal system incorporating law enforcement agencies to provide the protection being sought.

How, then, are these goods and services produced? It is clear that individuals working independently would be unable to meet our complex physical and social needs. Therefore society has developed a system where people join together to form organisations. These bodies are extraordinarily diverse. They manufacture products, which they distribute and sell. They also provide all the services that we need. Thus, both the BBC and the Ford Motor Company are organisations, although their products are very different.

Clearly, then, if individuals within society are to have all their various needs satisfied, there must be co-operation between workers. Each must specialise in a certain aspect of the supply process. These workers must be organised and allocated a specific role in which to perform co-ordinated tasks. These tasks are normally organised with the aim of producing a given product or service, although there are some organisations which do not specialise and which make an extremely diverse range of products. In the private sector of the economy, such businesses will usually have the objective of making a profit for their owners. Of course, this is just one example of an organisation. As we have already noted, the state is another form of organisation which is clearly more complex than a business, and it has a variety of objectives, such as increasing the wealth of citizens, improving their quality of life and protecting them if they are threatened. We are all members of organisations, some of which are formal while others are informal. Your family is an example of an informal organisation, as is the group of friends you mix with. Other more formal organisations to which you may belong or may have belonged are the school you attended as a child, your employing body, or your trade union.

The tendency to form groups is a characteristic of human nature. Human beings are highly socialised, they need to 'belong' and will generally find it uncomfortable and disturbing if they cannot find 'acceptance' within a social group. An employee who is capable and confident in his or her job, and who is in turn regarded by the employer and the rest of the work force as a professional, gains a 'role' satisfaction through identifying as a vital part of the group. So organisations have an important role to fulfil in meeting the social needs of man. However, perhaps more important in the context of this course of study is the function of organisations as the satisfiers of needs. They allow individual workers to develop their specialist skills, and this in turn allows productive capacity to increase.

Since differing organisations concentrate on the supply of different goods and services, there must be a system established whereby products can be distributed to the consumers. Thus shops, wholesalers, transport companies and so on must all be involved. The fabric of the social and economic environment is based on a process whereby individuals form organisations which are dependent upon other organisations to survive. In just the same way as the needs of the individual cannot be met by that individual alone, so the same also holds true for organisations. They are interdependent. Organisational activity involves a perpetual interaction, one organisation with another, as society steadily evolves in a direction that individually and collectively we try to guide. However, as we shall see, even though the overall aim of society is the advancement of our physical well-being, the methods for achieving this are the subject of much disagreement.

Characteristics common to all organisations

The specific reasons for the formation of organisations are many and varied, and may not, of course, always be clearly defined. Some are the result of the need for individuals to find company for a social or leisure reason, for example by forming a sporting or working-men's club. Others are formed with a more precise economic objective in mind, such as the desire to make a profit for the person who has established a business organisation. Some, such as the organisations which make up the state and government, evolve as a result of the emergence of particular needs in society which require government intervention. For example, the Government established the National Health Service in 1946 to meet the needs of society for a high standard of free health care, available to all. Nevertheless, most formal organisations have some common characteristics. These may be simply stated as follows:

(i)   The establishment of an organisation is usually for a specific purpose.

For example, the Automobile Association was founded with the precise objective of promoting the interests of motorists within this country. Other organisations may be launched with one prime aim, but may later diversify in order to follow alternative causes or objectives. For instance, Guinness, the brewery company, was established to produce alcoholic drinks, but now has subsidiaries making a variety of products such as fishing tackle boxes and cassette cases. This illustrates how a business may try to evolve as the commercial environment changes and new commercial opportunities emerge.

(ii) Organisations usually have a distinct identity.

People belonging to a specific organisation can identify themselves as being part of a group either as a result of where they work or of what they do. A Manchester United footballer wears a red shirt to show he is part of the particular organisation. A member of a trade union is given a membership card to signify he belongs to that union. Manufacturing companies promote their brand names through advertising. This sense of identity, which we have already seen is an important need for most people, can produce extreme loyalty to the organisation.

(iii) Most organisations require some form of leadership.

We have seen that organisations are normally formed for a specific purpose. In order to achieve this purpose, it is necessary to co-ordinate the efforts of the members of the organisation. This requires management, or leadership. Formal organisations such as companies or a club have a specified management hierarchy which may be appointed by the owners of the organisation. For instance, the shareholders of a company appoint the directors. Alternatively, the leadership may be elected, as in the case of a club or society where the members vote to have a chairman, secretary and committee. However, once appointed this management team has the responsibility for ensuring the organisation achieves its objectives.

(iv) Organisations are accountable.

Such accountability applies both to those the management team deals with and those it employs.

Objectives of organisations

The objectives of an organisation are the targets it hopes to achieve. Clearly the objectives which are set will vary considerably between different types of organisation. As we shall see later in this section, the objectives of commercial organisations will largely be based around the goal of profit. For organisations within the public sector, profit may not be the sole aim. Factors such as benefit to the community or the creation of jobs may also feature as targets for the public sector. It should be noted, however, that the profit motive has grown substantially in importance in recent times.

A classification of organisations

Initially, it is convenient to categorise organisations as follows:

❑ public service;

❑ commercial and industrial.

Public service organisations

Many public services are provided by central and local government (the public sector) Central government takes responsibility for a wide range of services and has specific organisations, referred to as Departments, to manage each. Thus, there are separate departments, each responsible for the provision of, amongst others, health, education, defence and social welfare services. The role of local government is continually changing as successive governments pursue policies which tend to centralise power, or devolve it to locally elected council bodies. The provision of water, electricity and gas services used to be provided by 'public utilities', but they have been 'privatised' and now operate as commercial and industrial businesses. Some services, traditionally provided by the public sector, are now partly in the private sector; for example, some prisons are privately owned and private companies may carry out the work of refuse collection. Even so, overall control of such services is still the responsibility of central and local government departments. Table 56.1 lists some major central government organisations and briefly describes the responsibilities of each. Table 56.2 does the same, in respect of local government.

Government departments	Responsibilities
Education	Schools
Transport	Road and building
Home Office	Law and order, police and prison services policy
Health	Hospitals,
Trade and Industry	Business and industrial policy
Social Security	Benefits such as income support.
Treasury	Economic policy
Defence	Armed Forces

Table 56.1. *Central Government Departments and areas of responsibility*

It should be noted that although the government departments retain overall responsibility for the areas listed in the Table, private companies carry out some of the work. For example, some hospitals, prisons and schools are privately owned. As part of the government's 'privatisation' programme, local councils have to allow private businesses to tender for (compete for) work traditionally carried out by their own departments; this is called Compulsory Competitive Tendering (CCT).

For example, private businesses can tender for contracts to carry out street sweeping or refuse collection. In addition, some schools have 'opted out' and receive their funding directly from central governments.

Local Government departments	Responsibilities
Social Services	Home helps, children's homes, meals on wheels, day nurseries, residential homes and day centres for the mentally ill.
Education	Nursery, and secondary schools.
Housing	Council housing provides affordable accommodation for those who cannot buy their own homes.
Environmental Services	Refuse collection and disposal, street sweeping and pollution control.
Police and Fire Services	Although there is co-operation between forces, these services are still locally controlled.
Planning and Building Control	Consider applications for local building and enforce regulations on building standards.

Table 56.2. *Local Government Departments and areas of responsibility*

Industry and commerce

The term 'industry' covers a wide range of organisations which form part of a country's economy. We tend to link factories with the idea of industry, but the term also covers: *extraction* industries, such as coal-mining and fishing; *manufacturing* businesses which take raw materials and process them into finished products, such as cars and clothing, as well as those assembling ready-made components into, for example, computers and televisions; *retail* and *wholesale* businesses, concerned with buying, selling and distributing goods for personal and business consumption; *service* industries, such as hotel, catering, travel and banking. The word 'commerce' overlaps with 'industry' and includes all forms of trading organisation and those which support trade, such as banking and insurance.

Organisational structures

A structure can be defined as having component parts, which are connected in a particular way. Structures are designed to fulfil purposes. For example, a house is a structure, consisting of rooms, windows, floors, ceilings, doors and connection passages; the mix of these component parts and the way they are put together determines the design of the house. Two main types of organisational structure are considered here: *hierarchical*; *flat*.

Hierarchical structure

An organisation with a hierarchical structure includes different levels of authority and responsibility. Heads of Department may be directly responsible to one of the Directors. For example, the Accounts Department Head may be subject to the authority of the Financial Director. Such authority relates to the operation of the organisation and enables tasks to be completed. There may be Section Supervisors who are responsible to their respective Heads of Department for particular functions within departments. Each section supervisor may have authority over a number of clerks. Generally, there are more 'workers' than 'bosses', so a hierarchical structure can be viewed as a pyramid, as shown in Figure 56.1; the lower down the pyramid you descend, the larger the number of staff you are likely to find employed. The jobs at the top of the pyramid carry the most authority and the greatest responsibility for the success or failure of the organisation. Operatives and clerical staff are unlikely to have any authority in the organisation, but they have responsibility for the completion of their own jobs.

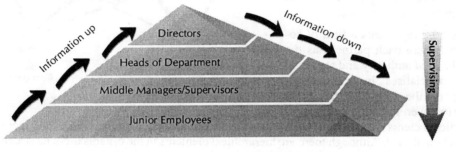

Figure 56.1. *Hierarchy of authority, responsibility and information flow*

Downward communication

Figure 56.1, shows that, within the pyramid, communications go up and down. Policy decisions taken at board level by the directors are implemented by instructing the relevant departmental heads to see that the policy is carried out. The heads of department brief their middle managers and the final stage in the process is the communication between middle managers and their subordinates.

Upward communication

The communication also passes from the bottom upwards. Staff provide feedback to their seniors. This may take many forms; it may involve monitoring shortages of materials, absences of staff, production problems, grievances and suggestions for improving work methods. Anything which requires the authority or approval of someone further up the organisational hierarchy and which has been generated or identified below, will pass back up the system. Only in extreme circumstances is it likely that an issue arising at the bottom of the pyramid will pass right back to the top for consideration and decision. For the most part, an immediate senior is likely to have sufficient authority to make a decision; ultimately however, it is a question of the extent of *delegated* responsibility held by senior employees that determines whether they can deal with it personally, or must pass it back to their own superiors. As organisations grow bigger it is inevitable that communications have much further to travel. This is not ideal since it is likely to take longer to transmit information and there is greater distancing between the giver and the receiver, which can lead to a 'them and us' view of the organisation by junior staff. However, it is clear that as the organisation grows, so its communication system must be become increasingly refined. Information technology support is crucial to the efficiency of communications.

Flat structure

In contrast to a hierarchy, a flat structure generally has a single level of management, as shown in Figure 56.2. Except for the smallest organisations, very few will have an entirely flat structure. It is possible, that an organisation wishes to avoid a cumbersome hierarchy and attempts to keep the number of management levels to a minimum; they are thus aiming for a 'flatter' structure. As mentioned earlier, hierarchies with many levels of authority can make communication difficult. A flatter structure can encourage 'team spirit' through the avoidance of the 'them and us' feelings, which can be characteristic of hierarchies

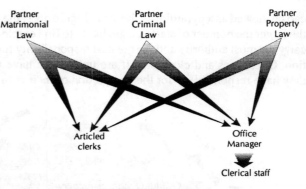

Figure 56.2 represents a firm of solicitors, where each partner has the same level of authority and responsibility, specialises in a particular aspect of the law and has joint authority over the Office Manager

Figure 56.2. *Flatter structure*

and articled clerks ('apprentice' solicitors). The Office Manager is responsible for supervision of the clerical staff. Although there are hierarchical elements in the organisation, its structure is fairly 'flat'.

✎Exercises

1. Choose three formal organisations with which you are familiar and for each:
    (i)   identify its main *purpose*;
    (ii)   select an aspect which gives it its distinct *identity*;
    (iii) briefly describe how it is *lead* - its top management structure;
    (iv)   identify to whom the management are ultimately *accountable*.
2. The water industry used to be in the public sector, but is now run by private companies, overseen by a regulator (OFFWAT). Briefly list features which allow the privatised water company to be classified as both commercial and public service.
3. (i)   Choose a hierarchically structured organisation with which you are familiar and using Figure 56.1 as a guide, draw a pyramid structure to show the main levels of authority.
    (ii)   Identify two benefits and two drawbacks of the structure for the chosen organisation.

This Topic investigates some of the main functional areas to be found in organisations, namely:

- ❑ financial accounting (sales, purchasing and general ledger);
- ❑ invoicing and stock control;
- ❑ marketing;
- ❑ payroll and personnel;
- ❑ design and production;
- ❑ IT services.

Financial accounting

Financial accounting or 'book-keeping' is the process of recording financial transactions arising from the day-to-day operation of a business. The sale of goods to a customer and the subsequent settlement of the debt are two examples of financial transactions. Apart from their function as a control mechanism over the financial transactions of a business, accounting records can be analysed to provide information on the performance of a business over a period. Typically, such information is extracted annually or every six months, in the form of a *balance sheet* and *trading and profit and loss account*. These financial statements are also required by *external agencies*, such as the Inland Revenue (for tax assessment) and the bank, if loan facilities are required.

Financial accounts need to record:

- ❑ *debtor* transactions; debtors are people or organisations who owe money to the business for goods or services provided (credit sales);
- ❑ *creditor* transactions; creditors are people or organisations to whom the business owes money, for the supply of goods (credit purchases).

These transactions are recorded in the *sales ledger* and the *purchase ledger* respectively. A third ledger, the *nominal* (or *general*) ledger is used to record the overall income and expenditure of the business, with each transaction classified according to its purpose.

Sales accounting

When credit sales are made to customers, a record needs to be kept of amounts owing and paid. Payment is normally requested with an invoice, which gives details of goods supplied, quantities, prices and VAT. Credit sales are usually made on for example, a 14, 21 or 28 day basis, which means that the customer has to pay within the specified period to obtain any discounts offered. Overdue payments need to be chased, so sales accounting systems normally produce reports analysing the indebtedness of different customers. Debt control is vital to business profitability and computerised systems can produce prompt and up-to-date reports as a by-product of the main application.

Purchase accounting

This function is concerned with controlling amounts owed and payments made to suppliers of services, goods or materials which are used in the main business of the company. For example, a car manufacturer will need to keep records of amounts owing to suppliers of car components and sheet steel manufacturers. Delayed payments to suppliers may help cash flow, but can harm an organisation's image, or even cut off a source of supply when a supplier refuses to deliver any more goods until payment is made.

General ledger

The general ledger keeps control of financial summaries, including those originating from pay-roll, sales and purchase accounting and acts as a balance in a double entry system. Computerised systems can automatically produce reports at the end of financial periods, including a trial balance, trading and profit and loss account and balance sheet.

Other finance-related functions

Stock control

Any organisation which keeps stocks of raw materials or finished goods needs to operate a stock control system. Although stock constitutes an asset, it ties up cash resources that could be invested in other aspects of the business. Equally, a company must keep sufficient quantities of items to satisfy customer demand or manufacturing requirements. To maintain this balance a stock control system should provide up-to-date information on quantities, prices, minimum stock levels, and re-order quantities. It should also give warning of excessively high, or dangerously low levels of stock. In the latter case, orders may be produced automatically. A stock control system may also generate valuable management reports on, for example, sales patterns, slow-moving items, and overdue orders.

Sales order processing

This function will normally be concerned with:

❏   the validation of orders, checking, for example, that the goods ordered are supplied by the business or that the customer's credit status warrants the order's completion;

❏   the identification of individual items ordered. A customer may request several different items on the same order form and any particular item will probably appear on many different order forms, so the quantities for each are totalled to produce picking lists to enable warehouse staff to retrieve the goods for despatch;

❏   the monitoring of back orders. If an order cannot be fulfilled, it may be held in abeyance until new stocks arrive, so all outstanding back orders need to be available on request.

Invoicing

This function deals with the production of customer invoices, requesting payment for goods or services delivered. Information stored in the customer files and stock files is used to produce invoices, usually on pre-printed continuous stationery.

Payroll

Payroll systems are concerned with the production of payslips for employees and the maintenance of records required for taxation and other deductions. In a manual system, the preparation of payroll figures and the maintenance of payroll records is a labour intensive task. Although tedious and repetitive, it is a vitally important task. Most employees naturally regard pay as being the main reason for work and resent delays in payment or incorrect payments, unless of course it is in their favour! The repetitive nature of the task makes it a popular candidate for computerisation, especially with organisations which employ large numbers of people. The automatic production of reports for taxation purposes also provides a valuable benefit. Smaller organisations with only several employees probably do not regard payroll as a high priority application for computerisation. The benefits are not as great if the payroll can be carried out by one or two employees who also carry out a number of other tasks.

Personnel

The personnel function is responsible for the selection (usually by interview), recruitment, training and development of staff. Personnel records will store all the information needed by Salaries and Wages to make the correct payments to employees; this will include details of, for example, gross salary, tax code, statutory sick pay and holiday entitlement. Depending on the size of the organisation, information may also be held concerning: qualifications, courses attended; personal and career development plans.

Design

The design function is present where an organisation develops its own products and services; a trader who simply buys and sells goods has no need of a design team. Design is part of the research and development ® & D) function, which is vital to organisations wishing to radically develop their product range. The nature of design teams depends on the product or service being designed. The skills and talents of a car design team are clearly very different from those of a team designing a cover for a magazine.

Production

The production function should, ideally, be driven by the market for the business's products. In other words, it should be geared to produce the necessary mix and quantities of products required by customers. If goods are perishable within a short time, and large reserve stocks cannot be held, then production should be flexible and responsive to the day-to-day sales requirements. Of course, this is an ideal and production plans cannot always be changed at short notice; ships and other large items take months or years to build. The production department must know exactly what is required and when; it must also have the staff with the necessary skills and any machinery must have the appropriate facilities and production capacity. For example, a production department which is geared to produce 1000 units of a product per day, will probably find it difficult to produce 2000 units, without modification of the system of production.

Marketing

A marketing function is a vital part of many large national and international businesses; it aims to generate information, from a wide range of data sources, to support marketing decisions. Three such decision areas are:

(i) *strategic* and relating to, for example, expansion of the company's existing market share and the identification of new marketable products;

(ii) *tactical*, for example, planning the marketing mix;

(iii) *operational*, for example, day-to-day planning of sales calls and ad hoc promotions.

At the operational level, for example, data gathered from sales invoices, sales force staff and accounting information can be used to establish customer types. Thus, customers can be classified as 'low', 'medium' or 'high' volume users according to the frequency and volume of their orders. This information can help sales staff to target particular categories of customer and to plan the timing of sales calls. At the tactical level, invoices provide information on sales variance between different market segments over time or sales projections based on current patterns.

Information Technology (IT) Services

Apart from small firms, most organisations need specialist staff to develop, introduce, maintain and update the various systems which make use of information technology. The term 'information technology' covers all computer-based information processing systems, plus those which make use of data communications, such as computer networks, fax machines, photocopiers and telephone systems. The responsibilities of IT Services are, therefore, much broader than those traditionally held by wholly centralised computer services or data processing departments. The development of cheaper and more powerful microcomputer systems, which can be networked with one another, as well as with larger mini and mainframe systems, has resulted in computer facilities being distributed more widely. For this reason, IT Services needs to provide a much more flexible service and support user systems at the point of use. For example, users of network workstations need support when equipment, such as a shared printer, breaks down or they may require help in the use of software on the network. This contrasts with a centralised department, which holds all the computer equipment, carries out all computer processing and restricts user access to specialised applications, run through dedicated terminals. IT Services may be known variously as Computer Services, Management Information Services or less commonly now, the Data Processing Department.

Role of IT Services

IT Services fulfils a servicing function for the whole organisation. In larger organisations, there is a centralised computer facility, possibly in the shape of a mainframe or mini-computer system, with the responsibility for major applications, such as payroll and stock control. User departments may have access to the centralised facility through attached terminals or networked microcomputers. Individual members of staff may also use stand-alone microcomputer systems or portable devices, such as notebooks and personal digital assistants (PDAs). IT Services staff need to support users in the use of these distributed facilities, as well as control the operation of any centralised system. IT Services provides facilities to satisfy both *operational* and *managerial* information needs.

Operational requirements

Each functional area has its own operational information needs. For example, Wages and Salaries need payroll details and payslips, and Sales Order Processing require the production of customer invoices. Common examples of routine operations include:

- ❑ keeping stock records
- ❑ sales accounting and purchase accounting;
- ❑ payroll;
- ❑ invoicing and production of delivery notes;
- ❑ routine costing;
- ❑ filing of customer orders.

Managerial requirements

Routine processing work forms the bulk of the activity within IT Services, but there is an increasing demand for management information. This includes assistance with functions which require management involvement and thinking, but which can be partially automated or assisted by computers. Examples of such functions include:

- ❑ production planning;
- ❑ short term and long term forecasting;
- ❑ setting of budgets;
- ❑ decision-making on financial policies;
- ❑ marketing decisions and sales management;
- ❑ factory maintenance and management;
- ❑ price determination;
- ❑ selection of suppliers.

Function of IT Services

Figure 57.1 shows the typical functions within an IT Services department.

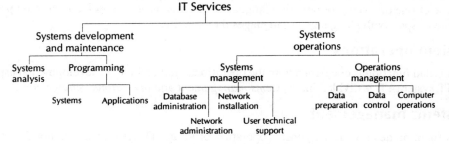

Figure 57.1. *Typical structure of IT Services department*

Systems development

This function relates to the development of new computerised systems and the maintenance of existing ones. This function is staffed primarily by *systems analysts* and *programmers*. In small organisations, hybrid skills are often needed, so job titles such as *analyst programmer* may be used.

Systems analysis

Systems analysis is a process used in the design of new systems, as requested by corporate management. Systems analysis follows stages of *investigation*, *design* and *implementation*. Each stage should involve close consultation with potential users, in the various functional areas of the organisation, to ensure that their information and operational requirements are met.

The design stage should produce a *system specification* which, rather like an architect's plans for a building, details all necessary materials and procedures needed to fulfil the specification. The specification should detail the necessary clerical procedures, hardware requirements and the inputs, processing and outputs required of the computer software.

After implementation of a system, it will require continual monitoring and probably, occasional modification, when the operational or information requirements of users change. This maintenance task is the responsibility of the systems analysts,

Programming

Programming lacks some of the creative aspects of systems analysis and involves the use of a programming language (for example, C++, COBOL, Visual BASIC) to code the necessary computer programs. The program requirements are detailed in the *program* or *software specification*, which forms part of the system specification prepared by systems analysts.

Most programmers who work in an IT Services department are likely to be *applications programmers*, responsible for the development or modification of applications, such as stock control or payroll. Systems programmers are concerned with the development of operating systems and utilities (see Topics 11 and 12), which are normally developed by large computer manufacturers or software companies, such as Microsoft. An IT Services department may also employ *systems programmers*, but they are likely to have a more limited role than applications programmers. Much software is now in commercial package form, but not all applications can be satisfied by such means and applications programmers continue to be needed for tailoring of programs specifically for their employer. The growth of network use has created the need for *network programmers*, who have specialist knowledge of such systems. Apart from specialising in systems, applications or network programming, a programmer is likely to be skilled in the use of one or more programming languages. An organisation seeking to employ programmers will specify the language or languages they require.

System operations

This broad function is concerned with the operational, rather than the developmental aspects of the IT systems. It is divided into *systems management* and *operations management*.

Systems management

This function deals with the general operation of all the IT systems and is not directly concerned with particular applications.

There are a number of separate areas within this function: *network installation*; *network administration*; *user technical support; database administration*.

Network installation and administration

Computer networks are a feature of most organisations and tasks of selecting, purchasing and installing the hardware and software, both systems and applications, may be carried out by specialist staff in this area. Staff employed in this area need to be familiar with the network operating system and its utilities. They are responsible for setting up and managing network user accounts, controlling passwords, managing printer queues, allocating and maintaining and backing up network storage and monitoring the performance of the network.

User technical support

The distribution to users, of computer resources through networks, desktop and portable computer systems has hugely expanded the need for IT user support. Users often have access to a range of different devices, such as printers, scanners, plotters and fax modems and apart from needing initial training in their use, they also require occasional support when things go wrong. Support staff may also give guidance in the use of software and help trouble-shoot problems which users will inevitably encounter at some stage. User technical support is extremely important if users are to use IT resources efficiently and for the benefit of the organisation.

Database administration

If applications are implemented through a database system, then specialist staff, known as database administrators, are employed to control access to the database by applications and ensure consistency in the use of data within it. Systems analysts and programmers involved in the development of database applications need to work closely with the responsible *database administrator* (DBA).

Operations management

This function, led by an operations manager, has three main areas of responsibility: *data control*; *data preparation*; *computer operations*; *media library*. These responsibilities relate particularly to centrally controlled applications.

Data control

Data control staff are responsible for the co-ordination and control of data flowing through the operations section. For example, data received from Salaries, to update the payroll master file and produce payslips, have to be controlled to ensure their accuracy and completeness at all stages of processing. The methods of control are described in Topic 19.

Data preparation

Batch processing systems require the transcription and encoding of data gathered from source documents, such as order forms or invoices, on to magnetic storage. The input is then effected directly from the magnetic tape or disk on which the data has been accumulated. On-line, transaction processing systems, do not usually require this data preparation stage.

Computer operations

Computer operators are responsible for the day-to-day running of the computer hardware. In the case of mainframe computer systems, their responsibilities include the loading and unloading of magnetic tape reels or magnetic disk packs, according to the on-line requirements of applications currently in use. For example, before a payroll run, the media containing the master and transaction files have to be loaded onto the relevant devices, so that they can be accessed by the computer which is running the payroll program. The computer hardware is under the control of operating system software (Topic 11) and an operator needs to communicate with the operating system regarding jobs to be processed and to deal with error conditions which may arise. A separate terminal is normally dedicated as an *operator console* and access to it is restricted both physically and through software-controlled passwords.

✍Exercises

1. Machem Ltd is a large manufacturing business. It buys in raw materials from a number of suppliers and uses the raw materials to produce its range of specialist outdoor clothing and equipment, which it sells to retailers. It has a warehouse next to the factory, to store the stocks of raw materials and finished goods.

   (i)   Explain the circumstances when Machem Ltd is a *debtor* and when it is a *creditor*.

   (ii) Explain circumstances when Machem will receive *invoices* and when it will issue them.

   (iii) List the processes involved in invoicing a retailer and settlement of the debt.

   (iv) Identify features of a typical *stock control* system which Machem Ltd could use to maintain sufficient, but not excessive levels of stock.

   (v)   Machem Ltd is planning to extend its range of products and needs to ensure that there will be sufficient demand for the new products to make a profit. As well as its production function, the company has its own research and development (R&D) and marketing departments. Suggest ways in which these three functions may co-operate to maximise Machem Ltd's chances of success.

2. Machem Ltd has its own *IT Services* function, employing systems analysts, programmers, network engineers, network administrators and user technical support assistants.

   Briefly outline the likely role of each of these categories of staff at Machem Ltd.

Role of information

In business, making decisions or taking actions without all the relevant information can be risky. For example, if a company decides to increase the price of a product because the product is selling well and ignores information that competitors have launched similar products, it is acting without all the relevant information. Similarly, fulfilling a customer order without checking their credit record risks an increase in bad (unrecoverable) debt. Information can vary in quality (Topic 2) and to provide the best possible basis for decision-making, organisations should attempt to control the quality of the information they use. If it is to act with any purpose, an organisation needs information about itself, its customers (or clients) and suppliers (if any) and the *environment* in which it operates. Environment includes influences which are external to an organisation, such as government legislation and bank lending rates. Without such information, an organisation cannot properly plan for the future (*strategic planning*), or control and monitor its present performance (*operational control*).

Strategic planning

Planning for the future is never risk-free, but with a range of appropriate information the risks of decision-making can be minimised. Suppose, for example, that a manufacturing company is planning its production output for the next month; it needs to specify the particular product mix and the number of units of each product to be manufactured. In making these decisions, it is likely to draw on two main sources of information:

❑   past sales figures;

❑   market research results.

Decisions of this nature are likely to be made at corporate (Board of Directors) level and fall into a category known as *strategic* decision-making.

Operational control

When a company monitors its production figures, its stocks of raw materials and finished products, its is controlling its day-to-day, manufacturing operations. Other functions in the company, such as sales, payroll and accounts require similar operational control. Operational information permits day-to-day control to be exerted and allows measurement of present performance, as opposed to future prospects. Common examples of operational information include:

❑   balances of customer accounts;

❑   invoices for customer sales;

❑   delivery notes for goods received from suppliers.

Periodic monitoring through Annual Accounts

The production of statements, such as a Trading and Profit and Loss Account and Balance

Sheet, provides information on the financial health of a company, at the time the statements are produced. These statements are a legal requirement for all but the smallest businesses, but are useful for periodic monitoring of performance. Accounting records are essential to effective decision-making and also produce information demanded by, for example, shareholders, the Inland Revenue or the VAT authorities. Not all information generated within or used by an organisation can be categorised as wholly operational or corporate. Information which is classed initially as operational can become part of corporate information. For example, the operational information that a customer has failed to pay their account in two successive months may result in a suspension of further credit. Subsequently, this information may be combined with details of similar customer accounts to produce a bad debts report, which results in a corporate decision to alter customer credit and debt collection strategy.

Information systems

The production of information needs to be a controlled process, exercised through the use of information systems. An organisation can be divided into a number of *internal* functions, such as Sales, Marketing, Production and Accounts and each function requires its own information systems or sub-systems. The information system for any one functional area should not be considered in isolation, because it forms only part of an organisation-wide information system. This is made particularly clear when database systems are used. The various information systems within an organisation interact and affect one another. An organisation also interacts with and is influenced by organisations, such as banks and the Inland Revenue, in the surrounding environment; these are *external* functions. Co-ordination of an organisation's separate information systems or sub-systems is essential if its common aims are to be achieved.

Information needs

To operate, different functions within an organisation need access to particular types of information, some examples of which are briefly described below.

Design specifications; before a product is manufactured a specification is produced detailing, for example, the types, qualities and quantities of required materials, physical features, performance requirements (such as for a car) and so on. Some products, such as computer software, need to include design features concerning, for example, the user interface.

Construction drawings. As the term indicates, these are used to guide the person or persons building or constructing the product. An architect produces construction drawings for the house builder to follow; design specification details are also included, so that the builder knows the types and quantities of materials.

Market research. This information is often gathered through surveys, either using questionnaires or monitoring consumer buying patterns. A company should carry out market research before beginning the production or sale of a new product in its range.

Advertising is essential to any organisation wishing to promote its image or product range. Advertising uses market research information to target the most appropriate areas of the population. For example, market research may indicate that a product is most likely to be bought by professional people living in the south of England; advertising can be directed, perhaps through mails shots, to that section of the population.

Sales orders detail customer order requirements, including item details, quantities and delivery dates; *purchase orders* detail the organisation's purchase requirements from suppliers.

Payments and receipts. These may relate to sales orders or purchase orders. Receipts are amounts received from debtors. Payments are made by a business to settle debts with creditors (suppliers to the business).

Transport requirements. This information will detail, for example, a goods list, the delivery address, special requirements, such as refrigeration and possibly the route to be taken.

Information flow diagrams

Figure 58.1 illustrates some information flows within a typical manufacturing and wholesaling organisation.

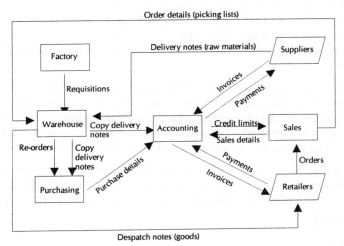

Figure 58.1. *Information flows between functions*

An examination of Figure 58.1 shows that each functional area is dependent on one or more other areas for the information it needs to operate. For example, to charge the retail outlets (their customers) for the goods supplied, the Accounting function requires the necessary sales information, which is supplied by the Sales function. The information allows the Accounting function to prepare the necessary invoices to send to customers. Similarly, Purchasing must be kept informed by the Warehouse (stock control) of raw materials which need re-ordering from suppliers, to replenish stocks.

These examples of *operational* information allow day-to-day decisions to be made on the operation of the business. To keep the diagram fairly simple, certain vital functions, such as Production Control and Marketing, are not shown. Obviously, their inclusion would increase the number of information flows and the complexity of the diagram.

The information flows shown in Figure 58.1 are all 'triggered' by *events*. For example:

(i)   a customer order is generated when a customer orders goods;

(ii)   credit limit details flow from Accounting to Sales, when a customer order is checked;

(iii)   an invoice is raised when goods are despatched to a customer;

(iv)   a payment to a supplier is triggered when the invoice payment falls due.

ICT support of information flows

To illustrate the role of ICT in managing information flow, we use a simple example of a small electrical company, Wingrove Electrical Ltd, based on the outskirts of London. It employs 38 people and produces electrical components for use in central heating equipment. The following examples of activities and information flows are used to show the potential benefits of using IT.

An enquiry from a potential buyer

A telephone enquiry from a potential customer is received by the company's telephonist, who attempts to connect the caller with the company sales manager, who is out of the office. She makes a note of the caller's name and the nature of the enquiry and promises to pass these details on to the sales manager when she returns to the office. Unfortunately, the paper with the message is lost and so is the potential order. Clearly, the system could have been improved by a number of methods.

If Wingrove had a local area network, the telephonist could have obtained sufficient product information to meet the initial enquiry of the potential buyer. The message could have been transmitted through the electronic mail system, for the sales manager to access when she returned. If the sales manager used a notebook computer, she could download such messages remotely, through the telecommunications or mobile phone network.

It is also possible that the customer's enquiry could have been satisfied through the company web site. Information on products, prices, anticipated delivery times, technical support details and the answers to frequently asked questions (FAQs) can be stored and kept up to date through customer support pages.

Receipt of an order

Wingrove receives a substantial order by post. The manual procedures involve copying the order, sending a copy to Accounting and a copy attached to a 'job sheet' to Production. When the order is completed and despatched, Accounting will invoice the customer and await payment. Unfortunately, when the customer eventually pays, he submits a cheque for an incorrect amount, but the clerk fails to notice that the amount on the invoice and the amount on the cheque do not agree; as a result, he processes the invoice as paid. Wingrove has thus lost some of its profit.

The company could improve its financial control by installing a computerised order processing and invoice verification system. As each order is received into the company, the appropriate details, such as customer, item, quantity, price and so on, are entered into its computer, which automatically generates an invoice, statements and increasingly harshly worded reminders, until the customer settles the debt. When the cheque arrives, its value is also entered and the program automatically checks to ensure that the amount matches both the original price quoted and the invoice value. As protection against the miskeying of the cheque amount, a further check involves the automatic reconciliation, each month, of totals for paid and unpaid invoices.

Production of a quotation

Wingrove's managing director is informed that Birmingham City Council is intending to replace the central heating systems in all its public buildings, over the next three years and is seeking tenders for the component parts of the system. Wingrove would very much like to gain the contract and decide to submit a detailed quotation document. The quotation is 28 pages long and contains an extensive amount of technical detail, as well as product specifications, prices and delivery details. Typed manually, reference would have to be made to numerous files for component specifications and prices and the inevitable modifications to the tender would involve extensive re-typing. The following improvements are possible.

Using a word processor and quotation template, the task can be completed much more quickly. Layout alterations and editing can easily be done before a final copy is printed. A high quality printer, possibly with colour facility, will contribute to a highly professional appearance and improve the image of the company. Component specification and price data can be imported from the company's database of such information, directly into the document. If speed is important, the document could be faxed or e-mailed to Birmingham City Council.

ICT applications for strategic decision-making

Management information systems (MIS)

Although computers can perform routine processing tasks very efficiently, it is generally recognised that limiting a computer's use to the processing of operational information constitutes a waste of computer power. An MIS is designed to make use of the computer's power of selection and analysis to produce useful management information. An MIS has a number of key features:

- ❑   it produces information beyond that required for routine data processing;

- ❑   timing of information production is critical;

- ❑   the information it produces is an aid to decision-making;

- ❑   it is usually based on the database concept (Topic 22).

The claims for MIS are sometimes excessive. It is rarely the complete answer to all a company's information needs, but when successfully implemented, it provides a valuable information advantage over competitors.

Decision support systems (DSS)

A DSS aims to provide a more flexible decision tool than that supplied by a MIS which tends to produce information in an anticipated, pre-defined form and as such, does not allow managers to make ad hoc requests for information. DSS tend to be narrower in scope than MIS, often making use of general-purpose software packages. Examples of DSS include electronic spreadsheets, such as Microsoft Excel and relational database management systems such as Access and Paradox. Additionally, *financial modelling* (Topic 61) and statistical packages are considered to be DSS tools. A major benefit is the independence they allow for information control by individual managers and executives. When, for example, a sales manager requires a report on sales figures for the last three months, a microcomputer with database package may provide the report more quickly than a centralised data processing department.

✍️Exercises

1. Study the information flow diagram in Figure 58.1 and answer the following questions.

   (i) When a customer places an order with Sales, to which function must they refer for a credit limit?

   (ii) When a customer order is accepted why are the details passed to Accounting?

   (iii) What information does accounting need from the Warehouse function before paying an invoice sent from a supplier?

   (iv) What use does the Warehouse function make of the requisitions it receives from the Factory?

Before we look at some of the training requirements and approaches, it should be helpful to consider some of the effects which the introduction of new ICT systems may have on different categories of staff. The effects on staff within an organisation will be extremely varied and the degree of effect will depend on the extent of involvement individual staff have with a new ICT system. Consider the following situation in a commercial trading organisation:

(i)　　Assume that Sales Order Processing (SOP) is computerised and that the output includes Picking Lists (these are lists of products and quantities of each that need to be retrieved from the warehouse to satisfy customer orders).

(ii)　　Assume further that Stock Control in the warehouse is not computerised but that the staff will receive computer printed picking lists.

(iii)　　Assume finally that the Accounting function is not computerised. Staff in Accounting will receive sales details on computer printout from SOP from which they will produce invoices to send to customers.

Effects on clerical staff

The staff in these three departments, SOP, Stock Control and Accounting are all affected by computerisation but to varying degrees. Least effected are staff in Stock Control and Accounting who only receive computer output. They have to become familiar with the reading and interpretation of computer printouts. This is not a difficult task, but one which requires some adjustment on the part of staff. At a more complex level, the staff in SOP are more significantly effected. The effects will require education and training for staff in the various parts of the computerised process as follows.

Preparation of input data

Computerisation imposes a discipline on clerical and management procedures. To deal with data correctly it needs to be presented accurately and in a form suitable for input to the computer. Usually, prior to data entry, all source data, (in this case customer orders) have to be recorded on standard, specially designed *source documents* which match the order of data requested by the computer software. For example, if the first item of data required by the computer is an order number, then this should be the first data item on the source document. The second data item required should be next and so on. Therefore, however the orders are received, by telephone, by word of mouth at the sales desk or by post, the first job is to transcribe the details onto the source document. Such tasks need to be documented in office procedure manuals and staff need to be instructed in their proper execution.

Data entry

Staff involved in this task require keyboard (and possibly mouse) skills and training will be needed in the day-to-day operation of the software. These include 'signing on' with codes and passwords, familiarity with computer screen prompts and the correct responses to make, dealing with simple error conditions when an incorrect key is pressed and correcting or editing keying errors during data entry.

Where the volume of data entry is such that a member of staff can be fully occupied with this task there are health and safety considerations to be examined. There are for example recommended guidelines concerning time limits for personnel operating VDU's. Headaches and eye strain can result from prolonged viewing of a computer screen. Where the volume of data entry is limited, the specialist staff may not be justified and a number of clerical staff with a variety of duties may have to 'take their turn' at the keyboard. Thus more staff will need some basic training in the use of the system.

Effects on managerial staff

The day-to-day clerical routines will not usually directly involve managerial staff although this will depend on the size of the organisation and the hierarchical staffing structure. However, their necessary involvement in the development, introduction and implementation of an ICT system and their responsibilities for the efficient running of their departments mean that the effects of computerisation on the working lives of managers can be even more emphatic than the effects on clerical staff. To continue the Sales Order Processing example, the manager of that department may:

(i)   be closely involved in a consultative role with systems analysts in the analysis of the old manual system and the design of the new ICT system;

(ii)   have to maintain communication with the staff in the SOP department to ensure that:

(a)   their views are taken into account;

(b)   envisaged changes are reported to them.

This communication is vital if the staff are to feel 'involved'.

(iii)   require some computer education and training. A prerequisite of communication between staff is that the manager has developed some computer 'awareness' and computer 'literacy' sufficiently to understand the role of the computer and the changes in procedures within his department which are necessary. A desktop or notebook computer is also likely to be an essential tool for a manager.

This educational or training need has to be satisfied if the manager is to be effective in the role of ensuring that the operational procedures are being followed and that efficiency is being maintained. Without knowledge of the powers and limitations of an ICT system a manager cannot assess its effectiveness or suggest improvements.

Other computer applications involving management

There are a number of computer applications which make use of 'content free' software. This refers to software which is not fixed to one application or type of data. Such software packages are available for spreadsheet work, and database or file management.

Managers and executive staff will wish to support their decision-making with the use of computer-based decision support systems (DSS) and management information systems (MIS). For example, spreadsheet packages can be used for the preparation of cash budgets and sales forecasting with the added facility of generating 'what if' projections. So a cash budget based on current and anticipated figures of cash due in and out of the organisation over the next few months, can be quickly modified to present the results of an alternative strategy of say, an injection of cash from a bank loan. Database packages can be used by managers for their own local information store on which they can make enquiry. In addition, where a database is held centrally, a manager could access files through the use of a Query Language (Topic 39). To use such a language requires training, similar to that required by a programmer albeit at a simpler level.

The efficient and effective use of such packages demands a high level of knowledge and skill which will probably require some sort of training programme, perhaps with the software supplier.

Effects on managers not yet involved

The use of such facilities by one departmental manager or the issue of a general directive from top management within an organisation will place pressure on other managers to follow suit. Of course the pressure may be in the other direction where departmental managers wish to get involved and pressurise top management for training and the introduction of new ICT systems.

Effects on functional relationships

ICT affects the ways in which different functions such as Sales and Accounts relate to each other, in terms of how information flows between them and the activities in which each is engaged.

Without computers, the Sales and Accounting departments would maintain their own files. Transaction data such as a customer order would be used to update each of the department's files separately. Each department would be responsible for maintaining its own files thus creating separate autonomous areas within an organisation, each led by a Head of Department or similar executive staff member. Each department would tend to have its own working practices and provided information was presented to other departments in a form they could use, there would perhaps be little need for change.

Computerisation imposes discipline and standardisation. Information flows between departments may have to pass through a computer process and although the user requirements should take priority over what is convenient for the computer, some modifications will need to be made to the ways in which data is presented to the computer for processing. Earlier in this Topic, the example was used of customer order details being transcribed onto Source Documents designed to be compatible with the order of input to the computer. A feature of manual systems is the separateness of related operations. For example a customer order will be used to update the customer file, the stock file and to produce a customer invoice in separate operations carried out in each separate functional area. A computerised system could allow these tasks to be carried out with a single input of the data.

Inter-departmental conflict

Organisations are formed to allow a rational and co-ordinated approach to the achievement of certain aims which may be the provision of a service or product for which there is a profitable market. The problem is that organisations are made up of individuals who may not always be rational. Each individual has his or her own ambitions, fears and emotions. Management styles may well stem from such personal characteristics. This may lead to competition between department heads rather than co-operation in achieving the common aims of the organisation as a whole.

Personal fears

To many people, computerisation is a venture into the unknown and many individuals feel threatened because they have insufficient knowledge or experience to give them adequate control over their own futures. Being made to look a fool, or worse, the possibility of being made redundant by computerisation can be the main obstacle to the acceptance of change.

Resistance to change

Sometimes because of inter-departmental rivalry or simply incompetence, a manager may keep secret certain facts which computerisation may make available. This is another reason for resistance to the introduction of ICT systems. Managers are forced to change their style of management because of the introduction of computers and may attempt to resist the threat to their power, by doing less than they might to make the innovation work and by constantly finding fault, without making constructive suggestions.

The Enthusiast

An alternative reaction, which is usually irrational, is the whole-hearted, eager acceptance of computerisation as being the ideal solution to every problem. There are many circumstances where computerisation is inappropriate or where the immediately available standard package is far from ideal. Because organisations are made up of individuals, computer systems should be designed with the full co-operation of management and staff, enlisting their help wherever possible so as to take proper account of their individual or at least departmental information needs.

Effects on management style

Many managers work intuitively and have confidence in their own methods which have served them well. Such 'flying by the seat of the pants' often leads to a natural derision for any system designed by 'experts' and 'theorists'. Of course such confidence is usually based on previous success and the specialist in computer systems will often be young and, as far as the experienced manager is concerned, 'wet behind the ears'. Thus the computer specialist may have a difficult job in convincing existing management that a new ICT system will be an improvement on the old. The systems analyst will need to have the interpersonal skills to deal with such resistance. One feature of ICT systems is the increase in the volume of information available to a manager and the speed with which it can be obtained. A resulting danger is that the manager may become too concerned with the low level decisions within his department, thus interfering with the responsibilities of lower levels of management or supervisory staff. The problem can be more serious if it extends upwards from departmental to corporate management. Information which should have been seen by the department manager may have been seen by the chief general manager first. Too much information and the wrong type of information can be worse than insufficient information.

Training requirements and options

The education and training of an ICT system's users is vital if it is to be operated correctly and the full benefits are to be obtained. Management staff need to be educated, so that they can recognise the ways in which the system can meet their information requirements. Generally, managerial staff do not carry out routine data entry, but often make use of computers, for example, to produce budgets, gather ad hoc reports and communicate through e-mail. The training requirements of managerial staff will differ from those of operational staff.

The main categories of staff requiring training include:

- ❑ management;
- ❑ clerical;
- ❑ data control and data preparation;
- ❑ computer operations.

By the time a system is ready to 'go live', all involved staff should be competent to operate it efficiently. They should also have sufficient knowledge to assess its effectiveness, that is, answer the question, "Does it do what it is supposed to reliably and at the right time?".

Deciding when to carry out training can be difficult. If too early, some staff will have forgotten what they have been taught by the time the system is introduced. If too late, staff may feel panicked, because they have not been properly prepared. Training programmes should, as far as is possible, be designed to suit the working conditions of staff and the time-scale for implementation. It may be that residential courses will be needed for supervisory staff, who can then carry out in-house training of subordinate staff. This latter task may necessitate some staff working overtime, because the existing system may still have to be operated prior to implementation and for some time afterwards, during a period of parallel running (Topic 42). Alternative training methods make use of computer-based training (CBT) and with modern multimedia techniques they can be extremely effective. The Internet can allow staff to be trained remotely by being given access to CBT systems provided through an organisation's intranet (Topic 52). More personalised training can be provided through video conferencing.

✍️Exercises

1. When a new computerised system is to be implemented, it is important that staff are *trained* to use it effectively.
   (i)   Identify three topics you would expect to be covered on a course for new *data entry* staff
   (ii) Identify two topics you would expect to be part of a course for *managerial* staff.

Part 3

Applications development

Sections

Modelling and simulation

Topics

The term *modelling* is used in information technology for computer applications which, for example, are used to investigate, analyse or plan a complex activity, or to *simulate* a complex process. Some models are concerned with investigating financial systems using a software tool such as a *spreadsheet* program. For example, a manufacturing company might use a spreadsheet-based model to determine the minimum number of items the company must produce in order to make a profit (see Topic 61). Other computer models are concerned with representing physical systems. For example, before a new chemical plant is built, its designers often will first model the complex arrangement of pipes and other equipment using a 3-D computer graphics program, and also simulate its operation with other types of software. In this way many potential problems can be identified and solved before construction work is started. This Topic begins by describing the nature and purpose of mathematical models and simulations. Some of the areas that have benefited from modelling and simulation are also discussed.

Mathematical models

Physical models are usually simplified versions of actual objects or objects that may be constructed at some later date. Thus, a car manufacturer might produce a scaled-down model of a new car to investigate its wind-resistance characteristics. Though the model accurately represents the shape of the car, it is much easier to construct than a full-sized working version. Producing a model therefore provides a convenient and cheap method of investigating certain aspects of the final product. A *mathematical model* takes modelling a stage further: it provides a means of investigating something without the need to make a physical model. Mathematical models are symbolic representations of things that we want to know more about. For example, a mathematical model of the distance travelled by a body accelerating from rest is

$$s = \frac{1}{2}at^2$$

where s is the distance travelled, a is the acceleration of the body and t is the time period. This mathematical model now allows us to investigate the effects of different accelerations and different time periods on the distance travelled by the body, without having to build a working model. Using this model it can be predicted that a body uniformly accelerating at 5 metres/sec^2 for ten seconds will have travelled

$$\frac{1}{2} \times 5 \times 10^2 \text{ metres,}$$

that is, 250 metres. Of course not all mathematical models are as simple as this. Some mathematical models attempt to describe much more complex things such as human behaviour or weather patterns. Such complex models involve defining the relationships between the many variables of the system being modelled, and they almost invariably require the use of very powerful computers to investigate them.

Simulation

In computer science, *simulation* refers to the use of computers to model and investigate systems which involve some changing process. Thus a computer simulation will generally incorporate a mathematical model of the system of interest. The purpose of a computer simulation often is to enable experimental measurements to be made or to predict behaviour. Simulation can provide an experimental system for designers to investigate behaviour under a variety of different circumstances, or it may be used to provide a teaching aid for the system being simulated.

The prime reason for developing a simulation is that the cost of experimenting with the actual system is prohibitive, and since simulations are themselves expensive, there must be very sound economical reasons for justifying their use. For example, it is much cheaper and quicker to test a large number of design variations of a nuclear reactor by using a simulation rather than by building prototypes. More possible reasons for simulating a complex system are:

❏ *Testing* - it is necessary to test the system to destruction, that is, identify the factors that will cause it to fail and a complex device might be too expensive to use for the investigation.

❏ *Safety* - it is too dangerous or expensive to use the actual equipment. An example is teaching an aircraft pilot to respond to a range of emergency situations.

❏ *Prediction* - an accurate model is needed of an existing system so that its future behaviour can be predicted accurately. A good example of this is weather forecasting.

❏ *Speed and flexibility* - the system might require frequent modification and development. For example, in control systems electronically-based instruments can be simulated by a computer. These so-called virtual instruments allow devices, such as meters and indicators, and other electronic components, to be represented by software which is cheaper and easier to modify or replace than physical devices.

Simulation parameters

A mathematical model of a system usually consists of a linked set of formulae in which the result of one formula may affect others. These formulae will generally use one or more key factors, or *parameters*; altering the value of a parameter will generally alter the overall behaviour of the system. A number of different types of parameters can be identified:

❏ *Controllable inputs*. These are factors, or *variables*, which are under the direct control of the system designers. For example, in a stock control simulation where items of stock are continually being sold to customers and received from suppliers, two of the controllable inputs are likely to be the re-order quantity and re-order level. In a traffic lights simulation, the timing of the red/green cycle is also under the control of the system designers.

❏ *Non-controllable inputs*. These are factors which are not under the direct control of the system designers. For example, in a simulation of a supermarket checkout queue, the arrival rate of customers is an input variable which cannot be controlled, but there will be some statistical information regarding its characteristics. Similarly in a traffic lights simulation, the arrival and departure rates of vehicles at the junction are not directly under the control of the designers. These types of variables frequently have characteristics which can be described using probability.

❏ *Seasonal variations.* Some factors, again not under the control of the system designers, can vary significantly according to the time of day, the day of the week, or the season of the year. For instance, traffic density is usually heavier in the morning when people are travelling to work and in the evening when people are returning home, than at other times of the day. Supermarkets often attract more customers at the weekend and just before bank holidays, than on other days.

Monte Carlo simulation

One common technique used in simulation is called the *Monte Carlo* method which uses random numbers to solve problems. The method is particularly suitable for problems which involve statistical uncertainty. For example, when you throw a die, you are never certain which number is going to show: there is an equal probability of each of the number 1 to 6 appearing. A computer program could be used to generate a random number in the range 1 to 6 in order to simulate a die being thrown. This is a simple application of the Monte Carlo method.

Most high-level programming languages and spreadsheet programs provide random number generators. However, the random number function usually will return a fraction between 0 and 1, but this can be converted into the required range quite simply. For instance, if we multiply the random number by 6, add one and ignore the fractional part of the number, we will have a random number between 1 and 6. Thus if the random number was 0.3245 then when multiplied by 6 it gives 1.9470. Adding 1 gives 2.9470, and ignoring the fractional part gives us our random number 2. The queue simulation example in Topic 61 uses random numbers produced by a spreadsheet to simulate traffic arriving at traffic lights.

Applications of modelling

Mathematical models and simulation are used in many areas including:

Marketing

This involves activities related to getting goods from the producer to the consumer. Marketing research involves the use of surveys, tests, and statistical studies to analyse consumer trends, to identify profitable markets for products or services and to produce sales predictions. Such research and forecasts require mathematical models of social behaviour and consumers' needs for various products. The cost implications of predicted demands for goods can also be modelled so that a company can be fully prepared to cope with the production, distribution and sale of the products.

Sociology

Sociology is a social science that deals with the study of human social relations or group life. Quantitative sociology, which attempts to analyse sociological phenomena using mathematics, ranges from the presentation of large amounts of descriptive statistical data to the use of advanced mathematical models and computer simulations of social processes. One popular area of investigation is identification of the factors that are mainly responsible for people succeeding or failing in their chosen occupations.

Social psychology

Social psychology is a branch of psychology concerned with the scientific study of the behaviour of individuals as influenced, directly or indirectly, by social factors. Social psychologists are interested in the thinking, emotions, desires, and judgements of individuals, as well as in their outward behaviour. Numerous kinds of research methods and techniques are being used in social psychology. In recent years accurate mathematical models of social behaviour have been used increasingly in psychological studies. Such models allow predictions of social behaviour to be made, given a system of social relationships.

Educational psychology

This involves the application of scientific method to the study of the behaviour of people in instructional settings. Different theories of learning help educational psychologists understand, predict, and control human behaviour. For example, educational psychologists have worked out mathematical models of learning that predict the probability of a student making a correct response to a multiple-choice question. These mathematical theories are used to design computerised instruction in reading, mathematics, and second-language learning.

Weather forecasting

Weather forecasting involves reporting, predicting, and studying the weather, including temperature, moisture, barometric pressure, and wind speed and direction. In addition to their regular and special services to the public, weather services conduct research projects. In their meteorological investigations, primarily concerned with forecasting techniques and storm behaviour, these agencies make use of the findings from studies of mathematical modelling of the general circulation of the atmosphere, advances in radar meteorology, high-speed computer methods, and earth-orbiting artificial satellites.

Fluid mechanics

This is a physical science dealing with the action of fluids at rest or in motion, and with applications and devices in engineering using fluids. Fluid mechanics is basic to such diverse fields as aeronautics, chemical, civil, and mechanical engineering, meteorology, naval architecture, and oceanography. Turbulent flows cannot be analysed solely from computed predictions and depend on a mixture of experimental data and mathematical models for their analysis, with much of modern fluid-mechanics research still being devoted to better models of turbulence. The nature and complexity of turbulent flow can be observed as cigarette smoke rises into very still air. At first it rises in a stable streamline motion but after some distance it becomes unstable and breaks up into an intertwining eddy pattern.

Population biology

Population biology is the study of populations of animals and plants. A population is a group of interbreeding organisms in a specific region - for example, the members of a species of fish in a lake. Populations are analysed in terms of their variability, density, and stability, and of the environmental and other processes and circumstances that affect these characteristics. Among such key features of a given population are birth and death rates; the distribution of ages and sexes; behavioural patterns of competition and co-operation; predator-prey, host-parasite, and other relationships with different species; food supplies and other environmental considerations; and migration patterns. To analyse populations biologists try to develop mathematical models of the group under study that incorporate as many of these variables as possible. Such models enable scientists to predict what effect a change in any one factor may have on a population as a whole.

Catastrophe theory

This is the term for an attempt to develop a mathematical modelling system for dealing with abruptly changing natural events. One such physical 'catastrophe', for example, could be an avalanche resulting from a gradual build-up of snow. In the area of human relations, a 'catastrophe' could be someone suddenly losing his or her temper after being patient for a long period. Catastrophe theory was primarily intended to be useful for describing events in the biological and social sciences.

Science education

Laboratory experiments to determine the characteristics of falling bodies, colliding balls, pendulums and projectiles can all be simulated quite easily by a computer. Students can investigate the effects of changing various parameters such as the weight of the pendulum, or the speed of colliding objects, or the angle at which an object is projected, or any one of a number of other factors that affect the experiment of interest.

Medical education

Medical diagnosis is a very complex activity and very difficult to learn. Though the typical symptoms of most ailments are well-known, the manner in which a given illness manifests itself varies from patient to patient. This means that physicians must acquire the ability to assign the correct level of importance to each recognisable symptom in order to make a correct diagnosis.

Computers can help with this task by simulating illnesses and associated symptoms. The computer model of the illness can be set up so that the symptoms vary each time the same illness is simulated. The computer might present a case study of a patient, supplying the student with the type of information gained from tests and by questioning the patient. The student is then required to arrive at a diagnosis of the ailment and suggest appropriate treatment. The student's diagnosis and suggested treatment can then be compared with the correct ones stored in the computer in order to provide feedback concerning the accuracy of the student's analysis. In this way, students can very quickly 'experience' many different manifestations of a particular illness, a situation which could be very difficult to organise using actual patients.

Computers can also be used to show the effects of drugs on the human body. How long a drug remains active in the bloodstream and the concentration of the drug after repeated doses are very important factors. However, because of the complexity of the human body and the great number of factors which contribute to the effects of a particular drug, predicting the effects of a drug is very difficult. Computer simulations which use complex theoretical models of the human body can allow students to experiment with typical drug dosages and observe the resulting effects. A common approach is to present the student with a number of screens of text and/or graphical information. After this information has been assimilated, the student is then in a position to understand the purpose of the simulation and what information must be supplied. By providing typical drug characteristics and dosages, the student can observe the predicted affect of the drug as simulated by the computer. Finally, the student completes a multiple-choice test which is marked by the computer. Any weaknesses in the student's understanding of the material can thus be identified and remedied by suggesting that the student repeats certain parts of the simulation program. With the enormous increase in desk top computing power over recent years, it is now feasible to produce computer programs which use graphics to allow students to explore the human body in great detail. Software simulates the structure and function of the nervous, circulatory, immune and other systems of the body using multimedia. Though they are not used as replacements for actually dissecting cadavers, these products can give students a useful grounding in physiology and anatomy.

Queuing theory

This deals with the analysis of the waiting lines that occur in many areas of modern life. Whenever something is in demand, there is the possibility of a queue of some description forming, resulting in restricted access to resources, or losses in time, money and patience. Efforts to avoid and control congestion are therefore of great interest to providers of services which can cause queues, and this has led to the study of waiting lines using mathematical models and simulation. An area which has benefited greatly from queuing theory is that of time-shared computer systems in which each user is given a small amount of processing time and users waiting their turn are put in a queue; the computer decides which job will be serviced next and for how long using a scheduling algorithm based on queuing theory.

Instrumentation

Computer measurement systems frequently involve monitoring a physical system, analysing the data gathered and displaying the results. Traditionally, many such systems have used hardware components, such as filters, frequency analysers, meters and LED displays, but computers can be used to replace many of these devices. *Virtual instruments* allow many physical devices to be simulated using a computer. A virtual instrument uses software components to

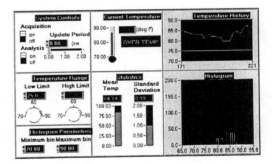

Figure 60.1. *Virtual instrument*

process the data measured externally to the computer, and to present results of processing using realistic representations of instrument panels containing meters, switches, digital and other types of displays. (See Figure 60.1). Graphically based programming languages allow complex processing tasks to be programmed by connecting together symbols which represent electronic devices. The advantage of this approach is that new devices can be constructed, tested and modified without the need to produce costly, purpose-built hardware devices.

Three-dimensional models

Many software products are available for simulating the structure of solid objects. These programs allow designers to create three-dimensional drawings of objects which can be viewed from

Figure 60.2.
Three-dimensional model

any angle, rotated, and modified using a wide variety of software tools. Many 3D drawing pro-grams also allow objects to be animated. For example, detailed computer models of buildings are used as the basis of *fly-throughs* in which a simulated camera navigates through the build-ing, going from room to room, zooming in and out. Simulations such as this, animated or otherwise, allow complex objects to be visualised prior to production, thus speeding up and re-ducing the design process.

Exercises

See Exercises following Topic 61.

In this Topic we look at the use of spreadsheet for performing a break-even analysis to investigate a manufacturing business, to simulate a stock control system and to simulate traffic arriving at traffic lights. Here we limit explanations to special functions that are required for simulation purposes and to the formulas that are required for the various calculations involved.

Financial planning - break-even analysis

The prime objective of most organisations is the achievement of profit. In order to make a profit the organisation must earn sufficient revenue from the sale of its products to exceed the costs that it has incurred in operating and producing. It is usually a relatively simple task to calculate revenue: simply determine the number of goods which have been sold and multiply this quantity by the price per item. The calculation of cost is slightly more complicated owing to the fact that the organisation incurs a variety of different costs in producing its products. *Fixed costs* remain constant irrespective of the number of items produced. Examples include rent on the premises or local council rates. Therefore, as production rises the fixed cost per item reduces. Other costs, however, increase with production. These are called *variable costs*. Raw materials are an example of variable costs since as more items are produced, more raw materials are required. Combining fixed and variable costs gives the organisation its total costs and it is these which must be exceeded by its total revenue before it can make a profit. Clearly then, an organisation may make a loss if its output is low, but as it produces and sells more it will eventually move through a *break-even point* into profit. As the name suggests, the break-even point is where the organisation neither makes a loss nor a profit – it simply breaks even. Management are obviously very interested to know the level of production required to exceed the break-even point and make a profit. Combining the revenue and cost figures in order to determine the break-even point is called *break-even analysis*, and a graphical representation of the figures is termed a *break-even chart*. An example of a break-even analysis and the equivalent chart are shown in Figures 61.1 and 61.2, respectively.

PRODUCED	FIXED COSTS	E COSTS	TOTAL COSTS	REVENUE	PROFIT
0	500	0	500	0	500
100	500	200	700	270	430
200	500	300	800	540	260
300	500	350	850	810	40
400	500	450	950	1080	-130
500	500	600	1100	1350	-250
600	500	800	1300	1620	-320
700	500	1050	1550	1890	-340
800	500	1350	1850	2160	-310
900	500	1700	2200	2430	-230
1000	500	2100	2600	2700	-100

Figure 61.1. *Break-even analysis model*

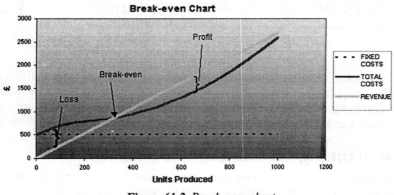

Figure 61.2. *Break-even chart*

The formulas used in the spreadsheet are shown in Figure 61.3.

	D	E	F	G	H	I
7	UNITS PRODUCED	FIXED COSTS	VARIABLE COSTS	TOTAL COSTS	REVENUE	PROFIT
8	0	=$G$4	0	=E8+F8	=D8*$G$5	=G8-H8
9	100	=$G$4	200	=E9+F9	=D9*$G$5	=G9-H9
10	200	=$G$4	300	=E10+F10	=D10*$G$5	=G10-H10
11	300	=$G$4	350	=E11+F11	=D11*$G$5	=G11-H11
12	400	=$G$4	450	=E12+F12	=D12*$G$5	=G12-H12
13	500	=$G$4	600	=E13+F13	=D13*$G$5	=G13-H13
14	600	=$G$4	800	=E14+F14	=D14*$G$5	=G14-H14
15	700	=$G$4	1050	=E15+F15	=D15*$G$5	=G15-H15
16	800	=$G$4	1350	=E16+F16	=D16*$G$5	=G16-H16
17	900	=$G$4	1700	=E17+F17	=D17*$G$5	=G17-H17
18	1000	=$G$4	2100	=E18+F18	=D18*$G$5	=G18-H18

Figure 61.3 . *Formulas for break-even analysis in Figure 61.1*

The UNITS PRODUCED and VARIABLE COSTS columns of the spreadsheet are constant values. FIXED COSTS are copied from the Fixed Costs(FC) parameter cell. The TOTAL COSTS column is the sum of FIXED COSTS and VARIABLE COSTS. The REVENUE is calculated by multiplying the units produced by the Unit Cost(UC) parameter. Finally, the profit is found by subtracting the TOTAL COSTS from the REVENUE.

The break-even chart, shown in Figure 61.2, graphs the three costs and the revenue figures; the break-even point is where the TOTAL COSTS curve crosses the REVENUE line. Profit occurs to the right of the break-even point, and you can see that in this case, when the fixed costs are at £500 and the selling price is £2.70, the break-even point occurs when just over 300 items are produced. Interestingly, the graph also shows that maximum profit occurs when between 600 and 700 items are produced and that at about 1000 items the company again breaks even.

Stock control simulation

Suppose that Agros is a large retail outlet which sells a wide range of household materials. It has a computerised stock control, or *inventory*, system which deals with obtaining, storing and supplying the goods it offers to the general public. Agros provides free catalogues containing descriptions of items which customers can obtain by visiting one of their outlets. The items shown in the catalogue are kept in a warehouse attached to the outlet. It is of vital importance to Agros to ensure that it has a full range of items in stock so that customers can immediately obtain those that they require.

If an item is out of stock, the potential customer might decide to shop elsewhere thus causing Agros to lose the sale, and possibly future sales too. Agros attempts to prevent this situation by ordering quantities of those items that are in danger of being sold out. However, the time taken for the items to arrive from the suppliers may be several days, by which time the goods still could have sold out. Moreover, if the demand for an item is overestimated, and there are a large number of the item in the warehouse, Agros again loses money because each item incurs a warehouse storage cost.

Agros must try to achieve a balance between over-ordering and under-ordering goods. This would be an easy problem to solve if Agros knew exactly what the demand for a particular item is likely to be at any one time, but unfortunately this is never the case. Possibly the best prediction of demand will still involve a large amount of uncertainty. For example, past experience might provide an estimate of the average demand per day for an item, but the actual demand on a particular day will probably fluctuate fairly randomly.

A possible means of investigating this type of system is therefore a Monte Carlo simulation in which demand is simulated using a random number generator such as that described in the previous example. Before showing how a spreadsheet can be used for such a simulation, a number of terms commonly used in stock control systems, are described.

Demand – the quantity of a product that customers are willing to purchase.

Opening stock – the number of items of stock immediately available for purchase at the start of trading on any day.

Closing stock – the number of items of stock that remain in the outlet at the close of trading on any particular day.

Re-order quantity – the number of items of stock ordered from a supplier at any one time.

Re-order level – the minimum number of items held in stock before the item is re-ordered. As soon as the level of stock reaches this level, or drops below it, the re-order quantity is ordered from the supplier.

Carrying costs – the cost of storing an item waiting to be sold.

Stock out costs – the financial loss incurred when the demand for an item exceeds the stock level. In other words, a company loses money when it cannot supply an item to a customer because that item is out of stock. The term *Loss of Goodwill* also applies to this type of loss, because the disappointed customer might not use the outlet in the future.

Order costs – the cost to the company of making an order or a re-order quantity of a product; this in addition to the actual cost of buying the items from the supplier. Each time an order is generated, there is an order cost.

Lead time – this is the time it takes to receive an item from the supplier once the order has been generated.

The simulation shown in Figure 61.4 illustrates the effects of the stock control parameters, shown at the top of the spreadsheet, over a period of fourteen days.

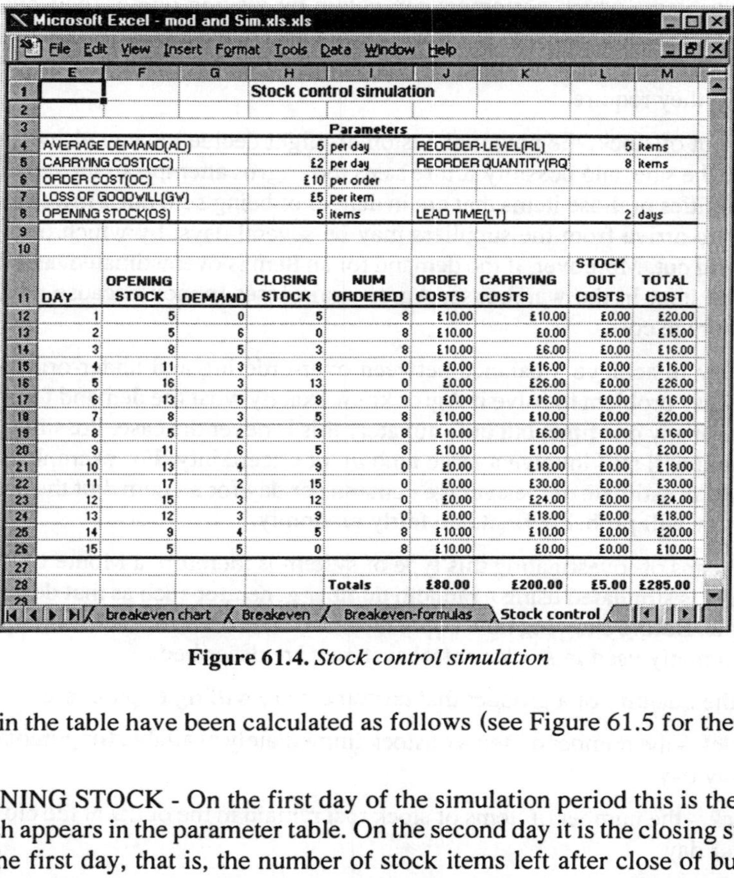

Microsoft Excel - mod and Sim.xls.xls

File Edit View Insert Format Tools Data Window Help

Stock control simulation

Parameters

AVERAGE DEMAND(AD)	5	per day	REORDER-LEVEL(RL)	5	items
CARRYING COST(CC)	£2	per day	REORDER QUANTITY(RQ	8	items
ORDER COST(OC)	£10	per order			
LOSS OF GOODWILL(GW)	£5	per item			
OPENING STOCK(OS)	5	items	LEAD TIME(LT)	2	days

DAY	OPENING STOCK	DEMAND	CLOSING STOCK	NUM ORDERED	ORDER COSTS	CARRYING COSTS	STOCK OUT COSTS	TOTAL COST
1	5	0	5	8	£10.00	£10.00	£0.00	£20.00
2	5	6	0	8	£10.00	£0.00	£5.00	£15.00
3	8	5	3	8	£10.00	£6.00	£0.00	£16.00
4	11	3	8	0	£0.00	£16.00	£0.00	£16.00
5	16	3	13	0	£0.00	£26.00	£0.00	£26.00
6	13	5	8	0	£0.00	£16.00	£0.00	£16.00
7	8	3	5	8	£10.00	£10.00	£0.00	£20.00
8	5	2	3	8	£10.00	£6.00	£0.00	£16.00
9	11	6	5	8	£10.00	£10.00	£0.00	£20.00
10	13	4	9	0	£0.00	£18.00	£0.00	£18.00
11	17	2	15	0	£0.00	£30.00	£0.00	£30.00
12	15	3	12	0	£0.00	£24.00	£0.00	£24.00
13	12	3	9	0	£0.00	£18.00	£0.00	£18.00
14	9	4	5	8	£10.00	£10.00	£0.00	£20.00
15	5	5	0	8	£10.00	£0.00	£0.00	£10.00
				Totals	**£80.00**	**£200.00**	**£5.00**	**£285.00**

breakeven chart / Breakeven / Breakeven-formulas / Stock control

Figure 61.4. *Stock control simulation*

The columns in the table have been calculated as follows (see Figure 61.5 for the spreadsheet formulas:

- OPENING STOCK - On the first day of the simulation period this is the value OS which appears in the parameter table. On the second day it is the closing stock value for the first day, that is, the number of stock items left after close of business the previous day. On the third and subsequent days it is the closing value for the previous day plus any stock that was ordered two days previously. Thus, for day four, the opening stock (10) is the sum of the third day's closing stock (2) and the quantity ordered on the second day (8).
- DEMAND - This is produced using a random number generator which produces a random number between half the average demand and one and a half times the average demand. For example, if the average demand is 6 items per day, a random number between 3 and 9 is generated. This represents the actual demand for the item on a particular day, and this is where the uncertainty factor is introduced.
- CLOSING STOCK - the number of items remaining in the warehouse/storeroom at close of trading on that day.

	E	F	G	H	I	J	K	L	M
11	DAY	OPENING STOCK	DEMAND	CLOSING STOCK	NUM ORDERED	ORDER COSTS	CARRYING COSTS	STOCK OUT COSTS	TOTAL COST
12	1	=OS	=INT(AD/2*(1+2*RAND()))	=IF(F12<G12,0,F12-G12)	=IF(H12<=RL,RQ,0)	=IF(I12>0,OC,0)	=H12*CC	=IF(H12<0,GW*(G12-F12),0)	=SUM(J12:L12)
13	2	=H12	=INT(AD/2*(1+2*RAND()))	=IF(F13<G13,0,F13-G13)	=IF(H13<=RL,RQ,0)	=IF(I13>0,OC,0)	=H13*CC	=IF(H13<0,GW*(G13-F13),0)	=SUM(J13:L13)
14	3	=H13+I12	=INT(AD/2*(1+2*RAND()))	=IF(F14<G14,0,F14-G14)	=IF(H14<=RL,RQ,0)	=IF(I14>0,OC,0)	=H14*CC	=IF(H14<0,GW*(G14-F14),0)	=SUM(J14:L14)
15	4	=H14+I13	=INT(AD/2*(1+2*RAND()))	=IF(F15<G15,0,F15-G15)	=IF(H15<=RL,RQ,0)	=IF(I15>0,OC,0)	=H15*CC	=IF(H15<0,GW*(G15-F15),0)	=SUM(J15:L15)
16	5	=H15+I14	=INT(AD/2*(1+2*RAND()))	=IF(F16<G16,0,F16-G16)	=IF(H16<=RL,RQ,0)	=IF(I16>0,OC,0)	=H16*CC	=IF(H16<0,GW*(G16-F16),0)	=SUM(J16:L16)
17	6	=H16+I15	=INT(AD/2*(1+2*RAND()))	=IF(F17<G17,0,F17-G17)	=IF(H17<=RL,RQ,0)	=IF(I17>0,OC,0)	=H17*CC	=IF(H17<0,GW*(G17-F17),0)	=SUM(J17:L17)
18	7	=H17+I16	=INT(AD/2*(1+2*RAND()))	=IF(F18<G18,0,F18-G18)	=IF(H18<=RL,RQ,0)	=IF(I18>0,OC,0)	=H18*CC	=IF(H18<0,GW*(G18-F18),0)	=SUM(J18:L18)
19	8	=H18+I17	=INT(AD/2*(1+2*RAND()))	=IF(F19<G19,0,F19-G19)	=IF(H19<=RL,RQ,0)	=IF(I19>0,OC,0)	=H19*CC	=IF(H19<0,GW*(G19-F19),0)	=SUM(J19:L19)
20	9	=H19+I18	=INT(AD/2*(1+2*RAND()))	=IF(F20<G20,0,F20-G20)	=IF(H20<=RL,RQ,0)	=IF(I20>0,OC,0)	=H20*CC	=IF(H20<0,GW*(G20-F20),0)	=SUM(J20:L20)
21	10	=H20+I19	=INT(AD/2*(1+2*RAND()))	=IF(F21<G21,0,F21-G21)	=IF(H21<=RL,RQ,0)	=IF(I21>0,OC,0)	=H21*CC	=IF(H21<0,GW*(G21-F21),0)	=SUM(J21:L21)
22	11	=H21+I20	=INT(AD/2*(1+2*RAND()))	=IF(F22<G22,0,F22-G22)	=IF(H22<=RL,RQ,0)	=IF(I22>0,OC,0)	=H22*CC	=IF(H22<0,GW*(G22-F22),0)	=SUM(J22:L22)
23	12	=H22+I21	=INT(AD/2*(1+2*RAND()))	=IF(F23<G23,0,F23-G23)	=IF(H23<=RL,RQ,0)	=IF(I23>0,OC,0)	=H23*CC	=IF(H23<0,GW*(G23-F23),0)	=SUM(J23:L23)
24	13	=H23+I22	=INT(AD/2*(1+2*RAND()))	=IF(F24<G24,0,F24-G24)	=IF(H24<=RL,RQ,0)	=IF(I24>0,OC,0)	=H24*CC	=IF(H24<0,GW*(G24-F24),0)	=SUM(J24:L24)
25	14	=H24+I23	=INT(AD/2*(1+2*RAND()))	=IF(F25<G25,0,F25-G25)	=IF(H25<=RL,RQ,0)	=IF(I25>0,OC,0)	=H25*CC	=IF(H25<0,GW*(G25-F25),0)	=SUM(J25:L25)
26	15	=H25+I24	=INT(AD/2*(1+2*RAND()))	=IF(F26<G26,0,F26-G26)	=IF(H26<=RL,RQ,0)	=IF(I26>0,OC,0)	=H26*CC	=IF(H26<0,GW*(G26-F26),0)	=SUM(J26:L26)
27					Totals	=SUM(J12-J2)	=SUM(K12:K	=SUM(L12:L27)	=SUM(M12:M
28									

Figure 61.5. *Formulas for stock control simulation*

❑ NUM ORDERED - the number of items ordered that day. This will be either the re-order quantity, if the closing stock level is equal to or below the re-order level, or zero if the CLOSING STOCK level is greater than the re-order level.

❑ ORDER COSTS - each time the item is re-ordered, there is an order cost incurred.

❑ CARRYING COSTS - there is a charge for each item in stock at the close of trading on each day. Thus, on day 5, CLOSING STOCK was 9 and the order costs at £2 per item means that the CARRYING COSTS amount to £18.

❑ STOCK OUT COSTS - a fixed cost is incurred for each item out of stock that a customer was willing to buy. This is calculated by subtracting OPENING STOCK from DEMAND and multiplying the result by the LOSS OF GOODWILL cost shown in the parameter table.

❑ TOTAL COSTS - calculated by summing ORDER COSTS, CARRYING COSTS and STOCK OUT COSTS.

The column totals for the four costs calculated are shown below the appropriate columns. Note that the OPENING STOCK parameter is a constant value that can be changed in this particular simulation only by changing the formulas in the OPEN STOCK column. Each time the spreadsheet is recalculated (by pressing F9 in Excel) new DEMAND random numbers are generated for each day, and the resulting costs are displayed. This allows investigation of the effects of changing the various parameters, for example, the investigation of the effect on the total costs of increasing the re-order level, or of reducing the re-order quantity, or the effect of changing both of these parameters together.

Simulating vehicles arriving at traffic lights

At a road junction controlled by traffic lights, vehicles arriving at the junction form a queue when the lights are on red. The size of the queue depends on two factors: the length of time the lights remain on red and the rate at which vehicles arrive at the junction. When the lights turn to green, the queue reduces as vehicles pass through the junction. At the same time, however, vehicles are still arriving at the junction while the lights are on green. In this simple simulation (Figures 61.6 and 61.7), we use four *parameters*, which affect the size of the queue:

1. The average rate of arrival of vehicles at the lights. We assume that if the average rate is say, A, then during any stop period the actual rate is modelled by generating a random number between A/2 and 3A/2. For example, if the average arrival rate is 4 vehicles per minute, then we generate a random number between 2 and 6 and use this as the actual arrival rate for one instance of the lights being on red. We generate a new value for the actual arrival rate the next time the (simulated) lights turn to red.

2. The average rate of departure from the lights. We use the same scheme as for the arrival rate: if the average departure rate is L vehicles per minute, then we generate a random number between L/2 and 3L/2 to represent the actual departure rate for one instance of the lights being on green. We generate a new value for the actual departure rate the next time the lights turn to green.

3. The length of time (in minutes) the lights are on red. This affects the build-up of the vehicle queue, since the longer the lights are on red, the greater is the number of

vehicles that will arrive at the junction and join the end of the queue.

4. The length of time (in minutes) the lights are on green. This controls how many vehicles can leave the queue.

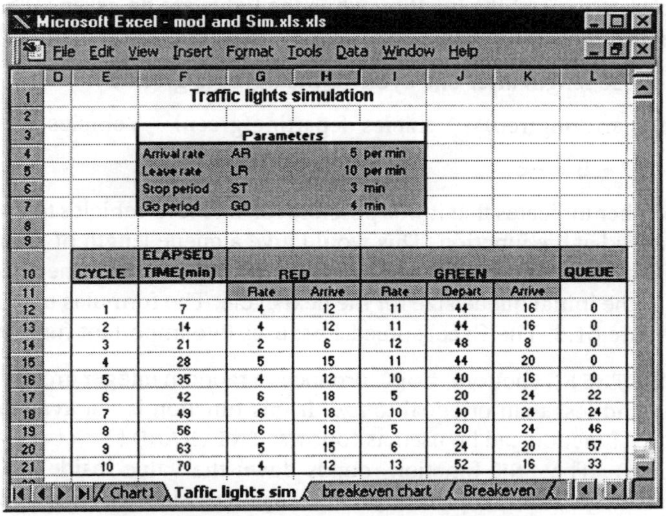

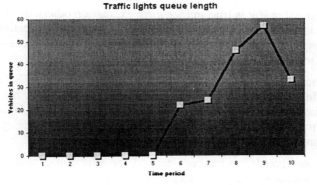

Figure 61.6. *Traffic lights queue simulation*

Traffic lights queue length

Figure 61.7. *Chart for traffic lights queue simulation*

A complete cycle of the lights is one stop (i.e. red) period followed by one go (i.e. green) period. The simulation calculates the size of the queue after each of these cycles. As an example, suppose that the average arrival rate at the lights (called *AR* on the spreadsheet) is 5 vehicles per minute, the average departure rate (*LR*) is 20 vehicles per minute, the lights are on red for 3 minutes (*ST*) and green for 4 minutes (*GO*), then for the first cycle, assuming that there were no vehicles waiting, the calculation might go as follows:

1. Vehicles arriving when lights are on red : $3 \times R1 = 3 \times 2 = \mathbf{6}$ to the nearest whole number (assuming R1 was 2), where R1 represents a random number between 1.5 and 4.5

2.   Vehicles leaving the junction when lights are on green : $4 \times R2 = 4 \times 5 = 20$ to the nearest whole number (assuming R2 was 5), where R2 represents a random number between 2 and 6.

3.   Vehicles arriving at the junction while the lights are on green : $4 \times R1 = 4 \times 2 = 8$ to the nearest whole number.

Therefore, the queue length after one cycle of the lights is given by

4.   Vehicles arriving(red) – Vehicles departing(green) + Vehicles arriving(green)

        $= 6 - 20 + 8 = -6$.

The negative number indicates that it was possible for six more vehicles to go through the lights than actually arrived at the junction. This would give a queue length of zero. A positive value would mean that a queue of vehicles still remained after the lights turned back to red, and this would be used as the initial queue size for the next cycle. The formulas used in the spreadsheet are shown in Figure 61.8. The Excel spreadsheet uses two important functions:

❑   RANDBETWEEN (bottom, `top`) produces a random integer greater than or equal to *bottom* and less than or equal to *top*. If this function is not available, the standard RAND() function can be used as follows: INT (RAND() * (top-bottom+1) + bottom). The INT function rounds down the value inside the brackets to the nearest integer; the complete expression again produces an integer between *top* and *bottom* inclusively.

❑   IF(condition, true, false) tests the specified *condition* and executes the *true* expression if it is true and the *false* expression otherwise. The IF function is required to check whether the queue length is negative, indicating that no vehicles were left in the queue at the end of the green period. If the queue length is negative, it is set to zero.

Note that the simulation parameters have been given names (AR, LR, ST and GO) in order to clarify their use in the formulas. The spreadsheet recalculation facility has been set to manual so that function key F9 must be pressed in order to generate a new set of random numbers and for their effects to be shown. The graph automatically reflects the change in the queue after each recalculation.

Once the simulation spreadsheet has been created, the effects of changing the parameters can be investigated. This allows the parameters to be set to values which reduce the probability of a large queue of vehicles forming. The parameter that is least likely to change frequently is the departure rate of vehicles, and the arrival rate is not under the direct control of the system designer; however, the timing of the signals is under the control of the designer and this type of simulation provides the opportunity of doing detailed analysis of how crucial the timing is likely to be in the reduction of large traffic jams. The principles used in this study could equally be used to investigate other types of queues, for example, supermarket checkouts or entrances and exits to football stadiums. Finally, note that this simulation could be improved in a number of ways. For instance, more accurate models could be devised for the arrival and departure rates, or perhaps another parameter representing the number of available lanes could be introduced, or the time of day could be taken into account, since this would affect the volume of traffic.

	E	F	G	H	I	J	K	L
	CYCLE	LAPSED TIME(min)	RED Rate	Arrive	GREEN Rate	Depart	Arrive	QUEUE
11								
12	1	=(ST+GO)*E12	=INT(AR/2*(1+2*RAND()))	=ST*G12	=INT((LR/2*(1+2*RAND())))	=GO*I12	=GO*G12	=IF(H12+K12-J12>=0,H12+K12-J12,0)
13	2	=(ST+GO)*E13	=INT(AR/2*(1+2*RAND()))	=ST*G13	=INT((LR/2*(1+2*RAND())))	=GO*I13	=GO*G13	=IF(H13+K13-L12-J13>=0,H13+K13-L12-J13,0)
14	3	=(ST+GO)*E14	=INT(AR/2*(1+2*RAND()))	=ST*G14	=INT((LR/2*(1+2*RAND())))	=GO*I14	=GO*G14	=IF(H14+K14-L13-J14>=0,H14+K14-L13-J14,0)
15	4	=(ST+GO)*E15	=INT(AR/2*(1+2*RAND()))	=ST*G15	=INT((LR/2*(1+2*RAND())))	=GO*I15	=GO*G15	=IF(H15+K15-L14-J15>=0,H15+K15-L14-J15,0)
16	5	=(ST+GO)*E16	=INT(AR/2*(1+2*RAND()))	=ST*G16	=INT((LR/2*(1+2*RAND())))	=GO*I16	=GO*G16	=IF(H16+K16-L15-J16>=0,H16+K16-L15-J16,0)
17	6	=(ST+GO)*E17	=INT(AR/2*(1+2*RAND()))	=ST*G17	=INT((LR/2*(1+2*RAND())))	=GO*I17	=GO*G17	=IF(H17+K17-L16-J17>=0,H17+K17-L16-J17,0)
18	7	=(ST+GO)*E18	=INT(AR/2*(1+2*RAND()))	=ST*G18	=INT((LR/2*(1+2*RAND())))	=GO*I18	=GO*G18	=IF(H18+K18-L17-J18>=0,H18+K18-L17-J18,0)
19	8	=(ST+GO)*E19	=INT(AR/2*(1+2*RAND()))	=ST*G19	=INT((LR/2*(1+2*RAND())))	=GO*I19	=GO*G19	=IF(H19+K19-L18-J19>=0,H19+K19-L18-J19,0)
20	9	=(ST+GO)*E20	=INT(AR/2*(1+2*RAND()))	=ST*G20	=INT((LR/2*(1+2*RAND())))	=GO*I20	=GO*G20	=IF(H20+K20-L19-J20>=0,H20+K20-L19-J20,0)
21	10	=(ST+GO)*E21	=INT(AR/2*(1+2*RAND()))	=ST*G21	=INT((LR/2*(1+2*RAND())))	=GO*I21	=GO*G21	=IF(H21+K21-L20-J21>=0,H21+K21-L20-J21,0)

Figure 61.8. *Formulas for traffic lights queue simulation*

✍️Exercises

1. Describe three distinct areas that make use of computer models. Explain the purpose of each model and its benefits compared to alternative methods (see Topic 60).

2. Develop a computer-based model to simulate customer queues at supermarket checkouts.

    (i) Explain the factors governing arrival rates and time taken to process purchases.

    (ii) Identify other factors which may need to be taken into account when developing the model.

    (iii) Carefully describe the rules for the operation of the model and how they have been represented in the spreadsheet.

    (iv) Explore the effects on queue lengths of changing key variables, such as average arrival rates, service rates and number of checkouts open.

    (v) Use a graph to show how the queue length at a typical checkout fluctuates over a period of time.

    (vi) Evaluate the effectiveness of your simulation, commenting on any inadequacies and ways in which it might be improved.

Section 14

Programming using Visual Basic

Topics

Visual Basic programming concepts

Overview

Even for experienced programmers, creating a program that runs under the latest Microsoft Windows *Operating System* can be a daunting task, particularly when using traditional programming languages such as Pascal, C or C++. Consequently, many program developers are using Visual Basic (VB) for application prototype development, or even for producing the final application program. The reason for the widespread adoption of VB is that it hides the complexities of Windows programming by the use of special graphical tools. These tools provide a convenient graphical user interface allowing complex windows components to be incorporated in a program with great ease.

Typically, a Visual Basic program is a collection of control objects that respond to user actions such as mouse operations and keyboard use. These actions generate events that are linked to program code. For example, a commonly used control is a *command button* that simulates a physical switch such as that used for door bells. 'Pushing' the button by clicking the mouse over it is a mouse-click event that can cause a specific section of code to be executed. Each type of control has one or more related events, each of which can be programmed. For this reason Visual Basic is classed as an *event-driven programming language*. The collection of control objects forms the user interface, the basis of most Visual Basic programs. Program design starts with creating the user interface which defines the functionality of the program. Then code is written to perform the required functions. Because control objects can be added to the user interface independently of other control objects, programs can be developed and tested in a modular fashion. A new control can be created, configured, modified, programmed and tested independently of existing controls. Moreover, the effects of any changes to the program can be examined immediately simply by clicking a button on the Visual Basic toolbar. This is one of the great strengths of Visual Basic, that programs can be created and modified very quickly and easily.

However, although VB can help novice programmers to produce professional-looking Windows programs relatively easily, it introduces a number of concepts additional to other more traditional languages. The VB programmer needs to know about objects, methods, properties and events in addition to such traditional programming concepts as variables, constants, control structures, files and subprograms.

Consequently we have divided the task of learning to program in Visual Basic into three parts:

1. **Programming Basics**. Traditional programming concepts are examined using VB as the programming language. A sequence of short, independent Topics introduce the concepts. Once VB has been set up for the tutorial, the first example programs that illustrate programming concepts can be run without the complications of having to create procedures or screen objects.

2. **Introduction to Event-driven Programming**. A number of simple programs illustrate elementary event-driven programming principles. Objects such as Forms, Command buttons, List boxes and Text boxes are introduced.

3.   **Case study**. More advanced event-driven programming concepts are introduced by means of a sequence of Topics that progressively develop a single, fairly complex project.

Pre-requisites

To use this Visual Basic tutorial you need access to Microsoft Visual Basic version 4 or above running under Windows 95 or above, and you must be familiar with the Microsoft Windows 95/98 operating system. You should know how to run applications, maximise, minimise, resize and scroll windows, use a mouse to select and drag items and be able to save and load documents using standard File menu commands.

You also need to set up a simple project in Visual Basic, as explained after the next section, to be able to run the example programs in the first topic, "Programming Basics".

The Visual Basic Programming Environment

The screenshot of the Visual Basic 6 programming environment shows the main features (described below) used in this tutorial. Note that in other versions of Visual Basic the toolbox, project window, properties window and form may initially appear in separate, movable windows.

Menu and Toolbar

The Menu bar provides access to all of VB's utilities. We will mostly make use of the File, Edit, Debug and Run menus. The Toolbar provides quick access to some VB features. We will use some of these in the course of the tutorial.

Form

A Form is the container for user interface controls. These controls can be visually positioned and moved by using the mouse. The next Topic will illustrate how controls are established on a form.

Toolbox

The Toolbox allows you to select, position and configure various controls on a Form. It displays all the standard Visual Basic controls plus any custom controls and insertable objects you have added to your project with the Custom Controls dialog box. You can display ToolTips for the Toolbox buttons by selecting the Show ToolTips option in the Environment tab of the Options dialog box. To open the Toolbox, choose Toolbox from the View menu.

The tools used in this introduction to Visual Basic are briefly described below. You can learn about other tools from VB Help.

Pointer. This is the only item in the Toolbox that doesn't draw a control. Use it to resize or move a control after it has been drawn on a form.

PictureBox. Use to display graphical images (either decorative or active), as a container that receives output from graphics methods, or as a container for other controls.

Label. Use for text that you don't want the user to change, such as a caption under a graphic.

TextBox. Use to hold text that the user can either enter or change.

Frame. Use to create a graphical or functional grouping for controls. To group controls, draw the Frame first, and then draw controls inside the frame.

CommandButton. Use to create a button the user can choose to carry out a command.

CheckBox. Use to create a box that the user can easily choose to indicate if something is true or false, or to display multiple choices when the user can choose more than one.

OptionButton. Use in a group of option buttons to display multiple choices from which the user can choose only one.

ComboBox. Use to draw a combination list box and text box. The user can either choose an item from the list or enter a value in the text box.

ListBox. Use to display a list of items from which the user can choose one. The list can be scrolled if it has more items than can be displayed at one time.

Timer. Use to generate timer events at set intervals. This control is invisible at run time.

DriveListBox. Use to display valid disk drives.

DirListBox (directory list box). Use to display directories and paths.

FileListBox. Use to display a list of files.

Shape. Use to draw a variety of shapes on your form at design time. You can choose a rectangle, rounded rectangle, square, rounded square, oval, or circle.

Line. Use to draw a variety of line styles on your form at design time.

Image. Use to display a graphical image from a bitmap, icon, or metafile on your form. Images displayed in an Image control can only be decorative and use fewer resources than a PictureBox.

OLE Container. Use to link and embed objects from other applications in your Visual Basic application.

CommonDialog. Use to create dialog boxes for operations such as opening, saving, and printing files, or selecting colours and fonts. CommonDialog is a custom control.

Project window

The Project window shows the project forms and modules and allows you to view code or forms.

To view the code associated with a form, click the code icon.

To view the form itself, click the form icon.

Creating a project allows you to keep all of the files associated with the project together.

Properties window

Objects such as forms and controls used in a project have properties associated with them. For instance, the width, height and colour of a form are properties. The Properties window allows you to set and modify all of the properties associated with an object.

Setting up Visual Basic to run example programs in "Programming Basics"

You will need to create a simple project called "VBConcepts.vbp" to allow you to create and run the example programs. (Note that the project is available on the CD in the folder "Tutorial1" and is called "VBConcepts.vbp". You can open this project in VB as an alternative to following the instructions given here).

To create the VBConcepts project, follow the instructions below:

First launch VB and start a new project.

1. Open the project window by pressing Ctrl+R.

2. If there is a Form in the project window delete it by clicking the mouse right-hand button and selecting "Remove".

3.   Create a new Module (Menu: Insert|Module, VB4 or Menu: Project|Add Module, VB6). The code window for the module should appear.

4.   Create a procedure called "Main" (Menu: Insert|Procedure.. VB4 or Tools|Add procedure.. VB6)

The code window should look much like this:

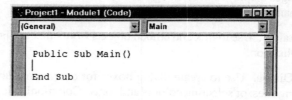

5.   Finally, open the Debug window by pressing Ctrl+G.

Now save the project as "VBConcepts".

Creating and running example programs in "Programming Basics"

We will create example programs by first opening project *VBConcepts.vbp* and then entering code between the lines Public Sub Main() and End Sub in the code window. To run the program you click the **Run** button on the toolbar. Any output from the program will be shown in the Debug window. (**Note:** if the Debug window is not visible prior to running a program, press Ctrl+G).

All of the example programs in this topic are stored on the CD in directory Tutorial1, using names such as Example01.bas.

Programming basics

Overview

This topic introduces basic programming concepts common to languages such as Pascal and C/C++ as well as Visual Basic, the language used here. We cover the following subjects:

- ❑ Variables and Constants
- ❑ Data Types
- ❑ Simple input and output
- ❑ Performing calculations
- ❑ Loops
- ❑ Decisions
- ❑ Arrays
- ❑ Strings
- ❑ Visual Basic functions

A first VB program

As a simple example to illustrate creating and running a program, Listing 63.1 shows a program which calculates the total cost of a purchased item by calculating VAT and adding it to the price of the item.

The algorithm on which the program is based is as follows:

1. *Ask the user to enter the price of the item*

2. *Store the price*

3. *Calculate the VAT at 17.5% (i.e. multiply the price by 0.175)*

4. *Calculate the total price by adding the VAT to the price*

5. *Display the total cost on the screen.*

Listing 63.1. A simple program to calculate the total cost of a purchase (Example01.BAS)

```
Public Sub Main()
' ====== Program to calculate the total cost of an item ======
10 Const VAT = 0.175
20 Dim Price As Single
30 Dim Tax As Single
40 Dim TotalCost As Single
50 Price = InputBox("Enter price of the item")
60 Tax = Price * VAT
```

```
70 TotalCost = Price + Tax
80 Debug.Print "The total cost is: "; TotalCost
End Sub
```

Note: line numbers are optional in VB, and we have used them to allow us to describe the operation of the example programs in detail.

The operation of program Example1

The first two lines (without line numbers) identify the program. "Sub" stands for *Sub*program or *Sub*routine and "Main" is the name of the program (this will be the name of all our example programs in this tutorial). The single quotation mark identifies the rest of the line as a comment. Comments are ignored by VB and are used to annotate programs.

Lines *10* declares that VAT is a *constant* value.

Lines *20* - *40* declare three *variables* Price, Tax and TotalCost each as being of type single. (This means *single* precision real number - ie a number having figures after the decimal point). Variables are used to store data, which in this case are in the form of real numbers, that is, numbers which are not whole numbers. Every variable used in a VB program must be declared in this way.

Up to this point the programmer has defined a number of *identifiers* that will be used in the procedural part of the program which follows.

Line *50* causes the message 'Enter price of the item' to be displayed on the screen in an input box. That appears like this:

The user types in the value for the price of the item and then clicks OK or presses the Enter key on the keyboard. The value entered by the user is stored in the variable Price.

Line *60* stores the result of Price multiplied by VAT in the variable Tax.

Line *70* stores the result of adding Price and Tax in TotalCost.

Line *80* then displays the text, 'The total cost is: ' followed by the value stored in TotalCost in the Debug window. The Debug.Print statement indicates that the variables and/or text following is to be printed in the Debug window. As its name suggests, the Debug window is generally used for debugging , that is finding and correcting programs, but it is used in this context to simplify learning VB concepts. Print is known as a *Method* of the Debug window *Object*. We will be discussing *Objects* and *Methods* later in the tutorial.

Finally, End sub indicates the end of the program. When the program is run, if the user entered the value 20 in the input box, the output from the program would look like this:

Some general remarks

Before going on to explore VB in more depth, it is worth mentioning a few general points at this stage:

1. VB does not distinguish between the use of capitals and lower-case letters. Thus it regards `Price`, `PRICE` and `price` as being exactly the same.

2. It is a good idea to include comment lines - text beginning with a single quote (') - to describe the purpose of lines or sections of your program. Particularly for large, complex programs, this is very helpful if it is necessary to change the program at some later date.

3. Using spaces, blank lines and indentation can greatly improve the appearance and the clarity of a program, thus making the program easier to read and understand if it has to be modified later for any reason.

4. Programming involves meticulous attention to detail; omitting punctuation marks, including them in the wrong place or making spelling mistakes will usually cause VB to report a syntax error on a program line, but sometimes such slips might cause errors which are more difficult to detect, so be very careful to form instructions precisely.

5. Line numbers are used in VB as labels for the `GOTO` instruction. Our example programs contain line numbers only so that we can identify lines that we want to explain; you do not need to include these line numbers in your own programs.

6. The Debug window (also called the Immediate window) is mainly used as a debugging aid. In this tutorial we are using it to simplify showing the output from example programs. When VB programs are compiled into stand-alone applications, the debug window would not appear. Topics later in the tutorial will deal with more usual methods of displaying program output.

Identifiers and data types

The term *identifier* is a general term used for *variables*, *constants* and other programmer-defined names such as *procedures* and *functions*. Variables and constants are normally associated with a data *type*. *VB does not require that variables are given a type* such as `Integer` or `Single` but it is good practice do so by using `Dim` and `Const` declarations.

Variables

A variable, which represents an item of data such as a single number, has a name and a current value. Variables are given names such as `Amount`, `Total` or `Numb3` and are assigned values by program instructions. These values are stored in the memory of the computer and they are accessed whenever a variable is referenced in a program instruction. So, for example, in the instruction

```
Total = Price + Tax
```

the value associated with the variable `Price` is added to the value of the variable `Tax` and the sum is then assigned to the variable `Total`. If in a previous instruction `Total` had already been assigned a value, that value would be replaced by the new one.

Constants

Constants too are assigned values but only once after the word `Const`. The constant `VAT` in Listing 1 is an example. Constants retain their values throughout the execution of a program; VB does not allow you to use a constant in an instruction which tries to change the value of the constant. Thus, if in Listing 1, you included an instruction such as

```
VAT = 0.2;
```

in the main program, VB would report an error.

Reserved words

Words that form part of the VB language are not allowed to be used as identifier names. For instance, if you included in your program the line

```
Print = 3
```

VB would report an error because `Print` is a reserved word that is part of the VB language. VB also provides a large number of predefined constants that programmers can use but not change. Many, but not all, of these constants start with the letters vb, for example,

```
vbMultiSelectNone
```

Some of VB's reserved words are shown below. You will soon learn to avoid using reserved words as identifiers by careful choice of identifier names, but be aware that illegal use of reserved words will cause an error.

Reserved words		
And	Wend	Not
Case	Next	Xor
End	Set	Until
Dim	To	Do
Or	Step	
If	Then	
For	Goto	
While	On	

VB imposes a number of restrictions concerning the formation of names for identifiers:

1.   The name must consist only of alphabetic and numeric characters.

2.   The name must start with an alphabetic character.

3.   The name must not be a reserved word or predefined VB constant.

Examples of valid identifiers

```
firstNum     NUMBER1     abc31        Counter     x
```

Examples of invalid identifiers

```
12abc
```
                         (starts with a numeric character)

first-number   (contains a non-alphabetic/numeric character)

var 1   (contains a space)

End   (a reserved word)

As well as having a names and values, variables are also given a *type*. Three commonly used types are `Integer`, `Single` and `String`. Variable data types are declared before the variables are used in the program. For the purposes of this tutorial, we will use the `Dim` statement to declare variables, but note that this is not the only way it can be done.

The *type* must be shown after the name of the variable in the `Dim` statement. Some examples of type declarations are shown below.

```
Dim Amount As Single
Dim Address as String
Dim NumberOfItems As Integer, Count As Integer
```

The third example illustrates that more than one variable can be declared in a single `Dim` statement.

The type `single` means that these variables can be used for numbers such as $123 \cdot 456$, $0 \cdot 22$ or $-9 \cdot 93$, that is, *signed* numbers that are not whole numbers. The computer holds `Single` numbers in 32-bit floating-point form so that very large, and very small numbers can be stored.

Signed whole numbers, that is, `Integer` values are stored as two's complement binary values in the computer. Some examples of integers are 23, 0, –1, 32767 and –559.

Type `String` means that the named variable (`Address` in the example above) can store a number of alphanumeric characters such as "24 Railway Terrace, Shilbottle, Countyshire".

A further standard data type is the type `Boolean`. This type of variable has only one of two possible values, namely `True` or `False`. A boolean variable declaration is made as follows:

```
Dim MoreValues As Boolean
```

VB provides the two reserved words `True` and `False` which can be used to assign a value to a boolean variable, as in:

```
Morevalues = True
```

The use of boolean variables will be explored in a later section. The following table shows all the data types supported by VB, including their storage sizes and ranges.

Data type	Storage size	Range
Byte	1 byte	0 to 255
Boolean	2 bytes	True or False.
Integer	2 bytes	–32,768 to 32,767
Long (long integer)	4 bytes	–2,147,483,648 to 2,147,483,647

Single (single-precision floating-point)	4 bytes	−3.402823E38 to -1.401298E−45 for negative values; 1.401298E-45 to 3.402823E38 for positive values
Double (double-precision floating-point)	8 bytes	−1.79769313486232E308 to −4.94065645841247E-324 for Negative values; 4.94065645841247E-324 to 1.79769313486232E308 for positive values.
Currency (scaled integer)		−922,337,203,685,477.5808 to 922,337,203,685,477.5807
Date	8 bytes	January 1, 100 to December 31, 9999
Object	4 bytes	Any Object reference
String (variable-length)	10 bytes + string length	0 to approximately 2 billion
String (fixed-length)	Length of string	1 to approximately 65,400
Variant (with numbers)	16 bytes	Any numeric value up to the range of a Double
Variant (with characters)	22 bytes + string length	Same range as for variable-length String
User-defined	Number required by elements	The range of each element is the same as the range of its data type

Performing calculations

Probably every program that you will ever write will contain at least one calculation, and this is true of the majority of programs. It is not surprising therefore that VB and other high-level languages make calculations easy to perform. Arithmetic instructions simply involve defining what arithmetic operations are to be performed on numeric identifiers and constants. The four common arithmetic operations: add; subtract; multiply; divide, use the symbols +, −, * and /, respectively.

The examples of arithmetic operations provided in Table 63.1 on the next page assume that the following data declarations have been made.

```
Const PI = 3.14
Dim Length As Integer, Width As Integer, Perimeter As Integer
Dim Area as Single, Radius as Single, Gallons as Single, Miles As
Single, Mpg As Single
Dim x As Single
```

Expression	VB statement
Area = length × width	`Area = Length*Width`
Area = π × radius^2	`Area = PI*Radius*Radius`
Perimeter = 2 × (length + width)	`Perimeter = 2*(Length + Width)`
Mpg = gallons ÷ miles	`Mpg = Gallons/Miles`
x = 0	`x = 0`

Table 63.1. *Examples of arithmetic operations with real variables*

Another point to note is that VB provides two divide operators. The '/' divide operator may be used with any values, real or integer, and it produces a real result, that is a non-integer value. The second divide operator, '\', produces an integer result. If the result of a division does not produce a whole number, the fractional part is ignored. In other words, the result is rounded down to the nearest integer. The remainder when one integer is divided by another is produced by the Mod operator. Some examples of different combinations of real and integer divisions are shown in Table 63.2. VB automatically rounds any non-integer values used with \ and Mod.

Operands	Example	Answer	Answer type
real / real	7.3 / 0.2	36.5	real
	0.5 / 0.25	2.0	real
real / integer	13.9 / 5	2.78	real
integer / real	1116 / 7.2	155.0	real
integer / integer	33 / 11	3.0	real
	33 / 10	3.0	real
	3 / 5	0.6	real
integer \ integer	33 \ 11	3	integer
	33 \ 10	3	integer
	3 \ 5	0	integer
integer \ real	33\3.3	11	integer
	33\3.8	8	integer
real \ integer	15.9\4	4	integer
real \ real	14.9/3.3	5	integer
integer mod integer	33 mod 10	3	integer
	10 mod 33	10	integer
integer mod real	10 mod 3.3	1	integer
real mod integer	14.4 mod 4	2	integer
real mod real	13.9 mod 3.3	4	integer

Table 63.2. *Examples of divide operations*

Listing 63.2 is an example of the use of integer division. The program converts a number of seconds into hours, minutes and seconds.

Listing 63.2.   The \ and Mod integer division operators (Example02.BAS)

```
Public Sub Main()
' ====== Program to illustrate integer division ======

' Declare identifiers
10 Const SECONDSPERMINUTE = 60
20 Const MINUTESPERHOUR = 60
30 Dim Hours As Integer
40 Dim Minutes  As Integer
50 Dim Seconds As Integer
60 Dim Duration As Integer
70 Dim Temp  As Integer

' Get the duration in seconds
80 Duration = InputBox("Enter the length of time in seconds")

'Calculate equivalent hours minutes and seconds
90 Seconds = Duration Mod SECONDSPERMINUTE
100 Temp = Duration \ SECONDSPERMINUTE
110 Minutes = Temp Mod MINUTESPERHOUR
120 Hours = Temp \ MINUTESPERHOUR

'Display the results
130 Debug.Print Duration; " seconds is: "
140 Debug.Print Hours; " hours "
150 Debug.Print Minutes; " minutes "
160 Debug.Print Seconds; " seconds."

End Sub
```

On line *80* the user is requested to enter the time to be converted from seconds to hours, minutes and seconds:

The number of seconds is stored in the variable `Duration`. The first stage in the calculation is to calculate the remainder when `Duration` is divided by the number of seconds per minute stored in the constant `SECONDSPERMINUTE` which has the value 60. Suppose, for example, the user entered the number 6573 when asked for the time in seconds. Line *90* would produce the value 6573 mod 60, that is, 33. This is assigned to the variable, `Seconds`. Next, the temporary variable `Temp` is given the value 6573 \ 60, that is, 109. The remainder when this last number is divided by the number of minutes per hour, that is 60, gives the value for `Minutes`: 109 mod 60 = 49. The number of hours is calculated using 109 \ 60 = 1. Thus, when the program is run, it produces the following output:

```
Immediate                                    [X]
    6573  seconds is:
    1  hours  49  minutes  33  seconds.
```

Operator precedence

The term *operator precedence* applies to the order in which the operators in an arithmetic expression are used. For example, to evaluate the expression

$$x = y + 3z$$

z is multiplied by 3 before the result is added to *y*; the multiply operator thus has precedence over the addition operator. If *y* had a value of 2 and *z* had a value of 4, *x* would be calculated as

$$x = 2 + 3 \times 4 = 2 + 12 = 14$$

The higher the precedence of an operator, the sooner it is used in the evaluation of an expression. The use of parentheses within an expression can alter the way a calculation is performed. So, in the above expression, to force the addition to be performed before the multiplication, we would write x = (y + 3) × z. This would result in y being added to 3 before multiplying by z. Thus,

$$x = (2 + 3) \times 4 = 5 \times 4 = 20$$

In VB, the operators *, /, div and mod have equal precedence; this means that in an expression involving two or more of them, they are simply used in the order that they appear in the expression. These four operators all have higher precedence than + and –. Again, + and – have the same precedence. As a further example, consider the program in Listing 63.3.

Listing 63.3.   Illustration of operator precedence (Example03.BAS)

```
Public Sub Main()
' ====== Program to illustrate operator precedence ======

10 Dim x1 As Single
20 Dim y1 As Integer
30 Dim n As Integer

40 n = 11
50 y1 = 5
60 x1 = 1 / 2 * (y1 + n \ y1)

70 Debug.Print x1

End Sub
```

The order of evaluation of line *60* is as follows:

1. $\frac{1}{2}$ i.e.   0.5

2.   n \ y1   i.e.   11 \ 5 = 2
3.   y1 + n \ y1   i.e.   5 + 2 = 7
4. $\frac{1}{2}$*(y1 + n \ y1)   i.e.   0.5*7 = 3.5

Loops

The For..Next statement

A very frequent programming requirement is to perform a set of instructions several times. Rather than writing the set of instructions several times (which is impractical for all but a small number of repetitions), they are controlled by a special instruction which causes them to be re-peated as many times as desired. Such program constructs are called *loops*, and each repetition of a set of statements is often called an *iteration*. For example, suppose a program is required to read 10 numbers, add each one to a running total and then display the final total.

The program in Listing 63.4 accomplishes this task using a loop.

Listing 63.4.   Using a loop to add numbers (Example04.BAS)

```
Public Sub Main()
' ====== Program to add ten numbers    ======

' Declare variables
10 Dim Number  As Single
20 Dim Total As Single
30 Dim Count As Integer

' Initialise running total variable
40 Total = 0

' Get numbers and add to running total
50 For Count = 1 To 10
60    Number = InputBox("Please enter a number")
70    Total = Total + Number
80 Next Count

' Display final total
90 Debug.Print "The total is: "; Total

End Sub
```

Listing 63.4 uses a For loop to repeat the two instructions which repeatedly read a number and add it to a running total. The For loop requires that a control variable, called Count in this ex-ample, is defined as type integer. The control variable is automatically given the first value specified (1 in this example) and, each time the statements within the loop are repeated, it is in-creased by 1 until it finally reaches the second value specified (10 in this example). Thus the same program, but with the value 10 replaced by the required number, could be used to add any number of numbers. Statements to be repeated are enclosed between For and Next Count.

Listing 63.5 is a further example of the use of the For loop.

Listing 63.5.   Using a For loop to display a conversion table (Example05.BAS)

```
Public Sub Main()
' ====== Program to display a conversion table for
'          inches to  centimetres using a For loop   ======

' Declare constants and variables
10 Const CONVERSIONFACTOR = 2.54, MAXINCHES = 12
20 Dim Inches As Integer
30 Dim Centimetres As Single


50 Debug.Print "Inches", "Centimetres"
60 Debug.Print "——", "———-"


70  For Inches = 1 To MAXINCHES
80     Centimetres = Inches * CONVERSIONFACTOR
90     Debug.Print Inches, Centimetres
100 Next Inches

End Sub
```

The output produced looks like this:

Notice that the end value in the For statement on line *100* is a constant called MAXINCHES; this could also have been defined as a variable, its value to be supplied by the user using an InputBox instruction.

A variation in the format of a For statement allows the count variable to go down from a high value to a low value. For example, you could write

> For i= 12 To 1 Step -1

which would cause the variable i to start at 12 and go down to 1 in steps of 1.

Immediate	
Inches	Centimetres
------	-----------
1	2.54
2	5.08
3	7.62
4	10.16
5	12.7
6	15.24
7	17.78
8	20.32
9	22.86
10	25.4
11	27.94
12	30.48

The While..Wend statement

The For statement is a very useful means of implementing a loop, but certain programming problems require a different approach to repeating a set of instructions. For example, consider the following outline program description:

> *Read a set of real numbers representing the cost of a number of items. Accumulate the total cost of the items until a value of zero is entered, then display the number of items purchased and their total cost.*

Here it is not known how many times the loop is to be repeated: the user decides when to terminate the loop by entering a *rogue value*, (zero in this case). The rogue value is used in another type of loop instruction, the While instruction.

Listing 63.6 shows how a While loop can be used in conjunction with a rogue value.

Listing 63.6.   Using a While loop and a rogue value (Example06.BAS)

```
Public Sub Main()
' ====== Program to illustrate the use of a rogue value
'         to terminate a loop                          ======

' Declare constants and variables
10 Const ROGUEVALUE = 0
20 Dim Count As Integer
30 Dim Amount As Single
40 Dim Total As Single

' Initialise variables
50 Total = 0
60 Count = 0
' Get the cost of the first item
70 Amount = InputBox("Enter the cost of the first item, or 0 to end:")
' Loop to get the remaining items
80   While Amount > ROGUEVALUE
90     Count = Count + 1
100    Total = Total + Amount
110    Amount = InputBox("Enter the cost of the next item, or 0 to
end:")
120  Wend
' Display the restults
130 Debug.Print Count; "items were purchased"
140 Debug.Print "The total cost was: £"; Total
End Sub
```

The rogue value is defined as a constant on line *10*. Because the user may want to terminate the program immediately, without entering any values, the program asks for a purchase amount before entering the loop starting on line *80*. The While instruction requires that a true/false expression is included after the word 'while'. Thus the expression, Amount > ROGUEVALUE, will be true if Amount entered is greater than zero, and it will be false if Amount is not greater than zero, that is if it is equal to, or less than zero. When the expression is true, the statements between While and Wend, that is lines *90* to *110*, will be executed; as soon as the expression becomes false, the loop terminates and the program goes on to line *130*. Notice that the last instruction in the lines to be repeated is the instruction to read another value: this means that because the next instruction to be executed is the While instruction, the value typed in by the user is immediately compared with the rogue value. This ensures that the rogue value is not processed as an actual data item. Here is a typical run of the program:

```
Enter the cost of the first item, or 0 to end :23.45
Enter the cost of the next item, or 0 to end :6.12
Enter the cost of the next item, or 0 to end :5.99
Enter the cost of the next item, or 0 to end :0
```

Notice that the assignment instruction on line *90*, Count = Count + 1, is used as a means of counting the number of times the loop is executed. The instruction simply adds 1 to the variable, Count, each time the instructions within the loop are repeated. The true/false expression on line *80* in the While statement uses the *relational operator*, >,

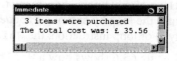

```
Immediate                        _ □ ×
    3 items were purchased
    The total cost was: £ 35.56
```

meaning 'greater than', to compare `Amount` with `ROGUEVALUE`. There are six different relational operators that can be used in such logical expressions, and these are shown in Table 63.4.

relational operator	meaning
>	Greater than
>=	Greater than or equal to
<	Less than
<=	Less than or equal to
=	Equal to
<>	Not equal to

Table 63.4. *Relational operators used in logical expressions*

The operators in Table 63.4 are used according to the relationship to be established between two values. Whatever logical expression is used, the result of the comparison will either be true or false - if true, the `While` loop will repeat; if false the loop will terminate. More examples of the use of these operators are provided in the next part of this Topic, which deals with the use of logical expressions in making program decisions.

Decisions

The If statement

Suppose a program is required to display multiple-choice questions with one correct answer out of three possible choices. For example, one of the questions could be:

```
A BYTE is the name given to

    (a) Four bits
    (b) Eight bits
    (c) Sixteen bits

Your answer is:
```

The program is also required to display the message

```
Correct - well done!
```

if the answer is correct, and display a message such as

```
Sorry, the correct answer is (b)
```

if the answer provided is incorrect. The program must therefore be able to take two alternative courses of action depending on the answer supplied. An `If` statement is one possible way of achieving this requirement.

The appropriate form of the `If` statement is illustrated in Listing 63.7 which shows the VB code required to display the question above and provide the response appropriate to the letter 'a', 'b' or 'c', typed into the Input box that appears.

Listing 63.7.   Using an If statement (Example07.BAS)

```
Public Sub Main()
' ====== Program to illustrate the use of the If statement =======


' Declare constants and variables
10 Dim Answer As String

' Ask the question
20 Debug.Print "Please enter a, b, c or d"
30 Debug.Print "in the Answer Box provided:"
40 Debug.Print
50 Debug.Print "A BYTE is the name given to"
60 Debug.Print "(a) Four bits"
70 Debug.Print "(b) Eight bits"
80 Debug.Print "(c) Sixteen bits"
90 Debug.Print

' Get the answer and display it
100 Answer = InputBox("Your answer is?", "Answer Box")
110 Debug.Print "You answered ("; Answer; ")"

' Check the answer and report
120 If Answer = "b" Then
130    Debug.Print "Correct - well done!"
140 Else
150    Debug.Print "Sorry, the correct answer is (b)"
160 End If

End Sub
```

The If statement extending over lines *120* to *160* shows how the program can take one of two possible courses of action depending on the value of a variable. We saw in the last Topic concerning the use of the While statement that logical expressions are either true or false. This is also the case with the logical expression Answer = "b" in the If statement on line *120*. If the letter stored in the character variable Answer is the letter 'b', then the logical expression Answer = "b" will be true, otherwise it will be false. If it is true, the statement following the word Then is executed (that is, line *130*), otherwise the statement after Else is executed (that is, line *150*). Notice the different form of the input box on line *100*:

```
100 Answer = InputBox("Your answer is?", "Answer Box")
```

The text after the prompt text ("Your answer is?") is the title of the input box shown below:

The general form of the If statement is

```
        If {logical expression} Then
```

```
         {statement 1}
     Else
         {statement 2}
     End If
```

Note that {statement 1} is the instruction that is performed if {logical expression} is true; {statement 2} is performed if {logical expression} is false. Note also that either {statement 1} or {statement 2}, or both of them, can contain more than a single instruction, as illustrated below:

```
If Answer = "b" Then
   Debug.Print "Correct - well done!"
 Else
   Debug.Print "Sorry, the correct answer is (b)"
   Debug.Print "There are eight bits in a byte"
 End If
```

Sometimes it is necessary to choose between more than just two courses of action in a program. For example, Listing 63.8 shows a program which converts a percentage mark to a pass, merit, distinction or fail grade. The program repeatedly accepts marks and converts them to grades until the mark entered is the rogue value –1 (or any negative integer value) signifying the end of the mark inputs. The rules that are used to determine the grade are as follows:

For a distinction the mark must be equal to or over 80.

For a merit the mark must be greater than or equal to 60 and less than 80.

For a pass the mark must be greater than or equal to 40 and less than 60.

Below 40 is a fail.

Listing 63.8.   The If..Else If construction (Example08.BAS)

```
Public Sub Main()
' ====== Program to illustrate the use of the If statement =======


' Declare constants and variables
10 Const DIST = 80, MERIT = 60, PASS = 40
20 Dim Mark As Integer, Grade As String

'Get the first mark
30 Mark = InputBox("Please enter the first mark(-1 to end): ",
"Marks")

' Check the grade
40 While Mark >= 0
50    If Mark >= DIST Then
60       Grade = "Distinction"
70    Else
80       If (Mark >= MERIT) And (Mark < DIST) Then
90        Grade = "Merit"
100      Else
110       If (Mark >= PASS) And (Mark < MERIT) Then
120          Grade = "Pass"
130        Else
```

```
140          Grade = "Fail"
150         End If
160    End If
170    End If

'Report mark and grade
180 Debug.Print "Mark: "; Mark,  "Grade: "; Grade

' Get the next mark
190 Mark = InputBox("Please enter the next mark(-1 to end): ",
"Marks")
200 Wend

End Sub
```

The If statement between lines *50* and *170* reflects this logic exactly. It is possible to chain If statements in this way to cope with quite complex lines of reasoning. Added flexibility is provided by the use of the logical And operator used for the logical expressions on lines *80* and *110*. The And operator requires that both of the minor logical expressions it connects are true for the complete logical expression to be true. If either or both are false, then the whole expression is false. Logical operators are discussed in more detail in the next section. Here is the output from the program for a set of four marks:

```
Immediate                                    ☒
Mark:   67      Grade: Merit
Mark:   83      Grade: Distinction
Mark:   51      Grade: Pass
Mark:   32      Grade: Fail
```

Logical operators

Logical operators allow you to combine logical expressions. There are three logical operators in VB: And, Or and Not. An example of the use of the And operator was provided in Listing 8. The And and the Or operators are always placed between two logical expressions, and they each combine these logical expressions to produce a value of true or false. Table 63.5 shows the rules that are applied by VB to determine whether a compound logical expression is true or false. This type of table is usually called a *truth table*.

(Expr 1)	(Expr 2)	(Expr 1) Or (Expr 2)	(Expr 1) And (Expr 2)
true	true	true	true
true	false	true	false
false	true	true	false
false	false	false	false

Table 63.5. *Truth table for the* **And** *and* **Or** *logical operators*

Look at Listing 63.8, on line *80*, where the compound logical expression (Mark >= MERIT) And (Mark < DIST) is used to determine whether the mark is equivalent to a merit grade. In the expression, (Mark >= MERIT) is an example of (Expr 1) and (Mark < DIST) is an example of (Expr 2) shown in Table 63.5.

The next table (Table 63.6) shows how the And operator combines these two logical expressions for a number of cases.

Mark	(Mark > = Merit)	(Mark < Dist)	(Mark > = Merit And (Mark < Dist)
45	false	true	false
86	true	false	false
67	true	true	true

Table 63.6. *Truth table for the* **And** *logical operator*

Thus, both logical expressions must be true for the complete expression to be true; with the Or operator, however, only one of the expressions needs to be true for the complete expression to be true. For example, consider the program in Listing 63.9 which reads some text and counts how many vowels it contains. The program uses a For loop to test each letter in turn in the text against each possible vowel. If the current letter is a vowel, that is 'a', 'e', 'i', 'o' or 'u', a count is incremented.

Listing 63.9. Illustrating the use of the Or logical operator (Example09.BAS)

```
Public Sub Main()
' ====== Program to illustrate the use of the Or operator =======

' Declare constants and variables
10 Dim VowelCount As Integer
20 Dim Letters As String
30 Dim LengthOfText As Integer
40 Dim c As Integer

' Initialise vowel count variable
50 VowelCount = 0

' Get the text to process
60 Letters = InputBox("Type text followed by ENTER: ", "Vowel count")
70 LengthOfText = Len(Letters)

' Count the number of vowels
80  For c = 1 To LengthOfText
90    If (Mid(Letters, c, 1) = "a") Or
         (Mid(Letters, c, 1) = "e") Or
         (Mid(Letters, c, 1) = "i") Or
         (Mid(Letters, c, 1) = "o") Or
         (Mid(Letters, c, 1) = "u") Then
100     VowelCount = VowelCount + 1
110   End If
120 Next c

'Display the results
130 Debug.Print "You entered "; Letters
140 Debug.Print "The text contains "; VowelCount; " vowels"
End Sub
```

The text is held in a string variable called Letters. Each letter in Letters is accessed by specifying its position within the text. For example, if the text entered was the string 'hello there', then Mid(Letters,1,1) is the letter 'h', Mid(Letters,2,1) is the letter 'e', Mid(Letters,3,1) is the letter 'l', and so on. The function Mid allows us to access one or more characters from a string. The first item in the brackets is the string to search, the second is the position in the string to start, and the third is the number of characters to access. So `Mid(Letters,5,2)` would return two characters starting at position 5 and `Mid(Letters,c,1)` returns the single character at position c.

The `For` loop control variable, c, starts at 1 and goes up in steps of 1 to the length of the string (11 for the string 'hello there'). The length of the string is determined by the VB function `len()`, on line *70*, which requires a string as its single argument.

Here is the output from the program when the string, 'the cat sat on the mat' is typed in:

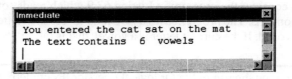

```
Immediate
You entered the cat sat on the mat
The text contains   6   vowels
```

Note that the program will only work with lower-case text. The reason is that lower-case letters 'a', 'b', 'c', etc are represented in a computer using a different set of codes from the equivalent upper-case letters 'A', 'B', 'C', etc.

The third logical operator is the `Not` operator which simply reverses the logical value of a logical expression. Thus, the logical expression `Not (x >3)` is true only when x is less than or equal to 3. Similarly, the logical expression `Not (Balance <= 0)` is true only when Balance has a value that is greater than zero. The truth table shown in Table 63.7 defines the operation of the `Not` logical operator.

Expr	not Expr
true	false
false	true

Table 63.7. *Truth table for* `not` *logical operator*

The Select..Case statement

The `Select` statement is an alternative method to the `If` statement for choosing between alternative courses of action within a program. It has the following general format:

```
Select Case {expression}
Case value list 1
   statement 1
            Case value list 2
                statement 2
      etc...
      ......
Case Else
     statement N
Select End
```

The expression after `Select Case` can be a single variable or an expression involving several variables. VB matches the value of this single variable or expression against the values specified in the Case value lists; when a match is found, the corresponding statements are executed after which the Select statement is immediately exited without considering any remaining values. If there are no values that match the variable, the Select statement does nothing unless the Else option is used, in which circumstances the supplied statement or statements (shown as statement N above) are executed.

In Listing 63.10, the Select statement is used to find the number of days in a month given the month number (1 to 12):

Listing 63.10. Illustrating the use of the Select statement (Example10.BAS)

```
Public Sub Main()
' ====== Program to illustrate the use of the Or operator =======


' Declare constants and variables
10 Const Title = "Days in month"
20 Const Buttons = vbOKOnly
30 Dim Month As Integer
40 Dim Response As Integer

' Get month number
50 Month = InputBox("Enter a month number(1 to 12)", Title)

' Determine days in month
60   Select Case Month
     Case 1, 3, 5, 7, 8, 10, 12
70     Msg = "There are 31 days in month " & Month
     Case 4, 6, 9, 11
       Msg = "There are 30 days in month " & Month
     Case 2
       Msg = "There are 28 days in month " & Month
80   Case Else
90     Msg = "Invalid month number: " & Month
     End Select

' Report days in month using a message box
100 Response = MsgBox(Msg, Buttons, Title)
End Sub
```

Month contains a number corresponding to the month of the year, where January = 1, February = 2 ..... December = 12. The Select..Case statement is used to store, in the variable, Days, the number of days in the month whose number is stored in Month. Thus if Month contained the number 8 corresponding to August, Days would be assigned the value 31. The example uses a Message Box function on line *100* to display the number of days in the specified month. The message box displays a window with a title, a message and a single OK button as illustrated alongside.

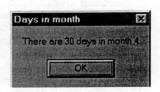

A Message box can display a variety of different buttons that can be specified by using appropriate VB constants as shown below:

Constant	Value	Description
vbOKOnly	0	Display OK button only
vbOKCancel	1	Display OK and Cancel buttons
vbAbortRetryIgnore	2	Display Abort, Retry, and Ignore buttons
vbYesNoCancel	3	Display Yes, No, and Cancel buttons
vbYesNo	4	Display Yes and No buttons
vbRetryCancel	5	Display Retry and Cancel buttons

The function returns the value corresponding to the button that the user selects:

Constant	Value	Button chosen
vbOK	1	OK
vbCancel	2	Cancel
vbAbort	3	Abort
vbRetry	4	Retry
vbIgnore	5	Ignore
vbYes	6	Yes
vbNo	7	No

This allows us to take different forms of action depending on the button clicked. (See Listing 63.11). However, in our example this value is not used - we simply display a message and stop.

The message to display is stored in the variable Msg and is set according to the Case clause that corresponds to the Month entered by the user. Notice that to join together strings (*concatenate*) we use the & operator, as in line *70 :*

```
70    Msg = "There are 31 days in month " & Month
```

In the next example we use another form of the Message box function in combination with the Select statement.

Listing 63.11.   Illustrating the use of the Select statement (Example11.BAS)

```
Public Sub Main()
' ====== Program to illustrate the use of Select..Case =======

' Declare constants and variables
10 Const Title = "Smoking"
20 Const MsgYes = "Smoking is bad for you!"
30 Const MsgNo = "Good for you!!"
40 Dim Response As Integer

' Display message box
50 Response = MsgBox("Do you smoke?", vbYesNo, Title)

' Determine whether smoker or non-smoker and report
60 Select Case Response
    Case vbNo
70    Response = MsgBox(MsgNo, vbOKOnly, Title)
```

```
      Case vbYes
80    Response = MsgBox(MsgYes, vbOKOnly, Title)
      End Select

End Sub
```

If the user clicks the Yes button in the Message box that is displayed by line 70 variable, Response is assigned the value vbYes(6) ; if the user clicks the No button, Response is assigned the value vbNo (7). The Select statement then determines which button was clicked and displays the appropriate message.

Arrays

An *array* is a data structure which allows you to store a number of items of data without having to allocate separate variable names to them. Arrays must be declared before they are used. For example, the following declaration is for an array of five integers:

```
      Dim Array(5) As Integer
```

This single declaration is in effect defining five variables called Array(1), Array(2), Array(3), Array(4) and Array(5), each of which can store a single integer value. The integer value inside the square brackets is called the array's index, and it is allowed only to take the range of values specified in the declaration (1 to 5 inclusive in this example). Each of these identifiers can be used just like any ordinary integer variable. For instance, to set each of them to zero could be accomplished as follows:

```
      Array(1) = 0
      Array(2) = 0
      Array(3) = 0
      Array(4) = 0
      Array(5) = 0
```

However, we could accomplish the same operation by using an integer variable as an *index* and by putting a single assignment statement in a For loop:

```
      For i = 1 to 5
        Array(i)= 0
      Next i
```

Now the count variable i takes on the integer values 1 to 5 and again each element in the array is set to zero. The obvious advantage of using a variable for an index is that arrays can then be used very effectively within loops, and they allow the manipulation of as many or as few numbers as appropriate to the task in hand; notice that the same For loop could initialise 5000 array elements as easily as 5 elements:

```
      For i = 1 to 5000
        Array(i) = 0
      Next i
```

This would be an exceedingly difficult task to accomplish without the use of an array.

Listing 63.12 illustrates the use of an array of real numbers. The program reads five numbers into an array and then finds the position within the array of the smallest number. It then swaps this number with the first number in the list before displaying the re-ordered array.

Listing 63.12.   Using an array (Example12.BAS)

```
Public Sub Main()
' ====== Program to illustrate the use an array =======

' Declare constants and variables
10 Const MAXNUMS = 5
15 Dim Array1(MAXNUMS) As Integer
   Dim Temp As Integer
   Dim i As Integer

' Get the numbers
20 For i = 1 To MAXNUMS
30    Array1(i) = InputBox("Enter number " & i & " of " & MAXNUMS)
35 Next i

' Find the smallest and store in first array element
40 For i = 2 To MAXNUMS
50    If Array1(i) < Array1(1) Then
60       Temp = Array1(1)
70       Array1(1) = Array1(i)
80       Array1(i) = Temp
      End If
   Next i

' Print the new list
   Debug.Print "The new list is as follows: "
90 For i = 1 To MAXNUMS
      Debug.Print Array1(i);
   Next i
 End Sub
```

The program first defines a constant MAXNUMS to be the maximum size of the integer array, Array1. Lines *20* to *35* are to read in the five numbers with appropriate user prompts. Thus the first number is read into Array1(1), the second into Array1(2), and so on up to the last number which is read into Array1(5). The second For loop starting on line *40* compares each number in the array in turn with the first number; if one is found that is less than the first, they are swapped over. By the time the last number in the array has been compared with the first one, the smallest number is in the first position in the array. A typical run of the program might be:

```
Enter number 1 of 5 :5
Enter number 2 of 5 :3
Enter number 3 of 5 :9
Enter number 4 of 5 :1
Enter number 5 of 5 :8
```

```
Immediate
The new list is as follows:
 1  5  9  3  8
```

The output appears as shown alongside.

As a final example in this section on arrays, Listing 63.13 shows a program which uses a random number generator to select five lottery numbers in the range 1 to 49.

Listing 63.13.   Random numbers and array to generate lottery numbers (Example13.BAS)

```
Public Sub Main()
' ====== Program to use random numbers to use an array
'        to generate 5 lottery numbers          =======

' Declare constants and variables
10   Const NUMOFNUMS = 5
20   Const MAXNUM = 49
30   Dim LuckyNums(MAXNUM) As Boolean
40   Dim Num As Integer
50   Dim i As Integer
60   Dim Count As Integer

'Display heading
     Debug.Print "Lottery random number generator"
     Debug.Print

' Initialise array
70   For i = 1 To MAXNUM
80      LuckyNums(i) = False
90   Next i

' Initialise count for numbers generated
100 Count = 0

' Initialise random number generator
110 Randomize

' Generate the lottery numbers
120 While Count < NUMOFNUMS
130   Num = Int(MAXNUM * Rnd()) + 1
140    If LuckyNums(Num) = False Then
150       Debug.Print Num;
160       LuckyNums(Num) = True
170       Count = Count + 1
180    End If
190 Wend

200  End Sub
```

The random numbers are generated using the function Rnd() which produces a random number less than 1 but greater than or equal to 0. To produce a random number in the range 0 to MAXNUM, we use the statement

```
130   Num = Int(MAXNUM * Rnd()) + 1
```

This instruction multiplies the random number by MAXNUM (i.e. 49) to produce a number in the range 0 to less than 49. The Int function then rounds this number down to the nearest integer, thus giving a number in the range 0 to 48. Then 1 is added to produce a number in the range 1 to 49.

The randomize instruction on line *110* simply initialises the random number generator so that it does not produce the same sequence of random numbers every time the program is run.

Lines *70-90* initialises each element to False in the array LuckyNums() which is to be used to record the five numbers that are generated.

The reason for the If statement on lines *140* to *180* is to ensure that the same random number is not used more than once. When a number is generated, the appropriate element in the LuckyNums array is checked to see if it has a value of False which indicates that the number has not been generated before. Then, to record that the number has been generated, that element is set to True in the LuckyNums array. For example, if the first random number generated on line *130* was the number 36, then this would be stored in Num. The If statement checks that 36 has not been used already by checking if LuckyNums(36) still has its initial value of False. If this is the case, 36 is displayed (line *150*), LuckyNums(36) is set to True and Count is increased by 1. Thus if 36 is generated again, the If statement will prevent it from being used. The While loop repeats until five different numbers have been generated.

Here is an example from the output of Example 13:

```
Immediate
Lottery random number generator

14   24   37   41   28 |
```

Strings

A string is a set of characters such as "24, Railway Terrace, Willington" or "Hello" or "123abc". Strings can be stored by string variables and they can be manipulated in various ways using special Visual Basic functions. In this section we will briefly review a number of common functions used for handling strings and then apply them in an example program.

Declaring strings and assigning strings to variables

Use the Dim statement to declare a variable as a string variable. For example, to declare the variable "Myname" as a string use the statement

```
Dim Myname As String
```

Declare Myname before it is used in the program.

There is no practical limit on the size of a string (up to about 2 billion characters).

To store characters in a string you simply use an assignment statement such as

```
Myname = "Ivar Peregrine Trews"
```

The right-hand side of this statement, that is the text in quotation marks, is called a string *literal*.

To clear a string variable, store the empty string, "" (double quotes with nothing between), in it:

```
Myname = ""
```

To join strings together (concatenate) use the & operator. The following example illustrates how to concatenate strings:

```
Dim Firstname As String,  Surname As String, Fullname As String
Firstname = "John"
Surname = "Smith"
Fullname = Surname &  ", " & Firstname
```

The variable Fullname would then contain the string "Smith, John"

String length - Len()

This function returns the length of a string, that is, the number of characters in the string.

Example

```
Mystring = "Hello there"
L = Len(Mystring)
```

(L would be assigned the value 11)

Substrings - Left(), Right() and Mid()

These three functions are used to extract parts of strings (*substrings*) from strings.

Left(string,length) returns a specified number of characters (length) from the left side of a string (string).

Examples

```
MyString = "Hello There"       ' Define string.
Str1 = Left(MyString, 1)       ' Returns "H".
Str2 = Left(MyString, 7)       ' Returns "Hello T".
Str3 = Left(MyString, 20)      ' Returns "Hello There".
```

Right(string,length) returns a specified number of characters (length) from the right side of a string (string).

Examples

```
MyString = "Hello There"       ' Define string.
Str1 = Right(MyString, 1)      ' Returns "e".
Str2 = Right(MyString, 5)      ' Returns "There".
Str3 = Right(MyString, 20)     ' Returns "Hello There".
```

Mid(string, start, [length]) returns a specified number of characters (length) starting from position start in a string (string). length is optional and if omitted all characters from start to the end of the string are returned.

Examples

```
MyString = "Hello There"       ' Create text string.
Str1 = Mid(MyString, 1, 3)     ' Returns "Hel".
Str2 = Mid(MyString, 7, 5)     ' Returns "There".
Str3 = Mid(MyString, 7)        ' Returns "There".
Str4 = Mid(MyString, 5, 1)     ' Returns "o".
```

Searching strings - Instr()

InStr([start,]string1, string2[, compare]) returns the position of the first occurrence of string2 within string1 starting from position start in string1. The optional parameter compare can be used to specify whether the search is to be case sensitive (compare = 0) or not (compare = 1). If compare is omitted the comparison is case sensitive (binary comparison). The `start` value is also optional - if omitted the search starts from the first character in `string1`. If the search string, `string2`, is not found in `string1`, the function returns a value of 0, otherwise it returns the position of the first character of `string2` within `string1`.

Examples

```
MyString = "Information and Communications Technology"
Pos1 = Instr( MyString, "c", 0)      ' Returns 24 - case sensitive
Pos2 = Instr( MyString, "com", 1)    ' Returns 17 - case insensitive


Pos3 = Instr( MyString, "com")       ' Returns 0 - case sensitive
Pos4 = Instr( 25, MyString, "c")     ' Returns 34 - start position 25
```

Example program to illustrate string handling

This example program splits a sentence into separate words by looking for a space at the end of a word. It is assumed that there are no extra spaces between words or any spaces at the beginning or end of the sentence, and that the sentence contains no punctuation marks.

Listing 63.14.   String handling (Example14.BAS)

```
Public Sub Main()
' ====== Program to use illustrate the use of some string
'         handling functions                              =======
' Declare constants and variables
 Dim Sentence As String, Word As String
 Dim CurPos As Integer, SpacePos As Integer, L As Integer

' Get the sentence
10 Sentence = InputBox("Please type in a sentence")

' Add space at end to simplify coding
20 Sentence = Sentence & " "

' Set the starting point for searching sentence
30 CurPos = 1

' Get the length of the sentence
40 L = Len(Sentence)

' Look for spaces and extract words
50  While CurPos < L
60    SpacePos = InStr(CurPos, Sentence, " ")
70    Word = Mid(Sentence, CurPos, SpacePos - CurPos)
80    Debug.Print Word
90    CurPos = SpacePos + 1  ' update search start position
100 Wend
End Sub
```

The user is requested to type in the sentence on line *10*. Line *20* adds a single space to the end of the sentence to simplify the programming required to extract single words. (this allows us to assume that all words in the sentence are followed by a space).

The starting position for the search is set at the beginning of the sentence on line *30*. CurPos will store the start position of each new word located.

On line *40* the length of the sentence is stored in the variable L.

The main part of the program is the While loop from lines *50* to *100*. The position of the next space in the sentence is located using the Instr() function. It is not necessary to use the compare option because a space does not have upper and lower case.

Line *70* extracts a word using the Mid() function. SpacePos contains the position of the space at the end of the word and CurPos is the position of the first letter in the word; thus the length of the word is given by SpacePos - CurPos.

Finally, the extracted word is printed, CurPos is set to the beginning of the next word and the loop repeats.

The loop ends when CurPos exceeds L, the length of the sentence.

Some Visual Basic Functions

We have already used a few functions in the example programs. The previous lottery number program used rnd() to generate random numbers and int() to convert a real number to an integer. We have also used the MsgBox() function to display a window and return a value to indicate which button the user clicked. Functions are pre-written subprograms that perform frequently required tasks. There are a great number of Visual Basic functions available to the programmer, and you can use the VB Help facility to research them and to see examples of how they can be used. Here we list and briefly describe a selection of them.

Function	Purpose
Abs	Returns the absolute value of a number
Asc	Returns the character code corresponding to the first letter in a string
Atn	Returns the arctangent of a number
Chr	Returns the character associated with the specified character code.
Cos	Returns the cosine of a number
CurDir	Returns the current path
Date	Returns the current system date.
Dir	Returns the name of a file or directory that matches a specified pattern or file attribute, or the volume label of a drive.
DoEvents	Yields execution so that the operating system can process other events
EOF	Returns a value that indicates whether the end of a file has been reached

Error	Returns the error message that corresponds to a given error number.
Exp	Returns e (the base of natural logarithms) raised to a power
Input	Returns characters from an open sequential or binary file
InStr	Returns the position of the first occurrence of one string within another
Int	Returns the integer portion of a number
IsNumeric	Returns a Boolean value indicating whether an expression can be evaluated as a number
Left	Returns a specified number of characters from the left side of a string
Len	Returns the number of characters in a string or the number of bytes required to store a variable.
Log	Returns the natural logarithm of a number.
Ltrim, Rtrim, Trim	Returns a copy of a string without leading spaces (LTrim), trailing spaces (RTrim), or both leading and trailing spaces (Trim).
Mid	Returns a specified number of characters from a string
MsgBox	Displays a message in a dialog box, waits for the user to choose a button, and returns a value indicating which button the user has chosen.
Now	Returns the current date and time according to the setting of your computer's system date and time
Right	Returns a specified number of characters from the right side of a string.
Rnd	Returns a random number
Sgn	Returns an integer indicating the sign of a number.
Shell	Runs an executable program
Sin	Returns the sine of an angle
Space	Returns a string consisting of the specified number of spaces
Sqr	Returns the square root of a number
Str	Returns a string representation of a number
StrComp	Returns a value indicating the result of a string comparison
String	Returns a repeating character string of the length specified
Tan	Returns the tangent of an angle.
Timer	Returns the number of seconds elapsed since midnight.
Val	Returns the numbers contained in a string

Programming Exercises

Decisions

1. Read a number and display a message which states whether the number is positive, negative or zero.

2. Read a number and print it only if it is between 10 and 20.

3   Read a number and a single letter code. The number represents the price of an item and the code indicates whether tax is to be added to the price. If the code is "V" then the tax is 20% of the item's cost. If the code is "X" then the item is not taxed. Display the total cost of the item.

4   Read three positive, non-zero integers which may represent the sides of a triangle. The numbers are in ascending order of size. Determine whether or not the numbers do represent the sides of a triangle. (The largest side must be smaller than the sum of the other two sides).

5   Extend the previous question to determine the type of triangle if one is possible with the values provided. Assume that the only types of triangles to consider are:

> scalene- no equal sides;
>
> isosceles - two equal sides;
>
> equilateral - three equal sides.

6. Read in a single character and display a message indicating whether or not it is a vowel.

Loops

7. Write separate programs to produce conversion tables for:

   (i)   Inches to centimetres (1 to 20 inches, 1 inch = 2.54 centimetres);

   (ii) Pounds to kilograms (1 to 10 pounds, 2.2 pounds per kilogram);

   (iii) Square yards to square metres (10, 20 ,30,..., 100 sq yds 1yd = .91 m)

8. The cost and discount code of a number of items are to be entered by a user. The program must print out each item's cost, discount and cost less discount. The discount codes are as follows:

Code	Discount
A	5%
B	10%
C	15%

The program will terminate when the user enters 0 for the cost of the item. The program must then display the total cost of all the items entered.

9. A program reads an integer representing the number of gas bills to be processed, followed by that number of customer details. Each set of customer details consists of a customer number, a single character code representing the type of customer and the number of units used. Customers are of type 'D' (domestic) or 'B' (business). Domestic customers are charged 8p per unit and business customers are charged 10p per unit. For each customer display the customer number, the number of units used and the cost of the gas used. Print the total number of units used for this batch of customers and the total amount charged.

10. Repeat the previous question assuming that all the domestic users are first and that separate totals are required for domestic and business users.

Strings

11. Read two strings and compare them. Display a message to indicate whether or not they are identical.

12. Repeat the previous problem but ignore case. For example, your program should regard the strings "Hello There", "HELLO THERE", and "hello there" as being identical.

13. Read a string representing a sentence and display average length of the words in the sentence. Assume that words are separated by no more than one space and that there are no punctuation marks in the text.

14. Write separate programs to enter and store a string of up to 80 characters and then:
    (i) Count the number of leading spaces;
    (ii) Count the number of trailing spaces;
    (iii) Count the number of embedded spaces;
    (iv) Count the number of leading, trailing and embedded spaces;
    (v) Remove leading and trailing spaces from a string, and reduce multiple embedded spaces to single spaces.

15. Read a string containing a sentence and display the words in reverse order. For example, the sentence "the cat sat on the mat" would become, "mat the on sat cat the".

16. Read a string and determine whether it is purely alphabetic, purely numeric or a mixture of alphabetic and numeric characters.

Arrays

17. Read 5 values into a numeric array and then:
    (i) display the contents the array;
    (ii) find the average of the numbers stored in the array;
    (iii) copy the array into a duplicate array, but in reverse order. Display the contents of both arrays.

18. Read a set of numbers and swap the first number with the largest in the set. Then, starting from the second value, find the largest number in the remaining list and swap it with the second value. Repeat this process until the list has been sorted into descending order of magnitude.

Validation

19. Post codes have the following possible formats:
    (i) *aa99 9aa*
    (ii) *aa9 9aa*
    (iii) *a9a 9aa*

    where *a* represents an alphabetic character and *9* represents a numeric character. Write a program to validate a post code, assuming that only uppercase letters are used and there is a single space separating the two parts of the post code.

20. As for the previous problem but allow upper and lower case letters, leading spaces, trailing spaces and more than one space between the two parts of the code.

Encoding

21. Many names that sound the same are often spelled differently and this can cause problems in information systems. For example, Waites, Waits and Whaites all sound the same though they are all spelled differently and contain different numbers of letters. A coding system called Soundex can be used to solve this problem by converting a name into a code based on the following algorithm.

    (i)   The first letter of the name is used as the first letter of the code.

    (ii)   All subsequent vowels, and the letters H, W and Y are ignored.

    (iii) Double letters are replaced by single instances of the letter.

    (iv)   Then this code, apart from the first character, is converted into a number by substituting the letters in the following table by numeric digits.

letter	substitute digit
BFPV	1
CGJKQSXZ	2
DT	3
L	4
MN	5
R	6

    (v)   The code is restricted to four characters including the leading letter.

    (vi)   If the code is less than four characters it is padded with zeros.

    Write a program to convert a name into its equivalent Soundex code. Some examples are given below.

    Morton becomes *M635*

    Morten becomes *M635*

    Waites becomes *W320*

    Whaites becomes *W320*

    Waits becomes *W320*

22. The following table illustrates the Morse code.

A	.-	N	-.
B	-...	O	—
C	-.-.	P	.--.
D	-..	Q	--.-
E	.	R	.-.
F	..-.	S	...
G	--.	T	-
H	....	U	..-
I	..	V	...-

J	.---	W	.--
K	-.-	X	-..-
L	.-..	Y	-.---
M	--	Z	--..

Write a program to read in a word (or a sentence if you wish) and output it in Morse code.

23. A form of encoding used on the Internet is called "rot13" encoding. It involves taking each letter of the alphabet and replacing it by the letter 13 positions further on in the alphabet as shown in the following table.

letter	replacement letter	letter	replacement letter	letter	replacement letter
A	N	J	W	S	F
B	O	K	X	T	G
C	P	L	Y	U	H
D	Q	M	Z	V	I
E	R	N	A	W	J
F	S	O	B	X	K
G	T	P	C	Y	L
H	U	Q	D	Z	M
I	V	R	E		

(i)   Write a program to read a block of text and encode it using rot13. Spaces and punctuation marks do not need to be encoded.

(ii) Enhance the above program by also encoding punctuation marks and spaces.

(iii) Write a program to decode text which has been encoded using rot13.

(iv) Invent and implement your own encoding and decoding scheme using a different form of substitution.

Overview

In this topic we progress to using Visual Basic as a Windows Programming Application Generator rather than as a traditional programming language. To do this we need to begin to use *Forms* and *Controls*, and understand what is meant by *Event-driven* programming.

In Visual Basic, Forms and Controls are primary *Objects*. They are classed as Objects because they have characteristics that are typical of Object-Oriented Programming (OOP). In particular, Forms and Controls have *Properties*, *Methods* and *Events* associated with them. Properties define the appearance or behaviour of an object, Methods are procedures that perform actions associated with Forms and Controls, and Events are actions - such as user mouse clicks - that trigger the execution of program code.

Forms and Controls

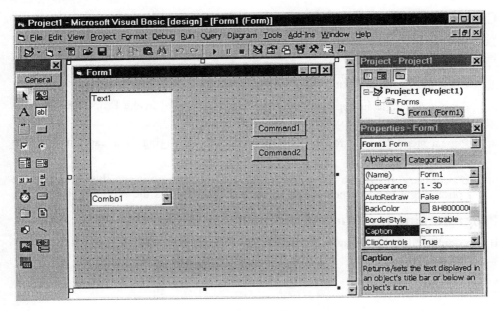

One of the great strengths of VB is the ease with which a complex graphical user interface can be constructed. The main component used for this is the Form on which Controls are placed. Controls are selected from the VB Toolbox and positioned on the form using the mouse. A Form and its Controls can be configured and modified using the Properties box. The screen shot above shows a Form (Form1) with the Toolbox on the left and the properties box on the right. There are four controls on the forms: two Command Buttons (Command1 and Command2), a Text Box (Text1) and a Combo box (Combo1).

Clicking on a control or a blank area of the form causes the properties box to display all of the properties for that object. These properties can be changed by clicking in the appropriate data cell to the right of the property name. For instance, the Form's Caption (the Caption is the text that appears in the title bar of the form) can be changed to, say, "MyForm" by editing "Form1".

To illustrate the creation of a simple Form and some associated Controls, we will design a program to perform a simple animation.

A Simple event-driven program - "Winking face"

When you launch VB and start a new project, you are automatically provided with a blank form called "Form1". Alternatively, if you wish you can add a Form to the current project by clicking the Add Form button on the toolbar. In this example we will start a new project and add three CommandButton controls to the blank Form. We will then use Click events to make the program respond to CommandButton Clicks. Our aim is to produce a Form as shown on the right.

Creating the Form and Controls

To create the Form and Controls, follow the steps listed below:

1.   Start a new project.

2.   Click the CommandButton tool on the Toolbox.

3.   Drag a rectangle in approximately the location shown. In the Properties window, change the Caption property to "Show face".

4.   Repeat steps 2 and 3 for the two other buttons, changing their captions to those shown.

5.   If necessary, resize the form by clicking a blank area on it and then dragging the bottom right-hand corner control node until the form is the required size.

Programming the CommandButtons

If you double click the "Show face" button, the code window will open:

```
Private Sub Command1_Click()
|
End Sub
```

The name of the button, "Command1", is displayed along with a blank procedure ("Command1_Click") for the Click event. The code that we will insert will be executed when Command1 (ie the "Show face" button) is clicked by the user when the program is running.

Add the following code to the `Command1+Click` event procedure:

```
Private Sub Command1_Click()
Form1.Cls
Form1.Print "    ---    "
Form1.Print " < 0  0 >  "
Form1.Print "  |  ^  |  "
Form1.Print "    \_/    "

End Sub
```

In this code we are calling two Form methods - `Cls` and `Print`.

`Form.Cls` clears Form1 of any text and graphics and `Form1.Print` prints the specified text.

Now run the program. When you click the "Show face" button you should see a face that looks something like this (it may be a bit distorted but we will correct this later):

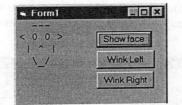

Next, add click event procedures for the other two Command buttons:

```
Private Sub Command2_Click()
Form1.Cls
Form1.Print "    ---    "
Form1.Print " < 0  o >  "
Form1.Print "  |  ^  |  "
Form1.Print "    \_/    "
End Sub
```

```
Private Sub Command3_Click()
Form1.Cls
Form1.Print "    ---    "
Form1.Print " < o  0 >  "
Form1.Print "  |  ^  |  "
Form1.Print "    \_/    "
End Sub
```

When you run the program again, all three buttons should now operate.

The face that appears will probably look different from those illustrated. The reason is that the default font for Form1 needs to be set to a font such as "Courier New". This property setting can be done manually using the Properties window for the form but, in order to illustrate the use of another event procedure, we will change the font with code.

To change the default font for Form1, do the following:

Double click on an empty area of Form1 to make the code window appear. The cursor will be in the blank `Form_Load` procedure. Add the line shown below:

```
Private Sub Form_Load()
  Form1.Font = "Courier New"
End Sub
```

Now, when you run the program, before Form1 appears, the `Form_Load` event procedure will be executed, thus setting the form font to Courier New. Then, when the Command buttons are clicked, the faces should appear undistorted.

ComboBox and TextBox Controls

The screenshot below shows a form containing two ComboBox controls and a TextBox control. A TextBox control, sometimes called an edit field or edit control, displays information entered by the user. In this example it allows a user to enter a currency amount to be converted to another currency. A ComboBox control allows users to enter information in the text box portion or select an item from the drop-down list portion of the control. The ComboBox controls in this example each provide the same drop-down list as shown.

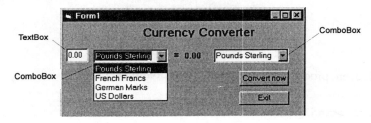

The form allows a user to enter in the TextBox control a number representing an amount of money in a currency specified by the first ComboBox. This amount is to be converted to the currency specified in the second ComboBox. When the "Convert now" command button is clicked, the equivalent amount of the target currency is calculated and displayed. For example, the next screenshot shows 230 Pounds Sterling converted to French Francs:

In this example we will:

❑   Create the form controls

❑   Configure the two ComboBox controls

❑ Create a global array to store exchange rates

❑ Initialise the program using the `Form_Load` event procedure

❑ Program the two Command buttons

Creating the Form and Controls

To create the Form and Controls, follow the steps listed below:

1. Start a new project.

2. Click the TextBox Control tool in the Toolbox

3. Drag a rectangle in approximately the location shown

4. In the Properties window, set the Text property to "0.00"

5. Click the ComboBox tool in the Toolbox

6. Drag a rectangle in the location shown for the leftmost ComboBox.

7. In the Properties window, set the Style property to "2 - Dropdown list"

8. In the Properties window, click in the List property box and Enter the following list of items: Pounds Sterling, French Francs, German Marks, US Dollars. You need to hold down the control key (Ctrl) while you press Enter after each item.

9. Repeat steps 5 - 8 for the second ComboBox

10. Click the Command Button tool in the Toolbox.

11. In the Properties window, change the Caption property to "Convert now"

12. Repeat steps 2 and 3 for the "Exit" button

13. There are three labels on the form: Label1, the Title ("Currency Converter"); Label2, the "=" sign; Label3, the converted amount immediately to the right of Label2. These are created using the Label tool. Use the Caption property to change these labels as follows:

    Label1: "Currency Converter"

    Label2: "="

    Label3: "0.00"

    Also use the Font property to increase the size of the title and use the ForeColor property to change the colour of the title.

14. If necessary, resize the form by clicking a blank area on it and then dragging the bottom right-hand corner control node until the form is the required size.

Initialising the Form

When the program runs, the `Form_Load` event triggers. We will use this event to modify the two ComboBoxes so that they show the first item in the list of currencies, ie "Pounds Sterling". We use the `ListIndex` property for the ComboBoxes to set the default item to the first one. Each item in a ComboBox has an index ranging from 0 to one less than the number of items in the list. In our case the items and indexes are shown in the first two columns of the following table:

Index	Item	ExchRate()
0	Pounds Sterling	1
1	French France	11
2	German Marks	4
3	US Dollars	1.5

The third column shows the appropriate exchange rates for the currencies stored in the array `ExchRate()`. This array is used in the currency conversion calculation explained later.

The code shown below sets the `ListIndex` values for both ComboBoxes to 0.

```
Private Sub Form_Load()

' Set each combo box to show the first item in the list
    Combo1.ListIndex = 0
    Combo2.ListIndex = 0

End Sub
```

Programming the Command Buttons

The code for the "Convert now" Command Button is shown below.

```
Private Sub Command1_Click()
' ===== Procedure to convert from one currency to another ======

' Declare variables used
10    Dim FromCurrency As Integer, ToCurrency As Integer
20    Dim AmountFrom As Single, AmountPS As Single, AmountTo As Single
      Dim ExchRate(4) As Single

' Set up exchange rates (these are not accurate figures!)
30    ExchRate(0) = 1     ' Pounds
40    ExchRate(1) = 11    ' Francs
50    ExchRate(2) = 4     ' Marks
60    ExchRate(3) = 1.5   ' Dollars


' Get the From and To currencies chosen
70    FromCurrency = Combo1.ListIndex
80    ToCurrency = Combo2.ListIndex

' Get the amount to convert from
90    AmountFrom = Val(Text1.Text)

' Convert to Pounds Sterling
100    AmountPS = AmountFrom / ExchRate(FromCurrency)
```

```
' Convert from Pounds to target currency
110    AmountTo = AmountPS * ExchRate(ToCurrency)

' Display equivalent amount by changing  Label3's caption
120    Label3.Caption = AmountTo

End Sub
```

The `Command1_Click` procedure contains the code required to convert from one currency to another. The method is to first convert the 'From' currency to Pounds Sterling by dividing by the exchange rate for that currency. Then this figure is converted to the 'To' currency by multiplying the number of Pounds Sterling by the exchange rate for the target currency. Lines *90* to *110* perform these calculations. The appropriate exchange rates are stored in the array `ExchRate()`, as shown in the earlier Table, so that the ListIndexes for the ComboBoxes matches the array indexes. For instance, if the user selects "German Marks" as the 'From' currency, this item's ListIndex is 2 and the exchange rate for Marks is stored in `ExchRate(2)`.

Line *70* determines the ListIndex for the 'From' Currency and line 80 determines the ListIndex for the 'To' currency.

Line *90* uses the Text property of the TextBox, `Text1`, to determine the amount of money to be used in the conversion. The `Val()` function converts a string to a numeric value that can be used in a calculation

Line *100* converts the 'From' currency to Pounds Sterling. Then on line *110*, this value is converted to the target currency.

Finally, the answer is displayed in `Label3` by using its Caption property.

Frames, OptionButtons and CheckBoxes

The next Form contains two Frames captioned "Select system required" and "Select options".

The first frame contains four OptionButtons that allow a user to select one computer system from the four choices available. When a user clicks one of a group of OptionButtons (sometimes called "radio buttons"), all of the other buttons are automatically deselected. In other words, a group of OptionButtons allow only one button in the group to selected at any one time. On the other hand, a user can select as many or as few CheckBoxes in a group as required.

The example Form shows the third OptionButton and two CheckBoxes selected. The Frame tool allows number of OptionButtons or CheckBoxes to be collected together so that they operate as an independent group. Frames thus allow a single Form to contain several independent groups of these controls.

The PC Configuration Calculator allows a user to select a PC system and a number of options. Whenever an OptionButton or a CheckBox is selected, the price of the system is immediately calculated and displayed. This facility allows a user to investigate the cost of different system configurations very quickly. The full listing of the program is shown below.

```
' ==== Global variables are defined here ====
10 Dim DVDOpt As Single
   Dim LCDOpt As Single
   Dim ZipOpt As Single
   Dim BasicCost As Single
   Dim SystemCost As Single
   Dim ExtraCost AS Single
```

```
Private Sub Command2_Click()
' Exit program
80 Unload Form1
End Sub
```

```
Private Sub Extras_Click(Index As Integer)
' CheckBox clicked
90 If Extras(0).Value = 1 Then
     DVDOpt = 100
   Else
     DVDOpt = 0
   End If

100 If Extras(1).Value = 1 Then
     LCDOpt = 500
   Else
     LCDOpt = 0
   End If

110 If Extras(2).Value = 1 Then
       ZipOpt = 150
   Else
     ZipOpt = 0
   End If

120 ExtraCost = DVDOpt + LCDOpt + ZipOpt

130 Call ShowCost
End Sub
```

```
Private Sub Form_Load()

' Initialise global variables when form loaded
140 DVDOpt = 0
    LCDOpt = 0
    ZipOpt = 0

' Initialise Cost variables
150 BasicCost = 600
    SystemCost = BasicCost

' Set first option (Basic system) as default
160 Option1.Value = True

' Display basic cost
    Label3.Caption = "Price: £ " & BasicCost

End Sub
```

```
Private Sub Option1_Click()
170 SystemCost = BasicCost
180 Call ShowCost
End Sub
```

```
Private Sub Option2_Click()
190 SystemCost = BasicCost + 200
200 Call ShowCost
End Sub
```

```
Private Sub Option3_Click()
210 SystemCost = BasicCost + 400
220 Call ShowCost
End Sub
```

```
Private Sub Option4_Click()
230 SystemCost = BasicCost + 600
240 Call ShowCost
End Sub
```

```
Public Sub ShowCost()
' Calculate system cost and display
250 Dim Price As Single
260 Price = SystemCost + ExtraCost
270 Label3.Caption = "Price: £" & Price
End Sub
```

Before looking at this program in more depth, we need to discuss *user-defined procedures* and *functions*, *parameters*, and the difference between *Global* and *Local* variables

User-defined Procedures

We have already used several Event Procedures in previous example programs. These are procedures that are linked to user interactions with a Form's controls. Visual Basic automatically provides empty procedures for all of a control's events. However, programmer-defined procedures can also be created. We can name and create code for our own procedures that are not directly linked to events. For example, in the program listing above, the procedure ShowCost has been created to calculate and display the cost of a computer system. It is invoked, or *called*, by a line such as

```
180 Call ShowCost
```

which causes VB to immediately execute the code in ShowCost before processing the next line. User-defined procedures allow us to split lengthy sections of code into manageable sizes, and also, most importantly, reduces the need to repeat code several times. Thus in the example program above for calculating the cost of a computer system, ShowCost is called from four other locations in addition to line *180*.

User-defined Functions

Functions, in addition to those that are provided by VB, can also be defined. Unlike Procedures, Functions can return a value calculated within the function's code. For example, look at the Function defined below:

```
Public Function Max(x, y)
If x > y Then
    Max = x
Else
    Max = y
End If
End Function
```

The Function Max() receives two numbers from code elsewhere in the program and determines the larger of the two. The value to be returned to the calling code must be assigned to the name of the Function, in this case, Max. To illustrate the use of this function, suppose that somewhere in a program is the line

```
Debug.Print "The larger of the two numbers, 3 and 5, is"; Max(3,5)
```

The value 5 would be displayed in the Immediate (Debug) window because the Function Max() returns the larger of the two numbers supplied to it. The two numbers supplied in brackets are called *Parameters* which are discussed next.

Parameters

A Parameter provides an important method of supplying data to a Procedure or Function. In the section on User-defined Procedures earlier we mentioned that one of their important uses was to avoid repeating code, and being able to use Parameters is essential to this. Passing data to a Procedure allows it to use different data each time it is used, thus greatly increasing its usefulness. For example, the Function Max() in the previous section allows any two numbers - not just 3 and 5 - to be compared. You will see several examples of using parameters in the next topic. (Visual Basic Case Study).

Global variables, Local variables and Scope

When we include a statement such as

```
Dim MyVar As Integer
```

in a procedure, it is classed as a *Local* variable. Local variables are available for use only within the procedure or function in which they are declared. In other words, the *Scope* of such a variable is limited to that procedure. For example, in the previous program listing, on line *250* the statement

```
250 Dim Price As Single
```

defines the Local variable `Price` which can be used only within the procedure `ShowCost`.

However, if a variable is defined in the *Declarations* section of a Form's program module (outside of any of the Form's procedure or functions), it can be used by any procedure or function in that module. For example, again referring to the previous program, the line

```
10 Dim DVDOpt As Single
```

occurs within the Declarations section of the Form and can therefore be used by any of the Form's procedures. Note that parameters used within functions and procedures are automatically local variables.

Creating the PC Configuration Calculator Form

Returning to the example program, we need to create two frames on the form and establish OptionButtons and CheckBoxes in them as shown in the screenshot below.

Proceed as follows:

1. Start a new project.

2. Double click the Frames tool to create a Frame on the form. This will be the "Select system required" Frame.

3. Position and size it to match the screenshot, and then set the caption property to "Select system required".

4. Now double click the OptionButton tool while the frame is selected. An OptionButton will appear in the frame. Set its Caption to "Basic system".

5. Create the three remaining OptionButtons in the same way, changing their Captions to those shown.

6. Next create the "Select options" Frame, and set its Caption.

7. Create the three CheckBoxes inside the frame. Set the name of each of the three checkboxes to "Extras" and set their captions to those required.

8. The title, basic system description and price are all labels (Label1, Label2 and Label3 respectively). Create these labels and change the text to that shown. Note that program code will be used to modify Label3 to show the price of the system chosen by the user so allow space in the label for this.

9. Finally create a CommandButton and change its caption to "Exit".

The code for the PC Configuration Calculator

When the program starts, the Form_Load procedure is executed:

```
Private Sub Form_Load()

' Initialise Extras global variables
140 DVDOpt = 0
    LCDOpt = 0
    ZipOpt = 0

' Initialise Cost global variables
150 BasicCost = 600
    SystemCost = BasicCost

' Set first option (Basic system) as default
160 Option1.Value = True

' Display basic cost
    Label3.Caption = "Price: £ " & BasicCost

End Sub
```

This procedure initialises the global variables which will be used to calculate the cost of the system selected by the user. The cost of the basic system is set to £600 on line 150 and on line 160 the first OptionButton, Option1, is selected. Finally, the price of the basic system is displayed by setting the Caption for Label3 to the basic cost using the & operator to concatenate the literal "Price: £" and the value held in the variable BasicCost (i.e. 600) .

When a user selects a PC system option from the "Select system required" frame, a click event associated with the relevant OptionButton is generated. Referring back to the program listing given earlier, you will see that the code is very simple. For example, when the second OptionButton is clicked, the following code executes:

```
Private Sub Option2_Click()
190 SystemCost = BasicCost + 200
200 Call ShowCost
End Sub
```

SystemCost and BasicCost are global variables defined in the Declarations section. The code simply adds 200 to `BasicCost` (which has been set to 600 in the `Form_Load` procedure) to give `SystemCost`. Similar code is used for the other three options. Then the user-defined procedure `ShowCost` is called. This procedure calculates the total system price, including extras, on line *260* and displays it in `Label3`:

```
Public Sub ShowCost()
' Calculate system cost and display
250 Dim Price As Single
260 Price = SystemCost + ExtraCost
270 Label3.Caption = "Price: £" & Price
End Sub
```

Every time an OptionButton or a CheckBox is clicked this procedure is called so that the new system price will be updated immediately.

The CheckBoxes procedure is handled using a different technique from that used for the OptionBoxes. Notice that we gave all of the CheckBoxes the same name, i.e. "Extras". This created a *Control Array* for the three CheckBoxes. A Control Array allows us to use a **single** event procedure no matter which control is clicked. The particular control within the Control Array that is clicked is identified by the `Index` parameter for the click event procedure, as shown below:

```
Private Sub Extras_Click(Index As Integer)
' CheckBox clicked
90 If Extras(0).Value = 1 Then
     DVDOpt = 100
   Else
     DVDOpt = 0
   End If

100 If Extras(1).Value = 1 Then
      LCDOpt = 500
    Else
      LCDOpt = 0
    End If

110 If Extras(2).Value = 1 Then
        ZipOpt = 150
    Else
        ZipOpt = 0
    End If

120 ExtraCost = DVDOpt + LCDOpt + ZipOpt

130 Call ShowCost
End Sub
```

This parameter is set to the appropriate control's index vale by VB automatically when the control is clicked.

Each of the controls in a Control Array is assigned an integer value for its Index property during the design phase. You can manually set these values but VB automatically assigns values 0, 1, 2 etc for you. In this example we do not need to use the Index value since we need to find out whether each one of the CheckBoxes has been checked or unchecked. For instance, the If statement staring on line *90* determines whether the first CheckBox, Extras(0), is checked - Extras(0).Value = 1 - or unchecked. If it is checked, the user wants this extra included and the appropriate cost is recorded - DVDOpt = 100. If the CheckBox is unchecked, DVDOpt is set to zero. The same logic is applied to the other two CheckBoxes.

On line *120* the total cost of all extras is calculated and then the ShowCost procedure is used to display the new system cost.

Drag and Drop Events

The final example program in this topic illustrates the use of Drag and Drop events using the noughts and crosses game. The terms Drag and Drop refer to using the mouse to move a control from its current position and placing it somewhere else. A control is dragged by moving the mouse pointer over it, pressing and holding the mouse button and then moving the control with the mouse; the control is dropped in its destination position by simply releasing the mouse button.

In drag and drop operations there are two objects involved: the source object (a control) that is being dragged and the destination object (a form or control) that receives the dragged control when it is dropped. In our example, described below, the source objects and the destination objects are all CommandButtons. The code that controls drag and drop operations is placed in two different locations:

❑ the source object contains the code to start, stop and cancel dragging

❑ the destination object contains the code for the drop event.

For our implementation of the game of noughts and crosses we use the computer to display the game's grid and allow two players to position their O and X symbols. The program allows each player in turn to *drag* their symbol to a position on the grid and *drop* it there and then indicates whose turn is next. If the position has already been used, the move is rejected and the user is "beeped". The program also detects a winner or whether it is a drawn game after 9 moves. A screenshot of the game's Form is shown on the right.

The first player drags the X button and drops it to a position on the grid. X appears in the required position. The X button becomes disabled and the O button becomes enabled allowing the second player to make a move. The next screenshot shows the position after the first player's third move:

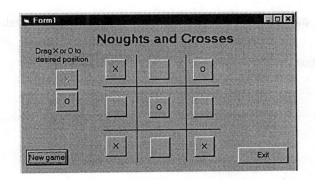

If a player has three symbols in a horizontal, vertical or diagonal line, a congratulatory message appears. A message also appears if the game is drawn. The board is cleared for a new game by pressing the "New game" button.

Creating the Noughts and Crosses Form

1. Start a new project and use the line tool to draw the grid lines.

2. Now create a CommandButton, size it and place it in the top left-hand corner of the grid. Clear its caption and name it OxoPos.

3. Now copy OxoPos to the clipboard (Ctrl C) and paste a copy of it to the Form (Ctrl V). You will be asked if you wish to create a Control Array. Answer "Yes" and position the new button to the right of the first one.

4. Paste the remaining 7 buttons (with Ctrl V again) and position them going from left to right. The Index value for the final button in the bottom right-hand corner should be 8.

5. Next, create the players' X and O CommandButtons. Name them OxoX and OxoO and change their captions to "X" and "O" respectively.

6. Create the "Exit" button.

7. Create the title label and use the ForeColor and Font properties to change the colour of the text and the size of the font.

8. Create the user instruction label that appears above the X and O CommandButtons.

Coding the Noughts and Crosses Form

To simplify checking for a winning line of Os or Xs we will use an array called Grid() to record moves. Grid() is an array of nine integer values representing the nine positions on the grid as illustrated below:

Grid(0)	Grid(1)	Grid(2)
Grid(3)	Grid(4)	Grid(5)
Grid(6)	Grid(7)	Grid(8)

X moves will be stored as a value of 1 and O moves as −1; unused positions will contain zero.

The diagram below shows a board position with the equivalent `Grid()` values:

Board position				Grid() values		
X		O		1	0	−1
	O			0	−1	0
X		X		1	0	1

We will test for a winner by finding the row, column and diagonal sums. A sum of 3 means that X has won and −3 means that O has won. Ignoring the sign of the sum, a value of 3 means that either X or O has won, i.e. there is a winner.

We will start by creating the code to initiate a drag operation when the mouse button is clicked over the X CommandButton. The X CommandButton is called OxoX and when it is clicked, the OxoX_MouseDown event procedure is executed. The code for this procedure is shown below:

```
Private Sub OxoX_MouseDown(Button As Integer, Shift As Integer, X As
Single, Y As Single)
' Initiate drag operation for X
  OxoX.Drag 1
End Sub
```

The parameters supplied by VB provide information regarding the button pressed, whether the Shift key was held down at the time, and the X and Y coordinates of the mouse pointer position when the button was clicked. In this example, we are only interested in the fact that OxoX was clicked. The code simply initiates a drag operation. This causes an outline of the button clicked to follow the movement of the mouse pointer while the mouse button is being held down.

The same coding principle applies to the O button:

```
Private Sub OxoO_MouseDown(Button As Integer, Shift As Integer, X As
Single, Y As Single)
' Initiate drag operation for O
  OxoO.Drag 1
End Sub
```

When the mouse button is released over one of the blank command buttons forming the game's grid, the OxoPos_DragDrop event procedure is triggered. This is the most complex part of the program, so we will discuss it in some detail.

```
Private Sub OxoPos_DragDrop(Index As Integer, Source As Control, X As
Single, Y As Single)
10   If OxoPos(Index).Caption = "" Then
20     OxoPos(Index).Caption = Source.Caption
30     Select Case Source.Name
40       Case "OxoO"
```

```
50       OxoO.Enabled = False
60       OxoX.Enabled = True
70       Grid(Index) = -1
80       Turns = Turns + 1
90    Case "OxoX"
100      OxoX.Enabled = False
110      OxoO.Enabled = True
120      Grid(Index) = 1
130      Turns = Turns + 1
140   End Select

150   Select Case Result()
160   Case "win"
170    MsgBox ("Well done, " & Source.Caption & ", you won!!")
180    OxoO.Enabled = False
190    OxoX.Enabled = False

200   Case "draw"
210    MsgBox ("Well played both of you - a draw")
220    OxoO.Enabled = False
230    OxoX.Enabled = False

240   Case ""
250   End Select

260 Else
270     Beep
280 End If
End Sub
```

Remember that because OxoPos is a Control Array when the OxoPos_DragDrop procedure is called VB provides the Index value of the control within the array that is the destination object of the Drop event. This will allow us to determine the position on the grid chosen by the user. In addition, the OxoPos_DragDrop procedure provides the Source control that has been dropped - either the X CommandButton or the O CommandButton - and the current mouse. We use the first two parameters in this procedure.

Line *10* determines whether the destination object has a blank caption. If this is the case, it means that that position in the grid has not yet been used and we can then set the caption of this control to X or O, depending on the Source object. However, if the caption is not blank, it means that it is either X or O and that grid position is not available. If this is the case, the else statement on line *270* emits a beep to indicate a problem and the procedure exits.

If the user's move is valid, the caption of the Destination control is changed to the caption of the Source control. Thus, if the user drags the X CommandButton over the middle position of the grid, OxoPos(4)'s caption will be changed to "X".

The Select statement starting on line *30* uses the Name property of the Source control to determine whether OxoX or OxoO was dragged and dropped. If it was an X move, Grid(Index) is set to 1, the X CommandButton is disabled, the O CommandButton is enabled and the variable Turns is incremented. Turns is used later to determine whether the game is a draw. If it was a O move, Grid(Index) is set to −1, the O CommandButton is disabled, the X CommandButton is enabled and the variable Turns is again incremented.

The next Select statement starting on line *150* uses the function Result() to determine whether the game has ended with a winner, whether it is a draw or whether the game has still not reached a conclusion. Result() - discussed below - returns one of three values:

1. "win" indicating that there is a winner - a congratulatory message for the winner is displayed and both X and O Command buttons are disabled to halt the game.

2. "draw" indicating that the game is drawn - a general congratulatory message is displayed and again both X and O Command buttons are disabled

3. "" (empty string) indicating that the game has not reached a conclusion - no action is taken.

The function Result() is shown below:

```
Public Function Result()

If Abs(Grid(0) + Grid(1) + Grid(2)) = 3 Or _
   Abs(Grid(3) + Grid(4) + Grid(5)) = 3 Or _
   Abs(Grid(6) + Grid(7) + Grid(8)) = 3 Or _
   Abs(Grid(0) + Grid(4) + Grid(8)) = 3 Or _
   Abs(Grid(2) + Grid(4) + Grid(6)) = 3 Or _
   Abs(Grid(0) + Grid(3) + Grid(6)) = 3 Or _
   Abs(Grid(1) + Grid(4) + Grid(7)) = 3 Or _
   Abs(Grid(2) + Grid(5) + Grid(8)) = 3 Then
   Result = "win"
Else
   If Turns = 9 Then
     Result = "draw"
   Else: Result = ""
   End If
End If

End Function
```

If there is a row, column or diagonal of Xs, the sum of the equivalent elements of the array Grid will add up to 3. For O's, the sum will be -3. The magnitude of the sum, ie the absolute value, in both cases will be 3. The expression Abs(Grid(0) + Grid(1) + Grid(2) finds the absolute value of the sum of the first row of Grid. The other similar expressions in the If statement find the absolute sums of the other 7 possible lines. Each of these expressions is compared with the value 3, and if any one of them has a value of 3, the If statement is true and Result returns "win". Note that the underscore character (_) is recognised as a continuation character to allow a long statement to be spread over more than one line.

If there is not a winning line, the variable Turns is checked. If it is equal to 9, this means that all of the grid positions are filled and, because there is no winner, the game must be a draw.

The "New game" Command button uses a loop to restore the grid to its initial state and to indicate that X is to start by Enabling X and Disabling O:

```
Private Sub NewGame_Click()
Dim i As Integer
```

```
For i = 0 To 8
 OxoPos(i).Caption = ""
 Grid(i) = 0
Next i
OxoX.Enabled = True
OxoO.Enabled = False
Turns = 0
End Sub
```

The "Exit" CommandButton simply closes the form:

```
Private Sub Exit_Click()
Unload Me
End Sub
```

Note that Me is a special VB word that represents the current object, that is, the Form in this instance.

Finally, to establish Grid as a Global array so that it can be accessed by all of the Form's procedures and to do the same for Turns, the following two lines are included in the Declarations section:

```
Dim Grid(9) As Integer
Dim Turns As Integer
```

Programming Exercises

1. Create a Form similar to the "Winking face" program described earlier in this topic. Design your own shape to animate.

2. Repeat the previous exercise but use simple geometrical shapes to animate instead of text. You will need to use CommandButton clicks to change the properties of the shapes to be animated. You can use the Line tool to draw lines and use the X1, Y1, X2 and Y2 properties to change the position of the lines in code, and you can use the Shape tool to create and modify circles and squares.

3. Use the "Currency converter" program as a guide to producing a program that will convert between different units of measurement. For instance, you could convert between pounds, ounces, grams and kilograms, or between inches, feet, yards, metres and centimetres.

4. Extend the" PC Configuration Calculator" program to allow a user to select from a number of separate option categories such as faster processors, amount of additional RAM and larger Hard drives.

5. Write a program that uses a range of VB functions to simulate a scientific calculator. You could also provide the calculator with memory store and recall functions.

6. Write a simple vector drawing program that allows a user to drag and drop predefined shapes (eg squares and circles of different sizes) onto a drawing area on a form and then move them around.

7. Modify the "Noughts and Crosses" program so that a user can play the computer. To keep

the coding as simple as possible, the computer's move can be chosen randomly from the available positions. You could later add some defensive tactics, such as blocking possible winning moves by detecting two of the same user's symbol in a vertical, horizontal or diagonal line and placing the computer's at the end of the line.

Once a program has been written, it must go through two stages in order to remove errors which almost inevitably will be present. No matter how much care has been taken in the design and coding of a program, it is still very likely to contain *syntax* errors, that is incorrectly formed statements, and probably errors in *logic* as well. *Debugging* is the term given to the process of detecting and correcting these errors or *bugs*.

The first stage in the removal of errors is the correction of syntax errors. Fortunately for the programmer, modern interpreters and compilers will provide a large amount of assistance in the detection of syntax errors in the source code. Badly formed statements will be reported by a compiler after it has attempted to compile the source code; an interpreter will report illegal statements as it attempts to execute them.

Logic errors, however, are largely undetectable by the translating program. These are errors which cause the program to behave in a manner contrary to expectations. The individual statements in the program are correctly formed, but when executed it does not operate correctly; it may give incorrect answers, or terminate prematurely, or not terminate at all. Hopefully, even the most puzzling logic errors, having been detected, eventually can be removed. But how can the programmer be confident that the program will continue to behave properly when it is in use? The answer is that the programmer never can be absolutely certain that the program will not fail. However, by the careful choice of test data in the second stage of the debugging process, the programmer can test the program under the conditions that are most likely to occur in practice. Test data is designed to determine the robustness of the program: how well it can cope with unexpected or spurious inputs, as well as those for which it has been designed specifically to process. The purpose of *documentation* is to provide the user with all the information necessary to fully understand the purpose of the program and how that purpose has been achieved. The precise form that the documentation takes will be determined by a number of factors:

❏ The type of program.

❏ Who is likely to use the program.

❏ Whether it will be necessary to modify the program coding after it has been finally tested and accepted.

General guidelines for the contents and a complete example of program documentation are given at the end of this topic.

Detecting logic errors

If after examining program code for a reasonable amount of time the cause of an error remains a mystery, there are a number of courses of action which probably will be much more productive than continuing to pore over the listing:

1. Ask a fellow programmer to listen while you explain the operation of the program and the way it is behaving. Quite often you will see the cause of the error as you are making the explanation. Alternatively, your helper might recognise the type of error

and its probable cause from his/her own experience, or might ask a question which makes you reconsider some aspect of the program which you have assumed to be correct or had no direct bearing on the problem. It is surprising how often this simple approach works.

2. Examine the values of key variables while the program is running by inserting temporary lines of code throughout the program to display the values of key variables. Comparison of the values actually displayed with expected values will normally identify the likely source of the error.

3. Use debugging utilities provided in the language itself or separately in the system software. Most high-level language development systems provide debugging aids. These allow the programmer to do such things as step through the program line by line and display the value of variables, or to insert break-points to interrupt the execution of the program so that the state of variables can be examined. It is the responsibility of the programmer to investigate the debugging aids available and make good use of them.

Test data

When the programmer feels that the more obvious program errors have been detected and removed, the next stage is to test the program using carefully selected data. The nature of the test data should be such that:

❑ every statement in the program is executed at least once;

❑ the effectiveness of every section of coding devoted to detecting invalid input is verified;

❑ every route through the program is tried at least once;

❑ the accuracy of the processing is verified;

❑ the program operates according to its original design specification.

In order to achieve these aims, the programmer must be inventive in the design of the test data. Each test case must check something not tested by previous runs; there is no point in proving that a program which can add successfully a certain set of numbers can also add another similar set of numbers. The goal is to strain the program to its limit, and this is particularly important when the program is to be used frequently by a number of different people. There are three general categories of test data:

1. *Normal data*. This includes the most general data for which the program was designed to handle.

2. *Extreme values*. These test the behaviour of the program when valid data at the upper and lower limits of acceptability are used. The process of using extreme values is called 'boundary testing' and is often a fruitful place to look for errors. For numeric data this could be the use of very large or very small values. Text could be the shortest or longest sequence of characters permitted. A program for file processing could be tested with a file containing no records, or just a single record. The cases where zero or null values are used are very important test cases, frequently highlighting programming oversights.

3. *Exceptional data*. Programs are usually designed to accept a certain range or class of inputs. If invalid data is used, that is data which the program is not designed to handle, the program should be capable of rejecting it rather than attempting to process it. This is particularly important when the program is to be used by people other than the programmer, since they may be unaware of what constitutes invalid data. A programmer should from the outset assume that incorrect data will be used with the program; this may save a great deal of time looking for program errors which may actually be data errors.

Two commonly used approaches to the generation of good test data, namely *black box testing* and *white box testing*, are described in the following sections. Note, however, that good program testing will use a combination of testing techniques to generate test data, since no single method is sufficient to test a program thoroughly.

Black box testing

In *black box testing*, test data is created from a knowledge only of the function of the program module in terms of its inputs and outputs. In other words, only a knowledge of what it is supposed to do is required, not how it has been written. This approach allows people with no knowledge of the actual program code or of programming languages to be able to derive test data. A frequently used form of black box testing is *boundary value analysis*, but before describing this technique in more detail it is necessary to consider the concept of *equivalence classes*.

Equivalence classes

Suppose that a program accepts an input in the range 1 to 10. Suppose also that we use the values 2, 6, 7 and 8 to test the program. The test cases 2, 6, 7 and 8 are all values from a single equivalence class, that is, the class of numbers within the range 1 to 10. Each of these test cases is equivalent to all of the other test cases and so there is little point in using more than one or two such values, since if the program functions correctly with one of them, it most probably will work for the others. (Note, however, that this is never absolutely certain, which is why it is impossible to be sure that a program is completely error-free). Two types of equivalence classes are always considered, namely those that are *valid* and those that are *invalid*; it is essential that the program is executed with both good and bad data. To be clear about valid and invalid equivalence classes, Table 65.1 shows a number of examples of programs which require simple inputs. For each input we can identify both valid and invalid equivalence classes.

Input	Class	Description	Type
Integer in range 0 to 99	1	All values between 0 and 99 inclusive	Valid
	2	Values less than 0	Invalid
	3	Values greater than 99	Invalid
	4	Non-integer	Invalid
	5	Non-numeric	Invalid
Between 2 to 8	1	2 to 8 characters	Valid

characters	2	Less than 2 characters	Invalid
	3	More than 8 characters	Invalid
Between 2 to 6 values	1	Between 2 and 6 values	Valid
	2	Less than 2 values	Invalid
	3	More than 6 values	Invalid
One of the set of single	1	'A'	Valid
letter codes, 'A', 'B', or	2	'B'	Valid
'C'	3	'C'	Valid
	4	Any other input	Invalid

Table 65.1. *Examples of programs requiring simple inputs*

Test cases

Having established the classes of test data, the next stage is to identify suitable test cases according to the following rules:

1.   Create as many test cases as necessary in order to cover all the *valid* classes of test. This means that a single test case may cover more than one valid class.

2.   Create a *separate* test case for each *invalid* class of test.

The following example illustrates the procedure for deriving test cases.

Example

A program requires the following three inputs to be entered:

`Quantity`	Integer in the range 1 to 99
`Item Code`	Single letter followed by any three numeric digits
`Payment Code`	Single letter code: 'P', 'C' or 'D'

The valid and invalid equivalence classes for the three inputs are shown in Table 65.2.

Input condition	Valid		Invalid	
`Quantity`		Class No		Class No
Value	1-99	*1*	<1	*8*
			>99	*9*
			non-numeric	*10*
			non-integer	*11*

Item code				
1st character	Alphabetic	*2*	non-alphabetic	*12*
Size	4 chars	*3*	< 4 chars	*13*
			> 4 chars	*14*
Last 3 chars	Numeric	*4*	non-numeric	*15*
Payment code				
Value	'P'	*5*	not 'P', 'C' or 'D'	*16*
	'C'	*6*		
	'D'	*7*		

Table 65.2. *Equivalence classes for three inputs*

The next stage is to devise test cases according to the two rules given earlier for valid and invalid classes. The test cases are shown in Table 65.3.

Test case	Inputs			Classes covered	Type
	Quantity	Item	Payment		
1	25	r123	'P'	*1,2,3,4,5*	Valid
2	33	X345	'C'	*1,2,3,4,6*	Valid
3	44	G786	'D'	*1,2,3,4,7*	Valid
4	0	h123	'D'	*8*	Invalid
5	123	D123	'C'	*9*	Invalid
6	1ab	S123	'P'	*10*	Invalid
7	1.26	f123	'P'	*11*	Invalid
8	25	0123	'P'	*12*	Invalid
9	36	e1	'P'	*13*	Invalid
10	65	a12345	'C'	*14*	Invalid
11	33	abcd	'D'	*15*	Invalid
12	10	v123	'B'	*16*	Invalid

Table 65.3. *Test cases for valid and invalid classes*

Twelve test cases have been created. Notice that the first three test cases for valid inputs test several equivalence classes at once. The remaining test cases for invalid data only test a single equivalence class as required by the rules described earlier. Note that this set of test cases represents the *minimum* set of values required to test the program; additional test cases could be easily justified. For example, in order to test Invalid class 16, that is, a Payment code other than 'P', 'C' or 'D', we have entered the letter 'B'. It would be advisable also to try entering numeric characters and other special characters such as '!' or '%' found on keyboards.

Boundary value analysis

Observation has revealed that many programs fail when data are at the extreme edges, that is *boundaries*, of expected input. For example, if a program is designed to accept a single numeric input in the range 1 to 10, what happens when values at the boundaries of these values are entered, that is, such values as 0 and 1 around the lower boundary and 10 and 11 around the higher boundary? Such test data are more likely to reveal problems than several values such as 2, 6, 7, 8 which are all within the expected input range. *Boundary value analysis* is the name given to a commonly used black box testing procedure for the identification of classes of test data at the boundaries of expected inputs and from which test cases can be created. Boundary value analysis extends the idea of equivalence classes by concentrating on the values at the boundaries of equivalence classes rather than those within them. For example, with a test class for a numeric value in a certain range, values at both ends of the range and just below and above the range would be selected for test cases. Where a number of values are to be entered, test cases would be chosen for the minimum number of values, the maximum number of values, one less than the minimum and one more than the maximum. The rules for applying boundary value analysis are:

1.　Identify the valid and invalid equivalence classes.

2.　Identify boundary values for the valid and invalid equivalence classes.

3.　Produce test cases using the rules for equivalence classes.

The procedure for determining test cases using boundary value analysis is illustrated in Table 65.4, using the same example provided earlier for equivalence classes. Note that sometimes a boundary value for a class does not exist; where this occurs there is no entry in the table below.

Input condition	Valid			Invalid		
Quantity		BV	Class No		BV	Class No
Value	1-99	1	*1*	< 1	0	*13*
		99	*2*	> 99	100	*14*
				Non-numeric		
				Non-integer		
Item						
1st character	Alphabetic	'a'	*3*	non-alphabetic		*17*
		'A'	*4*			
		'z'	*5*			
		'Z'	*6*			
Size	4 chars	4 chars	*7*	< 4 chars	3 chars	*18*
				> 4 chars	5 chars	*19*
Last 3 chars	Numeric	'000'	*8*	Non-numeric		*20*
		'999'	*9*			
Payment						
Value	'P', 'C' or 'D'	'P'	*10*	Not 'P', 'C' or 'D'		*21*
		'C'	*11*			
		'D'	*12*			

Table 65.4. *Determining test cases for boundary analysis*

Since the first character of Item can be either upper or lower case, there are in effect two lower boundaries, 'a' and 'A', and two upper boundaries, 'z' and 'Z', for the valid equivalence class. However, there are no boundary values for the invalid equivalence class; we can simply choose a non-alphabetic character as an invalid test case.

These boundary values lead to test cases such as those shown in Table 65.5.

Test case	Inputs			Classes covered	Type
	Quantity	Item	Payment		
1	1	a000	'P'	*1,3,7,8,10*	Valid
2	99	A999	'C'	*2,4,7,9,11*	Valid
3	44	z678	'D'	*5,12*	Valid
4	7	Z123	'D'	*6,12*	Valid
5	0	D123	'C'	*13*	Invalid
6	100	s345	'P'	*14*	Invalid
7	1ab	S123	'P'	*15*	Invalid
8	1·26	f123	'P'	*16*	Invalid
9	25	0123	'P'	*17*	Invalid
10	36	el	'P'	*18*	Invalid
11	65	a1234	'C'	*19*	Invalid
12	33	abcd	'D'	*20*	Invalid
13	10	v123	'B'	*21*	Invalid

Table 65.5. *Test cases for boundary values*

White box testing

Here the program code is examined in order to determine the various routes that can be followed through the program. This approach requires a knowledge of the language being used, and in particular being able to recognise and understand conditional and looping instructions. The following example illustrates the process for dealing with conditional instructions within a program.

Covering multiple conditions in a program

Suppose that a mail order firm supplies goods to locations all over the world. An order from a customer is given a code, and if this code is of type A, B or C a discount on the total cost of the order is given. In addition, providing the order exceeds a minimum value, postage is free for customers within the UK.

The pseudo-code in Listing 65.1 illustrates typical instructions which might be used to determine the total charge to the customer. It is assumed that the variables Quantity and UnitCost have already been assigned values.

Listing 65.1   Calculate total customer charge for order

```
1    {Calculate the order value}
2    TotalCost = Quantity * UnitCost
3
```

```
4    {Determine whether any discount can be allowed}
5    select
6      when OrderCode = 'A' or OrderCode = 'B' or OrderCode = 'C'
7         Discount  = TotalCost * DISCOUNT_RATE
8      when otherwise
9           Discount = 0
10   endselect
11
12   {Adjust the order value to allow for discount}
13   TotalCost = TotalCost - Discount
14
15   {Determine whether postage and packing needs to be charged}
16   select
17     when TotalCost > MIN_ORDER-VALUE and Country = 'GB'
18         Postage = 0
19     when otherwise
20         Postage = PP_RATE
21   endselect
22
23   {Adjust the order value to allow for postage and packing}
24   TotalCost = TotalCost + Postage
```

The code shows how the discount and the postage might be calculated given the three constants DISCOUNT_RATE, PP_RATE and MIN_ORDER_VALUE (assumed to be £100).

We need to ensure that the compound conditional instructions on lines *6* and *17* are fully tested. This is accomplished by identifying test classes which cause each part of the conditional instruction to be true and false. For instance, on line *6* we must use test data such that the order code is of type 'A' (so that the condition OrderCode = 'A' is true), and also such that the order code is not of type 'A' (so that the condition OrderCode = 'A' is false). The same applies to the other two order codes, 'B' and 'C'. A *truth table* of the type shown in Table 65.6 is a convenient way to organise these requirements.

	Order type		
Class no.	**'A'**	**'B'**	**C'**
1	T	F	F
2	F	T	F
3	F	F	T
4	F	F	F

Table 65.6. *Truth table for OrderCode types*

The entries under the column headings 'A', 'B' and 'C' show that for the first class, the order will be type 'A', in the second class test the order type will be 'B' and in the third class, the order will be of type 'C'. In addition, we must also use a fourth test for the case where the order type is other than these three types in the table. The same procedure needs to be used for the second conditional statement on line *17*. The truth table is shown in Table 65.7.

Class No.	Condition	
	TotalCost > MinOrderValue	Country = 'GB'
5	T	T
6	T	F
7	F	T
8	F	F

Table 65.7. *Truth table for second conditional statement on Line 17*

Again, all of the possible combinations of the two conditions are covered, adding a further four test classes.

Having identified all of the paths through the program, we must now devise test cases using data which ensures that all of the paths are covered.

Table 65.8 shows the data for four test cases which accomplish this requirement.

Test case	OrderCode	TotalCost	Country	Classes covered
1	'A'	123	'GB'	1, 5
2	'B'	720.45	'USA'	2, 6
3	'C'	62	'GB'	3, 7
4	'D'	27.34	'XXX'	4, 8

Table 65.8. *Data for four test cases*

Notice that this table illustrates that we can cover more than one test class with a single set of test data as long as all of the classes are covered by the total set of tests.

Covering loops within a program

We need to create test data, where possible, to cover the following situations:

- ❑ Going through the loop the minimum number of times (which may mean skipping the loop entirely).
- ❑ Executing the loop once (if not covered above).
- ❑ Executing the loop the maximum number of times.
- ❑ Executing the loop one less than the maximum number of times.
- ❑ Executing the loop several times (between the maximum and minimum number).

For example, consider the pseudocode program fragment in Listing 65.2 which counts items and accumulates their total cost).

Listing 65.2   Pseudocode program fragment to illustrate testing of loops

```
Total = 0
Count = 0
write 'Enter the cost of the first item, or 0 to end'
read Amount
while Amount > 0
```

```
   Count = Count + 1
   Total = Total + Amount
   write <newline>, 'Enter the cost of the next item, or 0 to end'
   read Amount
endwhile
write <newline>
write   <newline>, Count, 'Items were purchased'
write  <newline>
write 'The total cost was: £', Total
```

Suitable test data for the program fragment may be as shown in Table 65.9.

Test case	Test data (Amount followed by 0)	Comment
1	0	Minimum number of times through loop, i.e. none
2	12·23, 0	Once only through loop
3	25·67, 17·99, 222·05, 123·45, 6·91, 0	Several times through loop

Table 65.9. *Test data for program fragment*

In this instance, because there is no maximum limit to the number of amounts that can be entered, we cannot devise test data for the maximum repetitions or for one less than the maximum, but in the case of the next example this is possible. In this example the loop is set to repeat a fixed number of times determined by the constant, LoopLimit. To change the number of times the loop is repeated, we simply alter this constant in the program as shown below.

```
   LoopLimit = 10
   Count = 0
   while Count < LoopLimit
      {Instructions to be repeated are here}
      . . . . . . . .
      . . . . . . . .
      Count = Count + 1
   endwhile
```

The test cases for `LoopLimit` are shown in Table 65.10.

Test case	LoopLimit value	Comment
1	0	Minimum number of times through loop, i.e. none
2	1	Once only through loop
3	5	Several times through loop
4	9	One less than maximum
5	10	Maximum

Table 65.10. *Test cases for LoopLimit*

Test logs

Once the test cases have been devised, the program must be executed using the test data. The effect of using the test data is recorded in a *test log*. Since the point of program testing is to find errors, the log will indicate a <u>successful</u> test <u>if an error is found</u>, and an unsuccessful test otherwise. The test log will form part of the documentation of the program so that if the program is subsequently modified, the same test data can be re-applied to ensure that no program errors have been accidentally introduced by the modifications. For each set of test data, the expected output must be determined before running the program so that it can be compared with the actual output produced by the program. The test log could be set out in tabular form as follows.

TEST LOG

Date:

Program name:

Version:

Author:

Tested by:

Test case	Expected output	Observed output	Result	Comments
1				
2				
3				
4				
etc				

Validation

At some point the programmer must decide that the program has had sufficient testing. He or she will be confident that the program will operate according to specification and without 'crashing' or 'hanging up' under extreme or unexpected circumstances; the reputation of a professional programmer relies on this. Prior to release, the final testing is then performed by the user for whom the program was developed. The programmer may have overlooked areas of difficulty because it is often hard to consider a problem objectively or entirely from the viewpoint of the user. If this is the case, that the operation of the program is not entirely satisfactory, the program will be modified and re-tested until all user requirements are met.

Program documentation requirements

The documentation produced for a program will depend on a number of factors. For instance, a program which validates a temporary file prior to creating it permanently will probably require a minimum of user interaction and only a small number of user instructions. However, at some later date, it might be necessary for the author of the program, or a different programmer, to modify it. This possibility means that the structure of the program will have to be explained in great detail, and test procedures to ensure its correct operation will need to be provided.

A general purpose program such as a spreadsheet, designed for people who just want to use the computer as a tool, will require extremely detailed instructions regarding its function and use. Such programs are generally accompanied by detailed user manuals and tutorials. On the other hand, users would not be expected (and definitely not encouraged) to modify the program coding; thus no details would be provided regarding the way the program has been written. This latter type of documentation would only be required for the people responsible for producing the program. In addition to the documentation requirements of users and programmers, there is a third category of person to be considered. These are people such as managers who are neither likely to use programs extensively nor want to attempt to modify them. They merely need to have an overview of the program - its function, capabilities, hardware requirements etc.

Thus there are many factors governing the coverage of documentation, and for this reason in the next section it is only possible to provide a checklist of items which might reasonably be included.

Documentation checklist

The documentation for a simple program generally falls into four sections:

- ❑ Identification.
- ❑ General specification.
- ❑ User information.
- ❑ Program specification.

Most users will need access to the first three sections; in general the fourth section will only be needed if the program is to be modified. The amount of detail in each section will depend entirely on the particular application and, to some extent, the implementation language. COBOL, for example, is largely self-documenting: it contains an Identification Division containing all the information listed in the first section below; the Data Division of a COBOL program contains precise details regarding all of the files used by the program and which devices are required; the Procedure Division is written in 'English-like' sentences which are generally easy to understand, even by a non-programmer. Consequently, a program written in COBOL will generally require less documentation than one written in Pascal or C, languages which are not self-documenting. The following checklist is a guide to what might reasonably be included in the documentation for a program.

1. Identification.

- ❑ Title of program.
- ❑ Short statement of its function.
- ❑ Author.
- ❑ Date written.
- ❑ Language used and version if relevant.

❏ Hardware requirements.

2. General specification.

❏ Description of the main action(s) of the program under normal circumstances.

❏ File specifications.

❏ Restrictions and/or limitations of the program.

❏ Equations used or references to texts explaining any complex procedures /techniques involved.

3. Program specification.

❏ Structure charts/flowcharts/decision tables.

❏ Annotated listing.

❏ Testing procedure including test classes and test data with expected output and a test log.

4. User Guide.

❏ Installation instructions

❏ Detailed explanation of the operation of the program

❏ Tutorial

❏ Screen shots

❏ Troubleshooting guide

✏️Exercises

1. Explain the difference between white box and black box testing.

2. What valid and invalid equivalence classes would you define for programs which accept the following inputs:

(i) a single integer value in the range 1 to 99;

(ii) a single name containing only alphabetic characters;

(iii) a single numeric digit;

(iv) an integer representing the number of units of a certain item sold, followed by the unit cost of the item;

(v) three names separated by commas;

(vi) a post code of the form *AA99 9AA*, where *A* represents any alphabetic character and *9* represents any numeric digit;

(vii) a telephone number which starts with an area code followed by a space.

Devise test cases for your test classes.

3.   Use white box testing methods to devise test classes and test cases for the following fragments of pseudocode:

(i)

```
if (Letter = 'a') or
   (Letter = 'e') or
   (Letter = 'i') or
   (Letter = 'o') or
   (Letter = 'u')
then
   VowelCount:= VowelCount + 1
endif
```

(ii)

```
if a > b then
   Temp:= a
   a:= b
   b:= Temp
endif
if b > c then
   Temp:= b
   b:= c
   c:= Temp
endif
```

(iii)

```
Count:= 0;
if a = b then
   Count:= Count + 1
endif
if b = c then
   Count:= Count + 1
endif
if c = a then
   Count:= Count + 1
endif
select
   when Count = 0
      TriangleType:= 0
   when Count = 1
      TriangleType:= 2
   when Count = 2
      {not possible}
   when Count = 3
      TriangleType:= 3
endselect
```

(iv)

```
repeat
   {get character from keyboard using}
   {readkey function                 }
    key:= readkey

   {check that character is a numeric}
   {digit                            }
    if (key >= '0') and (key <= '9')
       then
          write(key)   {echo to screen}
    endif

until key = ' '{exit loop only when }
              {spacebar pressed     }
```

Further event-driven programming

1. The Tutorial Approach to learning Visual Basic

Introduction

This Topic builds on the previous Visual Basic Topics by means of a detailed tutorial which provides step-by-step instructions for the development and implementation of a substantial programming project. The tutorial is not intended to be a comprehensive guide to VB; it has been designed simply to introduce event-driven programming and to provide a basis for further learning. Treat the tutorial as a guide to creating an application in Visual Basic. There is no need to thoroughly understand every line of code, but try to grasp the techniques used to build the program and to create the user interface. If you understand the techniques used here, you can apply them to other projects.

Visual Basic ships with comprehensive on-line documentation covering every aspect of the language. Consequently it was felt unnecessary to repeat this wealth of information in the tutorial and you are advised to use the VB on-line Help to check unfamiliar topics.

The tutorial covers the development of an interpreter for a simplified version of *Logo*. The tutorial is organised as series of Lessons, each introducing one or more programming concepts. New concepts are carefully explained before being used in the project.

The VB source files of each stage in the development of the project have been provided, allowing you to start or restart the tutorial at any point.

Prerequisites

You will need access to a recent version of Visual Basic. Visual Basic 6 was used to develop the project, though Visual Basic 4 and above could be used instead. However, if you use a version other than Visual Basic 6 there may be minor differences in default settings and menu items.

If you have some previous programming experience in languages such as Qbasic, Pascal or C/C++, you should be able to work through the tutorial directly.

Because this tutorial concentrates on event-driven programming, you are assumed to understand fundamental programming concepts such as variables, scope, loops, decisions, procedures and functions. In addition, you should already be able to create simple applications in Visual Basic. If you are a complete beginner to programming, and you are not familiar with these concepts or you have no experience of using Visual Basic, you should first work through a basic 'getting started' tutorial such as that provided in Visual Basic Help.

Familiarity with the Windows operating system is assumed throughout the tutorial. Before attempting the tutorial you should know how to use the mouse and perform common tasks such as launching applications, opening and saving documents, and moving resizing and scrolling windows.

As you are working through the tutorial, use the opportunity to become familiar with VB's Help facility. It contains a VB language reference with code examples of all aspects of VB programming and you will benefit greatly by studying the material, particularly when you are learning new concepts and programming techniques.

As the project on which the tutorial is based progresses, you will periodically test new code to make sure that it works as required. You may make spelling or other syntax errors as you type in the code we provide. If this happens, VB may report an error, in which case refer back to the program code to make sure that you have entered it correctly. To reduce the likelihood of this occurring, at the start of each lesson open the appropriate project stored on the CD. This way you will know that you are starting with tested code that (as far as we are able to ensure) contains no syntax errors.

Objectives of the tutorial

As you work through the tutorial you will learn how to:

❏   structure a substantial programming project

❏   create, configure and program a variety of commonly used Visual Basic objects

❏   use object properties and methods

❏   respond to user and system events

❏   methodically test a program as it is being developed

❏   create event and general procedures

❏   use a variety of program control structures

❏   use global and local variables

❏   create a tailored menu and toolbar

❏   use comments liberally to clarify code

❏   create simple, on-line help for the project

Simple Logo

What is Logo?

As a learning aid for programming and as a problem-solving tool for children, Logo is widely used in education. The most well-known form of logo makes use of a graphic called a 'turtle'. The turtle takes various forms: sometimes it is a simple triangular cursor which can draw lines and move about a display screen; in other versions it is a more complex shape such as an aeroplane or even a robot-like object which can be controlled in three dimensions; and in some versions of Logo the turtle is a mobile device connected to the computer and through which it can be programmed to move over the floor.

Basic Turtle Commands

The turtle is traditionally shown as a small triangle with the apex pointing to its current direction of movement. The turtle is given simple commands that move it around a screen, drawing a line as it moves. For example, the command FORWARD 50 causes the turtle to draw a line 50 screen units long in the current direction of movement; RIGHT 90 changes the direction of the turtle by 90 degrees in a clockwise direction; BACK 50 makes the turtle draw a line 50 units long in the opposite direction to the current heading; LEFT 45 rotates the turtle 45 degrees anticlockwise.

The turtle can be hidden by using the HIDE command, and SHOW makes the turtle visible. PENUP tells the turtle to move without drawing lines and PENDOWN tells it to start drawing lines again. The following sequence of instructions would make the turtle draw a box of side 30 units on the screen.

PENDOWN

FORWARD 30

RIGHT 90

FORWARD 30

RIGHT 90

FORWARD 30

RIGHT 90

FORWARD 30

In addition to these simple turtle commands, Logo contains many other commands, including those for creating and executing procedures, performing calculations, accepting data from the keyboard and displaying text.

What is Simple Logo?

As its name suggests, Simple Logo is a simplified form of Logo created to illustrate program development in Visual Basic. As such it is not intended to be used for writing complex Logo programs, but it could provide the basis for a more complete version of Logo. It allows simple programs to be constructed from a small number of logo commands, namely FORWARD, BACK, RIGHT, LEFT, SHOW, HIDE, PENUP and PENDOWN. In addition, a complete program comprising a number of instructions can be repeated a specified number of times, and the speed of the turtle can be controlled using another special command. The user interface has been designed to make the creation of simple programs as easy as possible by strictly controlling and limiting program creation and editing.

The programming requirements for the project

The program is required to perform the following the following functions:

❑ Provide eight basic turtle commands: FORWARD, BACK, LEFT, RIGHT, PENUP, PENDOWN, SHOW, HIDE.

❑ Display the turtle as a simple graphic that responds to the turtle commands.

❑ Allow each command to be executed immediately or included in a program for subsequent execution.

❑ Show the effect of each command on the turtle.

❑   Allow the turtle graphic area to be reset.

❑   Allow Simple Logo program lines to be added, inserted and deleted.

❑   Provide *new*, *open*, *save* and *print* program filing controls.

❑   Provide controls for running and halting Simple Logo programs.

❑   Provide controls for repeating complete Simple Logo programs a specified number of times.

❑   Provide controls for controlling the speed of execution of Simple Logo program instructions.

❑   Allow Simple logo facilities to be accessed via a combination of menu items, toolbar buttons and command buttons.

❑   Provide online help

The Target Program

The screen shot below shows the Simple Logo target program for the tutorial.

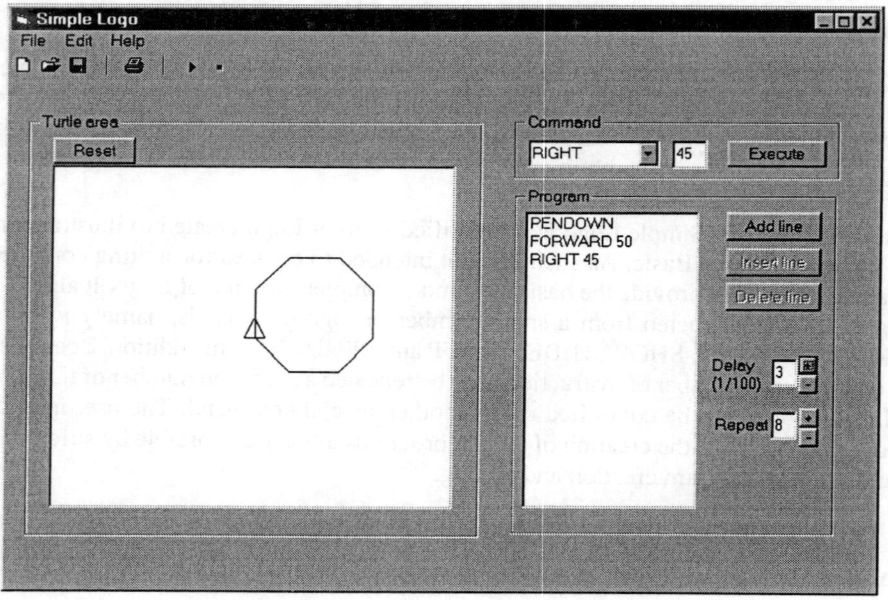

The programming environment comprises five major components:

1.   **Menu bar** at the top showing "File Edit Help". The File menu contains New, Open, Save, Print and Exit items. The Edit menu contains Add line, Insert Line and Delete line items. The Help menu contains Simple Logo Help and About Simple Logo.

2.   **Toolbar** just below the menu bar. From left to right, the toolbar buttons are New, Open, Save, Print, Run and Halt.

3. *Command* frame. This contains a drop-down list of commands and a text entry box for those commands that need a value to be supplied, eg FORWARD 10. The execute button executes the specified instruction immediately.

4. *Program* frame labelled "New Program". This contains the program lines in a no-editable list box, buttons for adding, inserting and deleting lines and four further program controls for repeating the program a specified number of times, setting the instruction execution delay value (in hundredths of a second) , running the program and terminating the execution of the program.

5. *Turtle area* containing the triangular turtle. This is where the turtle draws shapes according to programmed commands. The reset button clears the drawing area and resets the turtle.

The project is to develop this Simple Logo program incrementally according to the functions and facilities explained above.

2. Creating the user interface

Objectives

In this part of the tutorial you will start a new project comprising a single form module. On the form you will create the user interface which consists of a number of objects. You will create and configure the following VB objects:

❑ Command buttons   ❑ Picture box

❑ Text boxes   ❑ Labels

❑ Combo box   ❑ List box

❑ Lines   ❑ Frames

Creating a New Project

When you start Visual Basic 6 the New Project Window shown below appears. Choose the default option, Standard EXE, as shown and click the Open button.

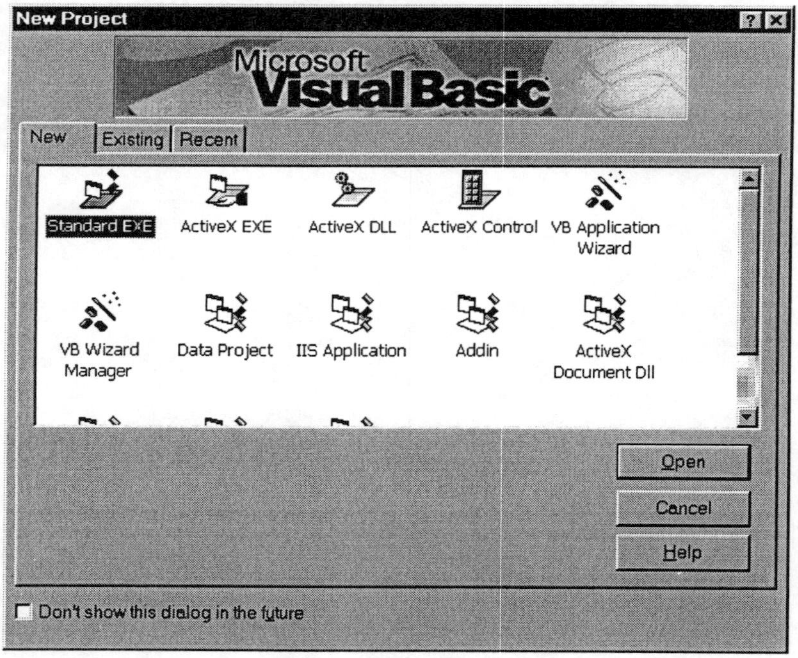

If this window does not appear, choose New Project. from the File menu.

Having created a new project (called Project1 by default) you will be presented with the screen shown alongside. A default form called Form1 is automatically created. We will rename this form "frmSL". To rename the form, click the title bar of the form to make sure that Form1's property window is visible. Then in the row labelled Name, replace "Form1" by "frmSL". Also change the Caption from "Form1" to "Simple Logo".

Now save your project by clicking the save icon on the toolbar or select Save from the File menu. You will be asked if you want to save the form. Save it using the name of the form, frmSL. Then save the project file using the file name "SimpleLogo".

The next task is to create the turtle area on form frmSL.

Create the Turtle Area Frame

The *turtle area* comprises a frame containing a *picture box* and a command button.

Frame Control

In the toolbox click on the *Frame* tool and then drag a rectangular frame in frmSL. In the properties window change the Name of the frame to "fmeTurtle" and the Caption to "Turtle area".

Picture Box Control

Next, click the *Picture box* tool and drag a roughly square area inside the frame. Leave space at the above the picture box for a command button.

In the properties window change the name of the picture box to "pbTurtle".

Command Button

Now click the *command button tool* and drag a small rectangular command button above the top left-hand corner of the picture box. Rename the command button "cmdReset" and change the caption to "Reset".

Note that at any stage you can adjust the size and position of any of these objects either by clicking and dragging with the mouse or by changing the entries in the object's properties window.

Before continuing save your project using the same file name as previously.

Turtle construction

The turtle consists of three lines forming a triangle. Later we will position and set properties of these three lines in code, but it is useful at this stage to practice setting properties using an object's properties window.

Line

Click the *Line tool* in the toolbox and drag a short horizontal line to form the base of the turtle. In order to position and size the turtle lines as accurately as possible, use the line's properties window to set the x and y co-ordinates of Line1's start and end points. X1 and Y1 define one end of the line and X2 and Y2 the other end. In the properties window for the line, change entries as shown. Also change the line colour to blue using the BorderColor property.

Line1 Line	
Alphabetic	Categorized
(Name)	Line1
BorderColor	■ &H00FF0000&
BorderStyle	1 - Solid
BorderWidth	1
DrawMode	13 - Copy Pen
Index	
Tag	
Visible	True
X1	1800
X2	2000
Y1	2000
Y2	2000

(Name)
Returns the name used in code to identify an object.

Create the other two lines and set their co-ordinates as follows:

Line2: X1=1800; X2=1900; Y1=2000; Y2=1800.

Line3: X1=2000; X2=1900; Y1=2000; Y2=1800.

Select BorderColor=&H00000000& (black) for both lines.

Save your project before continuing.

Creating the Command Frame and Controls

The Command frame contains three objects: a combo box for the eight commands, a text box to allow a command value to be entered where appropriate, and a command button that will cause the selected command to be executed immediately.

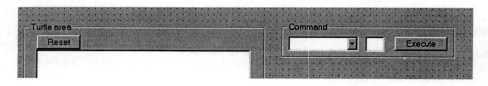

Frame Control

Begin by using the *frame tool* to create a small frame to the right of the Turtle area frame. Rename the frame "fmeCommand" and set the Caption to "Command".

Combo Box

Next use the *combo box tool* to create a *combo box* in the Command frame. Change the name of the combo box to "cbCommand". The List property allows you to enter a list of text items that will appear when the combo box is activated. Enter all eight commands, pressing control+enter after each one.

Run the program

To see the command combo box in operation, click the *Start button* on the toolbar.

Then click the down arrow in the combo box: the list of eight commands will appear. Click a command to select it.

Halt the program

Now click the *End button* on the toolbar to halt the program.

Text box

Next use *the text box tool* to create a small box that will allow a value to be entered for the FORWARD, BACK, RIGHT and LEFT commands. Call the text box "txtValue" and delete the default entry "Text1" for the Text property.

Command button

Finally, to complete the creation of the Command frame, create a button to the right of the value box, rename it "cmdExecute" and set its Caption property to "Execute".

Save your project before continuing.

Creating the Program Frame and Controls

The Program frame is the most complex of the three frames to be created for the project. The main object in the Program frame is a *list box* which can be used to contain and edit a complete Simple Logo program. The Program frame also contains several *command buttons* and two *text boxes*.

Frame

Begin by using the *frame tool* to create a rectangular frame below the Command frame. Rename the frame "fmeProgram" and set the Caption to "Program".

List box

Next use the *list box tool* to drag a rectangle inside the Program frame.

Rename the list box "lstProgram". This is where a complete Simple Logo program will appear.

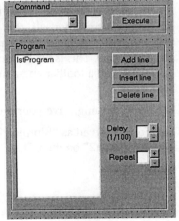

Program line-editing buttons

There are three buttons for editing programs: Add line, Insert line and Delete line. They are all created using the *command button* tool. Create these three buttons as shown, rename them "cmdaddline", "cmdinsline" and "cmddelline", and change their Captions to "Add line", "Insert line" and "Delete line" respectively.

The Delay control

The Delay control consists of a group of four items:

1.   a *Label* renamed "lblDelay" and with Caption set to "Delay (1/100)",

2.   a *Text box* renamed "txtDelay" and with Text set to blank,

3.   a *Command button* renamed "cmdDelayinc" and with Caption "+",

4.   a *Command button* renamed "cmdDelaydec" and with Caption "-".

In operation, the two command buttons will increment and decrement the delay value shown in the text box.

The Repeat control

The Repeat control also consists of a group of four items:

1.   a *Label* renamed "lblRepeat" and with Caption set to "Repeat",

2.   a *Text box* renamed "txtRepeat" and with Text set to blank,

3.   a *Command button* renamed "cmdRepeatinc" and with Caption "+",

4.   a *Command button* renamed "cmdRepeatdec" and with Caption "-".

In operation, the two command buttons will increment and decrement the repeat value shown in the text box.

The Form at the end of this section

The adjacent screenshot shows the Simple Logo form after all the controls detailed in this section have been created and positioned. This is not the final form, as we will add a toolbar and a menu in a later Topic.

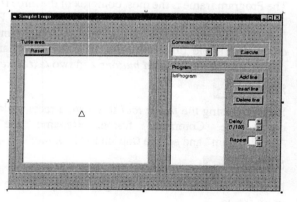

Before continuing, save your project.

This form is saved as "Slproject2" in the folder "Lesson2" on the CD.

3. Programming the turtle

Objectives

In this part of the tutorial you will start to develop code for the Command frame to respond to a user selecting and executing turtle commands.

You will learn how to:

- ❑ determine which item has been selected from a combo box
- ❑ enable and disable a text box
- ❑ add procedures to your project

You will write code to

- ❑ respond to a user selecting a turtle command from the Command drop down list
- ❑ respond to the Execute button being clicked
- ❑ hide and show the turtle
- ❑ rotate the turtle through a specified angle
- ❑ move the turtle to a new position
- ❑ draw a line as the turtle moves
- ❑ reset the turtle drawing area

Combo Box Click Event

When Simple Logo is run, users will select a command from the Command drop-down list (cbCommand). Four of these commands, FORWARD, BACK, RIGHT and LEFT require a value to be typed in - FORWARD and BACK require a distance and RIGHT and LEFT require an angle. To help the user, we will enable the Command value text box (txtCommand) if a value is required, and disable it otherwise.

However, first we need to be able to determine which command has been chosen by the user. Open the code window, select cbCommand from the Object drop-down list and then select the Click event from the Procedure drop-down list as shown. (To open the code window, select Code from the View menu).

```
Project1 - frmSL (Code)

cbCommand                  ▼    Click                    ▼

    Private Sub cbCommand_Click()

    End Sub
```

Now enter the following code:

```
Private Sub cbCommand_Click()

Select Case cbCommand.Text
  Case "FORWARD"
    txtValue.Enabled = True
    txtValue.BackColor = &HFFFFFF 'White
  Case "BACK"
    txtValue.Enabled = True
    txtValue.BackColor = &HFFFFFF 'White
  Case "RIGHT"
    txtValue.Enabled = True
    txtValue.BackColor = &HFFFFFF 'White
  Case "LEFT"
    txtValue.Enabled = True
    txtValue.BackColor = &HFFFFFF 'White
  Case "PENUP"
    txtValue.Enabled = False
    txtValue.BackColor = &HC0C0C0 'Grey
  Case "PENDOWN"
    txtValue.Enabled = False
    txtValue.BackColor = &HC0C0C0 'Grey
  Case "HIDE"
    txtValue.Enabled = False
    txtValue.BackColor = &HC0C0C0 'Grey
  Case "SHOW"
    txtValue.Enabled = False
    txtValue.BackColor = &HC0C0C0 'Grey
End Select
' ~~~ Enable the Execute button
CmdExecute.Enabled = True
End Sub
```

The Select statement uses the Text property of the cbCommand combo box control.

cbCommand.Text returns the current item selected from the list of commands. Case statements identify which of the eight possible commands has been selected.

The Enabled property of the txtValue text box is set to true or false depending on the command the user has selected. This enables the user to enter a value when one is required, and prevents the user from entering a value when one is not required. The BackColor property of txtValue is used to set its background colour to white when it is enabled and to grey when it is disabled.

The Execute button needs to be enabled now that a command has been selected. Hence the following two lines at the end of the procedure:

```
' ~~~ Enable the Execute button
CmdExecute.Enabled = True
```

At this point we also need to make sure that the Execute button is disabled when the program is first started by adding the following lines to the Form_Load procedure:

```
' ~~~ Disable the Execute button
cmdExecute.Enabled = False
```

Save the project.

Test the Program

Run the program and select each of the eight commands in turn to ensure that txtValue is enabled and disabled as required. The next step is to handle mouse clicks on the Execute button.

Execute Button Click Events

When the user clicks on the Execute button in the Command frame, the current command will be executed immediately. This will have some immediate effect on the turtle. The code shown below is procedure execute_instruction which has two parameters, command and value. When called, this procedure determines which command is to be executed and calls the appropriate procedure to perform the command, passing the value entered by the user where necessary.

```
Public Sub execute_instruction(cmd, str)
Dim num as Integer
num = Val(str)
Select Case cmd
  Case "FORWARD"
    Call forward_exe(num)
  Case "BACK"
    Call back_exe(num)
  Case "RIGHT"
    Call right_exe(num)
  Case "LEFT"
    Call left_exe(num)
  Case "PENUP"
    Call penup_exe
  Case "PENDOWN"
    Call pendown_exe
  Case "HIDE"
    Call hide_exe
  Case "SHOW"
    Call show_exe
End Select

End Sub
```

Add this code to your program by creating a procedure execute_instruction and typing in the code shown above. You can create procedures from the Tools|Add Procedure.. menu in VB6. In other versions of VB such as VB4, Procedure.. is found in the Insert menu. Make sure that you include the two parameters in the first line definition of the procedure as follows:

```
Public Sub execute_instruction(cmd, str)
```

Notice that eight other procedures are called from this procedure. At this stage of the project, we want to be able to test the program before writing these procedures. However, if the procedures do not exist, VB will report an error if we try to call any one of them. The solution is to use a *stub* for each of the eight procedures as follows. Create each procedure in turn, but do not add any code other than a line to show a message box that will display the command that is intended to be executed. For example, create `forward_exe` as shown below:

```
Public Sub forward_exe(val)
MsgBox ("Command: FORWARD " + str(val))
End Sub
```

The function `Str(val)` converts `val` to a string so that it can be displayed by the message box.

Do the same for `back_exe`, `right_exe` and `left_exe`. For the remaining four procedures, `hide_exe`, `show_exe`, `penup_exe` and `pendown_exe`, because the commands do not require a value, they will be of the form:

```
Public Sub hide_exe()
MsgBox ("Command: HIDE")
End Sub
```

Procedure `execute_instruction` needs to be called from the Click event procedure of the Execute button. The code is shown below. Add this code by selecting `cmdExecute` from the Objects drop-down list and `Click` from the Procedures drop-down list of the Code window.

```
Private Sub cmdExecute_Click()
  If valid_instruction Then
    Call execute_instruction(cbCommand.Text, txtValue.Text)
  End If
End Sub

Private Function valid_instruction()
Dim argval As Integer
  argval = Val(txtValue.Text)
  valid_instruction = True
  If txtValue.Enabled Then
    If argval <= 0 Then
      MsgBox ("Error: Please enter a positive integer value in the
      Value box")
      txtValue.SetFocus ' Move cursor to Value box
      valid_instruction = False
    End If
  End If

End Function
```

Before calling `execute_instruction` this procedure calls a validation function, `valid_instruction` which checks that a valid value for the current command has been supplied. The value, whether it represents a distance or an angle, must be a positive value integer. If the instruction is valid, `valid_instruction` returns a value of True, otherwise False is returned.

The method used in valid_instruction to validate txtValue.Text is to convert it into a numeric value using the Val() function in the instruction argval = Val(txtValue.Text). Non-numeric values such as letters or special characters will return a value of 0, whereas a numbers will be returned as numeric values. Notice that the variable argval has been declared in the Dim statement as an Integer type so that numeric values stored in this variable will be converted to integers automatically.

Test the program

The code so far must be thoroughly tested before proceeding. We need to ensure that

1. The program correctly identifies the command being executed by the user.

2. If one is required, a valid value has been supplied by the user.

3. The program does not try to process a command using an invalid value.

Use the entries shown in the table below as a guide to performing this testing methodically. Make sure that all eight commands are tested in this way.

Command	Value	Expected message displayed
FORWARD	10	FORWARD 10
FORWARD	0	Error: Please enter a positive integer value in the Value box
FORWARD	-1	Error: Please enter a positive integer value in the Value box
PENDOWN	N/A	PENDOWN
HIDE	N/A	HIDE
etc		

Turtle calculations

Before going any further we need to work out how to move and rotate the turtle. This is going to involve some fairly complicated mathematics. If you are not too interested in this aspect of the project, then just skip ahead to the next section where the relevant code is created.

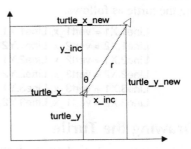

The adjacent diagram illustrates turtle geometry. In the diagram, `turtle_x` and `turtle_y` are the co-ordinates of the starting position of the turtle, `r` is the distance to move and θ is the angle through which the turtle has been turned. `x_inc` and `y_inc` represent the x and y components of the distance `r`. Hence, the new co-ordinates of the turtle are given by

```
turtle_x_new = turtle_x + x_inc
turtle_y_new = turtle_y + y_inc
```

where

```
x_inc = r * Sin(θ)
y_inc = r * Cos(θ)
```

This calculation gives us the new position of the middle of the base of the turtle. However, we also need to calculate the co-ordinates of the ends of the three lines that form the turtle. The following diagram shows an example of the turtle rotating through an angle θ about the mid point of the base.

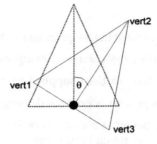

Suppose the corners of the turtle, labelled vert1, vert2 and vert3, have co-ordinates (vert1_x, vert1_y), (vert2_x, vert2_y) and (vert3_x, vert3_y) respectively, the base of the turtle is of length turtle_base and its height is turtle_height. Then, if the mid-point of the base has co-ordinates turtle_x and turtle_y,

```
vert1_x = turtle_x - (turtle_base / 2) * Cos(θ)
vert1_y = turtle_y - (turtle_base / 2) * Sin(θ)
vert2_x = turtle_x + turtle_height * Sin(θ)
vert2_y = turtle_y - turtle_height * Cos(θ)
vert3_x = turtle_x + (turtle_base / 2) * Cos(θ)
vert3_y = turtle_y + (turtle_base / 2) * Sin(θ)
```

From these calculations we can determine the co-ordinates of the ends of the three lines forming the turtle as follows:

```
Line1.X1 = vert1_x, Line1.Y1 = vert1_y
Line1.X2 = vert2_x, Line1.Y2 = vert2_y
Line2.X1 = vert2_x, Line2.Y1 = vert2_y
Line2.X2 = vert3_x, Line2.Y2 = vert3_y
Line3.X1 = vert3_x, Line3.Y1 = vert3_y
Line3.X2 = vert1_x, Line3.Y2 = vert1_y
```

Drawing the Turtle

Producing the code to draw the turtle requires a number of preparatory stages:

❑ Declare global variables in the Declarations section of the form module.

❑ Initialise global variables in the Form_Load event procedure.

❑ Create procedures to perform the turtle calculations.

❑   Write code to call these procedures.

Declare Global Variables

Module global variables are available to all procedures in that module, whereas variables defined within a procedure can only be used within that procedure. In this project we use global variables for turtle parameters. To define global variables use the code window to select 'General' from the Objects drop-down list and 'Declarations' from the Procedures drop_down list. Then define the global variables as shown below:

```
Option Explicit 'Ensure all identifiers are declared before use
Private Const turtle_base = 200, turtle_height = 200
Private turtle_x As Integer, turtle_y As Integer
Private turtle_angle As Integer
Private turtle_x_origin As Integer, turtle_y_origin As Integer
Private Const PI = 3.14159
Private Const MULTIPLIER = 10 'scaling factor for screen coords
```

Save the project before continuing.

Initialise Global Variables using Form Load

Generally, one of the first things that happens when you start a VB program is that the Form Load event is triggered. This allows you to initialise the form and associated variables before the Form is displayed. We use the `Form_Load` procedure here to initialise global variables as shown below.

First copy the following code into a new procedure called `turtle_init`. Later, we will use this procedure to reset the turtle and its drawing area.

```
Private Sub turtle_init()
' ~~~ Initialise turtle parameters.
' ~~~ The turtle origin is set to the
' ~~~ center of the turtle area.
  turtle_x_origin = pbTurtle.Width / 2
  turtle_y_origin = pbTurtle.Height / 2
  turtle_x = turtle_x_origin
  turtle_y = turtle_y_origin
  turtle_angle = 0


' ~~~ Set start and end values of the lines forming
' ~~~ the triangular turtle.
  Line1.X1 = turtle_x_origin + turtle_base / 2
  Line1.Y1 = turtle_y_origin
  Line1.X2 = turtle_x_origin - turtle_base / 2
  Line1.Y2 = turtle_y_origin

  Line2.X1 = turtle_x_origin - turtle_base / 2
  Line2.Y1 = turtle_y_origin
  Line2.X2 = turtle_x_origin
  Line2.Y2 = turtle_y_origin - turtle_height
```

```
Line3.X1 = turtle_x_origin
Line3.Y1 = turtle_y_origin - turtle_height
Line3.X2 = turtle_x_origin + turtle_base / 2
Line3.Y2 = turtle_y_origin

~~~ Set the colours of the lines.
Line1.BorderColor = &HFF0000 ' Blue
Line2.BorderColor = &H0& ' Black
Line3.BorderColor = &H0& ' Black

End Sub
```

Note that the position of the turtle origin (the middle of the base) is stored in (turtle_x_origin, turtle_y_origin) so that the turtle position can be reset by code that we will create later.

The start and end positions of each of the three lines forming the turtle are calculated from the turtle's base and height which are declared as constants in the Declarations section. This will allow us to redraw the turtle at its home position when the turtle area is reset.

Now, using Code window Object: Form, Procedure: Load, add the following lines to the Form_Load procedure:

```
Private Sub Form_Load()
' ~~~ Call procedure to initialise the turtle
  Call turtle_init

End Sub
```

Save the project before continuing

Turtle Display Procedures

We will begin by creating three procedures that use the turtle calculations described earlier. The first procedure, turtle_turn, will update the angular orientation of the turtle. The second procedure, turtle_move, will update the position of the turtle given the distance to be moved and its angle of rotation. The third procedure, turtle_draw, will actually draw the turtle in its new position and orientation.

Create these three procedures using the code shown below:

```
Public Sub turtle_turn(theta)
  turtle_angle = turtle_angle + theta
  turtle_draw
End Sub

Public Sub turtle_move(r)
  Dim x_inc, y_inc
  Dim theta As Double
  theta = turtle_angle / (180 / PI)
  r = r * MULTIPLIER
  x_inc = r * Sin(theta)
  y_inc = r * Cos(theta)
```

```
  turtle_x = turtle_x + x_inc
  turtle_y = turtle_y - y_inc
End Sub

Public Sub turtle_draw()
  Dim theta, vert1_x, vert1_y, vert2_x, vert2_y, vert3_x, vert3_y
' ~~~ Convert the turtle angle to radians
  theta = turtle_angle / (180 / PI)

' ~~~ Calculate the new positions of the turtle corners.
' ~~~ x, y start and end coordinates of the turtle lines
' ~~~ are calculated according to <turtle_angle> and
' ~~~ position of the middle of the turtle base given by
' ~~~ <turtle_x> and <turtle_y>
  vert1_x = turtle_x - (turtle_base / 2) * Cos(theta)
  vert1_y = turtle_y - (turtle_base / 2) * Sin(theta)
  vert2_x = turtle_x + turtle_height * Sin(theta)
  vert2_y = turtle_y - turtle_height * Cos(theta)
  vert3_x = turtle_x + (turtle_base / 2) * Cos(theta)
  vert3_y = turtle_y + (turtle_base / 2) * Sin(theta)

' ~~~ Set the new start and end coordinates of the 3 turtle
' ~~~ lines
  Line1.X1 = vert3_x
  Line1.Y1 = vert3_y
  Line1.X2 = vert1_x
  Line1.Y2 = vert1_y
  Line2.X1 = vert1_x
  Line2.Y1 = vert1_y
  Line2.X2 = vert2_x
  Line2.Y2 = vert2_y
  Line3.X1 = vert2_x
  Line3.Y1 = vert2_y
  Line3.X2 = vert3_x
  Line3.Y2 = vert3_y

End Sub
```

Save the project before continuing.

Linking the Turtle procedures

Finally, now that we are in a position to move and rotate the turtle, we will modify the appropriate procedure stubs that we created to test the program earlier. You need to make the following changes to four procedures:

```
Public Sub forward_exe(r)
'----------------------------------------------------------
' Call the <turtle_move> procedure to move the turtle <r>
' units forward. Then draw the turtle.
'----------------------------------------------------------

  Call turtle_move(r)
  Call turtle_draw
End Sub
```

```
Public Sub back_exe(r)
'-------------------------------------------------------------
' Call the <turtle_move> procedure to move the turtle <r>
' units back
'-------------------------------------------------------------
  Call turtle_move(-r)
  Call turtle_draw
End Sub
Public Sub left_exe(theta)
'-------------------------------------------------------------
' Procedure to turn the turtle anticlockwise <theta> degrees
'-------------------------------------------------------------
  Call turtle_turn(-theta)
  Call turtle_draw
End Sub
Public Sub right_exe(theta)
'-------------------------------------------------------------
' Procedure to turn the turtle clockwise <theta> degrees
'-------------------------------------------------------------
  Call turtle_turn(theta)
  Call turtle_draw
End Sub
```

Save the project before continuing.

Test the program

At this stage we need to make sure that the turtle responds correctly to commands. We will test FORWARD, BACK, RIGHT and LEFT, making sure that in each case the turtle behaves as expected.

Use the table below to guide your choice of test cases when you run the program.

Command	Value	Expected behaviour
FORWARD	100	Moves forward 100 units in the direction turtle is pointing
BACK	100	Returns to the previous position
RIGHT	90	Turns 90 degrees clockwise
LEFT	90	Turns 90 degrees anticlockwise
RIGHT	360	Stays pointing in same direction
LEFT	90	Turns 90 degrees anticlockwise
FORWARD	20	Moves 20 units west
LEFT	45	Turns 45 degrees anticlockwise
BACK	20	Moves 20 units north-east
etc		

Drawing lines with the turtle

When the PENDOWN command has been executed, the turtle draws a straight line when it is moved using the FORWARD and BACK commands. We will use a boolean global variable, `turtle_pendown`, which will have a value of True if PENDOWN has been executed and a value of False if PENUP has been executed. If `turtle_pendown` is true, whenever the turtle moves, it will draw a line from its current position to its destination. Whever the turtle is commanded to move, its current position will first be used to set the graphics cursor's x, y co-ordinates. Then, when we use the line drawing method to draw a line, we will need only to supply the end point of the line.

To implement the PENDOWN and PENUP commands we will need to:

❑ Declare the boolean variable `turtle_pendown` in the Declarations section.

❑ Initialise `turtle_pendown` in the Form_Load procedure.

❑ Initialise the position of the graphics cursor in the Form_Load procedure.

❑ Modify the current `pendown_exe` and `penup_exe` procedures so that the `turtle_pendown` variable defines the current pen state.

❑ Create a procedure to draw a line to the current turtle position.

❑ Modify the `forward_exe` and `back_exe` procedures to call the line-drawing procedure.

Declare Global Variable

To define a global variable use the code window to select 'General' form the Objects drop-down list and 'Declarations' from the Procedures drop_down list. Then add the global variable `turtle_pendown` as shown below:

```
Private turtle_pendown As Boolean
```

Initialise Variables

We need to initialise the `turtle_pendown` boolean variable to True, and set the position of the graphics cursor to the initial position of the turtle in the `turtle_init` procedure. Add the following lines to the end of the `turtle_init` procedure:

```
' ~~~ Set the turtle to PENDOWN
  turtle_pendown = True
' ~~~ Set graphics cursor of picture box to
' ~~~ x,y coordinates of current turtle position
  pbTurtle.CurrentX = turtle_x_origin
  pbTurtle.CurrentY = turtle_y_origin
```

Modify pendown.exe and penup.exe procedures

These two procedures are stubs at the moment. Replace the code as follows:

```
Public Sub penup_exe()
  turtle_pendown = false
```

```
End Sub

Public Sub pendown_exe()
    turtle_pendown = True
End Sub
```

Line Method

The Line Method allows you to draw lines in a picture box control such as our turtle area. We use one variation of the line method which draws a line from the current graphics cursor, defined by the picture box properties CurrentX and CurrentY, to the position specified in the Line method.

Create a new procedure called "turtle_line" and copy the code shown below into it.

```
Public Sub turtle_line()
'  ~~~ Draw a line from the previous turtle position to its new
'  ~~~ position if <turtle_pendown> is true
   If turtle_pendown Then
      pbTurtle.Line -(turtle_x, turtle_y)
   End If

'  ~~~ Set the graphics cursor of the turtle area to the
'  ~~~ x,y coordinates of current turtle position
   pbTurtle.CurrentX = turtle_x
   pbTurtle.CurrentY = turtle_y
End Sub
```

The statement

```
        pbTurtle.Line -(turtle_x, turtle_y)
```

uses the Line method of the pbTurtle picture box to draw a line to co-ordinates (turtle_x, turtle_y).

Before exiting the turtle_line procedure, the new base position of the turtle is used to set the current graphics cursor position ready for the next line to be drawn. This causes all lines to be joined by starting a new line at the end of the last one drawn.

Linking the turtle line drawing procedure

Now that all necessary code has been installed for drawing a line and responding to the PENDOWN and PENUP commands, all that remains is to call the the turtle_line procedure from the forward_exe and back_exe procedures as shown below:

```
Public Sub forward_exe(r)
' -----------------------------------------------------------
' Call the <turtle_move> procedure to move the turtle <r>
' units forward. Then draw the turtle and call the line
' procedure.
' -----------------------------------------------------------

   Call turtle_move(r)
   Call turtle_draw
```

```
  Call turtle_line
End Sub
Public Sub back_exe(r)
' ----------------------------------------------------------
' Call the <turtle_move> procedure to move the turtle <r>
' units back. Then draw the turtle and call the line
' procedure.
' ----------------------------------------------------------
  Call turtle_move(-r)
  Call turtle_draw
  Call turtle_line
End Sub
```

Save the project before continuing.

Test the Program

Before adding any further code we need to make sure that the line-drawing code works as required. When you run the program and execute a command such as FORWARD 100, a line should appear joining the new position of the turtle to its previous position. The line should extend from the middle of the base of the turtle.

There should be no line if the PENUP command is used immediately before FORWARD or BACK.

[NB If no line appears when you execute FORWARD or BACK commands, first make sure that the AutoRedraw property of pbTurtle (the turtle area picture box) is set to True.]

Test the program by using a variety of FORWARD, BACK, PENDOWN and PENUP commands.

Hiding and Showing Objects

Most objects have a Visible property. When set to True, the object is displayed; when set to False, the object is not displayed. We will use this property to implement the HIDE and SHOW turtle commands. To hide the turtle we will set the visible property of each of the three turtle lines to False; to show the turtle, we will set the properties to True.

Modify the procedure stubs hide_exe and show_exe as shown below:

```
Public Sub hide_exe()
' _____
' Hide the turtle
' _____
  Line1.Visible = False
  Line2.Visible = False
  Line3.Visible = False

End Sub
Public Sub show_exe()
' _____
' Show the turtle
' _____
  Line1.Visible = True
```

```
   Line2.Visible = True
   Line3.Visible = True
End Sub
```

Save the project before continuing

Test the Program

Now, when you execute the HIDE command, the turtle should disappear, and it should reappear when the SHOW command is executed. Run the program and make sure that this is the case.

Resetting the Turtle Drawing Area

To complete this section on programming the turtle, we will add a few lines of code to implement the Reset control for the turtle area. This requires us to:

Insert two lines at the beginning of the Form_Load procedure to clear the turtle picture box, pbTurtle:

```
Private Sub Form_Load()
' ~~~ Clear the Turtle drawing area of lines
  pbTurtle.Cls
' ~~~ Initialise turtle parameters
turtle_x_origin = pbTurtle.Width / 2 ' Center of picture box
etc.
```

Next add code for the Reset command button, cmdReset:

```
Private Sub cmdReset_Click()
' -----------------------------------------------------
' Reset the turtle drawing area
' -----------------------------------------------------
Call Form_Load

End Sub
```

This procedure simply calls the Form_Load procedure which initialises the program.

Test the Reset button

Now you can test the Reset button in the turtle drawing area.

Run the program and execute a FORWARD 100 instruction using the Execute button. A vertical line 100 units in length should appear.

Now click the Reset button. The line should disappear and the turtle should return to its starting position.

This stage of the project is saved as SLProject3 in the folder "Lesson3" on the CD.

4. Editing Simple Logo programs

Objectives

(This stage of the project is saved as SLProject3 in the folder "Lesson3" on the CD.)

In this part of the tutorial you will create code to deal with editing programs in the Program frame. This involves the simple program editing tasks of adding, deleting and inserting program lines.

You will learn how to:

❏ Make controls context-sensitive.

❏ Manipulate items in a List box using List box properties and methods.

You will create code to:

❏ Enable and disable controls

❏ Perform add, insert and delete operations on a List box control

❏ Run the current Simple Logo program

Enabling and disabling command buttons

The three editing buttons Add line, Delete line and Insert line, are intended to work as follows:

Add line: if there is a valid instruction in the Command frame, this button will be enabled and allow the instruction to be added to the end of the program currently in the Program frame.

Delete line: if an instruction in the Program frame has been selected by the user, this button will become enabled and allow the instruction to be removed from the current program shown in the Program frame. If no instruction is selected in the Program frame, the button is disabled.

Insert line: if an instruction in the Program frame has been selected by the user, this button will become enabled and allow the instruction to be inserted above the selected instruction. If no instruction is selected in the Program frame, the button is disabled.

As you can see, the availability of each of the editing buttons at any instant depends on whether use of the button is appropriate. In other words, we are making the use of the editing buttons *context sensitive*. This feature makes application programs easier to use and less prone to errors. In addition, by limiting user actions to only those that are possible, making a program context sensitive will often simplify coding.

To include the three editing functions in the program we will need to:

❏ Create a procedure called "edit_controls" to handle enabling and disabling the editing controls.

❏ Initialise the editing controls when the program is first started

❏ Enable the Add line control when a command has been selected by the user and add a line to the current program when Add line is clicked

❏ Enable the Delete line control when a program line has been selected by the user and delete the selected line when Delete line is clicked

❑   Enable the Insert line control when a program line has been selected by the user and insert the current command (if one is available) when Insert line is clicked

Enable/disable editing controls

We will start by creating a single procedure to handle enabling the three program editing buttons. The procedure will take three parameters, one for each of the three buttons. Each parameter will have three possible values, "off" (disable), *null string* (ignore) and "on" (enable). Note that a null string is simply a string containing no characters i.e. "".

Create the procedure shown below:

```
Public Sub edit_controls(add, del, ins)
' --------------------------------------------------------
' Procedure to enable and disable selected editing buttons
' --------------------------------------------------------
' ~~~ Add line
Select Case add
  Case "off"
    cmdAddline.Enabled = False
  Case "on"
    cmdAddline.Enabled = True
  Case ""
    ' null string - no action required
End Select
' ~~~ Delete line
Select Case del
  Case "off"
    cmdDelline.Enabled = False
  Case "on"
    cmdDelline.Enabled = True
  Case ""
    ' null string - no action required
End Select
' ~~~ Insert line
Select Case ins
  Case "off"
    cmdInsline.Enabled = False
  Case "on"
    cmdInsline.Enabled = True
  Case ""
    ' null string - no action required
End Select
End Sub
```

This procedure uses three Select statements, one for each editing control, to determine how to deal with each editing control. Each control is either enabled, disabled or ignored depending on the value of the parameters supplied to the procedure when it is called.

Initialise Editing Controls

When the program is first started, the editing controls need to be disabled, so add the following lines to the end of the Form_Load procedure:

```
' ~~~ Disable editing controls
  Call edit_controls("off", "off", "off")
```

Add line

When the user selects a command from the drop-down list in the Command frame, the Add line command button in the Program frame should become enabled. Add the following lines to the end of the cbCommand_Click procedure:

```
' ~~~ Enable Add line
  Call edit_controls("on", "", "")
```

This simply enables the Add line button.

Next, if the Add line button is clicked, the current command should be added to the program, providing it is valid. In the code window select Object: cmdAddline, Procedure: Click and enter the code shown below:

```
Private Sub cmdAddline_Click()
'_____
' Procedure to check that the current instruction is valid
' before adding to the current program in the Program Frame
'_____

  If valid_instruction Then
     Call edit_addline
  End If

End Sub
```

Now create a new procedure called edit_addline as shown below:

```
Public Sub edit_addline()
'_____
' Procedure to add the current instruction to the program.
' Checks whether the command requires a value
'_____

  If txtValue.Enabled Then
     lstProgram.AddItem cbCommand.Text + " " + txtValue.Text
  Else
     lstProgram.AddItem cbCommand.Text
  End If
End Sub
```

List box AddItem method

We use the AddItem method to add items to a List box control. Thus, 1stProgram.AddItem adds an item - a program instruction - to the 1stProgram List box. The value following the method reference is the value of the item to be added. In our case, this value is either the command -

cbCommand.Text - or the command and its value separated by a space - cbCommand.Text + " " + txtValue.Text. We use the enabled property of the command value text box, txtValue.enabled, to decide which of these two items to add to the list: if txtValue is enabled, we know that a value must be supplied for the command, whereas if txtValue is disabled, a value is not required.

Save the project before testing the Add line control. Now you are in a position to test the Add line control.

Test the Add line control

❑   Run the program. The three editing controls in the Program frame should be disabled.

❑   Now select PENDOWN from the command drop-down list. The Add line button should become enabled.

❑   Click Add line and PENDOWN should appear in the 1stProgram List box.

❑   Now select FORWARD and click Add line. You should get an error message saying that you need to supply a value.

❑   Supply a value and click Add line again. The FORWARD command should now appear after PENDOWN in the program box.

Delete line

When the user selects a program line by clicking it, the Delete line button should become enabled to allow the selected line to be removed from the program. This means that we must detect a List box click event and include code in the click-event procedure to enable the Delete line control. In the code window select Object: 1stProgram, Procedure: Click and enter the code shown below:

```
Private Sub lstProgram_Click()
' -----------------------------------------------------
' Procedure to respond to program line selection
' -----------------------------------------------------
' ~~~ Enable Delete and Insert
Call edit_controls("", "on", "on")

End Sub
```

Now that the Delete line control is enabled, we need to detect when it is clicked and be able to take the appropriate action.

In the code window select Object: cmdDelline, Procedure: Click and enter the code shown below:

```
Private Sub cmdDelline_Click()
' -----------------------------------------------------
' Calls the procedure to delete the selected line from the program.
The button is enabled only when a program line has been selected in
the program panel
```

```
'  ------------------------------------------------------
  Call edit_delline
End Sub
```

You may be wondering what the point is of having just a single line in this procedure that calls another procedure; the reason is that later we will be including a menu and a toolbar that will also allow provide editing functions, and they will also call this common procedure.

Now create a new procedure, `edit_delline`, to delete the selected line:

```
Public Sub edit_delline()
'  ------------------------------------------------------
'  Procedure to delete selected line from the current program
'  shown in the program frame. The <cmdDelline> control is
'  enabled only when a program instruction has been selected
'  ------------------------------------------------------
Dim itemIndex As Integer
'  ~~~ Determine the index of the selected program line
itemIndex = lstProgram.ListIndex

'  ~~~ Remove the line from the program
lstProgram.RemoveItem itemIndex

'  ~~~ Disable Delete and Insert line because no item now selected
Call edit_controls("", "off", "off")

End Sub
```

List box ListIndex and ListCount properties

The ListIndex property of the List box indicates which item is currently selected. It returns a value of -1 if no item is selected or the position of the selected item. The first position has a list index of 0, so, for example, the third item has a list index of 2. The number of items in a List box is given by the ListCount property.

In our case, the selected item index is given by `lstProgram.ListIndex`.

List box RemoveItem method

To remove an item from a List box use the `RemoveItem` method. This method requires you to specify the index of the item to be removed. Our `edit_delline` procedure first finds the index of the currently selected program line, using the statement

```
        selectedItem = lstProgram.ListIndex
```

and then removes the line using the method call

```
        lstProgram.RemoveItem itemIndex
```

Before continuing, save your project.

Test the Delete line control

1.   Run the program

2.   Select a command and add it to the program using the Add line control

3.   Repeat 2 several times with different instructions

4.   Click one of the program lines. The Delete line button should become enabled.

5.   Click the Delete line button. The program line should disappear and the Delete line button should be disabled. The Delete line and Insert line buttons become disabled because when an item is removed from a List box, no remaining item is left selected.

Insert line

The Insert line control requires two conditions to be satisfied:

1.   There must be a valid instruction in the Command frame

2.   A program line must be selected in the Program frame.

If these two conditions are both satisfied, then clicking the Insert line button will insert the current instruction above the currently selected program line. The second condition is taken care of automatically because until a program line is selected, the Insert line button will be disabled. We deal with the first requirements as follows. In the code window select Object: cmdInsline, Procedure: Click and enter the code shown below:

```
Private Sub cmdInsline_Click()
' -----------------------------------------------------------
' Calls the procedure to insert the selected line.
' The button is enabled only when a program line has been
' selected and the current instruction is valid
' -----------------------------------------------------------
  If valid_instruction Then
     Call edit_insline
  End If
End Sub
```

Now we need to create the procedure edit_insline to insert the program line:

```
Public Sub edit_insline()
' -----------------------------------------------------------
' Procedure to insert selected line shown in the program
' frame. The <cmdInsline> control is enabled only when a
' valid program is available in the Command frame.
' -----------------------------------------------------------
  Dim itemIndex As Integer
' ~~~ Determine the index of the selected program line
  itemIndex = lstProgram.ListIndex
' ~~~ Insert the line from the program
  If txtValue.Enabled Then
     lstProgram.AddItem cbCommand.Text + " " + txtValue.Text, itemIndex
  Else
     lstProgram.AddItem cbCommand.Text, itemIndex
  End If
End Sub
```

In order to insert an item in a List box we use the `AddItem` method as we did to implement the Add line button. However, this time the `AddItem` method requires an additional argument to specify the insertion position. We need to use the ListIndex property again for this purpose. The format for inserting an item in a List box at a certain position is

> *ListBoxName.AddItem String, Index*

Where *String* represents the item to add and Index is the position above which the item is to be added. In our case, for a command that requires a value, the statement to insert a line in the program is:

```
lstProgram.AddItem cbCommand.Text + " " + txtValue.Text, itemIndex
```

For a command that does not require a value, the statement to insert a line in the program is:

```
lstProgram.AddItem cbCommand.Text, itemIndex
```

Before continuing, save the project.

Test the Insert line control

1. Run the program

2. Select a command and add it to the program using the Add line control

3. Repeat 2 several times with different instructions

4. Click one of the program lines. The Delete line and Insert line buttons should become enabled.

5. Click the Insert line button. The current program line should appear above the selected line.

Running the Simple Logo program

To run the current program stored in the `lstProgram` List box we simply need to perform the following tasks for each instruction:

1. Take the first program line

2. Parse it to extract the command and the value if required

3. Call the execute_instruction procedure

At present there are no controls to run a Simple Logo program. Later we will create a toolbar containing a button to do this, but for the moment we will create a temporary Run button.

Display the main form and create a command button somewhere in the Program frame. Change the name of the button to "cmdRun" and set the Caption property to "Run". In the code window select Object: cmdRun, Procedure: `Click` and enter the code shown below:

```
Private Sub cmdRun_Click()
  Call program_execute
End Sub
```

This code is just temporary and will be removed at a later stage in the project.

Now create a procedure called `program_execute` as shown below:

```
Public Sub program_execute()
' ------------------------------------------------------------
' Procedure to execute the current program line by line
' ------------------------------------------------------------

  Dim curr_instr As Integer
  Dim proglen as integer
' ~~~ Determine number of lines in the program
  proglen = lstProgram.ListCount
' ~~~ Execute each instruction in turn
  For curr_instr = 0 To proglen - 1
    program_procInstr(curr_instr)
  Next curr_instr
End Sub
```

Now create `program_instrExecute` to parse and execute the specified instruction:

```
Public Sub program_procInstr(curr_instr)
' ------------------------------------------------------------
' Procedure to process the instruction at the program line
' passed by the parameter <curr_instr>. It first parses the
' instruction to extract the command and, if appropriate,
' the command value. It then calls the procedure,
' <execute_instruction()>, to execute the command, passing
' the command and value as parameters.
' ------------------------------------------------------------
  Dim spacepos As Integer
  Dim command As String, instruction As String, value As Integer
  instruction = lstProgram.List(curr_instr)
  spacepos = InStr(instruction, " ")
  If spacepos <> 0 Then
' ~~~ Instruction contains a command + value
    command = Left(instruction, spacepos - 1)
    value = Val(Right(instruction, Len(instruction) - spacepos + 1))
  Else
' ~~~ Just a command without a value
    command = instruction
  End If
End If

' ~~~ Call procedure to execute the instruction
  Call execute_instruction(command, value)
End Sub
```

Each instruction in the program is either of the form

        <command><space><value> or

        <command>

The `program_procInstr` procedure extracts the current program instruction from the program List box using the List property of `lstProgram`. The List property returns the item with the specified index - stored in `curr_instr` in our case - enclosed in parentheses.

```
        instruction = lstProgram.List(curr_instr)
```

Next, the procedure looks for a space in the extracted instruction using

```
spacepos = InStr(instruction, " ")
```

If a space is found, the command and value are separated, otherwise the instruction consists of just a command.

Once the current instruction has been parsed, it is executed by calling procedure

```
execute_instruction(command, value)
```

Now save the program before testing it.

Test the program

Run Simple Logo and create the program shown in the table below (or choose your own instructions) by repeatedly displaying an instruction in the Command frame and then clicking the Add line button. Then click the Run button to execute the program. The screen shot below shows the result.

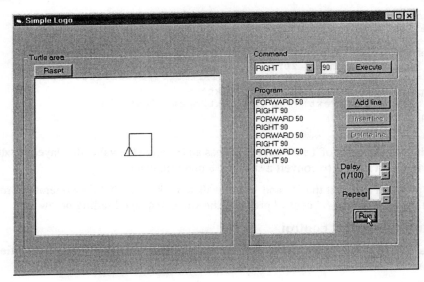

Repeating programs

The next stage in the project is to produce the code that will cause a Simple Logo program to be repeated a specified number of times. The Repeat control in the Program frame is used for this purpose. We will program the '+' and '-' command buttons to increment and decrement the repeat value to be displayed in the Text box txtRepeat.

Note that Visual Basic 6 has a special add-in tool for performing this type of function (see later for adding tools to the toolbox) , but for reasons of compatibility with other versions of VB, and for instructional purposes, we will create this type of control from 'scratch'.

Creating 'Spin Buttons'

Pairs of buttons that increase or decrease a displayed numeric value are often termed 'Spin Buttons'. Our spin buttons are the '+ 'and '- 'command buttons named cmdRepeatinc and cmdRepeatdec respectively. We will program these two buttons to change the value shown in the Repeat text box. To start, we will initialise txtRepeat in `Form_Load` so that it starts at a value of 1. Add the following lines to the end of `Form_Load`:

```
' ~~~ Initialise Repeat text box
  txtRepeat.Text = 1
```

Enter the code below for procedures `cmdRepeatinc_Click` and `cmdRepeatdec_Click` respectively:

```
Private Sub cmdRepeatinc_Click()
' -----------------------------------------------------------------
' Increments the <Repeat> value.
' -----------------------------------------------------------------
  txtRepeat.Text = Val(txtRepeat.Text) + 1
End Sub

Private Sub cmdRepeatdec_Click()
' -----------------------------------------------------------------
' Decrements the <Repeat> value. Prevents the value becoming
' less than or equal to zero
' -----------------------------------------------------------------
  txtRepeat.Text = Val(txtRepeat.Text) - 1
  If Val(txtRepeat.Text) < 1 Then txtRepeat.Text = 1
End Sub
```

We use the Text property of Text boxes to access and change the value displayed in txtRepeat. The `Val` function is used to convert a string to a numeric value.

Save the program then test the '+' and '-' controls to make sure that they operate as required. Note that the code for the '-' control prevents the value displayed falling below 1.

Integrating the Repeat control

Now we are ready to use the Repeat control to execute a Simple Logo program a specified number of times.

We modify the `program_execute` procedure as shown below:

```
Public Sub program_execute()
' -----------------------------------------------------------------
' Procedure to execute the current program line by line
' -----------------------------------------------------------------

  Dim curr_instr As Integer
  Dim proglen As Integer
  Dim reps As Integer, n As Integer
' ~~~ Determine number of lines in the program
  proglen = lstProgram.ListCount

' ~~~ Determine required number of repetitions of program
  reps = Val(txtRepeat.Text)
```

```
' ~~ Wrap program execution code in a loop
 For n = 1 To reps
' ~~~ Execute each instruction in turn
    For curr_instr = 0 To proglen - 1
       program_Procinstr (curr_instr)
    Next curr_instr                       ' Next instruction
 Next n                                   ' Repeat program
End Sub
```

We have simply wrapped the loop that executes the program in another loop which repeats the number of times stored in the Repeat box, txtRepeat.

Save your program before continuing.

Test the Repeat Control

To test the new Repeat control code, first create the program shown below by adding the two instructions to the program using Add line:

> FORWARD 50
>
> RIGHT 90

Now click the '+' control of the Repeat box until the value '4' appears.

Then click the Run button. The turtle should have drawn a square by repeating the two-line program four times.

Controlling Turtle Speed

The final task in this Topic is to control the speed of execution of turtle commands by introducing a user-defined delay between the execution of instructions. Visual Basic does not have a delay command, but we can create one using a timer.

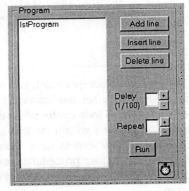

Timers

A Timer is a Visual Basic control that generates a Timer event. Select the timer tool from the toolbox and drag a rectangle on your form. The timer icon appears as shown to the right. Name the timer tmrDelay in the timer's property window. The timer does not appear on the form when you run the program, but when enabled it will be operating in the background. When a timer is enabled, it generates timer events continually at intervals determined by the timer's Interval property. The timer interval is in milliseconds. For example, if we want to set our timer to generate an event every 100 milliseconds, we would set `tmrDelay.Interval = 100`. To enable the timer we set `tmrDelay.enabled = True`.

Using a timer to pause a program

In the Code window Object: tmrDelay, Procedure: Timer enter the following code.

```
Private Sub tmrDelay_Timer()
' ---------------------------------------------------------
' Procedure to set global variable <timeUp> to true when a
' timer event occurs
' ---------------------------------------------------------
  timeUp = True

End Sub
```

Now create another procedure called wait():

```
Public Sub wait(d)
' ---------------------------------------------------------
' Procedure to set a program delay time.
' Uses a timer to effect the delay. If the delay time is
' greater than 0, the timer interval is set and the timer is
' enabled. When the timer event is triggered, the <timeUp>
' flag is set to true in the <tmrDelay_Timer> procedure
' allowing this procedure to exit and the next program
' instruction to be executed. Timer name is <tmrDelay>.
' ---------------------------------------------------------
  timeUp = False                    ' Global variable
  If d > 0 Then                     ' If delay > 0
    tmrDelay.Interval = d           ' Set interval
    tmrDelay.Enabled = True         ' Enable the timer
    While Not timeUp              ' While timeUp=False
      DoEvents                      ' Service all events
    Wend
  Else ' Return immediately
    tmrDelay.Enabled = False        ' Disable timer
  End If

End Sub
```

The procedure accepts a delay, d milliseconds, as a parameter and, providing it is greater than zero, uses it to set the interval for our timer, tmrDelay. The Timer is then enabled and a While..Wend loop cycles while the boolean global variable timeUp is set to False. The command DoEvents within the While..Wend loop makes Visual Basic check each time round the loop if any events have been generated. Thus, when a timer event is triggered, the tmrDelay_Timer procedure is executed causing the variable timeUp to be set to True. This ends the While..Wend loop and control returns to where the wait() procedure was called from.

To use the delay procedure, modify the procedure program_execute as follows.

```
Public Sub program_execute()
' ---------------------------------------------------------
' Procedure to execute the current program line by line
' ---------------------------------------------------------

  Dim curr_instr As Integer
  Dim proglen As Integer
```

```
Dim reps As Integer, n As Integer
Dim delay As Integer

' ~~~ Get delay value and convert to 1/10 secs
delay = Val(txtDelay) * 100

' ~~~ Determine number of lines in the program
 proglen = lstProgram.ListCount

' ~~~ Determine required number of repetitions of program
 reps = Val(txtRepeat.Text)

' ~~ Wrap program execution code in a loop
 For n = 1 To reps
' ~~~ Execute each instruction in turn
    For curr_instr = 0 To proglen - 1
        program_Procinstr (curr_instr)
        Call wait(delay)              'Wait <delay> msecs
    Next curr_instr                   ' Next instruction
 Next n                               ' Repeat program
End Sub
```

Now create the two procedures, `cmdDelayinc_Click` and `cmdDelaydec_Click` for the delay increment and decrement buttons respectively. Refer back to the creation of the two similar buttons for the Repeat control for guidance.

Finally add the following line to the `Declarations` section to establish `timeUp` as a boolean global variable:

```
        Private timeUp As Boolean        ' Used by delay control
```

Before continuing, save the project.

Test the delay control

Test the Delay control as follows:

1. Run the program.

2. Create the following Simple Logo program:

3. FORWARD 100

4. RIGHT 90

5. Set Repeat to '4'

6. Set delay to '10'

7. Click the Run button. The turtle should draw a square pausing 1 second between each instruction.

5. Creating a menu

Objectives

(This stage of the project is saved as SLProject4 in the folder "Lesson4" on the CD.)

In this part of the tutorial you will create code for a standard menu bar. The menu bar will have several main menu headings each of which leads to a number of items. The File menu will link to new functions for which code needs to be created; the Edit menu headings provide alternative access to functions already implemented. Later, we will add a Help menu.

You will learn how to:

- ❏ Use the Menu Editor to create a menu bar showing menu headings and menu items

- ❏ Create and access data files

- ❏ Use a Common Dialog Control for filing operations

You will create code to:

- ❏ Enable and disable menu items

- ❏ Create and access sequential files

- ❏ Open, save and print Simple Logo programs

- ❏ Link code to menu items

Menu Editor

The Menu Editor can be accessed by clicking the Menu Editor icon on the Standard Toolbar, by selecting Menu Editor from the Tools Menu or by using the keyboard shortcut, Ctrl + E .

The Menu editor window is shown on the right. Each menu item, whether a main heading or an item within a main heading, requires a Caption and a Name. The screen shot shows the main heading, "File", being edited. The Caption, that is the text that will appear on the menu bar, is "File", and the Name that will be used to link the item to a procedure when it is clicked, is `mnuFile`.

To create a sub item:

- ❏ first click the Next button,

- ❏ then click the right arrow to the left of the Next button to make the item a sub item

- ❏ enter the Caption and Name, e.g. "New" and "mnuNew" resp.

The right and left arrow buttons are used to set the level of the item - whether it is a main item or a sub item - and the up and down arrows allow you to move the selected item up or down the list of menu items.

Some items should be disabled initially when the Simple Logo program is run. Click the Enabled checkbox to enable and disable menu items. Later, program code will be used to make the menu items context sensitive. Separating lines are established by setting the Caption to a single hyphen, "-". They must be sub items and enabled.

Use the Insert button to insert a new item above the selected item.

Use the Shortcut drop-down list to assign a shortcut key to a menu item.

Create the menu using the table below:

Caption	Name	Level	Enabled	Shortcut
File	mnuFile	main	yes	
New	mnuNew	sub	yes	Ctrl+N
Open	mnuOpen	sub	yes	Ctrl+O
-	mnuSep1	sub	yes	
Save	mnuSave	sub	yes	Ctrl+S
Save as...	mnuSaveas	sub	yes	
-	mnuSep2	sub	yes	
Print	mnuPrint	sub	yes	Ctrl+P
-	mnuSep3	sub	yes	
Exit	mnuExit	sub	yes	Ctrl+E
Edit	mnuEdit	main	yes	
Add line	mnuAddline	sub	no	Ctrl+A
Delete line	mnuDelline	sub	no	Ctrl+D
Insert line	mnuInsline	sub	no	Ctrl+I

Press the OK button when you have entered the information shown above. If necessary, the menu can be edited later by starting the Menu Editor again.

The File menu items have all been enabled though later we will introduce code to make these items context sensitive by enabling and disabling them according to the current state of Simple Logo.

We will first program the "Edit" menu by linking its sub items to procedures already created.

Edit menu

There are three items in the Edit menu: Add line, Delete line and Insert line. Since we have already written code to perform these three functions, we will simply call the appropriate procedures when these menu items are selected. In addition, just as we did with the three editing buttons in the Program frame, we will also make them context sensitive.

Edit | Add line

In the code window, Object: mnuAddline, Procedure: Click, create the code shown below. Note that it is exactly the same as the code for cmdAddline_Click.

```
Private Sub mnuAddline_Click()
' -----------------------------------------------------------
' Procedure to check that the current instruction is valid
' before adding to the current program in the Program Frame
' -----------------------------------------------------------
  If valid_instruction Then
    Call edit_addline
  End If
End Sub
```

Edit | Delete line

In the code window, Object: mnuDelline, Procedure: Click, create the code shown below. Note that it is exactly the same as the code for cmdDelline_Click.

```
Private Sub mnuDelline_Click()
' -----------------------------------------------------------
' Calls the procedure to delete the selected line from the
' program. The button is enabled only when a program line
' has been selected in the program panel
' -----------------------------------------------------------

Call edit_delline
End Sub
```

Edit | Insert line

In the code window, Object: mnuInsline, Procedure: Click, create the code shown below. Note that it is exactly the same as the code for cmdInsline_Click.

```
Private Sub mnuInsline_Click()
' -----------------------------------------------------------
' Calls the procedure to insert the selected line.
' The button is enabled only when a program line has been
' selected and the current instruction is valid
' -----------------------------------------------------------
  If valid_instruction Then
    Call edit_insline
  End If
End Sub
```

Making the Edit menu context sensitive

When we were programming the Add line, Delete line and Insert line buttons, remember that we created a procedure, edit_controls, to enable and disable editing controls, depending on user actions. We will simply add instructions to this procedure to enable and disable menu commands in the same way. Modify edit_controls as shown below:

```
Public Sub edit_controls(add, del, ins)
' ------------------------------------------------------------
' Procedure to enable and disable selected editing buttons
' ------------------------------------------------------------
' ~~~ Add line
Select Case add
  Case "off"
     cmdAddline.Enabled = False
     mnuAddline.Enabled = False
  Case "on"
     cmdAddline.Enabled = True
     mnuAddline.Enabled = True
  Case ""
' null string - no action required
End Select
' ~~~ Delete line
Select Case del
  Case "off"
     cmdDelline.Enabled = False
     mnuDelline.Enabled = False
  Case "on"
     cmdDelline.Enabled = True
     mnuDelline.Enabled = True
  Case ""
' null string - no action required
End Select
' ~~~ Insert line
Select Case ins
  Case "off"
     cmdInsline.Enabled = False
     mnuInsline.Enabled = False
  Case "on"
     cmdInsline.Enabled = True
     mnuInsline.Enabled = True
  Case ""
' null string - no action required
End Select
End Sub
```

Save the program before continuing to test the Edit menu.

Test the Edit menu

The Edit menu items should now function in exactly the same manner as the three editing buttons in the Program frame. If necessary refer back to the headings "Test the Add line control", "Test the Delete line control" and "Test the Insert line control" for instructions on how to test the Edit menu items.

File menu

The File menu is going to add six new functions to Simple Logo. In order to do so, we will need to write procedures to:

❑   clear the current program when the New command is selected

❏   save the current program when the Save or Save as commands are selected

❏   load a stored program into the program frame when Open is selected

❏   print the current program when Print is selected

❏   quit the Simple Logo when Exit is selected

In addition, we will need to make the new commands context sensitive where necessary. Since we will be using Visual Basic's CommonDialog control to ease the tasks of opening, saving and printing data files, we will start by examining this control.

CommonDialog Control

The CommonDialog control provides a standard set of dialog boxes for operations such as opening, saving, and printing files or selecting colours and fonts. This VB control greatly eases the task of programming these functions. The CommonDialog control appears in the toolbox as this icon shown above.

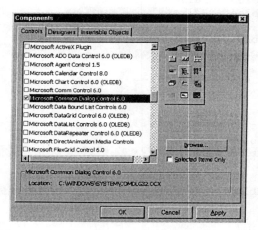

If you are using VB 6 and it is not in the toolbox you will need to perform the following actions:

❏   Click the Project menu

❏   Select Components ...

❏   Scroll the window down until you see "Microsoft Common Dialog Control 6.0".

❏   Check the adjacent tick box

❏   Click OK. The CommonDialog control icon should have been added to your toolbox.

Now click the CommonDialog tool and drag a rectangle on the Simple Logo form. Similar to the Timer control, the CommonDialog control appears as an icon when you are design a form, but is invisible when the program is running.

Name the control "cdcFile" in its property window.

To use the CommonDialog control you access its properties and methods. The properties that we will use for opening and saving files are:

cdcFile.FileName - to determine the name and location of a Simple Logo program file to be saved by the user.

cdcFile.DefaultExt - to define the default extension to be assigned to Simple logo program files

cdcFile.Filter - to define allowable file extensions for storing and retrieving Simple Logo programs.

cdcFile.CancelError - to detect when users cancel the CommonDialog window without loading, saving or printing a Simple Logo program.

The methods of the CommonDialog control we will use are:

cdc.ShowOpen - to allow a user to specify the name and location of a Simple Logo program to open.

cdcShowSave - to allow a user to specify the name and location of a Simple Logo program to save.

cdcShowPrinter - to allow a user to print the current Simple Logo program.

The use of these properties and methods will be explained in the following sections.

File|Save as...

Providing a user has transferred at least one instruction to the Program frame using Add line, we will allow the File|Save as... menu item to be accessed. When File|Save as... is selected, the "Save as" dialog box will open. This will allow the user to specify a file name and location for saving the current program. However, the user might decide against saving the program and press the Cancel button, in which case we will abort the Save as.. operation.

We will program the File|Save as... menu control in two stages: the first stage will be to produce the code to display the Save dialog box and to save a program under a user-supplied file name and path; secondly we will create code to configure the Save dialog box using CommonDialog control properties, and more code to make File controls context sensitive.

First create the following procedure:

```
Public Sub program_save()
' -----------------------------------------------------
' Procedure to save the current program.
' -----------------------------------------------------
  Dim filename As String
' ~~~ Show save dialog
  cdcFile.ShowSave
' ~~~ Get save filename/ path
  filename = cdcFile.filename
' ~~~ Call procedure to save program as text file
  Call save_file(filename)
```

```
' ~~~ Show program file name and path in the program frame
  fmeProgram.Caption = filename
End Sub
```

When the user clicks the Save button in the Save dialog box, the `cdcFile.FileName` property returns the name and path of the saved program. This filename is then passed as a parameter to procedure `save_file()` (listed and described below) which actually saves the program as a data file.

Next, the Caption property of fmeProgram , the program frame, is set to the name and path of the program with the line

```
        fmeProgram.Caption = filename
```

Now create the following procedure:

```
Public Sub save_file(filename)
' ----------------------------------------------------
' Procedure to save the current program as a text file
  ' ------------------------------------------------
  Dim lineNum As Integer, progsize as Integer
  progsize = lstprogram.ListCount

  Open filename For Output As #1          ' Open file for output
  For lineNum = 0 To progsize - 1
  Print #1, lstProgram.List(lineNum)      ' Write to file
  Next lineNum
  Close #1                                ' Close file
' ~~~ Set flag to show current program has been saved
  program_saved = True
End Sub
```

You will see that this procedure actually saves the program file by extracting and saving each entry of the lstProgram List box which contains the current program. The line

```
      Open filename For Output As #1 ' Open file for output
```

opens a file ready for writing and gives it the file handle "1". Then, each program instruction stored in the program list box, lstProgram, is saved by the statement

```
      Print #1, lstProgram.List(lineNum) ' Write to file
```

After the complete Simple Logo program has been saved, the file is closed.

Finally, the global variable `program_saved` is set to `True` to indicate that the current program has been saved. We will use this variable later for the File|New and File|Open commands.

Add this variable to the Declarations section with the line

```
  Private program_saved As Boolean
```

Then add these two lines to the `Form_Load` procedure to initialise this variable when the program is run:

```
' ~~~ Initialise program saved flag
  program_saved = True
```

To complete initial coding for the File|Save as.. menu command, create the following code in the Code window - Object: `mnuSaveas`, Procedure: `Click`:

```
Private Sub mnuSaveas_Click()
' ------------------------------------------------------
' Calls the procedure to save the current program
' ------------------------------------------------------

  cdcFile.CancelError = True        ' Enable Cancel error
  On Error GoTo saveas_cancelled
  Call program_save
  Exit Sub
  saveas_cancelled:
  cdcFile.CancelError = False        ' Disable cancel error
End Sub
```

The `mnuSaveas_Click` procedure first enables the CancelError property of the cdcFile CommonDialog control.

This causes VB to generate an error event when a user clicks the Cancel button after the Save as dialog box has been opened with the instruction `cdcFile.ShowSave`. If this Cancel event occurs, the `On Error GoTo` statement transfers control to the label `saveas_cancelled:`, the CancelError property is reset and the subroutine exits without saving the program.

Save the program before proceeding to test the File|Save as.. command.

Test the File | Save as... menu command

To test the new File|Save as.. command do the following:

1. Run Simple Logo

2. Create a short Simple Logo program by selecting commands and using Add line

3. Select File|Save as.. . The Save dialog box should appear.

4. Click the Cancel button. The Save dialog box should disappear and the Save operation should abort.

5. Select File|Save as.. again. The Save dialog box should re-appear.

6. Enter a file name such as "test.lgo", set the directory and drive and click the Save button. The Save dialog box should disappear and the program should have been saved. The Program frame should show the program name on the frame border.

7. Check that the program has been saved correctly by opening the program in Note Pad or another text editor.

CommonDialog control Filter and DefaultExt properties

A CommonDialog control Filter specifies the type of files that are displayed in the dialog box's file list box. For example, selecting the filter *.TXT displays all text files.

Use this property to provide the user with a list of file extensions that can be selected when the dialog box is displayed.

Use the (|) symbol to separate the description and filter values. Don't include spaces before or after this symbol, because these spaces will be displayed along with the description and filter values.

We will specify two special extensions for Simple Logo programs, .lgo and .txt, but we will also allow all file extensions to be displayed. The default extension will be .lgo - this will be added automatically to a file name if no extension is included in it.

Add the following statements to procedure Form_Load:

```
' ~~~ Set up save/open dialog extension filters
cdcFile.Filter = "Logo (*.lgo)|*.lgo|Text (*.txt)|*.txt
               |All files (*.*)|*.*"
cdcFile.DefaultExt = ".lgo"
```

The Filter property specifies that there are three file extension filters to be used, as shown in the table below:

Description	Filter
Logo (*.lgo)	*.lgo
Text (*.txt)	*.txt
All files (*.*)	*.*

Making File | Save context sensitive

Just as we did with the Edit menu items, we will make the File menu items context sensitive. To begin with, we will create a procedure to enable and disable File|Save, File|Save as.. and File|Print. Create the following procedure:

```
Public Sub file_controls(save, saveas, prnt)
' -------------------------------------------------
' Procedure to enable and disable selected file controls
' -------------------------------------------------
' ~~~ Save
Select Case save
  Case "off"
    mnuSave.Enabled = False
  Case "on"
    mnuSave.Enabled = True
  Case ""
    ' null string - no action required
End Select
' ~~~ Save as
Select Case saveas
  Case "off"
    mnuSaveas.Enabled = False
  Case "on"
```

```
      mnuSaveas.Enabled = True
  Case ""
      ' null string - no action required
End Select
' ~~~ Print
Select Case prnt
  Case "off"
      mnuPrint.Enabled = False
  Case "on"
      mnuPrint.Enabled = True
  Case ""
      ' null string - no action required
End Select
End Sub
```

You will notice that this procedure is very similar to the procedure `edit_controls` that we created for a similar purpose. Now we can use this procedure to initialise the File menu by adding the following lines to the end of the `Form_Load` procedure:

```
' ~~~ Disable File Save, Saveas and Print
  Call file_controls("off", "off", "off")
```

In addition, at this point we will also add another line of code to `Form_Load` to initialise the program frame Caption property to the default "Program":

```
' ~~~ Set the program frame caption to default value
  fmeProgram.Caption = "Program"
```

We need to do this because later we will need to implement the File|New menu command which will reset the program controls to their starting values.

Now we can add code to the `edit_addline` procedure to enable the three File controls when there is a program installed in the Program frame:

```
Public Sub edit_addline()
' -----------------------------------------------------------
' Procedure to add the current instruction to the program.
' Checks whether the command requires a value
' -----------------------------------------------------------
  If txtValue.Enabled Then
      lstProgram.AddItem cbCommand.Text + " " + txtValue.Text
  Else
      lstProgram.AddItem cbCommand.Text
  End If

' ~~~ Enable File Save, Save as and Print
Call file_controls("on", "on", "on")

End Sub
```

Save your program before testing the File|Save as.. menu control.

Test the File|Save as... menu control

1.   Run Simple Logo.

2.   Click the File menu. The Save, Save as... and Print items should appear disabled.

3.   Create a program of at least one line with the Add line control.

4.   Click the File menu again. The Save, Save as... and Print items should now be available.

5.   Select File|Save as.... The Save dialog box should appear.

6.   Click the Save as type drop-down list. Three extension types should be presented.

File|Save

The File|Save is almost exactly the same as File|Save as... The only difference is that it doesn't open the Save dialog box unless the current Simple Logo program has not been saved previously. Since we have produced most of the code already for this function, we need only add the following simple procedure to implement File|Save:

```
Private Sub mnuSave_Click()
' ----------------------------------------------------------------
' Calls the procedure to save the current program
' ----------------------------------------------------------------
  cdcFile.CancelError = True ' Enable Cancel error
  On Error GoTo save_cancelled
  If fmeProgram.Caption = "Program" Then ' Program not saved
    Call program_save
  Else
    Call save_file(fmeProgram.Caption)   ' Save using current filename
  End If
Exit Sub

save_cancelled:
  cdcFile.CancelError = False          ' Disable cancel error
End Sub
```

If the current program has not been saved, then the program frame, fmeProgram, Caption property will be the default setting, "Program" and we need to process File|Save as if it were File|Save as.... otherwise we simply save the program directly, using its current filename, without opening the Save as dialog box.

Save the program before testing File|Save.

Test the File|Save menu control

1.   Run Simple Logo

2.   Create a program of at least one line.

3.   Select File|Save. The Save as dialog box should appear.

4.   Save the program using a filename of your choice. The filename should appear as the Program frame caption.

5.   Check the contents of the program with Notepad.

6.   Add a line to the program.

7.   Select File|Save again. This time the Save as dialog box should not appear and the program is saved automatically using the current name.

8.   Check in Notepad that the program with the additional line has replaced the previous program with the same name.

File|New

When the user selects File|New to reset the program area, we need to:

1.   Check whether the user wants to save the current program if one exists

2.   Clear the program

3.   Initialise the Command, Program and Turtle frames

If the global boolean variable program_saved is True, we know that the current program has been saved and we can proceed with resetting Simple Logo. However, if program_saved is False, we need to open the Save as dialog box to allow the current program to be saved first before resetting.

The following procedure implements this logic:

```
Private Sub mnuNew_Click()
' ------------------------------------------
' Procedure to reset Simple Logo
' ------------------------------------------
Dim usrResponse, title, msg, msgBoxType

   ' ~~~ Set up parameters for message box
   title = "Save before continuing?"
   msg = "Do you want to save the current program?"
   msgBoxType = vbYesNo + vbApplicationModal

   cdcFile.CancelError = True
   On Error GoTo new_cancelled

   If program_saved Then          ' No need to save program
     Call Form_Load               ' Initialise Simple Logo
   Else
     usrResponse = MsgBox(msg, msgBoxType, title)
     If usrResponse = vbYes Then
       Call program_save          ' Open Save as dialog box
     End If
     Call Form_Load              ' Initialise Simple Logo
Exit Sub
new_cancelled:                    ' Exit without saving or initialising
  cdcFile.CancelError = False

End Sub
```

Because we may need to ask the user if the current program needs saving first, we set up the message box parameters. The three parameters that we use are:

title - the text appearing in the title bar of the message box

msg - the text that will appear in the body of the message box

msgBoxType - the form of the message box. The visual Basic constant vbYesNo indicates that the message box is to have a Yes button and a No button. The Visual Basic constant vbApplicationModal indicates that the message box must be closed before Simple Basic is allowed to continue.

A message box is a function that returns a value indicating what user action was taken. In our case, if the user clicks the Yes button, the constant value vbYes is returned by the message box function.

Next we ensure detection of the user clicking the Cancel button when the Save as dialog box is opened with the lines

```
cdcFile.CancelError = True
On Error GoTo new_cancelled
```

The Form_Load procedure, which is used to initialise Simple Logo, is called again here to reset Simple Logo. Note that Form_Load does not actually display the main form - it is simply a procedure that is called prior to displaying the form.

Save the program.

Test the File|New menu control

This is quite a complex control to test. We must ensure that all possible routes through the code are tested.

1. Run Simple Logo.
2. Display FORWARD 100 in the Command frame.
3. Click Execute. The turtle should draw a vertical line.
4. Click Add line to transfer the instruction to the program list box.
5. Select File|New. A message box should appear asking if the current program is to be saved.
6. Click Yes. The Save as dialog box should appear.
7. Click Cancel. The current program and controls should be unaffected.
8. Select File|New again. A message box should appear asking if the current program is to be saved.
9. Click Yes. The Save as dialog box should re-appear.
10. Enter a filename of your choice, eg "temp.lgo".
11. Press Save. The program should have been saved under the filename you specified and Simple Logo should have returned to its default state with the current program cleared. The turtle area should also be reset. Check that your program was saved by opening it in Notepad.

12. Display FORWARD 100 again in the Command frame.

13. Click Execute. The turtle should draw a vertical line.

14. Click Add line to transfer the instruction to the program list box.

15 Select File|New. A message box should appear asking if the current program is to be saved.

16. Click No. Simple Logo should have returned to its default state with the current program cleared. The turtle area should also be reset.

File|Open

Opening a program that was previously saved involves reading the file and transferring it to the program list box. However, just as we did with File|New, we need first to determine whether there is a current program that might require saving. Before opening a saved program we will also initialise Simple Logo as if File|New had been selected. The following procedure implements the required logic:

```
Private Sub mnuOpen_Click()
' ------------------------------------------
' Procedure to open a Simple Logo program
' ------------------------------------------
  Dim usrResponse, title, msg, msgBoxType

' ~~~ Set up parameters for message box
  title = "Save before continuing?"
  msg = "Do you want to save the current program?"
  msgBoxType = vbYesNo + vbApplicationModal

  cdcFile.CancelError = True
  On Error GoTo open_cancelled

  If program_saved Then               ' No need to save program
     Call program_open               ' Open program
  Else ' Possibly save first
     usrResponse = MsgBox(msg, msgBoxType, title)
     If usrResponse = vbYes Then
        Call program_save             ' Open Save as dialog box
     End If
     Call program_open                ' Open program
  End If
Exit Sub
open_cancelled:                       ' Exit without opening or initialising
  cdcFile.CancelError = False

End Sub
```

This procedure is almost identical to mnuNew_Click, the main difference being the call to a new procedure, program_open instead of Form_Load.

```
Public Sub program_open()
' ------------------------------------------------------------------
```

```
' Procedure to load a saved program into the program frame.
' ------------------------------------------------------------
  Dim filename As String, progline As String
  cdcFile.ShowOpen                       ' Display file open dialog
  Call Form_Load ' Initialise Simple Logo

  filename = cdcFile.filename            ' Get file name and path
  Open filename For Input As #1          ' Open file for input
  While Not EOF(1)
     Input #1, progline                  ' Get instruction
     lstProgram.AddItem progline         ' Add to program
  Wend
  Close #1                               ' Close the file
' ~~~ Show path and name of file in program frame
  fmeProgram.Caption = filename

' ~~~ Enable file controls
  Call file_controls("on", "on", "on")

End Sub
```

Procedure `program_open` first displays the ShowOpen dialog box using the Open method of the CommonDialog control:

```
  cdcFile.ShowOpen      ' Display file open dialog
```

After a file has been opened, Simple Logo is reset by the call to the `Form_Load` procedure which initialises all controls and variables.

Next, the file named in the Open dialog is opened for input:

```
  filename = cdcFile.filename      ' Get file name and path
  Open filename For Input As #1    ' Open file for input
```

The function `EOF(1)` returns the value False while there are more records (ie program instructions) in the program file and becomes True when an attempt is made to read past the end of the file. Thus the `While..Wend` loop reads all the instructions in the file, adding each one to the program list box, lstProgram, using the AddItem method:

```
  lstProgram.AddItem progline       ' Add to program
```

The program frame caption is set to the name of the program file and, finally, the three file controls, Save as, Save and Print are enabled.

Test the File | Open menu control

Though similar to File|New in many ways, File|Open is complicated by the possible need to use both the Save as dialog box and the Open dialog box. In each case, the user can either proceed with the operation or cancel it. Because these alternatives increase the number of paths through the program substantially, we will adopt a slightly more formal approach to testing this control than we have done with previous ones.

We need to make sure that at each decision point, every option is tested. So we need to test the `mnuOpen_Click` procedure for each of the following conditions:

1. `program_saved = True`. The Open dialog box should appear.

2. `program_saved = False`. The Message box should appear.

3. Message box - Yes clicked. The Save as dialog box should appear.

4. Message box - No clicked. The Open dialog box should appear

5. Save as dialog box - Save clicked. The program should be saved and the Open dialog box should appear.

6. Save as dialog box - Cancel. No changes should occur.

7. Open dialog box - Open clicked. The program should appear. The Command frame should be reset, the Program frame controls should be reset and the File controls should be enabled.

8. Open dialog box - Cancel. No changes should occur.

The following sequence of operations covers each of the above conditions at least once:

1. Run Simple Logo.

2. Create a simple program and save it. This sets `program_saved` to True, satisfying condition 1.

3. Select File|New to clear the current program.

4. Select File|Open. The Open dialog box should appear.

5. Open the program saved earlier. This satisfies condition 7. The program should appear and the appropriate controls set or reset. Check the File menu to make sure that Save, Save as and Print are all enabled.

6. Select File|Open. The Open dialog box should appear.

7. Click Cancel. This is condition 8. The dialog box should disappear and the Simple Logo controls should not have been affected.

8. Add an instruction to the current program. This sets `program_saved` to False, condition 2.

9. Select File|Open. The Message box should appear.

10. Click the Yes button. This is condition 3. The Save as dialog box should appear.

11. Click the Cancel button. This is condition 6. The dialog box should disappear and the Simple Logo controls should not have been affected.

12. Select File|Open. The Message box should appear.

13. Click the Yes button. The Save as dialog box should appear.

14. Enter a filename of your choice.

15. Click the Save button. This is condition 5. The Open dialog box should appear.

16. Click Cancel to exit the Open dialog box.

17. Add a command to the program.

18.   Select File|Open. The Message box should appear.

19.   Click the No button. This is condition 4. The Open dialog box should appear.

20.   Click Cancel and halt Simple logo.

This lengthy testing sequence has ensured that all routes through the procedure have been checked. This does not necessarily mean that there are no bugs in the program, but it does give confidence that each line of code in the procedure has been executed at least once. This is an essential requirement of program testing.

File | Print

When File|Print is selected, the Print dialog box will be displayed, allowing the user to configure the printer and print the current Simple Logo program.

To be able to display the Print dialog box we need to set the Flags property of the CommonDialog control using the statement

```
cdcFile.Flags = cdlPDReturnDC
```

The Flags property allows us alter printer settings using code; this particular setting, using the VB constant, `cdlPDReturnDC`, causes the Print dialog box to appear so that the user can select the printer to use or the number of copies to be printed, before printing commences. If this line is omitted, the program will be printed directly using the default printer.

First, create the following print procedure:

```
Public Sub program_print()
' -------------------------------------------------------------
' Procedure to print the current program. Displays the Print
' dialog control
' -------------------------------------------------------------
  Dim i As Integer

  cdcFile.Flags = cdlPDReturnDC
' ~~~ Returns a device context for the printer.
' ~~~ The device context is the link between VB,
' ~~~ the printer driver and the printer.

  cdcFile.CancelError = True         ' Enable error if print cancelled
  On Error GoTo print_error

  cdcFile.ShowPrinter                ' Show print dialog control

  cdcFile.CancelError = False        ' Disable Cancel error trap
  Printer.Print ""                   ' Print three blank lines
  Printer.Print ""
  Printer.Print ""

' ~~~ Print the program file name and path
  Printer.Print "Program: ", fmeProgram.Caption
  Printer.Print ""

' ~~~ Print each line of the current program
  For i = 0 To lstProgram.ListCount - 1
```

```
      Printer.Print lstProgram.List(i)
    Next i
    Printer.EndDoc                  ' Start printing
  Exit Sub
  print_error:
    If Err.Number <> cdlCancel Then
       MsgBox ("There appears to be a problem with your printer")
    End If
    cdcFile.CancelError = False      ' Disable error trap
  End Sub
```

We use the Print method of the Printer object to print the current program. To print a line of text on the printer, we use a statement such as

```
  Printer.Print x, y, z
```

The Print method is followed by a comma-separated list of items to print. These items can be variables or text enclosed in quotes. Thus the line

```
  Printer.Print "Program: ", fmeProgram.Caption
```

prints "Program: " followed by the Program frame Caption (which will normally be the file-name of the current program).

Each line of the program is printed by the loop:

```
  For i = 0 To lstProgram.ListCount - 1
      Printer.Print lstProgram.List(i)
  Next i
```

The printer is then activated by the line

```
  Printer.EndDoc              ' Start printing
```

Just in case there is a problem with the user's printer, we include an error trap that prints an appropriate message. If an error is generated by VB, control jumps to the label `print_error:` and, if the error was not generated by the user clicking the Cancel button (indicated by VB constant `cdlCancel`), a message reports that there is a problem with the printer. Finally, we need to link this procedure to the event procedure mnuPrint_Click as follows:

```
Private Sub mnuPrint_Click()
' ----------------------------------------------------
' Calls the procedure to save the current program
' ----------------------------------------------------
  Call program_print

End Sub
```

Create this procedure and then save your program.

Testing the File|Print menu control

To test File|Print do the following:

1.   Run Simple Logo

2. Open a stored program using File|Open or create a program.

3. Select File|Print. The Print dialog box should open.

4. Click OK. The program should be printed.

5. Select File|Print again.

6. Click Cancel. The Print dialog box should disappear and the program isn't printed.

File | Exit

The last item in the File menu to implement is the Exit option. When Simple Logo has been completely implemented, we will make it an executable file that can be run independently of the Visual Basic development environment. Thus we will need to provide this method of closing down Simple Logo. The only slight complication is that before quitting Simple Logo we must determine whether there is a current program that needs to be saved. We have dealt with this problem before when implementing File|New and File|Open so the code should look familiar:

```
Private Sub mnuExit_Click()
' ------------------------------------
' Procedure to exit Simple Logo
' ------------------------------------
  Dim usrResponse, title, msg, msgBoxType

' ~~~ Set up parameters for message box
  title = "Save before continuing?"
  msg = "Do you want to save the current program before quitting?"
  msgBoxType = vbYesNo + vbApplicationModal

  cdcFile.CancelError = True
  On Error GoTo exit_cancelled

  If program_saved Then              ' No need to save program
    Unload frmSL                     ' Close Simple Logo
  Else
    usrResponse = MsgBox(msg, msgBoxType, title)
    If usrResponse = vbYes Then
      Call program_save              ' Open Save as dialog box
    End If
    Unload frmSL                     ' Close Simple Logo
  End If
Exit Sub
exit_cancelled:                      ' abort Exit
  cdcFile.CancelError = False
End Sub
```

The VB command to close a form is the Unload command. Our main Simple Logo form is called frmSL, so we use the following statement to close Simple Logo:

```
Unload frmSL     ' Close Simple Logo
```

This completes the coding for the File menu. Save the program before continuing.

Test File | Exit

To test File|Exit do the following:

1. Run Simple Logo.

2. Create a simple program of one or more lines.

3. Select File|Exit. A Message box should appear.

4. Click the Yes button to save the program. The Save as dialog box should appear.

5. Click Cancel. Simple Logo should still be running.

6. Select File|Exit again. A Message box should appear.

7. Click the Yes button. The Save as dialog box should appear again.

8. Enter a filename for the program and click Save. The program should be stored and the Simple Logo form disappears.

9. Restart Simple Logo.

10. Open a program using File|Open.

11. Select File|Exit.

12. Simple Logo should exit.

13. Restart Simple Logo.

14. Create a simple program.

15. Select File|Exit. A Message box should appear.

16. Click the No button. Simple Logo should exit.

6. Creating a toolbar

Overview

(This stage of the project is saved as SLProject5 in the folder "Lesson5" on the CD.)

Windows application programs almost invariably provide a toolbar containing buttons for frequently used operations. We will follow this example of good practice and create a toolbar for Simple Logo. We will include buttons for the filing operations available in the File menu and two extra buttons to run and halt programs.

A toolbar is created in several stages. First an ImageList control is added to the main form. Then the images that will appear on the toolbar buttons are collected together in the ImageList control. Next the toolbar is created and linked to the ImageList control. Finally, the buttons that will appear on the toolbar are created and configured.

Once the toolbar has been created, button click events are linked to appropriate procedures. In the case of the buttons that duplicate existing filing operations available via the File menu, we will simply link a button click to the equivalent menu item event procedure. We will link the Run button to the procedure called by the temporary Run command button that we created earlier. However, we will need to write a small amount of code to deal with the Halt button which, as yet, has not been implemented.

ImageList Control

An ImageList control contains a collection of images, each of which can be referred to by an index or key. The ImageList control is meant to be used with other controls, such as the ToolBar control, as a repository of images. We will use the ImageList control to store the tool bar icons that will appear on the toolbar buttons. You create an ImageList control and specify images for it as follows:

1. Click the ImageList button in the toolbox and drag a rectangle somewhere on the main form. The ImageList control should appear. (If the ImageList tool does not appear in the Toolbox, you will need to add the "Microsoft Windows Common Controls " component to your project - see previous section, "5. Creating a menu" |File menu|CommonDialog Control for how to add a component to a project).

2. In the properties window for the ImageList, change the Name to "imgTbr", click in the (Custom) property and then click the button that appears. The Property Pages dialog for the ImageList control will appear.

3. Click the Images tab and then the Insert Picture... button. The Select Picture dialog opens.

4. The images for our tool bar buttons are on the CD in the folder Lesson6/Icons. Select the following images in turn, each time using the Insert Picture... button: "New.bmp", "Open.bmp", "Save.bmp", "Print.bmp", "Run.bmp" and "Halt.bmp". The Property Pages dialog should appear as shown on the next page.

5. Click OK to close the dialog box.

ToolBar Control

The next step is to create the tool bar buttons using the ToolBar control. Create the tool bar as follows:

1. Click the ToolBar control in the Tool box.

2. Drag a rectangle just below the Menu Bar.

3. In the Properties box for the Tool bar, set Name to "tbrSL".

4. Click in the Customise property and then click the button that appears. The Property Pages dialog should appear. Make sure that the General tab at the top is selected.

5. In the ImageList drop-down list select "imgTbr".

6. In the Appearance drop-down list select "0-ccFlat"

7. In the Style drop-down list select "1-tbrFlat".

8. Click the Buttons tab. Click Insert Button and enter the information in the first line of the table shown below. When you click the Insert button again to add the information for the next button, the first button should appear on the tool bar. Use the information in the table to create the remaining buttons and vertical line separators.

Index	Key	Style	ToolTipText	Image
1	btnNew	0-tbrDefault	New program	1
2	btnOpen	0-tbrDefault	Open program	2
3	btnSave	0-tbrDefault	Save program	3
4		3-tbrSeparator		0
5	btnPrint	0-tbrDefault	Print program	4
6		3-tbrSeparator		0
7	btnRun	0-tbrDefault	Run program	5
8	btnHalt	0-tbrDefault	Halt program	6

The toolbar should now look like this:

Save the project before continuing. Next we need to program the tool bar.

Programming the tool bar

When a toolbar button is clicked, the `tbrSL_ButtonClick` event procedure is invoked. VB supplies the appropriate button object as a parameter to this procedure to allow us to determine which button is involved. For each button we will call a procedure to handle the operation required. Fortunately, most of these procedures already exist for the File menu and for the temporary Run button we created earlier. Create the code as shown below:

```
Private Sub tbrSL_ButtonClick(ByVal Button As MSComctlLib.Button)
' ---------------------------------------------------------------
' This procedure is called when a button on the toolbar
' is clicked. The button object concerned is passed to the
' procedure in the object variable <Button>. Menu procedures
' are reused to implement toolbar button clicks.
' ---------------------------------------------------------------
' ~~~ The Button.Key property identifies the button name.
' ~~~ The appropriate procedure is then called.
  Select Case Button.Key
  Case "btnNew"
     Call mnuNew_Click
  Case "btnOpen"
     Call mnuOpen_Click
  Case "btnSave"
     Call mnuSave_Click
  Case "btnPrint"
     Call mnuPrint_Click
  Case "btnRun"
     Call btnRun_Click
  Case "btnHalt"
     Call btnHalt_Click
  End Select
End Sub
```

Next rename the existing `cmdRun_Click` procedure as `btnRun_Click` (just edit the procedure name) and delete the Run command button from the Program frame on the main form.

The Halt button requires a small patch to the `program_execute` procedure. When the Halt button is clicked while a program is running, the btnHalt_Click procedure will change the value of a global boolean variable. This variable will cause the program execution loop to exit without executing any instructions, thus terminating the program.

Add the following procedure:

```
Public Sub btnHalt_Click()
' ---------------------------------------------------------------
' Procedure to set global variable when Halt button clicked
' ---------------------------------------------------------------
  halt_program = True
End Sub
```

Add this line to the Declarations section:

```
Private halt_program As Boolean
```

Then modify the `program_execute` procedure as follows:

```
Public Sub program_execute()
'    ------------------------------------------------------------
' Procedure to execute the current program line by line
'    ------------------------------------------------------------
'........

'  ~~~ Determine required number of repetitions of program
  reps = Val(txtRepeat.Text)

'  ~~~ Init flag used by Halt control
  halt_program = False
'  ~~ Wrap program execution code in a loop
  For n = 1 To reps
'  ~~~ Execute each instruction in turn
    For curr_instr = 0 To proglen - 1
      If halt_program Then Exit For
      program_procinstr (curr_instr)
      Call wait(delay)              ' Wait <delay> msecs
    Next curr_instr                 ' Next instruction
  Next n                            ' Repeat program
End Sub
```

Now save the program before testing the toolbar.

Testing the ToolBar Controls

We will test the four toolbar filing buttons as we did the equivalent File menu items in the previous section, "5. Creating a menu". New, Open, Save and Print refer to the equivalent toolbar buttons in the following sections on testing.

Test the Save button

1. Run Simple Logo

2. Create a program of at least one line.

3. Click Save. The Save as dialog box should appear.

4. Save the program using a filename of your choice. The filename should appear as the Program frame caption.

5. Check the contents of the program with Notepad.

6. Add a line to the program.

7. Click Save again. This time the Save as dialog box should not appear and the program is saved automatically using the current name.

8. Check in Notepad that the program with the additional line has replaced the previous program with the same name.

Test the New button

This is quite a complex control to test. We must ensure that all possible routes through the code are tested.

1.   Run Simple Logo.
2.   Display FORWARD 100 in the Command frame.
3.   Click Execute. The turtle should draw a vertical line.
4.   Click Add line to transfer the instruction to the program list box.
5.   Click New. A message box should appear asking if the current program is to be saved.
6.   Click Yes. The Save as dialog box should appear.
7.   Click Cancel. The current program and controls should be unaffected.
8.   Click New again. A message box should appear asking if the current program is to be saved.
9.   Click Yes. The Save as dialog box should re-appear.
10. Enter a filename of your choice, e.g. "temp.lgo".
11. Click Save. The program should have been saved under the filename you specified and Simple Logo should have returned to its default state with the current program cleared. The turtle area should also be reset. Check that your program was saved by opening it in Notepad.
12. Display FORWARD 100 again in the Command frame.
13. Click Execute. The turtle should draw a vertical line.
14   Click Add line to transfer the instruction to the program list box.
15   Click New. A message box should appear asking if the current program is to be saved.
16. Click No. Simple Logo should have returned to its default state with the current program cleared. The turtle area should also be reset.

Test the Open button

Though similar to New in many ways, Open is complicated by the possible need to use both the Save as dialog box and the Open dialog box. In each case, the user can either proceed with the operation or cancel it.

1.   Run Simple Logo.
2.   Create a simple program and save it.
3.   Click New to clear the current program.
4.   Click Open. The Open dialog box should appear.
5.   Open the program saved earlier. The program should appear and the appropriate controls set or reset.

6. Click Open. The Open dialog box should appear.

7. Click Cancel. The dialog box should disappear and the Simple Logo controls should not have been affected.

8. Add an instruction to the current program.

9. Click Open. The Message box should appear.

10. Click the Yes button. The Save as dialog box should appear.

11. Click the Cancel button. The dialog box should disappear and the Simple Logo controls should not have been affected.

12. Click Open. The Message box should appear.

13 Click the Yes button. The Save as dialog box should appear.

14. Enter a filename of your choice.

15. Click the Save button. The Open dialog box should appear.

16. Click Cancel to exit the Open dialog box.

17. Add a command to the program.

18. Click Open. The Message box should appear.

19. Click the No button. The Open dialog box should appear.

20. Click Cancel and halt Simple logo.

Testing the Print button

To test Print do the following:

1. Run Simple Logo

2. Open a stored program using Open or create a program.

3. Click Print. The Print dialog box should open.

4. Click OK. The program should be printed.

5. Click Print again.

6. Click Cancel. The Print dialog box should disappear and the program isn't printed.

Test the Run button

1. Run Simple Logo and create the program shown in the screenshot overleaf.

2. Set Repeat to 18 and Delay to 5.

3. Then click the Run button to execute the program. The screen shot overleaf shows the result.

Test the Halt button

1. Repeat the test for the Run button.

2. As the program is executing, press the Halt button. The program should immediately stop executing.

Making the Tool bar context sensitive

Just as we did with menu items, we will make the tool bar buttons context sensitive. We already have a procedure, `file_controls`, to enable and disable filing operations. We will simply modify the code to incorporate the Save and Print buttons. Also note that if a program can be saved or printed, it can also be run, so we can add a line of code to `file_controls` to deal with the Run button too. Make the indicated additions to the procedure shown below:

```
Public Sub file_controls(save, saveas, prnt)
' ------------------------------------------------------------
' Procedure to enable and disable selected file controls
' ------------------------------------------------------------
' ~~~ Save
Select Case save
  Case "off"
    mnuSave.Enabled = False
    tbrSL.Buttons("btnSave").Enabled = False
    tbrSL.Buttons("btnRun").Enabled = False
  Case "on"
    mnuSave.Enabled = True
    tbrSL.Buttons("btnSave").Enabled = True
    tbrSL.Buttons("btnRun").Enabled = True
  Case ""
    ' null string - no action required
End Select
' ~~~ Save as
Select Case saveas
  Case "off"
    mnuSaveas.Enabled = False
    tbrSL.Buttons("btnSaveas").Enabled = False
    tbrSL.Buttons("btnRun").Enabled = False
  Case "on"
    mnuSaveas.Enabled = True
    tbrSL.Buttons("btnSaveas").Enabled = True
    tbrSL.Buttons("btnRun").Enabled = True
  Case ""
    ' Null string - no action required
```

```
End Select
' ~~~ Print
Select Case prnt
  Case "off"
     mnuPrint.Enabled = False
     tbrSL.Buttons("btnPrint").Enabled = False
     tbrSL.Buttons("btnRun").Enabled = False
  Case "on"
     mnuPrint.Enabled = True
     tbrSL.Buttons("btnPrint").Enabled = True
     tbrSL.Buttons("btnRun").Enabled = True
  Case ""
     ' Null string - no action required
End Select
End Sub
```

We access tool bar buttons by using the Buttons property with the button Key in brackets as shown in the example below:

```
tbrSL.Buttons("btnPrint").Enabled = False
```

Next, the Halt button needs to be enabled when the Run button is clicked and disabled when the program ends. We will insert two lines in the program_execute procedure to implement this. Add the following lines to the beginning of `program_execute`:

```
........................

' ~~~ Enable Halt
tbrSL.Buttons("btnHalt").Enabled = True

' ~~~ Get delay value and convert to 1/10 secs
delay = Val(txtDelay) * 100
```

etc

Add these two lines to the end of the procedure:

```
........................

' ~~~ Disable Halt
tbrSL.Buttons("btnHalt").Enabled = False
End Sub
```

Finally, we need to disable Halt when Simple Logo first starts and when it is reset. We do this by adding the following lines to the end of the Form_Load procedure:

```
' ~~~ Disable Halt
tbrSL.Buttons("btnHalt").Enabled = False
```

You can test the program to ensure correct enabling and disabling of tool bar buttons in exactly the same way as we tested the equivalent File menu items.

7. Adding help

Overview

(This stage of the project is saved as SLProject6 in the folder "Lesson6" on the CD.)

It is good practice to include help facilities in an application. Even for a relatively small application such as this one, all aspects of its operation and functions need to be explained to users.

Applications that run under Microsoft Windows 98 and above generally use HTML Help for Help. Microsoft provides "HTML Help Workshop" free of charge and it can be downloaded from Microsoft's Web site. This software aids the creation of professional-looking Help. However, creating a HTML Help file is quite complicated and beyond the scope of this tutorial, though it is well worth investigating yourself. For the purposes of this tutorial, we will create a simple help facility using VB tools.

We will extend the menu we created in the section, "5. Creating a menu", by adding an Edit menu with two sub items: "Contents" and "About Simple Logo". The first item will open a form that will provide information to help a user understand Simple Logo; the second item will open an 'About' form that all Windows applications include in the Help menu.

The Contents Form will display a panel containing the help outline consisting of topic headings, and the Help information will appear in a separate panel. The latter will contain the same headings along with information relating to the headings. When a user clicks on a topic in the outline panel, the information panel will scroll to the appropriate section.

Adding Help to the Menu

Click the Menu Editor icon on the tool bar and add the following three entries to the end of the existing menu:

Caption	Name	Level	Enabled	Shortcut
Help	mnuHelp	main	yes	
Contents...	mnuContents	sub	yes	Ctrl+H
About Simple Logo...	mnuAbout	sub	yes	

The menu should now appear as shown on the next page.

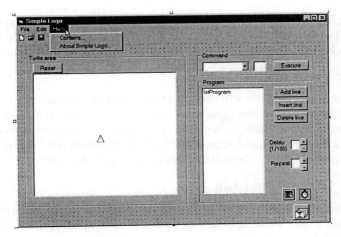

Creating a new Form

The next stage is to create a form that will be used to display the Help information. The form will contain two controls: a ListBox control and a RichTextBox control - see above. (Note: if the RichTextBox control does not appear in the Tool box (VB 6), it needs to added as a project component. Select Microsoft Rich Textbox Control from the Components dialog. See previous section, "5. Creating a menu" |File menu|CommonDialog Control for how to add a component to a project)

First create a new form by selecting Project|Add Form. Name the form frmHelp in Properties. Set the Caption to 'Help for Simple Logo'.

Next create a ListBox , Rich TextBox and the label "Topics" as shown below.

Rich Textbox Control

These controls allow us to create, edit and manipulate RTF files. They have numerous properties and methods that greatly ease the task of using text files stored in this format. RTF files can be created by all modern word processors. Because RTF files specify different text fonts, sizes and colours, as well as other types formatting such as tables, we can display information in a variety of attractive ways.

We will be using just two of the methods for this control: the `LoadFile` method to read an RTF file into a Rich Textbox control, and the `Find` method to search for the first occurrence of a string within the RTF file. Consult VB Help to find out more about this control.

Creating the Help outline

The list box at the left of the form will contain an outline of the help information. When a user clicks on a topic in the outline, the right-hand side panel will scroll to the appropriate section and display the required information. We need two text files - the outline stored as a plain text file and the help information stored as an RTF (Rich Text Format) file. The files, which are on the CD in the "Lesson7" folder, are called "HelpOL.txt" and "Help.rtf".

Reading the Outline text file

In section "5. Creating a menu", we created a program to read a program into the ListBox control in the Program frame; we need to do exactly the same thing here. Create the `Form_Load` procedure for the Help form as follows:

```
Private Sub Form_Load()
Dim l As String, filename As String
' ~~~ The location of the Help outline file - modify if necessary
  filename = "j:/A ICT/Vb/Tutorial/HelpOL.txt"
' ~~~ Load the Help outline file into the outline ListBox
  Open filename For Input As #1

' ~~~ Read file into list box
  While Not EOF(1)
     Input #1, l
     lstHelpOL.AddItem l
  Wend
End Sub
```

The procedure assumes that the text file contains lines of text terminated with a paragraph character so that each line in turn is added to the list box using the AddItem method. This procedure will be invoked as soon as the Help form opens.

Loading the Help form

When the user selects Help|Contents, the Help form should appear. We use the Form method, Show, to display a form and we invoke the method when Help|Contents is selected:

```
Private Sub mnuHelpContents_Click()
' -------------------------------------------------
' Opens the Help form
' -------------------------------------------------
  frmHelp.Show

End Sub
```

After creating this procedure, save the project.

Test the Help Form

To test the Help form we will make sure that the outline text file is correctly loaded into the outline panel. Make sure that the text file is in the correct location and then:

1. Run Simple Logo.

2. Select the Contents item from the Help Menu. The Help form should appear and the help outline should show in the ListBox control.

Load the Help file into the Rich Textbox control

Fortunately there is a Rich Textbox control method specifically for reading an RTF file into a Rich Textbox. Simply add the line shown below to the end of the `Form_Load` procedure for the Help file:

```
rtbHelp.LoadFile filename
End Sub
```

Linking the Outline to the Help information

We will use the ListBox click event to link the outline to the Help information. When a user clicks on a help topic in the Outline panel, the procedure `1stOL_Click` is invoked. Within this procedure we will write code to find the topic selected in the Rich Textbox control.

Create the following procedure:

```
Private Sub lstHelpOL_Click()
' -----------------------------------------------------
' Procedure to display appropriate Help info when
' a topic is clicked in the outline
' -----------------------------------------------------
  Dim topic As String
  topic = lstHelpOL.Text          ' Topic selected from outline
  rtbHelp.Find topic, 0           ' Find info in RTF control
End Sub
```

The code first gets the text of the item clicked in the outline using the Text property of the ListBox control. Then, this text is used by the Find method of the Rich Textbox control. The outline and information panels both contain the same topic headings, so that a topic clicked in the outline will always exist in the information panel.

Now save the project before testing the Help Form.

Testing the Help Form

To test the Help form, do as follows:

1. Start Simple Logo

2. Select Help|Contents. The outline and information panels should be filled with the appropriate files.

3. Click a topic in the outline panel on the left. The information panel on the right should scroll to that topic and highlight it.

4.   Repeat step 3 for several more topics chosen randomly.

About Form

We will create an About Form to provide details
about Simple logo. The form is shown alongside. As
you can see, it is very simple and contains a number of
labels and a single OK button.

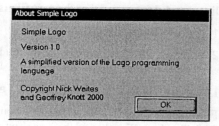

Add   four   labels   as   shown   and   use   the
CommandButton control to create cmdOK.

Set the Caption to "About Simple Logo".

Set the ControlBox property to False to prevent the
close and minimise window controls from appearing.

The code for the OK button procedure, cmdOK_Click, is shown below.

```
Private Sub cmdOK_Click()
' -----------------------------------------------
' Procedure to close the About form
' -----------------------------------------------

   Unload frmAbout

End Sub
```

Finally, to link the About form to the Help menu, create the following procedure in the main
form:

```
Private Sub mnuHelpAbout_Click()
' -----------------------------------------------
' Opens the About form
' -----------------------------------------------

   frmAbout.Show

End Sub
```

Save the project.

Test the About Form

1.   Run Simple Logo

2.   Select Help|About. The About form should appear.

3.   Click OK. The About form should disappear.

This completes the tutorial.

The final program is stored on the CD in the Lesson7 folder.

Glossary

A

ADSL (Asynchronous Digital Subscriber Line). Offers network access at up to 40 times faster than current modems.

ALU. An acronym for arithmetic-logic unit, a component part of the CPU or processor; used for arithmetic operations and logical comparisons of, stored data.

Analogue signal. A signal, such as that produced by the human voice, which is transmitted along a channel of, for example, the telephone network.

Analogue/digital converter (ADC). A device for converting analogue signals to the digital form useable by a digital computer. For example, the temperature measurements taken from a furnace can be digitised by an ADC and monitored by computer.

AND operation. A Boolean logical operation applied to two operands. If both are equal to 1 (TRUE) then the result or output is 1 (TRUE).

Applet. Small, self-contained application written in the Java programming language and executable by all modern Web browsers.

Applications software (programs). Programs to deal with user applications, for example, stock control or word processing. They may be packaged or specially written.

Artificial intelligence (AI). The ability of a computer to take on some attributes of intelligence, for example, learning and improving its performance through the use of repeated experience.

Assembler. Translator program to convert assembly language instructions into their machine code equivalents.

Assembly language. A machine-orientated programming language which uses mnemonic codes (memory aids) to identify instructions.

Asynchronous transmission. The transmission of characters along a channel at irregular intervals, for example, those produced by keyboard operation.

ATM. Stands for Asynchronous Transfer Mode and offers high bandwidth packet switching and multiplexing services.

Audit trail. A mechanism, usually built into the applications software, to allow the tracing of a transaction's history from input through to output. Auditing is an essential part of any accounting application as a guard against accidental or deliberate misuse of data.

B

Batch processing. A method of processing transactions which allows accuracy control totals to be associated with each batch. Each batch is dealt with as an entity, so that one error causes the rejection of the whole batch for correction and resubmission. Used where delay in updating is acceptable to users. Contrast with real-time.

Binary number system. A number system with the base or radix of 2 and in which only two digits are used, one and zero.

BIOS (Basic input output system). Utility held in ROM which holds the basic instructions for the machine's operation. Executed when the machine is switched on.

Bit. Contraction of binary digit (0 or 1). A bit is the smallest element of data or instruction representation in a computer.

Bridge. Device used to connect two LANs of the same type.

Browser. Client programs to help users to navigate through the World Wide Web. For example, Microsoft Explorer and Netscape Communicator.

Bucket. Area of direct access storage such as disk which may consist of a number of blocks of data and can be addressed as a unit.

Bug. A defect or malfunction in a computer program or system.

Bus. An electrical connection within a computer system and along which data is passed.

Byte. A group of bits handled as a unit by a computer system. Generally, a byte is formed from eight bits.

C

CAD. An acronym for Computer-Aided Design. A designer makes use of a computer, screen and light pen or similar device as aids to design.

Cell. In relation to spreadsheets, a single location identifiable by co-ordinate references.

Cellular (mobile) network. Wireless networks which use cellular radio communications to allow communication by hand-held or vehicle-based cellphones.

Central processing unit (CPU). The components of a computer system with the functions for control and processing, namely the control unit and the arithmetic/logic unit. Often known as the 'processor'.

COBOL. A high level programming language used for programming business and file processing applications. Acronym for COmmon Business Orientated Language.

Compiler. A program which translates high level source code into the object or machine code of the target machine.

Constant or literal. A value which is set at compilation time and does not change during program execution.

Control characters. Perform special functions, for example, carriage return on a printer.

Control total. A total accumulated on a batch of data to be processed. The computer accumulates the same total during data entry and checks its consistency. Used in batch processing.

Control unit. The functional component within the Central Processing Unit (CPU) of a computer which fetches instructions one by one, interprets them and 'triggers' the appropriate action.

Controlled redundancy. Used in connection with relational databases and refers to the duplication of certain key data items which allow connections to be made between different relations or files in a database.

CSMA/CD. Acronym for Carrier Sense Multiple Access with Collision Detector. A method of access control used on broadcast computer networks such as the 'bus' network.

Cylinder. A grouping of tracks in the same vertical plane, as for example, in a disk pack. Synonymous with seek area - all the tracks available whilst the read-write heads are in one position. The concept of the cylinder is used in addressing indexed sequential files.

D

Data. Collections of basic facts, meaningless until put into context or interpreted in some way, and also often in coded form.

Database. A collection of inter-related data stored together on a direct access storage medium to serve one or more applications.

Database Management System (DBMS). The programs required to control the use of a database. For example, Relational DBMS and Codasyl DBMS.

Data independence. The property of a database which allows the alteration of its overall logical or physical structure without changing the applications' views of the data.

Data transmission. The electronic transmission of data via a telecommunications link.

Debug. To remove errors from a computer system, for example, syntax or logic errors in a computer program.

Desktop publishing (DTP). A computer system with facilities for combined text and graphics presentation, 'cut and paste' and font selection, which are necessary for publishing.

Digital signature. Encryption method which authenticates both parties to an electronic transaction with a distinct public/private key pair.

Digitiser. A device to convert analogue signals into a sequence of digital values. For example, maps or pictures can be digitised for computer storage and processing.

Direct access storage. A facility which allows data to be retrieved directly from a storage device without reference to the rest of the file, for example, magnetic disk.

Distributed processing. A system where computer power is not centralised, but is distributed to geographically separate branches of an organisation, or amongst user systems within the same branch. This can be facilitated through the use of networked computers.

DLL (dynamic link library). Collection of functions and procedures (for commonly required programming tasks) forming part of the Application Programming Interface (API) or the MS Windows operating system.

Drivers. Files which enable a package to make use of the particular capabilities of different peripherals, for example, screen and printer drivers.

Dry running. A process of checking the logic of a computer program by hand and off-line.

Duplex or full duplex. Simultaneous transmissions of data in both directions with the use of two channels.

E

E-commerce. Conducting business transactions over electronic networks. Less formally, trading over the Internet (and, in the case of business to business trading, sometimes via private networks)

Electronic Mail. The transmission of mail by electronic means via a computer network. There is usually a 'mailbox' facility for the storage of messages awaiting collection.

Encryption. The transformation of data passing through a communications link into an encoded form which prevents its interpretation by unauthorised persons 'tapping' the line.

Expert system. A computer system programmed using artificial intelligence techniques to provide information or decisions relating to some narrow area of human expertise, for example, house conveyancing, house plant care, medical diagnosis. Also known as 'knowledge-based' systems.

F

Facsimile Transmission (FAX). The transmission of a copy of a document via a telecommunications link. Usually, it is transmitted in digital form.

Feasibility study. A study carried out by systems analysts and interested parties to ascertain possible solutions to an information processing problem.

Fetch-execute cycle. The activity of the CPU in fetching, decoding and executing program instruction one by one in a cycle.

Fibre optics. A means of transmitting data in light form.

Field. A subdivision of a record containing an item of information. Synonymous with data item.

Fifth generation computers. A combination of advanced hardware and software; characteristics include, faster processors, the use of multiple processors for 'parallel' processing, natural language processing and more human-orientated input-output devices, such as speech synthesisers, voice recognition devices and 'mice'.

File server. A local area network node which handles workstation access to shared storage and controls the exchange of files between network users.

Firewall. Firewalls protect Intranets from external networks such as the Internet. It may use both hardware and software components. Its purpose is to checks all packets before they enter or leave the

intranet, stopping any that do not pass the relevant security standards.

Foot-mouse. Mouse adapted for foot operation.

Footprint. The physical desk or floor space needed by a computer system or peripheral.

Foreign key. A field in one table (in a relational database) which links to the primary key in another table.

FORTRAN (FORmula TRANslator). A high level programming language particularly useful for programming scientific and mathematical applications.

Fourth generation languages (4GLs). Higher level languages which allow applications to be generated with the minimum of procedural programming; includes Applications Generators.

G

Gigabyte. One thousand million bytes.

Graph plotter. A computer output device which produces graphical material under computer control. There are two main types, the flat bed and the drum plotter.

GSM. Stands for Global System Mobile communications, which is the European standard for digital mobile communications.

H

Half-duplex. Data transmission in both directions, but not simultaneously.

Hashing. A technique using an algorithm to generate disk addresses for records within a random file. The technique aims to achieve an even distribution of records and to minimise overflow.

Hash total. A control total used in batch processing. Totals are derived from values such as account numbers and are thus meaningless apart from their control function. Also known as nonsense totals.

Hexadecimal ('Hex'). Number system with the base 16. Uses digits 0 to 9 and then A, B, C, D, E and F. Often used as shorthand for binary codes in technical manuals for computer systems and by programmers who make use of assembly language.

High level language. A language remote from any particular machine code. Each instruction in a high level language usually equates with a number of machine code instructions.

Hit rate. A percentage figure expressing the proportion of records in a file 'hit' during a processing run.

Home page. The opening page on a web site.

Host computer. A computer providing a central service to a number of other computers in a network.

HTML (Hypertext Markup Language). Language used to determine the appearance of web pages in browsers.

Hub. A device with multiple ports which allow devices to share a common connection point to the LAN cable.

Hyperlink. A text or graphical image which contains a link to another part of a document, or to another document.

I

Icon. A symbol on a screen menu representing a program option.

Indexed sequential. A method of organising a file on a direct access storage device such as disk, where records are organised in sequence according to a primary record key and indexes provide a means of referring to records directly.

Information. Derives from data, having been converted into a meaningful form.

Information flow diagram. A diagram which identifies the flows of information between different functional areas of a business.

ICT (Information Communication Technology). General term used to describe producing, storing, communicating and processing information using computers and other forms of electronic technology.

Initialise. To set variables to an initial value at the beginning of program execution.

Inter-block gap (IBG). The physical gap between blocks of data on magnetic tape to allow the starting and stopping of the tape between block transfers.

Interpreter. A translator program which interprets and directly executes program statements. Contrast with compiler.

Interrupt. A break in the activity of the central processor caused by an external event.

ISDN. Integrated Services Digital Network, a wholly digital service which provides quicker access to networks than is possible through dial-up, modem links. Likely to be superceded by ADSL.

Iterate. Commonly, to undertake a series of steps repeatedly, usually until a certain condition or result is achieved. More correctly, a process of calculating a result through a repeated series of steps, in which successive approximations are made until the desired result is achieved.

J

Java script. A programming language used in web site development.

K

Kilobyte (kb). A unit of computer storage - 1024 bytes.

Knowledge. Form of rules which can be used to arrive at conclusions in some area of expertise.

L

Linker. A program which incorporates any necessary machine code routines, from a library of standard routines, into an object program after compilation.

LISP (LISt Processing). A programming language where data elements are used in 'lists'. Its main application is in the field of artificial intelligence.

Local area network (LAN). A network of connected computers confined to a small area, say to a group of buildings on one site.

Logical operator. One of the logical functions, AND, or OR, NOT etc. used on variables.

Logo. A high level language designed by Seymour Papert to encourage an 'active' approach to computer-aided learning through the use of 'turtle' graphics.

Low-level language. A machine-orientated programming language as opposed to a problem-orientated high level language. Generally, each low level language instruction has a single machine code equivalent.

M

Machine code or language. The pattern of bits directly executable by a computer.

Macro-instruction. An instruction in a source language (high level or low level) which, when compiled, produces a number of machine code instructions.

Magnetic disk. A disk-shaped backing storage medium which provides direct access. Each magnetisable surface is divided into tracks and sectors addressable by the computer. Each addressable location may contain one or more logical records.

Magnetic tape. A serial access backing storage medium. It consists of a reel of plastic tape with a magnetisable coating to allow the representation of data. Generally, records are stored and accessed sequentially because the medium is non-addressable.

Magnetic ink character recognition (MICR). An input method whereby a reading device 'recognises' stylised characters printed in magnetisable ink. Used almost exclusively by the banking industry to read coded data from cheques.

Main memory. The primary memory of a computer system which stores programs and data currently being processed by the CPU. Contents are lost when the power is switched off and so is supplemented by backing storage.

Master file. A file which contains permanent or semi-permanent information on a subject. Usually affected by transactions during the updating process.

Megabyte (mb). Roughly one million bytes - a measurement of computer storage.

Message switching. A technique of switching messages between nodes in a network. Usually carried out by a mainframe or minicomputer at the 'hub' of the network.

Microprocessor. A central processor (control unit and arithmetic-logic unit) on a single chip.

Millisecond (ms). One thousandth of a second.

Modem (MOdulator-DEModulator). A device for converting the digital signal produced by a computer into an analogue form suitable for transmission along a telephone line. Also capable of carrying out the reverse process for incoming data.

Multiplexer (MUX). A device which transmits data arriving from several sources along a single transmission medium.

Multiprogramming. The processing of several jobs apparently at the same time. Programs and data relating to jobs are partitioned in memory and the CPU makes use of its high speed to switch control between them.

Multi-tasking. The concurrent processing of several tasks, relating to a single user, in memory at the same time.

Multi-user. A facility to allow more than one user to use a computer at the same time. Requires that the operating system can share the computer's resources and protect users' files from other users.

N

Nanosecond. One thousand millionth of a second.

Network. A number of computers connected together for the purposes of communication and processing.

Node. A component in a computer network, for example, one microcomputer station in a local area network.

Non-volatile memory. A storage medium which continues to hold data after the power is removed, for example, ROM, EPROM and PROM. Contrast with RAM which is volatile.

O

Object program. The machine code or object program produced after compilation of the source program. The object program is executable on the target machine.

Operating system. The basic suite of programs which supervise and control the general running of a computer system.

Optical character recognition (OCR). The recognition by an OCR device of characters (usually stylised) by measuring their optical reflectance.

Optical disk. A high capacity storage device (measured in gigabytes) which makes use of laser technology to record and read data on the disk.

Optical mark reading (OMR). Process whereby an OMR device identifies values on a pre-printed document by the position of pencil marks. Usually, boxes on the document are indicated as representing particular values and each can be indicated by a pencil mark in the relevant box.

OSI model. Open Systems Interconnection model. Developed by the International Standards organisation, it lays down standards for network systems.

P

Parallel processing. The technique of executing a number of computer instructions in parallel.

Parallel running. When a new system is implemented, the old system is continued until the users are satisfied that the new system is functioning correctly and reliably.

Parallel transmission. The transmission of bit groupings in parallel.

Parity. A minimal form of error checking in data

transmission, whereby an extra bit is added to a group of bits to make the total number of bit 1s even (even parity) or odd (odd parity). The parity is checked after each transmission.

Pascal. A high level, block-structured programming language named after Emile Pascal, a French mathematician.

Picosecond. One million-millionth of a second.

Pilot testing. A method of system implementation which only applies a new system to a portion of the live data. The remainder is processed by the old method until the users of the pilot data are satisfied concerning the system's accuracy and reliability.

Plotter. Flat bed or drum graph plotter.

Port. A place of entry to or exit from a central processor, dedicated to a single channel, for example, a printer port.

Primary key. A data item which ensures unique identification of an individual record.

Print server. A local area network node which shares its printer facility amongst all users on the network. Print jobs are queued and may be executed in turn or according to assigned priorities.

Processor. See central processing unit.

Program specification. A specification produced by a systems analyst as part of a system specification and detailing all the requirements of the related applications software.

Program testing. The process of running a program with test data to check the correctness and completeness of output.

Prolog. A programming language based on mathematical logic. It is used extensively in artificial intelligence (AI) applications and is particularly suitable for database applications. Adapted by the Japanese for programming their 'fifth generation' computers.

PROM (Programmable Read Only Memory). A chip which can be 'blown' or programmed by the user to produce non-volatile memory store (ROM).

Protocol. A set of rules governing the format of messages transmitted in computer networks. Compatibility needs to be established between communicating devices so that they can 'talk' to each other.

Q

Query language. A language designed for users to make ad hoc enquiries of a database.

R

RAM. Random access memory - the main memory of the computer.

Random access. A facility for accessing a storage medium for any record or data item, without reference to the rest of the file. Also known as direct access. Main memory and disk storage provide this facility.

Read only memory (ROM). Storage medium which allows only 'reading' and not 'writing'.

Real number. Positive or negative number with a fractional part.

Record. A group of related data items forming an entity. A subdivision of a file.

Referential integrity. Facility in Microsoft Access database to assist in maintenance of valid relationships between tables.

Relational database. A database made up of relations or two-dimensional tables.

Repeater. A signal amplifier, which passes packets of data onto the next node in a network.

Ring network. A network topology where computers are connected in a ring structure. Evolved in Cambridge and known as the Cambridge ring.

RISC. An acronym for Reduced Instruction Set Computer in which the decoding circuitry is limited to the most frequently used instructions, thus producing smaller, faster processors.

Router. A device used to connect two LANs, which may or may not be of different type.

S

Schema. The overall logical definition of a database.

Search. The scanning of data items for those in accord with specified criteria, for example, salaries in excess of 10,000 in a Personnel file.

Sector. A subdivision of a track on a magnetic disk. Constitutes the smallest addressable unit on a disk.

Seek time. The time taken for moveable read-write heads to move to the selected track or cylinder on a magnetic disk.

Sequential access. The retrieval of records according to the sequence of their organisation, for example, a customer file stored in Customer Account number order.

Sequential organisation. A method of storing a file so that records are sequenced according to a primary record key, for example, a Stock Code.

Serial access. Retrieving records in the order that they are physically stored, in other words, as they come.

Serial organisation. Simply, records stored one after the other, not necessarily in sequence, for example, an unsorted tape file.

Serial transmission. Transmission of data, usually via a telecommunications link, whereby the 'bits' follow one another in a serial fashion. Contrast with parallel transmission.

SET (Secure Electronic Transaction). The SET protocol was developed by Visa and MasterCard as a method to secure bankcard transactions over open networks, including the Internet. Compared with SSL, SET places greater importance on the validation of *both* parties to the transaction.

Simplex. Transmission of data in one direction only.

Source program. A program written in a programming language (high or low level). It must be translated into machine code before execution.

SQL. Structured query language. A non-procedural 4th generation programming language.

SSL (Secure Sockets Layer). The de facto standard for encryption between client browsers and Internet servers.

Star network. A network topology, whereby a main 'host' computer at the 'hub' services a number of peripheral systems.

Stop bit. A bit used to indicate the end of a character in asynchronous transmission.

Subroutine. A self-contained routine, coded once within a program, which may be 'called' at any point during the main program. After execution of the subroutine, control is returned to the instruction immediately following the call.

Subschema. A limited logical view of a database derived from the schema (overall logical database view) to be used by an applications program.

Synchronous transmission. The transmission of data in 'streams'. The sender and the receiver devices are synchronised so that individual characters are identified within the stream. No start or stop bits are needed. Special 'SYN' characters are transmitted periodically to maintain the synchronisation. Contrast with asynchronous transmission.

Syntax. The formal rules of grammar and structure governing the use of a programming language.

Syntax error. Where the syntax rules are broken in program coding. Generally, such errors are indicated by a compiler or interpreter.

Systems analysis. The study of an activity with a view to its computerisation.

Systems software. Program purchased as part of a computer system and which are concerned with the general running of the hardware and not with specific applications. Examples include, operating systems, utilities and compilers.

T

Teleworking. Working from home with the use of a computer link to the actual office.

Test data. Data specially prepared for the testing of program output for accuracy and consistency with the requirements of the program specification.

Timesharing. The technique, often used with interactive systems, whereby the CPU shares out its time amongst a number of users, with the aim of giving good response times to each. The allocation of time is known as 'time slicing'.

Token ring network. A local area network industry standard. Its main proponent is IBM.

Top-down design. Designing a program according to its overall logic, in terms of its identifiable components and then defining those components in further detail and so on, until the required level of detail is obtained.

Transaction file. A file containing transactions to be used in the updating of a master file.

Transaction logging. The recording of transactions on a separate serial file at the same time as they update the relevant master files.

Translator. A program for the translation of source code into object or machine code, for example, a compiler, an interpreter or an assembler.

Transputer. A processor with serial links to allow communication with other transputers. The basis of parallel processing computers.

U

Utility. A program which performs a common task such as sorting a file or copying a disk.

V

Validation. A process, usually carried out by a validation or 'data vet' program, to check that data falls within specified valid criteria, for example, that hours of overtime worked fall within a range from 0 to 20.

Verification. The process of checking the accuracy of data transcription, usually in a data encoding operation such as key-to-disk, prior to batch data input. Commonly, verification involves the re-keying of the data by another operator and the verifier machine compares keys depressed with data already stored.

Videoconferencing. The conducting of a conference through the use of computers, video cameras and telecommunications links.

Virtual memory. An extension of main memory to include on line disk storage, such that a programmer can regard the total memory space as being available for a program. Programs are written in segments or pages and are called into main memory as required.

Voice output. The technique of simulating the human voice by computer means.

Voice recognition. A technique to allow computer input to be supplied directly by a human voice.

Volatile. A property associated with computer memory, whereby it loses its data when power is removed.

W

Web server. An Internet server which physically stores or 'hosts' web sites.

Wide area network (WAN). A network which makes use of the telecommunications network to link computer systems over a wide geographical area.

WIMP. Acronym for Windows, Icons, Mice and Pull-down menus, all of which are commonly used in user-friendly, menu driven packages.

WML (Wireless Markup Language). Alternative to HTML for sites optimised for access by mobile phones, which may lack the transmission speed and power to access HTML sites.

Workstation. Usually used to describe a PC connected to a local area network. Typically consists of a processor, keyboard, high-resolution graphics monitor, mouse and hard disk drive. Also used to describe the powerful computer systems used by, for example, 3D design applications and has replaced the term *minicomputer*.

Write protect. A mechanism to prevent accidental or deliberate overwriting of a disk's contents.

Index